SPACE AGE

ASTRONOMY

SPACE AGE ASTRONOMY

An International Symposium
Sponsored by
Douglas Aircraft Company, Inc.
August 7–9, 1961
at the California Institute of Technology
in conjunction with the XI General Assembly
of the International Astronomical Union

EDITED BY

ARMIN J. DEUTSCH
Mount Wilson and Palomar Observatories
Carnegie Institution of Washington
California Institute of Technology

WOLFGANG B. KLEMPERER
Douglas Aircraft Company, Inc.
Santa Monica, California

ACADEMIC PRESS New York · London · 1962

ACADEMIC PRESS INC.
111 Fifth Avenue
New York 3, N. Y.

United Kingdom Edition
Published by
ACADEMIC PRESS INC. (London) Ltd.
Berkeley Square House, Berkeley Square, London W. 1

Library of Congress Catalog Card Number 62–21142

PRINTED IN THE UNITED STATES OF AMERICA

Roster of Participants

NAME	AFFILIATION	ADDRESS
Ables, H. D.	University of Texas	Austin, Texas
Adler, A. A.	Bell Aerosystems Co.	Boston, Massachusetts
Alfvén, Prof. H.	Royal Inst. of Technology	Stockholm, Sweden
Aly, Dr. M. K. M.	Helwan Obs.	Helwan, Egypt
Arnquist, Dr. W. N.	Douglas Aircraft Co.	Santa Monica, California
Atkinson, Dr. R. d'E.	Royal Greenwich Obs.	Hailsham, Sussex, England
Babcock, Dr. H. W.	Mt. Wilson & Palomar Obs.	Pasadena, California
Baum, Dr. W. A.	Mt. Wilson & Palomar Obs.	Pasadena, California
Beck, H. G.	Carl Zeiss Lab. Astron. Inst.	Jena, Germany
Becker, Dr. R. A.	Aerospace Corp.	Los Angeles, California
Bennett, Dr. R. D.	The Martin Co.	Baltimore, Maryland
Berger, R.*	Convair, General Dynamics	San Diego, California
Bergman, G.	Nat'l. Eng. Science Co.	Pasadena, California
Bhatnagar, Dr. P. L.	Indian Inst. of Science	Bangalore, South India
Biermann, Prof. L.	Max-Planck-Inst. für Physik und Astrophysik	Munich, Germany
Blamont, Prof. J. E.	Obs. de Meudon, Aéronomie	Meudon, France
Blasingame, Dr. B. P.	A. C. Spark Plug, G. M. Corp.	Milwaukee, Wisconsin
Blitzer, Prof. L.	University of Arizona	Tucson, Arizona
Boischot, A.	Obs. of Paris	Meudon, France
Boratynski, N. D.	Natl. Eng. Science Co.	Pasadena, California
Bowen, Prof. I. S.	Mt. Wilson & Palomar Obs.	Pasadena, California
Bower, Dr. E. C.	Mt. Wilson & Palomar Obs.	Pasadena, California
Boyd, Dr. R. L. F.	University College	London, England
Brandt, Dr. J.†	Mt. Wilson & Palomar Obs.	Pasadena, California
Brouwer, Prof. D.	Yale University Obs.	New Haven, Connecticut
Brown, Prof. H.	Cal.-Tech.	Pasadena, California
Brubaker, Dr. W. M.	Bell & Howell Research Ctr.	Pasadena, California
Bull, H. T.	Jet Propulsion Lab.	Pasadena, California
Butler, Dr. H. E.	Royal Obs.	Edinburgh, Scotland
Chamberlain, Dr. J. W.	Yerkes Obs.	Williams Bay, Wisconsin
Chapman, Dr. D.	NASA	Sunnyvale, California
Choisser, R. W.	Aeronutronics	Newport Beach, California
Clemence, Dr. G. M.	U.S. Naval Obs.	Washington, D.C.
Cohen, P. L.	Douglas Aircraft Co.	Santa Monica, California
Cole, Prof. J. D.	Cal.-Tech.	Pasadena, California
Cole, Dr. L. G.	Beckman Instrument Co.	Fullerton, California
Corben, Dr. H. C.	Space Technology Lab.	Redondo Beach, California
Davis, Prof. Leverett	Cal.-Tech.	Pasadena, California
Davis, M. E.	The RAND Corp.	Santa Monica, California

* Present address: Lockheed-California Co., Burbank, California.

† Present address: University of California, Berkeley, California.

NAME	AFFILIATION	ADDRESS
Delsemme, Dr. A. H.	Org. Europ. Econ. Co-Op.	Paris, France
Deutsch, Dr. A. J.	Mt. Wilson & Palomar Obs.	Pasadena, California
Dimeff, J.	NASA	Sunnyvale, California
van Driest, Dr. E. R.	North American Aviation, Inc.	Downey, California
Edlén, Prof. B.	Fysiska, Inst.	Lund, Sweden
Eimer, Dr. M.	Jet Propulsion Lab.	Pasadena, California
Ekstromer, J. E.*	Douglas Aircraft Co.	Santa Monica, California
Felling, W. E.	Raytheon Co.	Lexington, Massachusetts
Fowler, Prof. W. A.	Cal.-Tech.	Pasadena, California
Freden, Dr. S.	Aerospace Corp.	El Segundo, California
Fried, Dr. B.	The Garret Corp.	Phoenix, Arizona
Friedman, Dr. H.	U.S. Naval Research Lab.	Washington, D.C.
Friend, J. L.	North American Aviation, Inc.	Downey, California
Futthammar, C. G.	Royal Inst. of Technology	Stockholm, Sweden
Garber, Dr. D. H.	General Dynamics Astronautics	San Diego, California
Generales, Dr. C.	College of Space Medicine	New York, New York
Gibbons, H. B.	Chance-Vought Corp.	Dallas, Texas
Goedeke, A. D.	Douglas Aircraft Co.	Santa Monica, California
Goldbaum, G. C.	Douglas Aircraft Co.	Santa Monica, California
Goldberg, Dr. L.	Harvard and Smithsonian Obs.	Cambridge, Massachusetts
Greenstein, Prof. J. L.	Mt. Wilson & Palomar Obs.	Pasadena, California
Griesacker, I. M. C.	General Electric Co.	Philadelphia, Pennsylvania
Gunkel, R. J.	Douglas Aircraft Co.	Santa Monica, California
Güntzel-Lingner, Dr. U.†	Astrophys. Obs.	Potsdam, Germany
Haddock, Prof. F. T.	Univ. of Michigan Obs.	Ann Arbor, Michigan
Hagen, Dr. J. P.	NASA	Washington, D.C.
Hagihara, Prof. Y.	Utsunomiya University	Utsunomiya, Japan
Hallet, R. W.	Douglas Aircraft Co.	Santa Monica, California
Hege, D. W.	Rocketdyne, NAA Inc.	Canoga Park, California
Heller, G. B.	NASA	Huntsville, Alabama
Herrick, Prof. S.	Univ. of California, L.A.	Los Angeles, California
Hibbs, Dr. A. R.	Jet Propulsion Lab.	Pasadena, California
Hildebrand, R. B.	The Boeing Co.	Seattle, Washington
Hoh, Dr. F. C.	Royal Inst. of Technology	Stockholm, Sweden
Hori, Dr. G.-I.‡	Yale University Obs.	New Haven, Connecticut
Horner, R. E.	Northrop Corp.	Beverly Hills, California
Hoyle, Dr. F.	Kings College	Cambridge, England
Hudson, K.	Amer. Astrophysics Inc.	Monrovia, California
Hulett, H. R.	Advances Tech. Lab.	Mountain View, California
van de Hulst, Prof. H. C.	Sterrewacht te Leiden	Leiden, Holland
Hunter, M. W.¶	Douglas Aircraft Co.	Santa Monica, California

* Present address: Thiokol, Humetrics, Los Angeles, California.

† Present address: Astron. Rechen-Inst., Heidelberg, Germany.

‡ Present address: University of Tokyo, Japan.

¶ Present address: Natl. Aeron. & Space Council, Washington, D. C.

NAME	AFFILIATION	ADDRESS
Hyatt, A.	NASA	Washington, D.C.
Izsak, I. G.	Smithsonian Astroph. Obs.	Cambridge, Massachusetts
Johnson, R. L.	Douglas Aircraft Co.	Santa Monica, California
v. Karman, Prof. T.	Cal.-Tech.	Pasadena, California
Katz, A. H.	The RAND Corp.	Santa Monica, California
Kellogg, Dr. W. W.	The RAND Corp.	Santa Monica, California
Kienle, Prof. H. C.	Obs. Königstuhl	Heidelberg, Germany
Klein, Dr. A. L.	Douglas Aircraft Co.	Santa Monica, California
Kleinhans, S.	Douglas Aircraft Co.	Santa Monica, California
Klemperer, Dr. W. B.	Douglas Aircraft Co.	Santa Monica, California
Konecci, Dr. E. B.*	Douglas Aircraft Co.	Santa Monica, California
Kopal, Dr. Z.	University of Manchester	Macclesfield, England
Kovalevsky, Dr. J.	Bureau des Longitudes	Paris, France
Krieger, Dr. F. J.	The RAND Corp.	Santa Monica, California
Kvaas, T. A.	General Electric Co.	Santa Barbara, California
Larmore, Dr. L.	Lockheed Aircraft Corp.	Burbank, California
Laufer, Dr. A. R.	Office of Naval Research	Pasadena, California
Lauritsen, Dr. C. C.	Cal.-Tech.	Pasadena, California
Leighton, Prof. R. B.	Cal.-Tech.	Pasadena, California
Liepmann, Prof. H. W.	Cal.-Tech.	Pasadena, California
Lilley, Dr. A. E.	Harvard College Obs.	Cambridge, Massachusetts
Lyttleton, Dr. R. A.	St. John's College	Cambridge, England
Martin, Dr. A. B.	Atomics International, NAA Inc.	Canoga Park, California
Martina, E. F.	Aerospace Corp.	El Segundo, California
Massevitch, Dr. A. G.	Academy of Sciences U.S.S.R.	Moscow, U.S.S.R.
Mauro, J. A.	General Electric Co.	Pittsfield, Massachusetts
McGee, Prof. J. D.	Imperial College	London, England
McKee, Dr. J. W.†	Douglas Aircraft Co.	Santa Monica, California
Meinel, Dr. A. B.‡	Kitt Peak Natl. Obs.	Tucson, Arizona
Menzel, Dr. D. H.	Harvard College Obs.	Cambridge, Massachusetts
Message, Dr. P. J.	Gonville & Cajus College	Cambridge, England
Merrilees, D. S.	Douglas Aircraft Co.	Santa Monica, California
Mikhailov, Prof. A. A.	Pulkovo Obs.	Leningrad, U.S.S.R.
Milder, M.	Jet Propulsion Lab.	Pasadena, California
Moe, Dr. G.	Astropower, Inc.	Newport Beach, California
Moreton, G.	Lockheed Aircraft Corp.	Burbank, California
Münch, Prof. G.	Mt. Wilson & Palomar Obs.	Pasadena, California
Murphy, Dr. G. L.¶	Douglas Aircraft Co.	Santa Monica, California
Murray, Dr. B. C.	Cal.-Tech.	Pasadena, California
Neugebauer, Dr. G.	Jet Propulsion Lab.	Pasadena, California
Newburn, R. L.	Jet Propulsion Lab.	Pasadena, California
Nidey, R. A.	Kitt Peak Natl. Obs.	Tucson, Arizona
van Ornum, D. G.	Plasmadyne Corp.	Santa Ana, California

* Present address: NASA, Washington, D.C.
† Present address: General Electric Co., Santa Barbara, California.
‡ Present address: Steward Obs., Tucson, Arizona.
¶ Present address: Thiokol, Humetrics, Los Angeles, California.

NAME	AFFILIATION	ADDRESS
Pickering, Dr. W. H.	Jet Propulsion Lab.	Pasadena, California
Puckett, Dr. A. E.	Hughes Aircraft Co.	Culver City, California
Radhakrishnan, V.	Cal.-Tech.	Pasadena, California
Rechtin, Dr. E.	Jet Propulsion Lab.	Pasadena, California
Rense, Prof. W. A.	University of Colorado	Boulder, Colorado
Righini, Prof. G.	Obs. Astrophys., Arcetri	Florence, Italy
Ring, Dr. J.	University of Manchester	Manchester, England
Robertson, Prof. H. P.*	Cal.-Tech.	Pasadena, California
Robinson, S. M.	Douglas Aircraft Co.	Santa Monica, California
Rogerson, Dr. J. B.	Princeton University Obs.	Princeton, New Jersey
Roman, Dr. N. G.	NASA	Washington, D.C.
Roney, Dr. R. K.	Hughes Aircraft Co.	Culver City, California
Rosendahl, G. R.	General Electric Co.	Philadelphia, Pennsylvania
Rossoni, Dr. J. P.	IBM	Cambridge, Massachusetts
Rule, B.	Cal.-Tech.	Pasadena, California
Sadler, Dr. D. H.	Royal Greenwich Obs.	Hailsham, England
Sagan, Dr. C.	Univ. of Calif. at Berkeley	Berkeley, California
Satin, A.	Lockheed Aircraft Corp.	Burbank, California
Schatzman, Prof. E.	Astrophys. Inst.	Paris, France
Schmitt, Prof. O. H.	University of Minnesota	Minneapolis, Minnesota
Scott, W. H.	Grumman Aircraft Eng. Co.	Bethpage, L.I., New York
Sears, Dr. W. R.	Cornell University	Ithaca, New York
Seifert, Dr. H. S.	Stanford University	Stanford, California
Shef, A. L.	Douglas Aircraft Co.	Santa Monica, California
Singer, Prof. S. F.	University of Maryland	College Park, Maryland
Siry, Dr. J.	NASA	Greenbelt, Maryland
Smelt, Dr. R.	Lockheed Aircraft Corp.	Sunnyvale, California
Stehsel, Dr. M. L.	Aerojet Corp.	Azusa, California
Sternberg, S.	RCA	Princeton, New Jersey
Stewart, Dr. A. L.	Queens University	Belfast, N. Ireland
Stowell, R. D.	Douglas Aircraft Co.	Santa Monica, California
Stumpff, Prof. K.	University of Göttingen	Göttingen, Germany
Suemoto, Dr. Z.	Tokyo Astronomical Obs.	Mitaka-Tokyo, Japan
Suess, Prof. H.	University of California	La Jolla, California
Sutton, Prof. R. M.	Cal.-Tech.	Pasadena, California
Swings, Prof. P.	University of Liège	Liège, Belgium
Tousey, Dr. R.	U.S. Naval Research Lab.	Washington, D.C.
Undesser, Dr. K.	Ryan Aeronautical Co.	San Diego, California
Unsöld, Prof. A.	University of Kiel	Kiel, Germany
Urey, Dr. H.	Univ. of California	La Jolla, California
de Vaucouleurs, Dr. G.	Univ. of Texas	Austin, Texas
Vogl, T. P.	Westinghouse Electric Co.	Pittsburgh, Pennsylvania
Walker, J. C.	Douglas Aircraft Co.	Santa Monica, California
Wasserburg, Prof. G. J.	Cal.-Tech.	Pasadena, California
Watanabe, Dr. K.†	Aerospace Corp.	El Segundo, California
Weissler, Prof. G. L.	Univ. of So. California	Los Angeles, California

* Deceased August, 1961.
† Present address: University of Hawaii, Honolulu, Hawaii.

NAME	AFFILIATION	ADDRESS
Wen, W. L.	Ryan Aeronautical Co.	San Diego, California
Wheaton, E. P.*	Douglas Aircraft Co.	Santa Monica, California
Wilkins, Dr. G. A.	Royal Greenwich Obs.	Hailsham, England
Wilson, Dr. A. G.	The RAND Corp.	Santa Monica, California
Wilson, Dr. O. C.	Mt. Wilson & Palomar Obs.	Pasadena, California
Witunski, M.	McDonnell Aircraft Corp.	St. Louis, Missouri
Wood, Dr. R. M.	Douglas Aircraft Co.	Santa Monica, California
Wurm, Prof. D.	Hamburg Obs.	Hamburg-Bergedorf, Germany
Yanow, G.	Douglas Aircraft Co.	Santa Monica, California
Zwicky, Prof. F.	Cal.-Tech., Aerojet General	Pasadena, California

* Present address: Lockheed Missiles & Space Co., Sunnyvale, California.

Foreword

The Space Age Astronomy Symposium was organized as a contribution to greater international cooperation in the challenging tasks of space exploration and interplanetary travel.

It was pleasing to the Douglas Aircraft Company, as sponsor of the Symposium, that the participants, who represented a broad scope of scientific and technical accomplishment, came from nearly all of the world's continents.

The exploration and understanding of space—the solar system and beyond—require a mobilization of talent on a world-wide scale.

International cooperation is possible and highly desirable in man's efforts to move beyond the environment which has restricted him for thousands and thousands of years. Surely, in this respect at least, we can begin to transcend some of the political and ideological barriers which have compartmentalized our lives in other ways.

Comments of the almost 200 astronomers, physicists, astrophysicists, and engineers in attendance expressed a widespread feeling that the Symposium program was both effective and enlightening.

We at Douglas were deeply gratified to have a part in making the Symposium possible and we wish to extend our warmest thanks to the California Institute of Technology for its vital assistance and cooperation, to Dr. John P. Hagen, of the National Aeronautics and Space Administration, for his stimulating banquet remarks, and to the various committees for the efficiency of the Symposium arrangements.

DONALD W. DOUGLAS, JR.
President
Douglas Aircraft Company

Editors' Preface

The present book was compiled to record the transactions of the three-day Space Age Astronomy Symposium for the benefit of participants and nonparticipants alike. The transactions consisted of invited papers, some of them in the form of panel presentations, invited comments, and spontaneous discussions. The subjects had been carefully chosen by the Program Committee so that they would cover much of the wide field with which astronomy is going to be concerned in the space age. Deliberately omitted from the program were invited contributions on such important subjects as cosmic rays, the ionosphere and van Allen belts of the Earth, solar-terrestrial relations, and others more remotely related to astronomy proper.

The first day of the Symposium was devoted essentially to a review of the state of the art as reflected by current projects and techniques for making astronomically significant observations and for evaluating them. The speakers of the second day envisioned the cosmos, the galaxies (others and our own), and the stars (including our own Sun); they explained what the astronomers hope to learn about them and how. On the third day the view was focused on our solar system, particularly on its planets, moons, and comets, and the vehicles and instruments to which they will soon become accessible for closer look and eventually for actual visit.

The contributions of the Symposium participants, a most authoritative and articulate group, are reproduced here with the intervention of only minor editorial changes. In particular, we have made no effort to suppress the few minor instances where material is duplicated by different authors. A few of the papers which had been presented more or less extemporaneously have since been rewritten by the authors or reconstructed by reference to the tape recordings taken. We have taken care to avoid omissions or errors of transcription, but whatever errors may still remain should be charged to us. To ensure legibility, we had new versions made for some of the line drawings.

We have also taken the liberty of deviating slightly from a strict chronological transcript of the actual proceedings at the Symposium. Some of the topics were consolidated under a joint heading more appropriately encompassing the subject matter of related papers than the titles given in the original program. Therefore, the chapter numbers no longer agree with those of the original program. In reporting the discussions, we have taken certain small liberties of rearrangement in order to keep together the comments on any one topic and to remove unintentional repetitions or digressions.

The gulf between disciplines sometimes yawns as wide as the void between worlds. If our Symposium was a bridge, we owe this success to the people who made it. They are the scientists and engineers whose contributions are in this book. It has been a pleasure and a privilege for us to work with them.

Armin J. Deutsch
Wolfgang B. Klemperer

Welcome

On behalf of the sponsor, the Douglas Aircraft Company, Inc., *Elmer P. Wheaton,* Vice President of Engineering, formally greeted and welcomed the assembly. As Chairman of the Planning Committee which had undertaken to organize this Symposium in conjunction with the XI General Assembly of the International Astronomical Union, he expressed the sponsor's gratification at the large professional attendance, and the presence of many eminent scientists. He also conveyed the welcome of the American participants to their foreign colleagues and urged them to feel at home in this truly international gathering.

Dr. Ira S. Bowen, Director of Mount Wilson and Palomar Observatories and Professor of Astronomy at the California Institute of Technology, welcomed the Symposium on behalf of these institutions on the host campus. He outlined the long and distinguished history of astronomy in California, where progress in the science has been favored by the climate of the state. Drawing a parallel for the development of the aircraft and jet propulsion industries and research, he deemed it most appropriate that the Space Age Astronomy Symposium was convened here.

Contents

SECTION I

Accomplishments, Current Projects, and Proven Techniques

SECTION II

Desiderata for Future Astronomical Observations from Stations in Space (Solar, Interplanetary, Galactic, and Extragalactic Phenomena)

SECTION III

Celestial Mechanics Problems in the Solar System, Planetary Exploration, and Related Engineering Problems

SECTION I

Accomplishments, Current Projects, and Proven Techniques

CHAPTER 1

World-Wide Survey of Experiments Conducted, Running, Planned, or Scheduled

1.1 *The Astronomical Objectives of Space Research*

H. C. VAN DE HULST

LEIDEN OBSERVATORY, The Netherlands

Space Age Astronomy

It is essential to state a few things which are obvious but which, nevertheless, are necessary to define the subject.

The title of our Symposium—"Space Age Astronomy"—has a certain tension. One part—astronomy—is old; the other part—space age—is brand new. According to popular beliefs and popular terms: an astronomer wears a beard, sits in a lazy chair behind a long telescope, and *looks* at the stars; a space age astronaut wears a smile, sits in a capsule on top of a big rocket, and *goes* to the stars.

Fortunately, it is not necessary to take issue with popular beliefs in this company of insiders. Long ago astronomers abandoned *looking* as their principal method. The manifold ways of obtaining astronomical data by means of photometry, polarimetry, spectrography, cosmic-ray studies, and other methods, form an intrinsic part of the scientific progress which has brought about the space age. Astronautics, on the other hand, has hardly entered the "going" stage. The magnificent achievements of the two orbital flights made by Soviet citizens and the two suborbital flights made by Americans show that it can be done and holds big promise. However, until today, or at least until yesterday, 100% of all *scientific* results obtained by artificial satellites and spacecraft comes from the instruments built into those vehicles, just as 90%

of all astronomical results comes from the instruments attached to telescopes.

The big difference is in the distance scale. "Space" of space research and space craft and space travel is incomparably smaller than "space" in astronomy. The difference can be visualized in many ways, but perhaps most directly by considering the time it takes for light waves and radio waves to travel those distances. About 95% of today's space research deals with objects within 1 second of light time. The major part of present-day astronomy concerns objects beyond a century of light travel, and into the millions and billions of years. It follows that there are two distinct classes of astronomical research possibilities in the space age: (a) ambient studies and close-ups; (b) studies of distant objects. We shall comment briefly on the situation as it presents itself now.

Ambient Studies and Close-ups

For the nearer bodies, such as the moon, Mars, or Venus, which may be approached or visited before long, there will be no limit to the discoveries and surprises. It is almost certain that our present knowledge of these bodies will seem like a very poor and simplistic speculation (a kind of medieval science) once the new exploration has made some headway.

Our knowledge concerning the region of interplanetary space close to the earth already underwent this process. Ten years ago, all that was known about the physical conditions in interplanetary space was derived from data about the zodiacal light and the outer corona, from comet tails, and from meteors, coupled with indirect inferences from solar-terrestrial relationships and cosmic-ray studies. Now, the direct measurements of magnetic fields and particle fluxes made by means of the first interplanetary vehicles already carry the major weight of the observational data.

This is even more true for the upper layers of the earth's atmosphere. The results obtained from the drag on satellites and from instrumented geophysical rockets have become so numerous that the Committee on Space Research (COSPAR), established by the International Council of Scientific Unions, has compiled from them a set of reference tables which contain average densities, pressures, and temperatures up to 800 km.

The magnetic field studies have shown that it is logical to put the "boundary" of the earth at some 15 to 25 earth radii, the exact distance varying with the solar cycle. The Van Allen belts, therefore, form part of the earth. They provide the most striking example, so far, of the surprise discoveries that can be made by direct studies of ambient conditions by means of space vehicles.

Studies of Distant Objects

The second research possibility refers to distant objects. A space mission to Venus brings an astronaut as close to the center of the Galaxy as stepping up a doorstep brings him closer to the moon! (You may calculate the height of the doorstep from this equation.) This is astronomy in the classical sense, namely, the science of the world beyond reach. And the question naturally arises as to how this science can profit at all from the new tools of the space age. The answer is simply that the space vehicles may help us surmount certain natural obstacles presented by the earth and its immediate surroundings. Some such obstacles, which can be surmounted by various space tools, are now presented.

1. Ground Level Observations

We do not live on Venus. Hence, a good deal of astronomy can be done at sea level. This includes optical and near ultraviolet astronomy and radio astronomy.

2. Airplanes or High Mountains (5–10 km)

For accurate studies in the infrared (a few microns), and in the ultraviolet (beyond the Balmer limit), heights of 5 to 10 km are imperative for surmounting clouds, most water vapor absorption, and a good deal of the air scattering. It may also become necessary to establish radio telescopes at mountain sites for precision work in the centimeter and millimeter ranges. The gap which existed a few years ago between the photometric and polarimetric data on the corona, reaching to 2° from the sun, and those on the zodiacal light, starting at 30° from the sun, has now been successfully closed by the excellent observations of Blackwell (now at Oxford) from aircraft and from the mountain station at Chacultaya, Bolivia. This is just one example of significant progress made from conventional altitudes.

3. Balloons (30 km)

Altitudes reached by balloons are required and have been widely used for cosmic-ray studies, in which one wishes the majority count to come from primary particles. They have also proved to be excellent for optical studies in which it is important to improve the seeing drastically. The custom of whether or not to include balloon studies in the term space science varies. But they certainly give fine results as well as good practice for experiments with rockets and satellites.

4. Sounding Rockets (about 100 km)

5. Satellites (upwards from about 180 km)

6. Geophysical Rockets (about 400 km)

Let us consider these vehicles together to avoid repetition, and let us remember that we are discussing experiments aimed at the observation of distant objects. It is proper to include among these distant objects the sun, for the sun is certainly beyond reach of ambient measurements. (This is not true if we stretch the definition of the sun, as some recent authors have done, so that it includes a good part of the interplanetary matter and envelops the earth).

The transparency in the ultraviolet region becomes progressively better at the altitudes reached by rockets and satellites. A first attempt at detailing the precise absorption at each altitude and wavelength has been made by Hinteregger. Radio astronomy in two further decades (from about 10 Mc to 100 kc) becomes possible if the antenna is above most of the F-layer. This can be done with high satellites, and we shall have two reports on detailed plans.

The examples just mentioned refer to atmospheric absorption or reflection, but this is not the only way in which the high atmosphere can interfere with astronomical research. Some things, which we might wish to observe, penetrate through the atmosphere all right, but they are swamped by other effects unless we go to high altitudes. For instance, a dependable measurement of the electrons in the galactic cosmic rays would be crucial for the study of galactic magnetic fields. The connection is as follows: The cosmic-ray electrons circulate in the galactic magnetic fields and thereby emit a continuous radio spectrum. At most they form 1% of the primary cosmic rays of galactic origin, according to the present measurements. If it were possible to push this limit one order of magnitude further in accuracy, it would be possible to estimate from the observed radio spectrum rather precisely the magnitude of the magnetic fields in the galaxy. In turn, these fields would provide further clues to the problem of the dynamics and evolution of the spiral arms in our galaxy, a problem which occupies a central place in modern astrophysics.

7. Space Ships or Lunar Stations

Space ships or space probes sent to the moon or beyond enable us to surmount all obstacles presented by the earth at large. One of these is the general Lyman-α glare of the sky, which some time ago was attributed to solar radiation scattered by interplanetary hydrogen. Brandt's recent analysis, however, suggests that the scattering happens in a geocorona at 5 to 15 times the radius of the earth. This means that it is surmountable and that spacecraft could be used for studying Lyman-α emitters in the galaxy, as well as the multitude of important objects nearby.

8. Impossible Missions

It is possible to think that somebody a century from now may make fun about this word "impossible." However, this is the clearest manner of expressing that some obstacles appear insurmountable. One photograph taken with an amateur box camera from a vantage point some 10,000 light years away would give us a more precise idea of the spiral arms in our galaxy than the combined efforts of optical and radio astronomy of a full century are likely to give. But we had better forget about this tantalizing idea straightway. Another impossible mission is to measure the Lyman continuum radiation of the stars. The sharp boundaries of the Strömgren spheres, or ionized hydrogen regions, show how little this radiation can penetrate beyond ionized gas. Only a space ship sent to the vicinity of each star could observe the Lyman continuum.

Not quite as bad, but also nearly impossible, is the situation for radio astronomy below 100 kc/sec (wavelengths > 3 km). There is no problem with the ionosphere, for it has already been established by space experiments that enough of this radiation can penetrate the ionosphere. This is interesting by itself but is of little avail in doing distant astronomy, for interplanetary space may be entirely opaque to this radiation. The rather modest estimate of 100 electrons per cm^3 and no magnetic field places at 90 kc/sec the critical frequency below which no propagation takes place. The waves just above this frequency are strongly absorbed over distances of 1 astronomical unit. This implies an interesting combination of refraction and absorption effects at those frequencies. Combine these effects with those due to the magnetic field and to the continuous changes in density, temperature, and magnetic field brought about by solar streams; also, consider the possibility to conduct such measurements simultaneously from different points, and to combine natural noise studies with studies of propagation from artificial sources. The result is the recipe for a most fascinating and inexhaustible field of study. However, these experiments should properly be classed as ambient research. To observe the radio noise from the galaxy or other distant objects will require that we get "out of this mess" to a point well away from the dense parts of the solar system, which is again a next-to-impossible task.

Caution Required

This brief review is concluded by adding a few words of caution.

The first refers to the *communication* problem. We have silently assumed that once there will be an instrument on Mars taking measurements, it will be just a matter of technique to communicate these data to the earth. This is by no means true. First, mankind may be so busy with its nearby interests that the radio frequency spectrum offers no free channels to bring these data back to earth. World-wide agreement is vital to keep this opportunity open. For the first time, over a year ago, the International Telecommunications Union granted to radio astronomy and space research the status of "services" in their regulations. It is now necessary that the scientists should press their governments to see to it that proper allocations of frequency bands for these services are made and enforced. Otherwise, these two branches of science will be dead and we might as well cancel the rest of this Symposium.

Secondly, natural noise is a severe competitor of communication over such distances. The naive ideal of a continuous view by television of what is going on on Mars seems out of the question. One bit per second is quite feasible from that distance; 100 bits per second would be a fine achievement. This places severe restraints on the scientist who plans the program for this exploration, and a fair amount of reduction may have to be programmed before the data are sent back. The papers following will give many illustrations of this statement.

Even deeper should be our concern, and even firmer our determination, that man should not spoil conditions in space by ill-advised action. Thus far man has been described as going about space age astronomy as he has gone about ordinary astronomy: observing and trying to understand how things are, but not trying to change them. However, the space age has opened unmistakable opportunities for a more active, experimental type of approach. Such experiments have fascinating as well as dangerous aspects. Generally, they should be handled with the utmost caution and with due consideration of any detrimental effects on human existence and human values, including other sciences. A fine example of such an experiment, which gave important scientific results and had no bad effects, for all we can tell, was Project Argus, which created temporarily an artificial radiation belt. More questionable is, for instance, project West Ford, which was scheduled to put many resonant dipoles in orbit and may seriously affect normal astronomy and radio astronomy. And still highly problematic is the question of how to avoid with reasonable certainty that the first vehicle landing on Mars will poison all Martian life and thus destroy the very object which easily ranks highest in value among the scientific objects of space research.

1.2 Current Objectives of Astronomical Space Research (from Gamma to Infrared Radiation)

P. SWINGS

INSTITUT D'ASTROPHYSIQUE, Liege, Belgium

Introduction

In a short, general introductory report to a space age astronomy symposium, originality is not easy. There is a half-hour limit for a topic which would require a whole year course. Several books, monographs, and proceedings of symposia have been published in the course of 1960 and 1961, among which may be singled out "Science in Space," edited by L. V. Berkner and H. Odishaw; "Space Astrophysics," edited by William Liller; the Proceedings of the COSPAR Symposia, of the A.A.S. Symposium and of the Liège Symposium on the Far Ultraviolet Spectra of Astronomical Bodies. In the draft report of I.A.U. Commission 44, an attempt has also been made to review the present status of space age astronomy. In these books, reviews, reports, or proceedings, the problems have been classified either according to the vehicles employed, or according to the cosmic objects under consideration. Here we shall try to classify the problems according to the involved spectral range. It does not appear useful to give a bibliography here, which would necessarily be long. All the references may be found in the books mentioned above.

Happily, this task is simplified by several factors: our colleague van de Hulst has reviewed part of the general topic; scientists from various countries will certainly describe the work done or planned in their country; there will be technical reports on specific topics of a purely scientific nature (as, for example, the vehicles themselves, their instrumentation, the detectors of radiation, the tracking, and orbit determinations, the comunication problems, etc.). Moreover, quite a few chapters have been excluded, and rightly so, by the Program Committee.

For all these reasons it seems essential that we should concentrate on the fundamental problems and on illustrative examples, without going systematically into references to specific countries or to chronology. Although there is a close interplay between astronomy and engineering,

ments. In particular, one cannot too much stress the need for further spectroscopic laboratory work in the far ultraviolet and in the infrared regions, and for further spectroscopic study of the soft X-rays.

The following fields will be examined successively: γ- and X-rays; electronic transitions in atoms and molecules; vibration-rotation and pure rotation transitions in molecules; miscellaneous astrophysical phenomena concerned with radiation.

From the point of view of the covered spectral range, the line of demarcation between these fields is ill-defined. Originally, the term "X-ray" was applied only to radiation emitted by a metallic target bombarded by high energy electrons. Indeed, we shall see that this old point of view is still of astronomical interest for lunar, planetary, and satellitic explorations. The X-rays are essentially produced in two ways: either as discrete lines resulting from transitions in the inner electronic shells of atoms, or as continua due to thermal radiation, and collision and magnetic Bremsstrahlung. The γ-rays used to be considered as nuclear transitions of higher energy, hence shorter wavelengths. However, the spectral range is no longer a criterion: high energy electron or nuclear accelerators have produced X-continua at wavelengths which were considered the exclusive domain of γ-rays. Similarly, the line of demarcation of the X- and uv-spectra is no better defined. The optical ultraviolet spectra are due to energy transitions of an outer electron, but in the case of highly ionized atoms, an uv-photon may have a wavelength shorter than an X-photon of a light element: as an example, the resonance lines of ions such as Fe XIV which give rise to forbidden lines in the visible region of the solar corona fall mainly in the region $\lambda <$ 50 Å. We may continue in the same way: the electronic spectra of atoms and molecules extend approximately over the same spectral range, but they also overlap in the infrared with certain vibration-rotation transitions of molecules.

1.2.1 Gamma- and X-Rays

Gamma- and X-ray astronomy is an entirely new chapter of astrophysics; new mechanisms are involved, simple extrapolations from known data are generally impossible, and results of a wholly new character may be expected. Gamma-ray astronomy requires special coincidence-counting techniques for spectroscopic and angular resolution that are quite unfamiliar to astronomers. No one really has any definite idea of the amounts of γ- and X-energy which may be expected in stars or galaxies.

Gamma-ray astronomy was opened up by Explorer XI launched at Cape Canaveral on April 27, 1961 in an experiment by W. Kraushaar and G. Clark which, we understand, is giving good results. As for X-ray astronomy, it really started in 1948 when photographic emulsions protected by Be and Al filters were flown in a V2 and recorded solar X-rays. Since then the solar X-rays in the band 2–20 Å have been the object of many observations from rockets (U.S., U.S.S.R., Great Britain) and satellites (U.S., U.S.S.R.). Efforts to observe X-ray emission from astronomical objects other than the sun have yielded negative results with rockets; there is a need for the longer observing times available in satellites. How will X-rays from cosmic sources be observed? We shall have to sweep sectors of the sky in an endeavor to locate X-sources. Or we shall assume that certain objects are likely sources of X-radiation, point in their direction, and measure the flux of X-rays if there is any. Actually, a γ-mapping by a satellite such as Explorer XI should locate regions of particular interest for further detailed study of the γ-emission.*

Gamma rays may have various cosmic origins. In the soft range 2×10^{-3} to 6×10^{-2} Å they may result from the radioactive decay of excited nuclei,† from the fusion of light elements, and possibly from the annihilation of electrons and positrons. In the hard range 5×10^{-5} to 2×10^{-4} Å they may result from the decay of neutral pi-mesons produced in the interactions of nuclei with high energy particles and from the annihilation of nucleons and antinucleons. For example, when a fast proton, such as a cosmic-ray proton, encounters an interstellar nucleus (hydrogen or dust particle), the latter may be wrecked and give rise, after transformations, to a neutral pi-meson which decays rapidly into a pair of gamma rays traveling in opposite directions. The direction of the γ-ray points toward the region where the collision between the cosmic particle and the interstellar nucleus occurred.‡ We may expect to find production of γ-rays in the solar flares, in old supernovae (such as the Crab nebula), in the nucleus of our galaxy, in galaxies in collision, etc. Actually, we may expect γ- and X-emission in certain radio sources, in which the turbulent hydromagnetic regions give rise to radio noise through the synchrotron radiation of energetic electrons.

* Explorer XI is designed to map the sky (in intensity and direction) at about 10^{-4} Å with a field of view of about 15°; the instrument will discriminate against neutrons. The orientation of the satellite is determined by photocells serving as sun and earth sensors. Of course, the instrument will also observe solar γ-radiation, if there is any.

† S. P. Shen and S. N. Milford (1961) have considered the decay of intergalactic and interstellar radioactive nuclei (K^{40}; Tl^{208}) yielding monoenergetic γ-rays $\lambda > 3 \times 10^{-3}$ Å; this would give an intergalactic γ-ray flux well below the present detection limit.

‡ Contrary to the primary cosmic ray particles, whose trajectories are affected by the galactic, interplanetary, and terrestrial magnetic fields.

The stellar or interstellar production of continuous X-rays may be due to various mechanisms, besides thermal radiation and K-ionization. They may arise in (nonmagnetic) collision Bremsstrahlung, i.e., acceleration of electrons. A more powerful mechanism is the magnetic Bremsstrahlung (or Schwinger radiation, or synchrotron radiation). The energetic electrons moving through the magnetic fields which are present in our galaxy emit continuous radiation which may be strong in the X-region. We may anticipate that X-rays are emitted in the same cosmic sources as the γ-rays: the Crab nebula, the center of our galaxy, colliding galaxies, and other radio sources. Various hypotheses have been put forth for the origin of the energetic electrons by Hoyle, Ginsburg, and others.

It has also been suggested that nuclear reactions occur in the peculiar A-stars with rapidly changing magnetic fields; as a result, γ-rays would be emitted from the nuclei in excited states, and X-rays by Bremsstrahlung of electrons. At any rate, X-ray observations promise valuable information on the hydromagnetic forces in the sun, stars, and galaxies.

Observations from rockets have already provided a fair amount of information on solar X-rays, although one essential observation is still entirely lacking: the resolution of the soft X-ray region (say $\lambda < 80$ Å) where the discrete resonance lines of the highly excited coronal ions are located, in addition to any possible thermal and Bremsstrahlung continuum. That the X-rays originate in the corona has been established during total solar eclipses. Indeed, while the corona is a million times fainter than the solar disk in the visible region, it is the only contributor to the solar spectrum shortward of 100 Å. X-rays are emitted by the quiet corona, but they appear with much greater intensity in active regions believed to be coronal condensations overlying the plage formations.* The intensity of the solar flux in the range 10–100 Å is sufficient to explain the formation of the E-layer of the ionosphere. On the normal sun, some energy has also been observed shortward of 10 Å; during flares radiation shortward of 1 Å has been detected.

Actually, the solar radiation satellite No. I (SR I, 1960 η_2) is transmitting measurements of the solar X-intensity (2–8 Å) as well as of $L\alpha$.* The signals are received and recorded by four Minitrack stations, but the value of the experiment would be greatly enhanced if the signals were received at a much greater number of stations. The information on the forthcoming NRL satellite solar X-ray experiment (SR III, X-ray detectors in regions 2–8 Å and 8–20 Å) has been distributed to various

* The $L\alpha$-radiation is relatively constant even during solar storms, while the X-emission varies greatly.

COSPAR members who have been invited to participate in the measurements.

Many projects of solar X-ray experiments are in preparation in the U.S., the U.S.S.R., Great Britain, and other countries. The success of the NRL pinhole camera experiment from a rocket points the way to one interesting satellite experiment: the recording of X-ray images (which will be especially interesting during periods of solar activity). The NRL will map the sources of X-ray emission at 8 to 18 Å and 44 to 60 Å with pinhole collimation, giving a resolution of 2 or 3 minutes. Another experiment will be aimed at determining whether surge-ejected material acts as a source of X-rays (a single Geiger counter suffices for this!). Two cases of short bursts of solar flare X-emission (accompanying type III radio bursts) have been recorded by Winckler at balloon altitudes (one in the 0.02 Å range, duration 18 seconds; the other in the 0.4 Å range, duration 100 seconds); this problem will now be investigated from satellites.

Other experiments on solar X-rays are in preparation; they are often combined with γ-experiments. A solar X-ray telescope will give images of small regions of the sun in the range 3–8 Å. There will be measurements of fluxes of γ- and X-rays (from 2.10^{-5} to 10^{-4} Å, 10^{-2} to 10^{-1} Å, 0.1 to 1 Å, etc.).

Solar X-rays are known to be responsible for certain ionospheric phenomena; they also play a major role—together with solar ultraviolet radiation (see Section 1.2.2)—in the formation of ionospheres on other planets.

Should we expect to be able to observe X-radiations from objects other than the sun? For the latter star some theoretical work on the X-emission appears promising (C. W. Allen), and similar considerations have been applied to stars (C. de Jager and L. Neven; W. Grasberger and L. Henyey). But the uncertainties involved in the calculations of stellar X-emission are so large that we can hardly consider the present theoretical data as more than guesses. Do all main sequence stars have coronas similar to the solar corona ($T \sim 10^6$ degrees), or are stellar coronas exceptional features?* Do objects such as supernovae, novae, Wolf-Rayet, or supergiant stars have brighter coronas than the sun? Certainly we expect flare stars to be rich sources of X-emission, since they exhibit phenomena of the same sort as the solar flares. An object like the Crab nebula, whose visual and radio emission is probably due to synchrotron radiation, should be a strong source of X-emission. Catastrophic phe-

* Anyway, if a star does not emit more X-radiation than the sun there would be no possibility of observing it.

nomena such as collisions of stars, as may occur during the collision of two galaxies (S. N. Milford), would probably create X-radiation. Radio and gamma sources may also be X-sources.

A convincing decision on all these questions must await direct observations. Because of the interstellar absorption (continua of H, He I, and He II, and secondarily of the C, N, and O ions, see Section 1.2.2) no stellar radiation will appear between λ 912 and 20 or even 10 Å.

Several teams preparing the future lunar and planetary explorations are engaged in X- and γ-ray instrumentation. In the satellites for lunar exploration, a gamma-ray spectrometer will measure the radioactivity at the wavelength of the spectral line 8.5×10^{-3} Å associated with the decay of potassium 40; X-ray spectrographs and diffractometers are being designed. It is intended to study the moon's surface with an X-ray telescope. During flares the flux of solar X- and short uv-photons may give rise to fluorescence on the moon. Moreover, a beam of high energy particles may create a lunar X-ray primary flux. It does seem that an X-image forming device would be of great interest for studies of the surface of the moon.

This leads us to the problems involved in X-ray instrumentation. First we must distinguish between flux-gatherers and imaging instruments; the latter are definitely more complex. For a long time microscopy by X-radiation has been the object of many investigations; it would seem that by turning around such an instrument one may make a telescope. Actually, this problem—which had no practical interest before space astronomy—is indeed complicated if a good resolution is desired, and this is precisely one of the interests of short wavelengths. The reflection of X-rays requires an angle of incidence of almost 90°, depending on the wavelength and the material; nontotal reflection in the nongrazing incidence region is vanishingly small. For $\lambda \sim 10$ Å the total reflection requires an incidence angle i greater than 89°; for $\lambda \sim 1$ Å, i differs from 90° by only a few minutes of arc (for $\lambda = 100$ Å, $i \sim 85°$). Various geometrical systems have been designed: combinations of paraboloids and hyperboloids; double-cylinder crossed-mirror systems; two sets of plane mirrors at right angles. Focusing may also be accomplished by diffraction, rather than by reflection, through the use of Fresnel zone plates. These problems are studied extensively in the U.S. (P. H. Kirkpatrick, A. Baez, R. Giacconi, B. Rossi, etc.), in Great Britain, and in other countries.

The detectors require also careful selection; no single type of detector is suitable for all purposes or through a wide spectral range.

In order to obtain the resolved spectrum of the solar X-rays, grazing incidence (optical) grating spectrographs are used; laboratory experiments are also made with organic crystals. Actually, the whole field of the dispersing systems in the γ- and X-region requires much additional laboratory work.

1.2.2 Electronic Transitions in Atoms and Molecules

The permitted or forbidden, discrete or continuous transitions of the outer electrons in atoms and molecules cover a wide spectral range, extending from the far infrared (example: forbidden transitions $^3P_2$-$^3P_1$, $^3P_1$-$^3P_0$ of atmospheric OI at 63 μ and 147 μ) to the very short wavelengths (example: resonance lines of the highly ionized atoms of the solar corona). At the short-wavelength end they overlap with the X-rays, while, in the infrared, they fall in the same spectral range as the vibration-rotation and pure rotation transitions of molecules. In this section we shall be concerned with the ultraviolet region; the infrared will be considered in Section 1.2.3. Observations of the far ultraviolet spectrum of the sun from rockets have already furnished a fair amount of important information; but the investigation of the ultraviolet spectrum of other astronomical bodies is only at its beginning.

We shall not review here the remarkable results obtained on the far ultraviolet spectrum of the sun by four teams working with rockets: the NRL group (H. Friedman, R. Tousey, etc.), which has obtained the best photographed spectra down to λ 500 Å (plus important data on the behavior of solar $L\alpha$); the Colorado group (W. A. Rense), which has obtained photographed spectra down to 84 Å; the Geophysics Research Directorate group (H. E. Hinteregger), which has provided the best absolute intensity measurements down to λ 260 Å; and the Russian group, which has described the near ultraviolet solar spectrum. The excellent ultraviolet spectrograms—some stigmatic, revealing variations with location on the sun—show successively the photospheric, the chromospheric, and the coronal radiation as they extend to shorter wavelengths. There are still unassigned emissions. The admirable profiles of $L\alpha$ obtained by NRL must be secured over longer periods. The region 500–80 Å is still unsatisfactorily known, and we know nothing of the structure of the spectrum shortward of 80 Å. Actually, the spectrum of the corona is still unknown from λ 3000 Å to about λ 1500 Å; for these wavelengths, mirror coronagraphs are being designed in France, Great Britain, and the U.S. There are many projects in preparation in the U.S., the U.S.S.R., France, and Great Britain for additional ultraviolet spectroscopic information on the sun. Certainly, much important work remains to be done with rockets; it should be remembered that certain of them may be equipped in advance and launched rapidly for observation of sudden phenomena. Yet it clearly appears that we need the longer periods of observation provided by the astronomical satellites in order to progress substantially in solar ultraviolet spectroscopy. Despite all the recent observational results we have as yet no satisfactory model of the chromosphere and corona. We shall progress greatly in this field when we have several detailed profiles, besides $L\alpha$ (especially of He I and He II lines, and of lines of the C, N, and O ions), and when we know how the profiles, especially of $L\alpha$, vary with activity and with location on the sun.

The ultraviolet results obtained with rockets simplify greatly the planning of satellite solar experiments. These should and will give observations on the following topics: variations of the ultraviolet spectrum with time (especially variations of the high energy emissions of the chromosphere and corona during rapid solar events) and with location; profiles of various lines and their variations; spectroheliograms, especially in $L\alpha$,* λ 584 He I and λ 304 He II; coronal observations. Actually, the preparations for these experiments by satellites are well under way at various institutions, especially at NRL and at Harvard (L. Goldberg). The field of solar physics will receive a considerable impetus.

We shall not rediscuss the NRL results on the $L\alpha$-glow of the night sky. This glow is due to the scattering of solar $L\alpha$ by hydrogen gas of the geocorona† and/or the interplanetary space. On the other hand, no evidence is found for a glow in He I 584 or He II 304: the intensity of the night helium glow must be less than 10% of that of $L\alpha$. Experiments with rockets launched to greater altitudes ($L\alpha$-glow, and the narrow absorption core of solar $L\alpha$) will eventually reveal the exact role of the geocorona and of the interplanetary hydrogen.

The solar uv- and X-radiation are responsible for the ionization of the planetary atmospheres; this problem cannot yet be handled theoretically in a satisfactory manner (M. Nicolet) on account of our ignorance about the chemical composition of the planetary atmospheres, about the infrared emission of planets, and about certain absorption coefficients. In the case of Venus we also need the still uncertain period of axial rota-

* A $L\alpha$ solar disk image scanner will soon be placed on a satellite by NRL. Valuable information will be obtained from a comparison of spectroheliograms in $L\alpha$ (which arises far out in the chromosphere) and in $H\alpha$ (which comes from lower levels of the chromosphere). A stigmatic Wadsworth mounting will give a solar image in $L\alpha$, of 10 mm diameter with a resolution of 1 minute of arc (weight: 1.5 kg!).

† By geocorona we mean here the neutral component of the outer fringe of the earth's atmosphere, extending outward several earth radii. The neutral hydrogen geocorona originates probably in the photodissociation of atmospheric compounds containing hydrogen atoms (H_2O, CH_4); the H atoms diffuse upward. The ionized component of the geocorona—the protonosphere—consists of ionized hydrogen.

tion. The solar radiation is also responsible for the planetary airglows, which would give most valuable information on the planetary atmospheres, as would also planetary aurorae. The airglows and aurorae on Venus and Mars must differ greatly from each other, and also from their telluric counterparts. Unfortunately, the existence of emission from the unilluminated side of Venus remains uncertain (J. L. Weinberg and G. Newkirk).*

We are still very ignorant of the composition and physics of the interstellar gas, although the latter plays a dominant role in all the problems concerning the birth and evolution of stars. This is due to the fact that our present observations are limited to the absorption lines of a few neutral or ionized atoms and molecules which have their resonance transitions in the observable region. Actually, most of our information is based on the observations of the interstellar lines of Ca^+ and Na, combined with data on hydrogen; the other observed interstellar atoms or radicals (Ca, K, Fe, Ti^+, CH, CH^+, and CN) give only very weak lines. The situation will be quite different in the ultraviolet where we shall find the resonance absorption lines of C, N, O, Mg, and Fe in several ionization states. There is even a possibility that we may find the lines of the lowest ground state of diatomic hydrogen, λ 1108 Å and λ 1008 Å. The discovery of interstellar H_2 would be of great significance. Work is being prepared on high resolution spectroscopy of the ultraviolet interstellar lines at Princeton, under the direction of Lyman Spitzer, Jr.

However, the absorption continua of interstellar hydrogen and helium cause a great disappointment in blocking completely the region λ 912–λ 20 Å. Except for the nearest stars, no observation will be possible in this spectral range. Even in the nearest stars the profiles of the Lyman lines will be affected by the interstellar Lyman lines. The $L\alpha$-emission of galaxies which have a Doppler shift greater than 1000 km/sec will not be absorbed by the hydrogen atoms of our galaxy. We may expect to find hydrogen-rich and hydrogen-poor galaxies. If a galaxy has lost its hydrogen in a collision, this hydrogen may reveal itself by its $L\alpha$-emission in the space between galaxies.

In Section 1.2.1 we have already raised the question of the stellar coronas which would affect greatly the whole ultraviolet spectra of stars. The immense amount of information on stars which the region λ 912–λ 3000 Å will provide is obvious and has been stressed on many occasions. High-dispersion ultraviolet studies of single objects will furnish a wealth of new data. Even scans of fairly low resolution will give valuable information.

* Such observations may be easier from high altitude balloons.

The ultraviolet region is especially valuable in giving us a possibility to determine reliable abundances of the light elements in stars, nebulae, interstellar space, etc. For these light elements, ionized as well as neutral, the lines falling in the region from 3000 Å to 1 μ are due to transitions between excited states. In many astronomical conditions we do not know the temperature with accuracy, or conditions are far from thermodynamic equilibrium. As a result no accurate determination of abundance is possible for H, He, C, N, O, the halogens, and the noble gases. These abundances, which will be obtained in the far ultraviolet, are especially important because of their relationship to the process of thermonuclear energy generation in stars. The new abundances may possibly also help in disentangling the picture of stellar populations, since chemical composition is linked to population type.

The ultraviolet spectra of planetary nebulae, which will be obtained by orbiting telescopes, will give us valuable information on electron densities and temperatures, as well as on abundances. Except for surprises these spectra should be rather simple: the resonance lines of C, N, and O in various states of ionization; the recombination lines of He I, He II, C III, N IV, O II to O V; and a few forbidden lines. The Lyman lines will be reabsorbed in interstellar space or in the nebula itself. The ultraviolet spectra of the nuclei will permit further refinements of the Zanstra theory, a field well prepared by recent theoretical work, especially by Hummer and Seaton.

The preparation of space astronomy observations and their subsequent interpretation obviously require theoretical investigations on all cosmic objects. But it also requires a considerable amount of laboratory work. Even in the simple case of the far ultraviolet spectrum of the sun there remain a number of unassigned emissions. We may imagine that the number of puzzling lines will be much greater in stellar spectra of all kinds. Hence the urgent need for the measurement and analysis of spectra of many atoms and molecules of astronomical interest. In the ultraviolet we especially need wavelengths, term classifications, and intensities (theoretical and experimental) for highly ionized atoms. Edlén has stressed the unsatisfactory state of our knowledge in this field: even for the highly ionized atoms present or likely to be present in the solar corona some laboratory data are inadequate or entirely lacking, so that assignments must be based on extrapolations along isoelectronic sequences. Moreover, for future work on stellar coronas we should know the wavelengths, term classifications, and intensities for higher stages of ionization than those found in the solar corona. Such investigations involve the development of better sources of excitation. Similarly, despite the recent endeavors, we need much additional work on the far ultraviolet and the infrared spectra of molecules of astronomical interest: this includes wavelengths, classifications, and intensities of discrete lines, and also absorption coefficients in the molecular continua.* Of course, such progress involves the development of new sources of continua in the far ultraviolet, new excitation sources, and new calibration devices (H. Kienle, H. E. Hinteregger, etc.).

Far ultraviolet instrumentation requires developments on reflectivity of the mirrors and gratings, narrow band filters, phototubes and the corresponding calibrating devices,† television tubes, polarization effects, dispersing systems. Actually, quite a few of these problems apply to the infrared as well; we shall come back to this point in Section 1.2.3.

1.2.3 Vibration-Rotation and Pure Rotation Transitions of Molecules, and Other Spectroscopic Problems of the Infrared Region

The permitted and forbidden vibration-rotation transitions of molecules (example: organic molecules) occur in the near-infrared region, while the permitted and forbidden pure rotation transitions lie in the far infrared and in the millimeter-wave band. Very little astronomical work has been done in the infrared, and indeed much experimental work is also needed. While this section is essentially concerned with molecules, we shall add a few comments regarding atomic or other non-molecular questions concerned with the infrared.

Actually, much important infrared astronomical work which may be carried out from the ground or, at least, from balloon altitudes, has not been performed yet. The essential reason is instrumental: progress on high-sensitivity infrared receivers and adequate dispersing techniques will certainly be paralleled by astronomical observations. It is well known that certain infrared results, such as the detection of water vapor in the Cytherean atmosphere, may be obtained from balloons or high altitude aircraft. Much remains to be done in this field. Yet balloon observations will be subject to limitations: even at altitudes higher than 20 km there remain appreciable telluric absorption bands; moreover, the duration of the observations in balloons or aircraft is limited.

In the infrared we are chiefly concerned with fairly cool objects, but not exclusively. For example, as long ago as 1944, the desirability of obtaining the infrared spectrum of the solar corona was stressed, on account of the existence of infrared forbidden lines. Indeed, new infrared forbidden atomic lines will be found in nebulae and peculiar bright-

* Also in the atomic continua.

† An interesting example of improvement is the Bendix photomultiplier which makes double dispersion unnecessary to avoid the stray light of long wavelength in the grating scanning spectrographs.

line stars. Even the airglow of our atmosphere may reveal the [O I] lines at 63 and 147 μ. The infrared will furnish important information not only on cool objects, but also on sources which are very heavily reddened by interstellar dust (example: infrared emission of obscured population II regions, like the galactic center), and on particular emissions or absorptions of long wavelength.

The infrared spectrum of the sun, and especially of the sunspots, will certainly reveal new molecules. *A fortiori* we may expect new molecules, possibly polyatomic molecules, in the coolest M, S, and N stars; actually, we may even search for extremely cool stars (protostars!) in the long wavelengths. Certain peculiar stars, such as R Coronae Borealis, deserve a special infrared spectroscopic investigation. The infrared spectra of planets will provide a wealth of information.

Infrared observations on the interstellar matter may also bring rich rewards. One may possibly find the permitted vibration-rotation or pure rotation transitions of heteronuclear interstellar radicals such as CH, NH, OH, CN, CH^+. The forbidden H_2 lines have also been suggested, especially the pure rotation lines near 85 μ ($1 \leftrightarrow 0$), 42 μ ($2 \leftrightarrow 1$), and 28 μ ($2 \leftrightarrow 0$), and the fundamental (forbidden) vibration-rotation band near 2.4 μ. There also remains a possibility that unexpected interstellar bands may be discovered in the infrared, and may help in identifying the presently unassigned bands of the ordinary region. This would provide greatly desired clues to the chemical composition of interstellar matter.

Infrared instruments are being prepared in various institutions for space observations, especially in view of planetary explorations. As an example, an infrared grating spectrophotometer for spectral scanning, of the Ebert type, is in preparation. It will be used with a reflecting telescope and probably will employ a lead selenide detector. Many geographic elements of Mars should be resolved, and the signal should provide accurate values of the wavelengths, widths, and depths of the bands.

Much laboratory work remains to be done. As in the other sections of this report, we must first stress the fact that many data (wavelengths, classification, and transition probabilities) for atomic and molecular spectra of astronomical interest are still missing in the infrared.

It seems probable that interferometric techniques of infrared spectroscopy will help greatly. This is especially the case for spectrometry by the Michelson interferometer with Fourier transformation. The principle of this method dates back to Michelson himself (1891); actually, Rubens and Wood, in 1906, obtained the first spectra in the far infrared by using it. But it is the availability of modern electronic computers which has made the method really efficient and practical. Very promising applications have been made recently to the infrared spectra of the nightglow, Venus, Mars, and cool stars.

Other laboratory work which is obviously desired concerns high-sensitivity receivers, imaging devices, intensity-calibration devices, filters, reflecting and refracting materials. There should also be additional measurements of reflection, polarization, and thermal emissivity by planetary-type surface materials, including ices or snows of various compositions.

1.2.4 Miscellaneous Astrophysical Phenomena Concerned with Radiation

General Ultraviolet Survey of the Sky (Celescope project)

This project is as necessary as the BD-or HD-catalogs have been. It will reveal the objects or the regions which deserve special attention. It is in the hands of the Smithsonian Astrophysical Observatory (F. L. Whipple). The orbiting astronomical observatory will achieve the mapping of the celestial sphere in three ultraviolet ranges by television techniques using Westinghouse uvicon detectors. A slitless spectrograph with a resolving power of the order of 10 Å will also furnish valuable data, including possibly new population-linked spectral characteristics among the strong lines of the light elements. The first preliminary trial will be made with a sounding rocket.

Far Ultraviolet and Infrared Spectrophotometry

In stars with effective temperature from 4000° to 9000° most of the radiated energy lies in the observable portion of the spectrum; hence the bolometric correction is small, its relative error may be large without modifying substantially the estimated total amount of stellar radiation. The situation is entirely different for hotter and cooler stars, since the amount of unobservable radiation (ultraviolet or infrared) may be much greater than the observable. Yet in various fields of astrophysics it is essential to know accurately the total luminosities. An example is the case of the hot stars exciting nebular luminosities. Despite the important theoretical investigations on the far ultraviolet radiation of stars, great uncertainties remain, and direct ultraviolet intensity measurements would bring most welcome data.

Boggess and Dunkelmann have already determined some color indices (λ 2700 Å—visual) by rocket observations in the region λ 2530–λ 2880 Å. Stellar flux measurements in the middle ultraviolet (bands centered at 2700, 2600, and 2200 Å) have been made by A. Boggess, III. Using objective-grating spectrophotometers, T. P. Stecher and J. E. Milligan have obtained spectra for 10 stars between 1600 and 4000 Å. All this work was done with rockets.

Broad band photometry of individual stars (including intensities of emission lines in planetary and diffuse nebulae) will be carried in the same vehicle as the Celescope survey (A. D. Code). Absolute spectrophotometry of selected stars, nebulae, and galaxies will be performed by another team (James Milligan).

For the sun, measures of the ultraviolet energy curve and of the darkening or brightening toward the limb are in preparation at several institutions (France, U.S.). Experiments in the spectrophotometry of planetary atmospheres, especially Venus, using filters and polarizers, are in preparation. They will contribute greatly to our knowledge of the planets.

The topic of interstellar dust* has already been mentioned on various occasions. Infrared and, especially, ultraviolet spectrophotometry will be welcome in order to extend the law of interstellar reddening to a wider spectral range. This should furnish valuable information on the refractive index, the numbers, and the diameters of the interstellar grains. It is known that the scattering by solid grains of radius a is a function of the ratio a/λ and of the refractive index; when a/λ is near unity the function differs in a complex way from the Rayleigh law, and may even give rise to an "interstellar bluing" in the ultraviolet. The extension of the "interstellar coloring" curve over a wider spectral range would provide information which may eventually solve the problem of determining the nature and sizes of the scattering particles. Such a result would have a great number of applications, for example, to the gaseous nebulae, where the interstellar absorption alters the relative intensities of the bright lines. On the other hand, the determination of the relative intensities of certain emission lines of nebulae may also furnish information on the interstellar coloring; e.g., by comparison of the two forbidden lines from the same upper levels in [O III], λ 2322 ($^3P_1$-$^1S_0$) and λ 4363 ($^1D_2$-$^1S_0$).

An extension of the "coloring curve" is already possible from a high altitude balloon (T. Gehrels).

Satellite Solar Coronagraph

Coronagraphs for satellites (and rockets) are in preparation at various institutions; we mentioned in Section 1.2.2 those aimed at obtaining ultraviolet spectrograms. A coronagraph is being built by NRL to scan the white light corona and monitor its form and intensity over an

* We do not consider here the problems related to the interplanetary micrometeorites which have been detected by the Russian and American space probes.

extended period of time. Since atmospheric diffusion will be absent, the coronagraph, if properly built (perfect optics, protection from direct sunlight), could study the changes occurring in the K-corona (produced by free electrons; no Fraunhofer lines; strong radial polarization) and in the F-corona (due to dust scattering; presenting Fraunhofer lines; nearly unpolarized). The K- and F-coronas may be separated with polarization devices. Observations over a long period of time may possibly reveal the expulsion of the clouds of plasma which reach the earth following solar flares.

Let me conclude my part of this report by expressing my professional regret not to be 30 years younger. The young men who are now going into astronomy are those who will really make space age astronomy. They will have tremendous opportunities.

CHAPTER 2

Vehicle Systems and Instrumentation of Current Projects

2.1 NASA Launch Vehicle Development Program

ABRAHAM HYATT

NATIONAL AERONAUTICS AND SPACE ADMINISTRATION, Washington, D.C.

Before beginning the discussion of the NASA Launch Vehicle Program, it may be of value to briefly discuss the NASA itself. Many people are fairly well acquainted with this organization but there are many others who are not quite sure what it is, when it started, and what it does. In addition to explaining these items, the broad objectives of this organization will be discussed very briefly.

The National Aeronautics and Space Administration, frequently referred to as NASA, was established by an Act of Congress on October 1, 1958.

The declaration of policy and purpose by Congress states that:

(a) The Congress hereby declares that it is the policy of the United States that activities in space should be devoted to peaceful purposes for the benefit of all mankind.

(b) The Congress declares that the general welfare and security of the United States require that adequate provision be made for aeronautical and space activities. The Congress further declares that such activities shall be the responsibility of, and shall be directed by, a civilian agency exercising control over aeronautical and space activities sponsored by the United States, except that

> activities . . . associated with the development of weapon systems, military operations, or the defense of the United States (including the research and development necessary to make effective provision for the defense of the United States) shall be the responsibility of, and shall be directed by, the Department of Defense. . . .
>
> The Congress further states that the aeronautical and space activities of the United States shall be conducted so as to contribute materially to one or more of the following objectives. [There are a large number of these objectives: We will only mention three. They are:]
>
> [1] The expansion of human knowledge of phenomena in the atmosphere and space,
>
> [2] The development and operation of vehicles capable of carrying instruments, equipment, supplies, and living organisms through space: and
>
> [3] The preservation of the role of the United States as a leader in aeronautical and space science and technology and in the application thereof to the conduct of peaceful activities within and outside the atmosphere.

After the law was passed, the President of the United States by proclamation established the National Aeronautics and Space Administration. The first older government agency to be absorbed by the NASA was the National Advisory Committee for Aeronautics. It was a federal organization of some 9000 people and had been in existence for more than 40 years. The NACA operated three research centers, located at Langley, Virginia; Cleveland, Ohio; and Moffett Field, California. These centers were equipped with the most advanced laboratories. The engineers and scientists manning them formed the backbone of the new NASA.

Soon after the new organization also took over from the Army the Jet Propulsion Laboratory. This was an organization of some 3000 scientists, engineers, and technicians operated by the California Institute of Technology for the Federal Government. In this type of arrangement the government usually owns the land, buildings, and equipment. The university operates the laboratory for the government under a contract.

About 1 year later a decision was made by the President to transfer the technical team of the Army Ballistic Missile Agency to NASA. This group with their laboratories are located at Huntsville, Alabama. Not long ago this center was renamed and is now known as the George C. Marshall Space Flight Center. The director of this organization of some 5000 people is Dr. Wernher von Braun.

At the beginning of the NASA a new center was created which is now known as the Goddard Space Flight Center. It is located at Beltsville, Maryland, just outside of Washington, D. C.

To summarize what has been said about the organization, we have now on government payroll about 17,000 people. In addition to this number, there are 2400 people at the Jet Propulsion Laboratory. There are three research centers whose function is to do basic and applied research. The Jet Propulsion Laboratory is responsible for designing and developing the spacecraft for the lunar and planetary exploration program. Goddard Space Flight Center has the responsibility for designing and developing the spacecraft for satellites about the earth. Marshall Space Flight Center is charged with developing the rocket engines and the launching vehicles. They also have the job of launching all of the NASA vehicles. This is done at the Atlantic Missile Range, Pacific Missile Range, and at Wallops Island, Virginia.

Two other important groups must be mentioned. One is the Space Task Group at Langley which has the responsibility for carrying on the work necessary to put a man into orbit about the earth. The other group is the Edwards Flight Test Center in California, where the testing of the X-15 airplane is now going on.

What does this organization do? As the equipment, facilities, and manpower were being assembled, a broad program of space exploration was being put together. This program may be arbitrarily divided into four main categories.

(1) The first category is a program of scientific investigation in near-earth space, including solar phenomena and their effects.

(2) The second is a program of scientific investigations of the Moon and planets and the intervening space between them and the Earth.

(3) The third is the application of satellites for the direct and early benefit of our own and the world population.

(4) The fourth is a program for the development of the technology of manned space flight, leading to manned orbital flight around the Earth and eventual manned exploration of the Moon and near planets.

The President of the United States in his message to Congress of May 25, 1961, emphasized manned space flight by stating: ". . . This nation should commit itself to achieving the goal, before this decade is out, of landing a man on the Moon and returning him safely to Earth."

In order to carry out its assigned responsibilities of space exploration, NASA must of course promote the advancement of technology on a broad front, develop launch vehicles and spacecraft, and carry out numerous other ancillary functions.

Launch Vehicles

The principal launch vehicles that have been used to date in launching of our various spacecraft have been derivatives of our ballistic missile program. Naturally, since the first stage of these vehicles had been designed for other purposes, our various multistage vehicles have not had optimum staging. The only vehicle which has so far launched a payload into orbit and which has been designed from the start as a space vehicle is the Scout. Since the space program started, the development of a number of launch vehicles of various sizes has been initiated.

The principal launch vehicles that are now in use, those which will become available in the near future, and some now in the earliest stage of design, are shown in Fig. 1. The Scout, the Thor-Delta, the Thor-

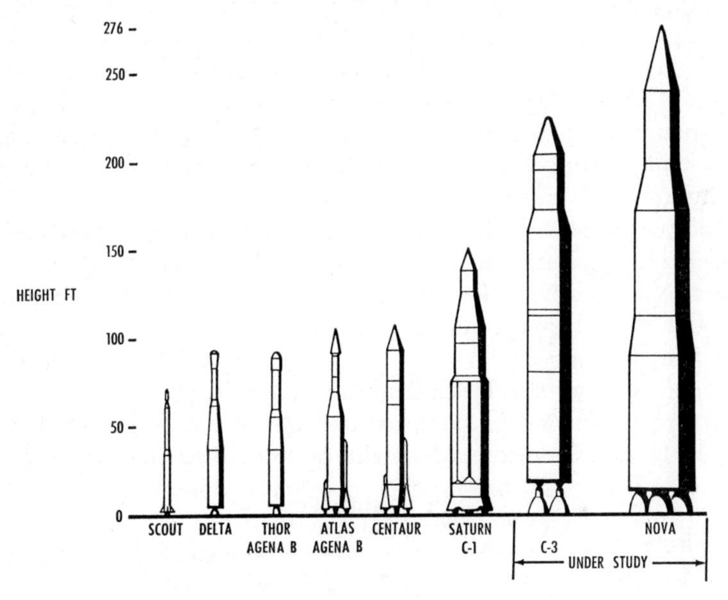

Fig. 1. U.S. launch vehicles.

Agena B, and the Atlas-Agena B have all been flown at least once. The Centaur and Saturn are at present under development, while the two launch vehicles on the right, designated the C-3 and Nova, are in an extensive study phase.

The principal features of the vehicles that are shown in Fig. 1 are described briefly.

The Scout is a four-stage solid propellant launch vehicle which provides a flexible capability to perform either orbital missions, high altitude probes, or reentry missions. As shown in Table I, the Scout can launch as much as a 150-lb weight into a 300 N. mile altitude orbit or can boost a 50-lb weight to an altitude of 8000 miles. To date we have launched five Scouts; two have been completely successful, one partially so, and two have failed.

TABLE I
SCOUT

Stages	Four solid stages
Mission capability	300 N. mile orbit, 150 lb
	8000 N. mile vertical probe, 50 lb
Employment	Satellite launcher
	High altitude sounding
Initiated	Late 1958
Launchings	July 1, 1960: probe, partial success
	October 4, 1960: probe, success
	December 4, 1960: orbit, failure
	February 16, 1961: orbit, success
	June 30, 1961: orbit, failure

The guidance system for Scout is a simple three-axis body-mounted gyro system. Rate gyros and a timer are also part of the package. The first three stages are controlled about all three axes from the same guidance package which is located in the third stage. Vector control is obtained from jet vanes in the nozzle of the first stage and by means of separate hydrogen-peroxide control jets for the second and third stages. The fourth stage is spin stabilized. There are no velocity cutoff features on the Scout.

The objective of the Delta launch vehicle is to provide a reliable vehicle for medium-weight satellites and small-weight space probes. Note in Table II that a maximum weight of 480 lb can be boosted into a

TABLE II
DELTA

Stages	1st stage, LOX/RP-1 Thor
	2nd stage, WIFNA/UDMH
	3rd stage, solid
Mission capability	300 N. mile orbit, 480 lb
	Space probe, 65 lb
Employment	Satellites
	Space probes
Initiated	Early 1959
Launchings	May 13, 1960: Echo, failure
	August 12, 1960: Echo, success
	November 23, 1960: Tiros II, success
	March 25, 1961: Explorer X, success
	July 12, 1961: Tiros III, success

300 N. mile altitude orbit and about 65 lb to escape velocity. So far this vehicle has demonstrated excellent (comparatively speaking) reliability. Of five launches, four have been completely successful.

A cross section of the Delta launch vehicle is shown in Fig. 2. It is a three-stage vehicle. The first stage is a modified Thor IRBM. The second stage is a rocket that was initially developed as a second stage for the Vanguard program. It is the only rocket of all those that will be

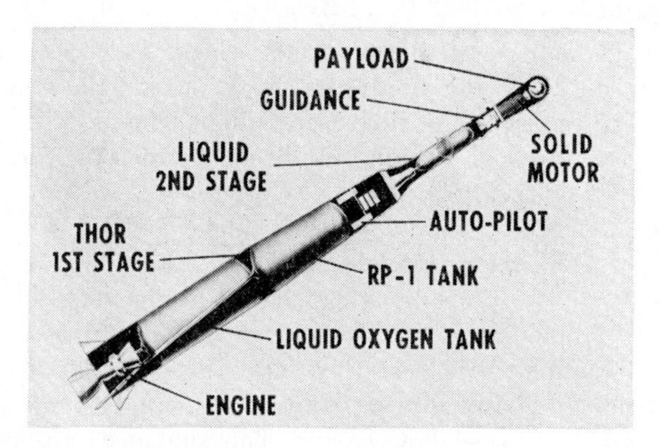

FIG. 2. Delta configuration.

shown in which the propellants are forced into the rocket combustion chamber by pressurizing the tanks rather than using pumps. The third stage of this vehicle is a solid rocket motor which was also initially developed for the Vanguard program. The propellant combination for the stages is shown in Table II.

In order to fly the Delta along a predetermined trajectory, a guidance and flight control system is incorporated in it. A combination inertial and radio command system is utilized. Therefore, a ground installation in the vicinity of the launch site, consisting of a tracking radar and high speed computer, is necessary.

The flight control system installed in the vehicle consists of a flight controller in both the first and second stages, and airborne radio guidance equipment located in the second stage. The flight controller consists of a programmer and a gyro reference system. Basically, the difference between the flight controller in the first and second stages is that rate gyros are included in the first stage to provide stabilization damping. The rate gyro output signals represent the rate of change of vehicle airframe movement.

During the first 90 sec, which includes a vertical rise, roll, and pitch-over, and flight along essentially a zero-lift path, the vehicle flies by a program stored in the first stage programmer. At the end of the first 90 sec, the airborne radio guidance systems located in the second stage start steering the vehicle by signals received from the ground. The steering signals from the airborne radio guidance system torque the flight control gyros in the first stage flight controller, thus overriding the first stage programmer. Staging commands at end of first stage burning are stored in the programmers before launch. The second stage flight controller takes over at main engine shutdown and continues to steer until third stage separation.

The radio guidance system commands second stage shutdown. After second stage shutdown, the system enters the coast phase and positions the vehicle for proper third stage separation. The third stage has no control system in it and is spin stabilized before separation from the second stage.

The Thor Agena B is a two-stage vehicle consisting of a slightly modified Thor IRBM first stage and a liquid propellant second stage. In the first stage the propellants are liquid oxygen and kerosene. The second stage propellants are unsymmetrical dimethyl hydrazine and inhibited red fuming nitric acid. The latter two propellants are hypergolic and hence do not require an ignition system. The Agena B engine can be restarted in space if necessary. The guidance system is a combination of ground command and inertial.

The Atlas Agena B is, as the name implies, an Atlas first stage and an Agena B second stage.

A more advanced type of rocket is shown in Table III. This is known as the Centaur and consists of a modified Atlas ICBM first stage and a

TABLE III
CENTAUR

Stages	1st stage, LOX/RP Atlas
	2nd stage, LOX/LH
Mission capability	300 N. mile orbit, 8500 lb
	Lunar probe, 2500 lb
Employment	Lunar and planetary exploration
	24-hr communications satellite
Initiated	Late 1958

newly developed second stage. The principal feature of the second stage is that it uses liquid oxygen and liquid hydrogen as propellants. The Centaur uses a fully inertial system for guidance, which is more completely described later. Once the launch vehicle leaves its pad, there are no further communications with the ground for guidance purposes. The payloads for different missions and the planned uses for the Centaur are also shown in Table III.

It is of interest to quickly enumerate the sequence of events in the operation of a Centaur vehicle (see Fig. 3). All three engines of the first stage are fired at launch. The two outer engines burn for a period of time and are then separated from the remaining vehicle. The center

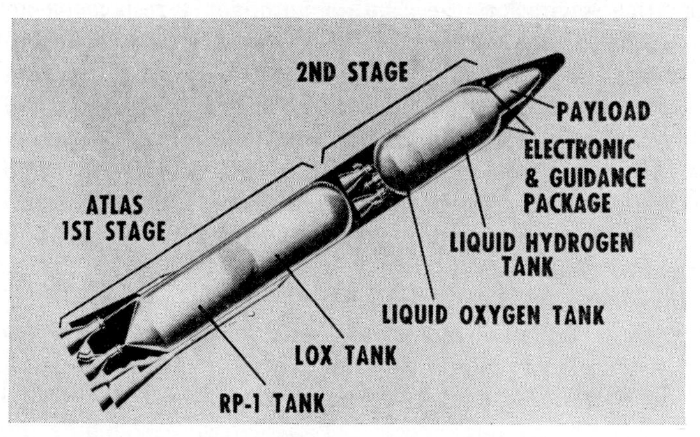

FIG. 3. Centaur configuration.

engine or sustainer engine continues to burn until propellant exhaustion of the first stage tanks. At that time the first stage is separated from the remaining vehicle. The second stage is then fired and burns for a prescribed period of time. Depending upon the mission, this stage can shut its engines off and fire them again several times. For a 24-hr synchronous orbit, this stage will fire and shut down three separate times.

The use of hydrogen brings us into a new area of rocket technology. To maintain hydrogen in a liquid state requires that the temperature be less than some —425°F. During an ascent to a 24-hr synchronous orbit, a coast period of several hours is involved. During this time, sunlight on the surface of the hydrogen tanks could very well heat the tanks to above a permissible level and thereby cause the loss of an unacceptable amount of liquid hydrogen through boil-off. For that reason, the guidance system is so designed and programmed that during the long coast period, it continuously orients the second stage so that the engines point toward the sun. It is hoped that the shielding from the engines plus orientation of the longitudinal axis of the tanks parallel to the sun's direction will reduce hydrogen boil-off to acceptable limits.

The Atlas-Centaur vehicle is controlled in flight by a single inertial guidance system; however, each stage has its own autopilot control system. The inertial guidance system consists basically of a gyro-stabilized platform and a general-purpose digital computer. The guidance system generates commands to the first stage autopilot by computing data on position, velocity and acceleration, and comparing the data with programming trajectory requirements. Changes in vehicle attitude and steering are then made by the autopilot which steers the vehicle until sustainer engine cutoff.

After Atlas separation, the Centaur autopilot is responsible for flight control. It accepts signals from the guidance system and initiates such events as engine starts and payload separation.

The Centaur suntracker, designed and built by Convair Astronautics, is an essential part of the flight control operation. It is the prime system for maintaining vehicle orientation during the coast period. Suntrackers mounted on each vehicle register exposure to sunlight and generate commands to the attitude control engines which fire to orient the vehicle's tail toward the sun. This reduces liquid hydrogen boil-off by keeping as much sunlight as possible away from the propellant tanks.

During mid-1962 it is planned to send an exploration probe to the vicinity of the planet Venus using the Centaur launch vehicle. The flight trajectory is shown in Fig. 4. On the left hand side of the figure are

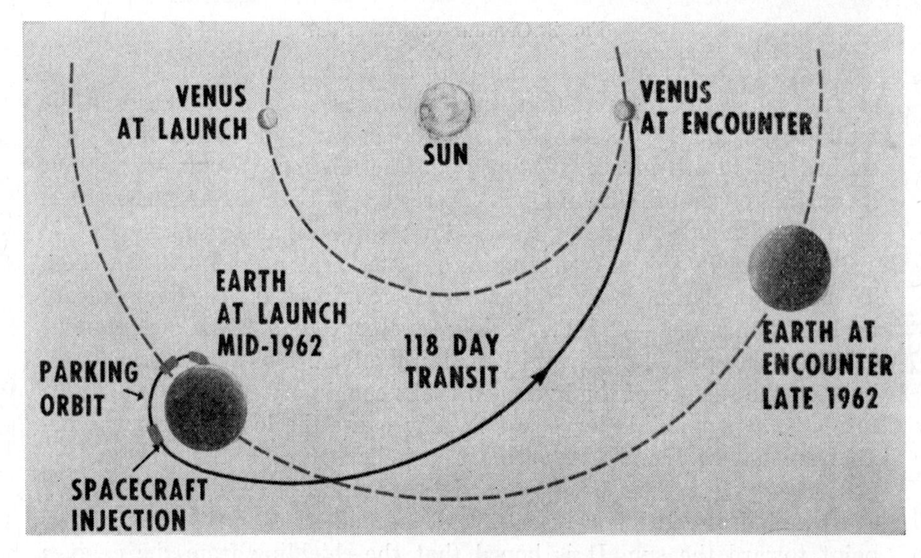

Fig. 4. Centaur Venus mission.

shown the orbital positions of Venus and earth at the time of Centaur launch. The Atlas-Centaur is launched from Cape Canaveral and the Atlas booster falls away when its propellants are exhausted. The first burning of the Centaur stage places it into an unpowered parking earth orbit wherein it coasts to a position over the South Atlantic Ocean. Here the Centaur engines are restarted and burn to propellant exhaus-

FIG. 5. Saturn C-1/Apollo 2nd stage separation.

Fig. 6. Saturn C-1/Apollo payload separation.

tion, injecting the separable spacecraft on its long 118-day journey toward Venus. On the right-hand side of the figure we see the relative positions of Venus and earth when the spacecraft arrives at Venus late in 1962.

Shown on Fig. 1 was an early configuration of the Saturn C-1 which shows it as a three-stage vehicle. This has now been modified and the C-1, at least in the early years of its life, will be a two-stage vehicle as pictured in Fig. 5. The first stage consists of a cluster of eight liquid rocket engines of a configuration very similar to that of the Thor and Atlas ballistic missiles. The tankage consists of eight outer tanks and one larger inner tank. Four of the outer tanks hold the kerosene fluid and the other four outer tanks and the inner tank are filled with liquid oxygen. Altogether the eight engines will in time develop 1,500,000 lb thrust.

So far the first stage has been static fired a number of times for the full duration of about 112 sec. The first stage has been shipped to Cape Canaveral where it will be launched in a ballistic trajectory for the first test some time late this year. Upper stages for the first few tests will be dummies.

The second stage (Fig. 6) of the Saturn will use liquid oxygen and liquid hydrogen as propellants and will have six 15,000-lb thrust engines. The first firing of both first and second stages is scheduled for 1963.

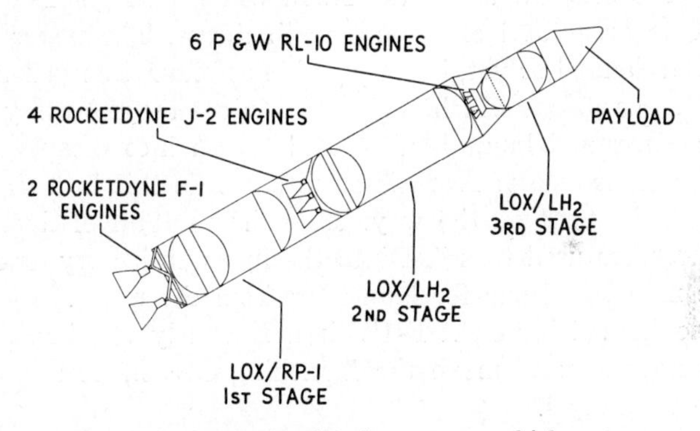

FIG. 7. Saturn C-3 three-stage vehicle.

The C-3 and the Nova are the kind of vehicles that are now under study and consideration for use in the manned lunar landing program.

The final configuration of the C-3 is not yet determined. Most likely it will be a three-stage vehicle of a configuration as shown in Fig. 7. The first stage will have no less than two F-1 engines. It will be recalled that the F-1 can produce 1,500,000 lb of thrust. Two of them therefore will give 3,000,000 lb of thrust at lift-off. As now contemplated, the second stage would have four engines with 200,000 lb thrust each, and the third stage six engines, each delivering 15,000 lb of thrust. The propellants of the first stage will be liquid oxygen-kerosene and the propellants for the upper stages will be liquid oxygen and liquid hydrogen. Because the weights needed for a "three-man" spacecraft for a moon trip have been going up, it now appears that the C-3 type of vehicle will be the first which could launch such a spacecraft in a circumlunar flight.

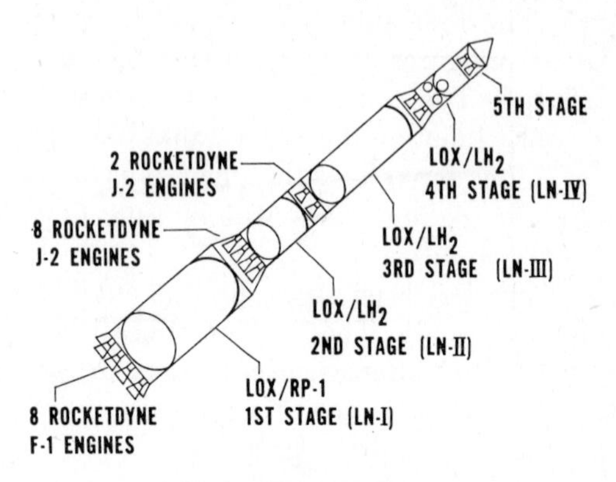

Fig. 8. Nova vehicle.

The largest liquid rocket launch vehicle now under discussion is called the Nova. It is estimated that the Nova will need eight F-1 engines in the first stage or a total of 12 million lb thrust. The upper stages are not very well defined as yet, but a possible configuration is demonstrated by Fig. 8. Three stages will be needed to inject the necessary estimated weight for a manned lunar landing and return into escape velocity. A launch vehicle the size of Nova is required to do this in a single launch without replenishment on the way. Note that a total of five stages are needed. Three are used to inject into the lunar trajectory, one for landing on the moon, and one for launching from the moon.

The noise from firing eight F-1's simultaneously will be so great that it may be necessary to move the launching site offshore several miles from Cape Canaveral.

The approximate payload values for two missions are summarized in Figs. 9 and 10. Figure 9 shows the payload capability of the vehicles now under development in a 300-mile earth orbit. In late 1963 or early 1964, we should have the ability to raise as much as 20,000 lb into orbit with the Saturn C-1. By that time, the Saturn should have completed a number of launchings and have attained a reasonable degree of reliability. By late 1964 and perhaps early 1965, the C-1 will be the launch vehicle that will be used to place multimanned satellites in orbit. It is

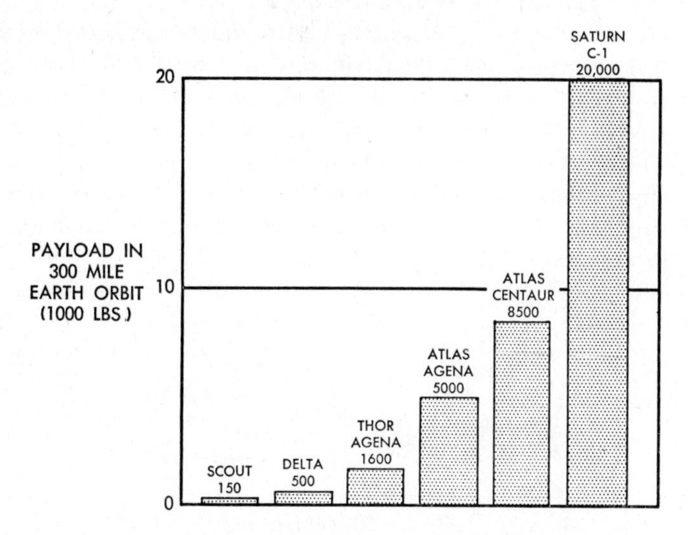

FIG. 9. Growth of launch vehicle payload capability.

also anticipated that the Saturn will be the vehicle that will be used as a workhorse for developing and improving the Apollo spacecraft which will eventually be used for the manned lunar landing and return operation.

Figure 10 shows the order of magnitude of weights that will be required for the manned lunar landing project. Shown by the top shaded region are the escape payloads required for a direct ascent method to send a three-man spacecraft to the moon and return to the earth. The

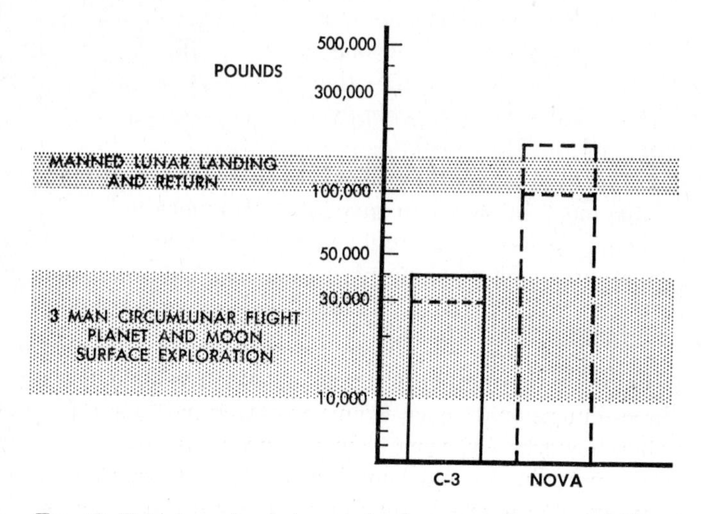

FIG. 10. Vehicle and mission payloads, escape large capability.

latest estimates indicate that the escape payloads needed will be near the upper portion of the shaded region. An escape payload of 150,000 to 200,000 lb will be required, and only a vehicle of the size of the Nova will be capable of doing that in a direct ascent method. The smaller C-3 will have the necessary performance to send a three-man spacecraft on a circumlunar flight, but not to land the spacecraft on the moon and return it to earth. The C-3 as indicated by the lower shaded region can be used in exploration of the surfaces of near planets as well as a possible supply vehicle for future surface exploration of the moon.

It is of interest to note that the configurations of the C-3 and Nova shown in Figs. 7 and 8 have the following approximate payload characteristics:

Vehicle	300 N. mile orbit (lb)	Escape (lb)
C-3	80,000	30,000
Nova	350,000	150,000

Future Requirements

A few years ago the average scientist and engineer would have dismissed the idea of a manned lunar landing trip with a shrug of the shoulders. Rocket technology was very young and only a very few people in certain innermost sanctums were doing concentrated thinking on the subject. Today, knowledge of rocketry and problems associated with space exploration has spread to many industrial and academic institutions. The result is that everyone appreciates that to achieve a manned lunar landing and return will be one of the most massive engineering undertakings of all history. On the other hand, few scientists or engineers believe that new discoveries or wholly new inventions will be necessary for a manned trip to the moon.

What can be said about the difficulties of more ambitious space exploration missions? In order to give a preliminary indication, let me first establish the concept of total velocity requirement of a particular mission, as used by rocket engineers in designing the propulsion systems.

Rocket Vehicle Performance

Consideration of the motion of a rocket launch vehicle along a trajectory in three-dimensional space from a rotating earth is quite complex. It is possible, however, by using elementary but fundamental principles, to arrive at approximate and simplified relationships which show how various physical characteristics of the vehicle and the trajectory parameters interact and affect performance. An approximate equation for the velocity tangent to the trajectory is the following (see Fig. 11, p. 43):

$$\underbrace{v}_{\substack{\text{Actual}\\\text{vehicle}\\\text{velocity}}} \approx \underbrace{\sum_{n=1}^{n=j} g_0 \bar{I}_{sp} \ln \frac{W_0}{W_e}}_{\substack{\text{vehicle velocity}\\\text{in gravity and drag}\\\text{free space}}} - \underbrace{\int g' \sin\theta \, dt}_{\substack{\text{velocity to}\\\text{overcome}\\\text{gravity}}} - \underbrace{\int \frac{W}{D} g_0 \, dt}_{\substack{\text{velocity to}\\\text{overcome}\\\text{drag}}} - \underbrace{|\Delta v|_{\text{coast}}}_{\substack{\text{velocity}\\\text{decrease}\\\text{during coast}}}$$

$$+ \underbrace{v_{\text{earth rotation}}}_{\substack{\text{earth's}\\\text{rotational}\\\text{velocity at}\\\text{launch point}}}$$

$$\underbrace{\left[v + \int g' \sin\theta \, dt + \int \frac{D}{W} g_0 \, dt + |\Delta v|_{\text{coast}} - v_{\text{earth rotation}}\right]}_{\substack{\text{total velocity requirement}\\\text{from earth's surface}}} = \underbrace{\sum_{n=1}^{n=j} g_0 \bar{I}_{sp} \ln \frac{W_0}{W_e}}_{\substack{\approx\text{ vehicle velocity in}\\\text{gravity and drag free}\\\text{space}}}$$

In this equation, the following definitions apply:

v = velocity referred to a nonrotating earth,
g_0 = standard sea level value of gravity,
g' = apparent value of gravity at altitude,
W_0 = gross weight of any stage including upper stages and payload,
W_e = empty weight of stage including upper stages and payload,
$\bar{I}_{sp}$ = average effective value of specific impulse during burning period of a stage,
D = drag,
W = instantaneous weight of the rocket,
t = time,
j = number of vehicle stages.

The velocity v required of the vehicle is determined by the mission. For a low earth orbit it is about 25,000 ft/sec, for escape about 36,000 ft/sec. Larger values are required for missions to the planets and for deep solar probes. The right side of the first equation contains vehicle and trajectory parameters. The first term is the well-known rocket performance parameter. It is the predominant term and emphasizes the two most fundamental parameters in rocket performance: the specific impulse, which depends to a large extent on the rocket nozzle exhaust velocity, and the ratio of the total mass or weight of the rocket at the beginning and end of any acceleration (burning) period. The weight ratio, W_0/W_e, is dependent on the proportion of the total mass which is propellant.

It is evident that increases in the first term may be obtained by increases in the specific impulse $\bar{I}_{sp}$, the weight ratio of each stage, W_0/W_e, and the number of stages. It is also evident that the term is independent of the rocket burning time. The second and third terms are dependent on burning time and represent the energy in terms of velocity that must be expended in overcoming gravity and drag. The coast term simply represents the decrease in velocity in coasting to a higher altitude and a conversion of kinetic to potential energy during the coasting ascent portion of the trajectory. It can be shown that in establishing orbits at relatively high altitude, about 300 miles and higher, it is highly desirable to have a coasting period near the end of the trajectory. The last term simply reflects the contribution that can be obtained if the launching occurs in the direction of the earth rotation. At the Atlantic Missiles Range this term has a magnitude of about 1300 ft/sec for an eastward launch.

TABLE IV

Typical Values of Rocket Performance Parameters

Vehicle velocity required	Function of mission
Velocity to overcome gravity	3000–5000 ft/sec
Velocity to overcome drag	500–900 ft/sec
Velocity decrease during coast	Function of trajectory
Earth's rotation	Contribution depends on launch site location and launch direction

Rearrangement of this equation, so as to equate the total velocity requirement to the fundamental rocket performance expression, is more convenient for investigation of the effect of the physical vehicle parameters, since for a given mission the total velocity requirement may be assumed constant. Typical values of the trajectory rocket performance parameter are given in Table IV.

Total Velocity Requirement for Future Missions

Using the approach outlined above, Fig. 12 was prepared. On the left-hand side of the figure are the calculated minimum energy velocity requirements from the earth's surface for three different missions to each of the planets. The total velocity requirements were obtained by assuming that the planetary orbits are coplanar, and circular, and for selection of reasonable values of trajectory parameters, as shown in Table IV. On the right-hand side of Fig. 12 are plotted payloads versus the velocity that a number of different vehicle designs can impart to those payloads.

Examination of the figure shows, for example, that to land a payload on the moon and return it to earth requires a total velocity equivalent of a little more than 60,000 ft/sec. As we move horizontally to the right, we see that a five-stage Nova can impart 60,000+ ft/sec to a payload of some 12,000 lb. Now, if a manned spacecraft can be designed within that weight, then the manned lunar landing and return can be accomplished with that vehicle and under the various assumptions made in these calculations.

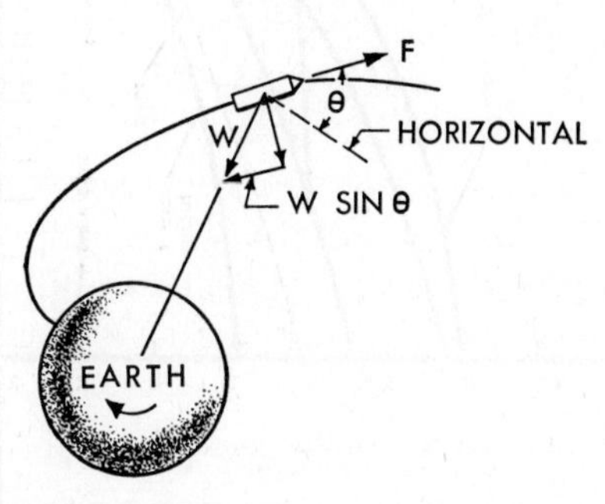

FIG. 11. Rocket performance. *W*, weight; *F*, thrust; *θ*, angle between horizontal and tangent to trajectory.

Further examination of the figure makes it apparent that chemical rockets will have to be very large indeed if we want to orbit, for example, the planet Jupiter. More efficient propulsion means will be necessary. Assuming certain anicipated weights and specific impulses, nuclear rockets and electric propulsion show great promise in very difficult missions requiring large total velocity equivalents.

Before showing the results of a comparative analysis of the weights required for a manned Mars mission, the operation of a nuclear rocket engine will be described briefly.

The nuclear heat transfer rocket is a type of engine that is now being developed. A diagrammatic sketch of the operation of a nuclear rocket engine is shown in Fig. 13. A number of similarities with the lipid engine are apparent. Beginning at the left, there is an expansion nozzle, throat, and pressure shell. In place of the combustion chamber, there is a nuclear fission reactor. The diagram then shows a radiation shield, turbine, pump, and propellant tank. Instead of having two different propellants, an oxidizer and a fuel which in the liquid rocket engine provide the chemical energy, there is only one working fluid. This will probably be liquid hydrogen. Other propellants may be used, but liquid hydrogen is the most efficient because the specific impulse, a measure of efficiency in rocket engines, is inversely proportional to the square root of the molecular weight of the propellants. Hydrogen, of course, having the lowest molecular weight, gives the largest specific impulse.

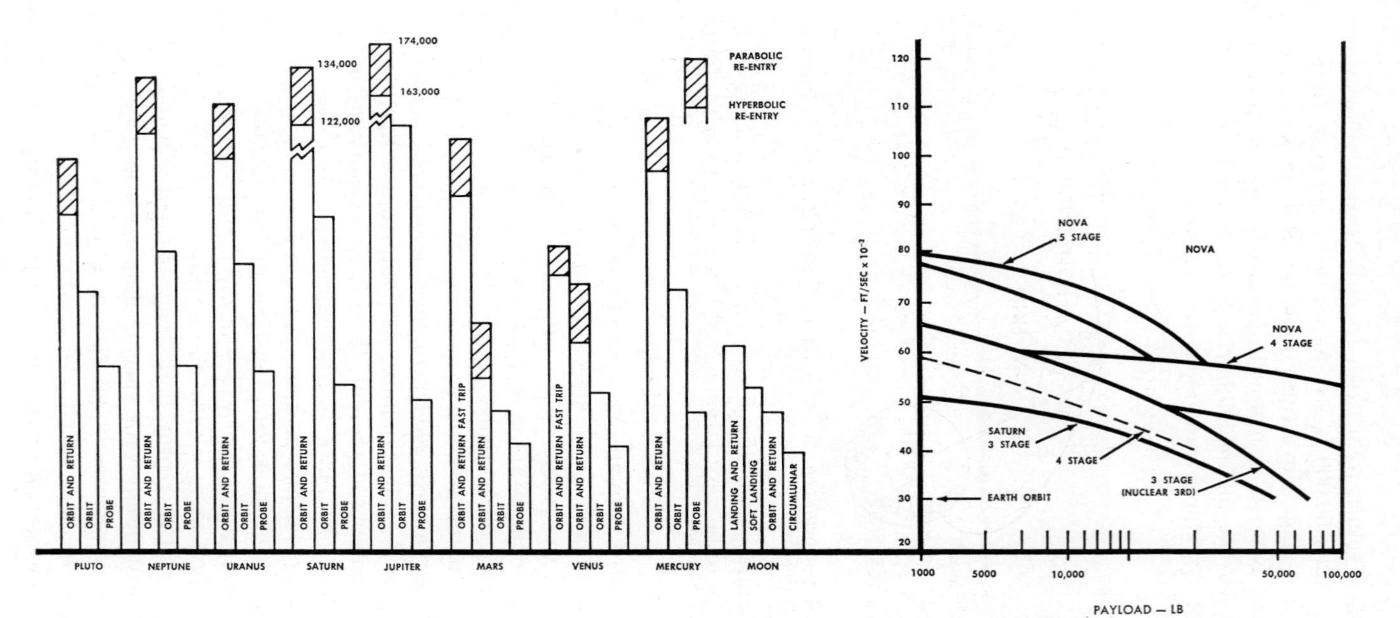

FIG. 12. Mission velocity and payload relationship. *Left:* medium energy velocity requirements from the earth's surface. *Right:* payload capability of Saturn and chemical Nova type vehicles.

In operation, the liquid hydrogen is pumped from the tank and is piped to some point in the expansion nozzle. From there it flows through the passages of the pressure shell, cooling its walls, and into a plenum chamber above the reactor and is heated in the process. It is then ejected through the nozzle and thereby provides thrust.

Whereas the specific impulse of a liquid rocket at sea level is of the order of 250 lb thrust per pound propellant flow per second, a nuclear

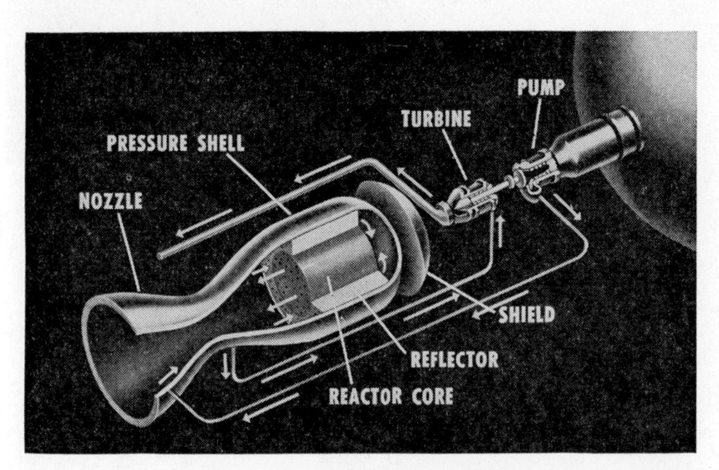

FIG. 13. Nuclear rocket engine.

heat transfer rocket may have a specific impulse under the same conditions of 800 to 1200 sec, depending on the temperature at which the reactor can operate. Specific impulse values of this order will markedly reduce the size of launch vehicle required for more difficult missions. A nuclear rocket engine (Project Rover) is now under development, and some highly successful early test firings have already been conducted.

The true potential of the nuclear rocket shows up to greatest advantage on distant and difficult missions. To illustrate this point, Mr. S. C. Himmel of NASA Lewis Research Center made some preliminary calculations based on the following assumptions:

1. weight of earth atmosphere reentry vehicle—20,000 lb;
2. atmospheric braking to decelerate to earth's surface;
3. as part of the mission an exploration party is landed on Mars using atmospheric braking;
4. total mission time is 360 days, including a 40-day stay time.

It must be emphasized that these calculations and results are of a preliminary nature and are valid for comparative purposes only. The results are shown in Fig. 14. You can see that the all-chemical vehicle using hydrogen-oxygen as propellants would have an initial weight in

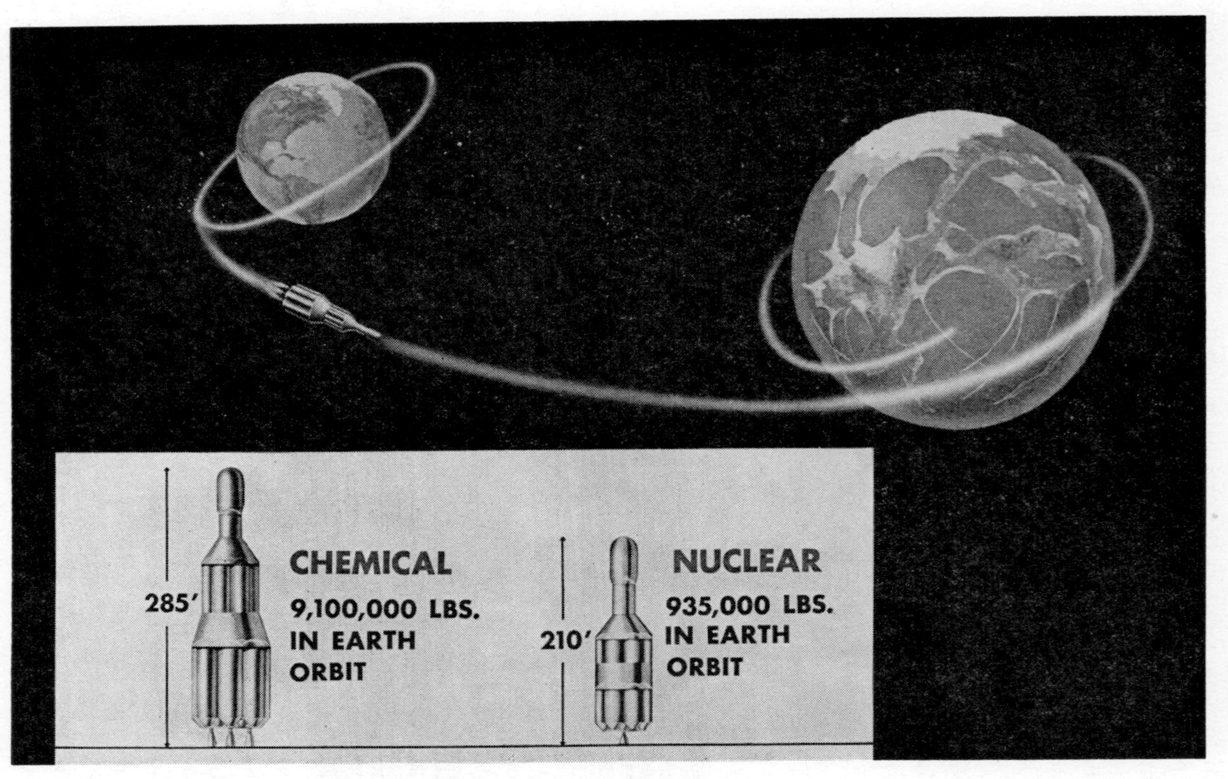

Fig. 14. Mars landing mission.

earth orbit of almost 10 million lb in order to perform the mission. The all-nuclear vehicle would have one-tenth the weight to do the same job. Just so we should not get too enthusiastic about the immediacy of all-nuclear vehicles, the calculations show that the all-nuclear vehicle requires 10,000 Mw of power for the first stage, 6000 in the second, and 1800 Mw in the third.

Earlier it was stated that electric propulsion also shows great promise for difficult missions. Electric propulsion is now in the early stages of development. A number of different types of electric engines have been proposed. We shall discuss very briefly only the ion engine. Figure 15

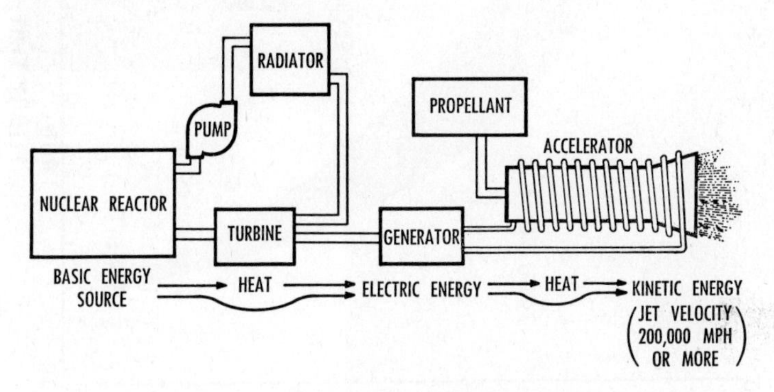

FIG. 15. Electric rocket propulsion principles.

shows the major elements of such an engine. The energy source is a nuclear reactor. The reactor provides heat to a working fluid, which then drives a turbo-generator system converting the thermal energy into electric energy. The working fluid itself, upon leaving the turbine, must go through some kind of radiator and be pumped back into the reactor to complete the thermal cycle.

The next element of the electric rocket engine is the accelerator or the propulsor as it is variously known. In the case of the ion engine, the propellant is likely to be cesium. This is passed through a heated porous tungsten plate, where it is ionized. The electric power from the generator is used to establish appropriate electric fields which accelerate the charged particles to very high velocities and expel them through some form of nozzle. Again, the reaction provides the thrust. The electric ion engine is highly efficient in terms of a very low usage of propellant. Specific impulses on the order of 10,000 sec or more are obtainable. On the other hand, the nature of the apparatus is such that a very low thrust to weight ratio is provided. In fact, some designs of a complete electric ion engine and payload are such that acceleration as low as 10^{-4} or 10^{-5} g are all that can be obtained. For this reason, such a device

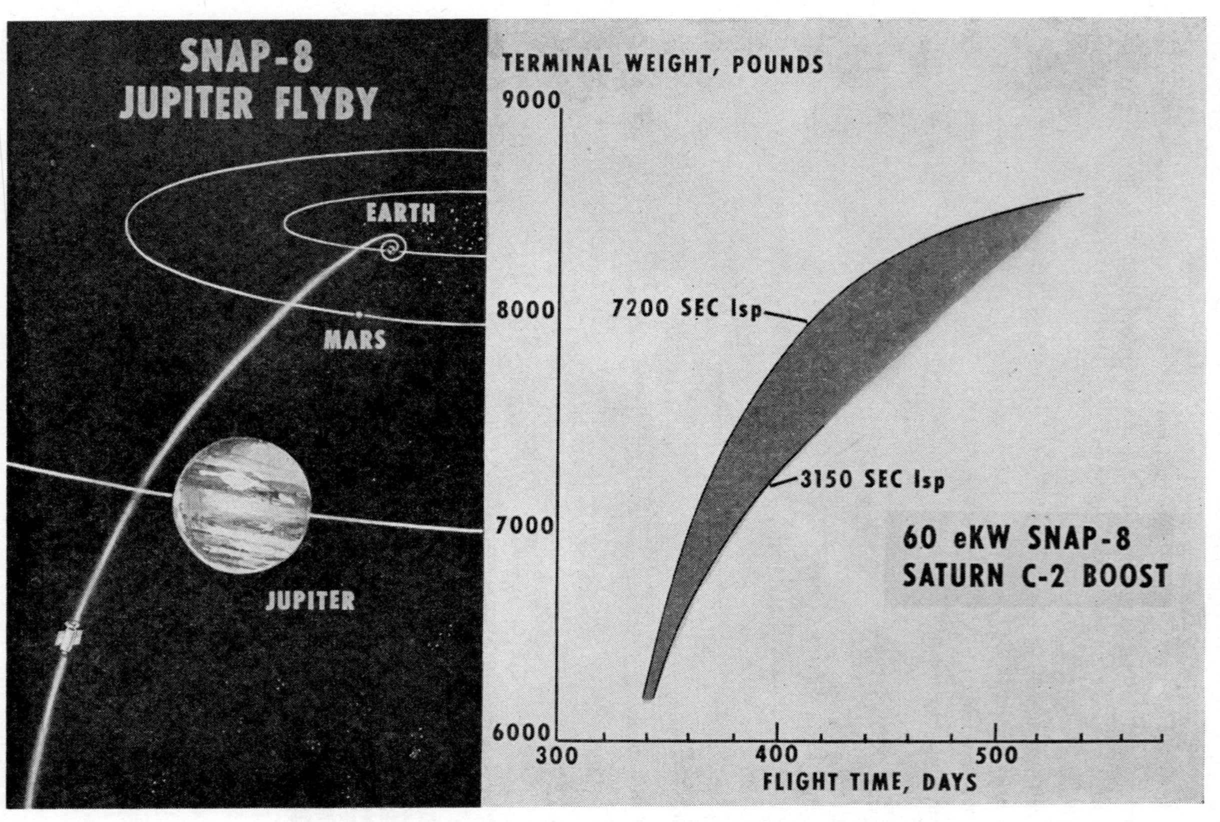

Fig. 16. Snap-8 Jupiter flyby; 60 ekw Snap-8 Saturn C-2 boost.

cannot be used to launch vehicles from the surface of the earth, but can be used for acceleration from earth-orbital velocities.

The pacing item in the development of electric rocket engines will be the power conversion system. At this time NASA has under development, in cooperation with the AEC, a 30 to 60 ekw power conversion system known as the Snap-8.

Although the Snap-8 system is low in power when compared with the powers that will ultimately be required, and is high in specific weight compared to possible future systems, it will have some interesting mission possibilities. Figure 16 shows the payload that can be delivered by a spacecraft propelled by a Snap-8 ion propulsion system on a mission flying by Jupiter. In this case, the Snap-8 spacecraft is launched by the Saturn vehicle. This analysis shows the variation of the payload with the flight time required to arrive at the planet Jupiter for specific impulses of the electrical system between 3200 and 7200 sec. The payloads are very respectable, especially since only about 3000 lb are devoted to the electrical propulsion system, and this can supply electric power when it is not used for propulsion.

2.2 Current Astronomy Program at NASA

NANCY G. ROMAN

NATIONAL AERONAUTICS AND SPACE ADMINISTRATION,
Washington, D.C.

Astronomy in NASA is defined as "the study of where you are not." More particularly, with a few minor exceptions, it covers the use of rockets and satellites to study the sun, stars, galaxies, and interstellar material. It also includes the study of the planets from near-earth satellites but not experiments designed to study planets at close range. However, since the projects in the Astronomy Program, particularly the Orbiting Solar Observatories and the Orbiting Astronomical Observatories, have been reported on before, most of this paper will be devoted to recent results in the NASA space science program: experiments which have been conducted in geophysics and interplanetary exploration, as well as in astronomy in the narrow sense.

The first major scientific discovery of the space program was that of the radiation belts of charged particles trapped in the earth's magnetic field. The study of energetic charged particles and the related study of magnetic fields continues to be a fruitful one. A series of rocket flights from the Canadian launch base at Fort Churchill provided interesting data on the spectrum of the solar protons following a solar flare. It was found, as might have been expected, that the spectrum becomes progressively stepper with time, as the large influx of softer particles arrives appreciably later than the more energetic ones (*1*). Moreover, these flights were able to extend the energy spectrum of the particle flux from the flare well beyond the limit previously set by balloons. Heavy particles were observed in these showers in the abundance found in the solar atmosphere (*2*). The nuclei of elements such as lithium and beryllium, which are scarce in the sun, are also scarce in the cosmic-ray flux following a solar flare. A high altitude recoverable rocket package launched from California contained nuclear emulsions which are being analyzed now. The preliminary results show changes in the energy spectrum of the inner belt with magnetic latitude (*3*). The results from Explorer VII showed that the energy spectrum of the inner belt is also correlated with solar activity (*4*).

Explorer X extended our knowledge of particle radiation and the magnetic field to an apogee of about 38.5 earth radii. Preliminary results (*5*) indicate the existence of a low energy plasma surrounding the earth to a distance of approximately 3 earth radii. Beyond approximately 21.5 earth radii, plasma coming from the general direction of the sun was observed on numerous occasions. This solar plasma consists of approximately 10 particles/cm^3 with kinetic energies of mass motion of the order of a few hundred electron volts. A smooth geomagnetic field closely resembling the predicted field was observed (*6*) out to at least 6.5 earth radii.

Between 20 and 27 earth radii, large scale fluctuations in the intensity of the magnetic field were observed. Beyond 20 earth radii Explorer X confirmed the existence of the strong interplanetary magnetic field, first detected by Pioneer V.

Pioneer V provided data for a much more extended region of space. This probe showed that the mechanism which produces the 11-year variation in cosmic-ray intensity is centered at the sun, and that the scale size for the volume of space in which the intensity of galactic cosmic rays is modulated was greater than 1 astronomical unit during the period of the solar cycle covered by the Pioneer V measurements (*7*). The solar flare corpuscular radiation which produces ionization in the polar atmosphere for many successive hours is not stored in the geomagnetic field, as simultaneous magnetic effects were observed at large distances from the earth and on the earth. On the daylight side of the earth, during periods of little geomagnetic activity, the termination of the geomagnetic field was observed near 14 earth radii; rapid fluctuations in this field were observed between 10 and 14 earth radii (*8*). During periods of low solar activity, an interplanetary magnetic field of about 2.7×10^{-5} gauss was found (*9*). During periods of high solar activity, fields greater than 50×10^{-5} gauss were observed in interplanetary space (*10*). Pioneer V also provided a determination of the astronomical unit, from which a solar parallax of $8''.79738 \pm 0''.00082$ was derived (*11*).

A closely related field in which many interesting results have been obtained is the study of the ionosphere of the earth. Rocket flights have indicated that the atmosphere is essentially isothermal between 350 km and at least 625 km. This conclusion was reached from an electron density profile obtained by Jackson and Bauer of the Goddard Space Flight Center. If one assumes thermal equilibrium, and that in this altitude region atomic oxygen is the predominant ionic constituent, then one obtains a temperature of 1650°K (*12*).

In the study of the un-ionized components of the upper atmosphere, perhaps the most interesting results have been obtained in the micrometeorite program. The Explorer VIII data have shown no altitude dependence in the momentum spectrum of the interplanetary dust (*13*). For the very low mass particles, less than about 10^{-7} gm, the slope of the number-frequency curve is much steeper than that observed for the higher mass particles at lower altitudes. However, the total influx is still estimated to be about 10^4 tons per day. In mid November an interplanetary dust event probably associated with the Leonid meteor stream was observed (*14*). During a 70-hour period, approximately as many impacts were observed as during the remaining 78-day life of the satellite. However, there were rapid fluctuations in the impact rate, and for several orbits no or very few impacts were observed even during this period. Very high impact rates were observed during several small segments of the orbits.

The dynamics of the lower atmosphere have been investigated by the release of sodium and other vapors from rockets. High turbulence is observed up to about 105 km with strong shears up to 120 km (*15*).

Returning to astronomy in the stricter sense, the most interesting results obtained so far have been from rocket observations of stars in the near ultraviolet (*16*). Both broad-band photometers and grating spectrometers have been flown with concordant results from the two types of instrumentation. With the grating spectrometer and a dispersion of 50 Å/mm, Sirius saturated the detector system but good spectra of about 10 stars were obtained. The spectrum of Alpha Carinae, an F0Ib supergiant, agrees well with the theoretical predictions, but the hotter stars are much fainter near 2000 Å than had been expected (*17*). Moreover, stars which look very similar in the visible region seem appreciably different in the 2000 Å region.

There are few results to report as yet from the first of the astronomical satellites, the gamma-ray telescope, Explorer XI, launched in late April. Events which are probably gamma rays are being observed at a rate of slightly more than one an hour, or approximately at the frequency which was expected (*18*). The angular resolution of the instrument is 15° but the analysis of the regions of the sky from which the gamma rays are coming has not been completed.

Some future projects in both the astronomical and geophysical areas can be mentioned briefly. The next astronomical satellite will be the Orbiting Solar Observatory. This satellite contains two instrument sections, a wheel spinning at the rate of 30 rpm and an instrument box on the "sail." The axis of rotation of the wheel is maintained within 5° of the plane perpendicular to the sun and the instrument box on the "sail" can be pointed at the center of the sun within about 1 minute of arc. The experiments on this satellite include gamma-ray spectrometers, X-ray spectrometers, ionization chambers, a Lyman-α profile spectrometer, and several experiments designed to measure features of the Van Allen belt and to answer engineering questions. A second satellite of similar design but with different instrumentation will be flown approximately 1 year later. Both ultraviolet spectrometers and spectroheliometers are planned for this satellite.

Further ahead in the program is the Orbiting Astronomical Observatory, currently scheduled for launch in about 2½ years. This will provide a stable platform for many types of astronomical instruments. Each satellite will provide power, accurate stabilization, telemetry, and data storage, and can be pointed to any region of the sky on command. The first satellite will contain two prime experiments: the Smithsonian Astrophysical Observatory plans to map the sky in several ultraviolet wavelengths using television techniques, and the University of Wisconsin is designing a broad-band photometry experiment for the same spectral region. These will be followed approximately a year later by a moderate dispersion ultraviolet spectrograph designed by the Goddard Space Flight Center, and a year after that, by a high dispersion ultraviolet spectrometer being designed by the Princeton University. In addition, these satellites can carry smaller auxiliary experiments.

A standard spacecraft also is being developed for geophysical experiments. This will accommodate instruments pointing in the direction toward the earth, the orbital plane, and the direction to the sun. In addition, booms are provided for instruments such as magnetometers which must be isolated from the remainder of the spacecraft. Two types of orbits are planned for this spacecraft. An eccentric orbit with an apogee of 100,000 km will be used for low frequency radio astronomy, ionospheric studies, and investigations of the radiation belts, geomagnetic field, and the transition from geophysical to interplanetary conditions. The first of these Eccentric Orbiting Geophysical Observatories (EGO's) will be launched in 1963. Approximately 1 year later, a Polar Orbiting Geophysical Observatory (POGO) will be launched into a polar orbit with an apogee of approximately 1000 km, for studies of the structure of the atmosphere, the auroral zone, and the lower Van Allen belts. We plan to continue launching solar, astronomical, and geophysical observatories at regular intervals to supplement the traditional techniques of ground-based astronomy with the possibilities which the use of rockets, satellites, and space probes can provide.

References

1. L. R. Davis, C. E. Fichtel, D. E. Guss, and K. W. Ogilvie, Rocket observations of solar protons on September 3, 1960, *Phys. Rev. Letters* **6**, 492 (1961).
2. C. E. Fichtel and D. E. Guss, Heavy nuclei in solar cosmic rays, *Phys. Rev. Letters* **6**, 495 (1961).

3. J. E. Naugle and D. A. Kniffen, Flux and energy spectra of the protons in the inner Van Allen belt, *Phys. Rev. Letters* **7,** 3 (1961).
4. Private Communication from J. Van Allen, State University of Iowa, to J. E. Naugle, NASA.
5. H. S. Bridge, C. Dilworth, A. Lazarus, E. F. Lyon, B. Rossi, and F. Scherb, MIT, a report to be published in the *Proc. Intern. Conf. on Cosmic Rays and the Earth Storm, Kyoto, Japan, September 1961.*
6. J. P. Heppner, N. F. Ness, T. L. Skillman, and C. S. Scearce, Goddard Space Flight Center, NASA, presentation at the American Geophysical Union Meeting, Washington, D. C., April 1961. A more comprehensive analysis will be published in the *Proc. Intern. Conf. on Cosmic Rays and the Earth Storm, Kyoto, Japan, September 1961.*
7. C. Y. Fan, P. Meyer, and J. A. Simpson, Experiments on the eleven-year changes of cosmic-ray intensity using a space probe, *Phys. Rev. Letters* **5,** 272 (1960).
8. E. J. Smith, P. J. Coleman, Jr., D. L. Judge, and C. P. Sonett, Characteristics of the extraterrestrial current system: Explorer XI and Pioneer V, *J. Geophys. Research* **65,** 1858 (1960).
9. P. J. Coleman, Jr., L. Davis, and C. P. Sonett, Steady component of the interplanetary magnetic field: Pioneer V, *Phys. Rev. Letters* **5,** 43 (1960).
10. P. J. Coleman, Jr., C. P. Sonett, and L. Davis, Jr., On the interplanetary magnetic storm: Pioneer V, *J. Geophys. Research* **66,** 2043 (1961).
11. J. B. McGuire, E. R. Spangler, and L. Wong, The size of the solar system, *Scientific American* **204,** No. 4, 64 (1961).
12. J. E. Jackson and S. J. Bauer, Rocket measurement of a daytime electron density profile up to 620 km, *J. Geophys. Research* **66,** 3055 (1961).
13. C. W. McCracken, W. M. Alexander, and M. Dubin, Direct measurement of interplanetary dust particles in the vicinity of earth, *Nature* **192,** 441 (1961).
14. W. M. Alexander, C. W. McCracken, and H. E. LaGow, Interplanetary dust particles of micron-size probably associated with the Leonid meteor stream, *J. Geophys. Research* **66,** 3970 (1961).
15. Private communication from M. Dubin, NASA.
16. A. Boggess, III, Stellar flux measurements in the middle ultraviolet, Abstract, *Astronomical J.* **66,** 279 (1961).
17. T. P. Stecher and J. E. Milligan, Stellar spectrophotometry below 3000 angstroms, Abstract, *Astronomical J.* **66,** 296 (1961). Paper to be published in *Astronomical J.,* July 1962.
18. Private communications from W. L. Kraushaar and G. W. Clark, MIT.

2.3 The Orbiting Astronomical Observatory

WALTER H. SCOTT, JR.

GRUMMAN AIRCRAFT ENGINEERING CORPORATION,
Bethpage, Long Island, New York

Introduction

The Orbiting Astronomical Observatory (OAO) is under development by the Goddard Space Flight Center of the NASA to serve as a standardized spacecraft for a variety of astronomical experiments. This requires a large spacecraft with ample power, exceptional stability and control, large data handling capacity, and long life. This paper will describe the spacecraft part of the system, which is under contract to Grumman Aircraft Engineering Corporation. The scientific equipment—different for each OAO—will be supplied to Goddard by direct contracts with the experimenters. The experiments currently under development will be discussed in other chapters. Therefore, this report will be confined to describing the spacecraft to show how we intend to provide for the experimenters' needs.

General Description

The first OAO is to be launched from the Atlantic Missile Range in late 1963, using an Atlas-Agena B booster. It is intended to orbit the earth in a 500-mile altitude circular orbit at approximately 30° inclination to the equator (Fig. 1).

The spacecraft weighs 3300 lb including 1000 lb of experimenters' equipment (Fig. 2). It is an octagonally shaped aluminum structure with a hollow central tube which houses the experiment container. The spacecraft is 118 in. high and 80 in. wide. The central tube provides for experiment equipment measuring 110 in. high by 40 in. in diameter. A sunshade is provided to prevent direct sunlight from entering the tube.

Power

The solar paddles (Fig. 3) are folded flat against the sides and the entire spacecraft is covered by a protective shroud during launch. Following shroud ejection and Agena B burnout, the solar paddles are extended and remain fixed. The spacecraft is designed to point to any part of the sky except within 45° of the sun. The roll angle of the vehicle

Fig. 1. Orbiting Astronomical Observatory.

(measured about the optical axis) is programmed to provide maximum solar cell exposure to the sun. The average power for the entire spacecraft is 350 watts. Thirty watts are provided for the experiment. Nickel-cadmium batteries are used to store energy to maintain operations on the dark side of the earth.

Thermal Control

The basic configuration of the spacecraft is determined primarily by thermal control requirements to maintain the proper temperature environment and minimize thermal distortion (Fig. 4). The central tube is protected from large excursions in temperature by the surrounding spacecraft structure. The structure and spacecraft equipment are in turn protected by the outer skin which is not structural and therefore can be mounted on insulated pads. Skin coatings are selected to provide the desired radiative properties. The central tube is normally insulated from heat generated by electrical equipment. Insulated equipment mounts are used to avoid conduction to the structure, and all heat is radiated to the outer skins. Careful attention is given to each piece of equipment to maintain local temperatures within tolerances.

FIG. 2. Structure and equipment details, OAO.

Attitude Control

The attitude control system for the observatory was evolved to satisfy the accuracy and stability requirements imposed by the experiments. The major function of the attitude control system may be divided into three tasks:

(1) To stabilize the spacecraft following booster separation and to establish its attitude with the required precision.

(2) To slew the spacecraft to any desired attitude as dictated by the experimenter's star observation program.

FIG. 3. Solar paddle mockup, OAO.

FIG. 4. Three bay thermal vacuum test specimen showing insulation pads and inner skin, OAO.

(3) To control the OAO to enable it to maintain a given attitude to the required accuracy over long periods of time.

The first task is accomplished by a series of steps which may require several orbits to complete. First, rate gyros and a coarse sun sensor are used to reduce the tumbling rates which exist after booster separation and to point the optical axis (roll) away from the sun. Nitrogen gas jets are used for control in this phase. Next, the fine sun sensors in combination with fine inertia wheels are used to bring the roll axis within a $\pm 0.5°$ alignment with the sun line.

The next step of orientation is to locate the pitch and yaw axes with respect to the celestial sphere. A system of six star trackers is used for this phase of operation. By rolling the spacecraft about the sun line, each of the trackers can be made to lock on a preselected bright star. The star trackers are mounted in two-degree-of-freedom gimbals such as to cover as large a solid angle as possible and to provide nearly complete coverage of the celestial sphere. Six star trackers are used in order to provide redundant signals for such situations as: (1) malfunctions, (2) bore sight errors, (3) guide star occulted by the earth, or (4) locked onto an improper signal such as stray illumination from the earth or sun.

To slew the spacecraft to any particular star for experimentation, the star trackers remain locked on guide stars, and commands are transmitted from the ground to provide new star-tracker gimbal angles for guidance. The coarse inertia wheels are activated, which can slew the spacecraft 30° in 3 min about any control axis. At the new heading, control is switched to the fine wheels for attitude hold. The star trackers are capable of pointing the spacecraft to ± 1 min of accuracy. The fine wheel control system is capable of holding to ± 0.1 sec of arc using error signals provided by the experiment.

An alternate pointing system consisting of a television camera with a 10°-field of view is capable of detecting sixth magnitude stars to ± 1 min accuracy. This camera is pointed along the optical axis of the experiment.

External torques due to solar pressure, atmosphere drag, gravitational forces and magnetic fields will tend to gradually force the inertia wheels to their limiting rpm. Therefore the wheels are periodically unloaded by a fine jet system and a back-up system consisting of magnetic coils used in conjunction with the earth's magnetic field to generate unloading torques.

Data Processing and Communications

The types of data to be processed and transmitted from the spacecraft include the basic data from the experiment, and data pertaining to the operational status of the spacecraft and its experiment.

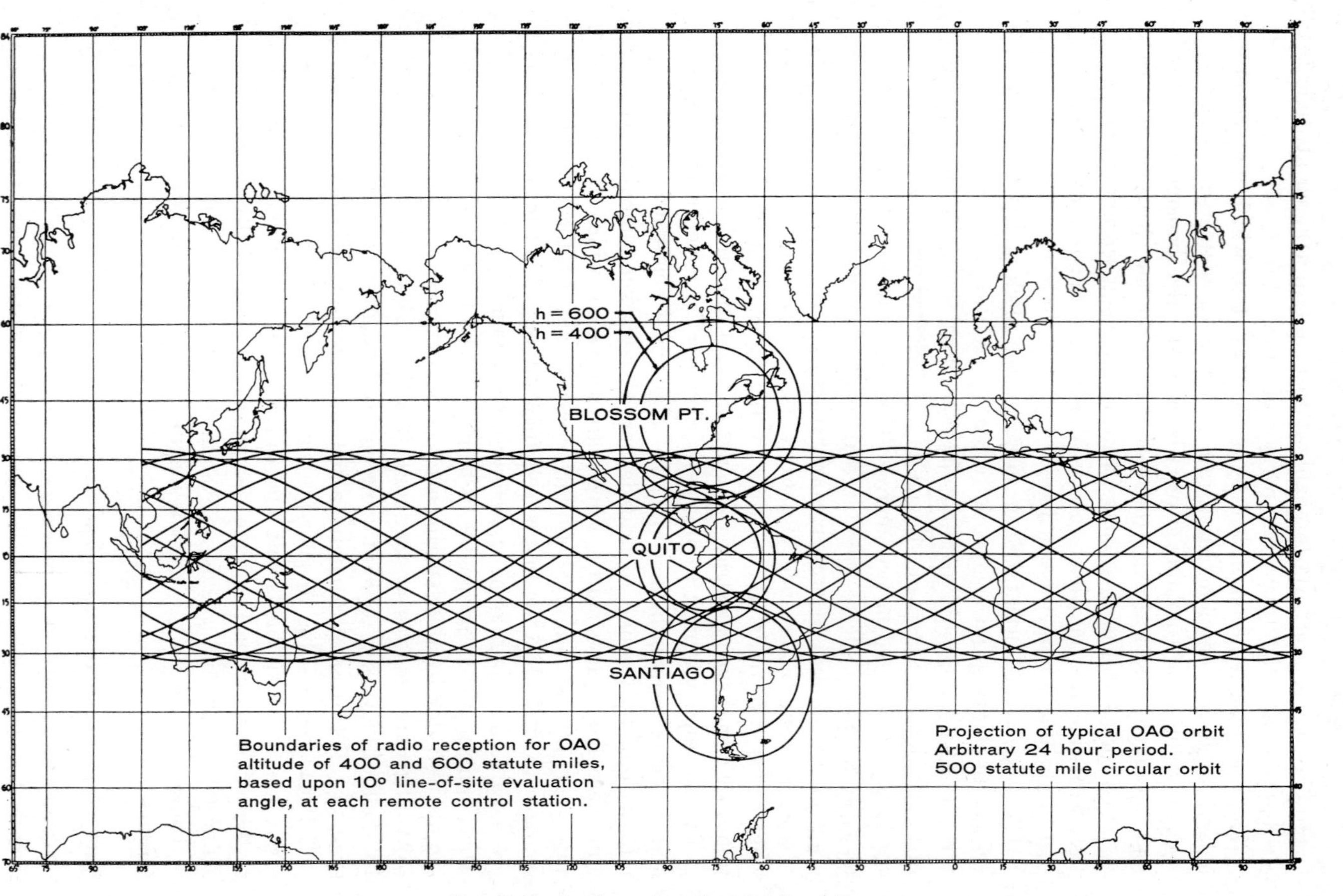

FIG. 5. Projection of typical OAO orbit.

All data are handled in digital form and are transmitted to the ground by the narrow-band and wide-band telemetry transmitters. A core memory with a capacity of 200,000 bits is provided to store data when beyond range of the ground stations.

A command receiver accepts commands from the ground which are then fed into a command decoder and distributor for either immediate execution in the case of real-time operation of the observatory from the ground or storage for later execution. A separate smaller core memory is used to store commands.

A tracking beacon is provided to aid in determining location and orbit information.

The ground equipment for the OAO consists of a central control station at the Goddard Space Flight Center, and three remote stations at Minitrack sites at Blossom Point, Maryland, Quito, Ecuador, and Santiago, Chile. With these station locations, the observatory will always be in line of sight for part of each orbit (Fig. 5).

Reliability and Long Life

The OAO is being designed and developed with strong emphasis on new approaches to long life reliability. Complex mechanical systems have been avoided wherever possible. Electronic systems such as the data processing system are designed with redundant components so that a transistor or diode failure will not make the system inoperative. Where redundancy cannot be applied on a circuit level, dual systems are provided, for example, the use of multiple star trackers, where any two of a total of six trackers are sufficient for stabilization.

The Orbiting Astronomical Observatory should provide astronomers with an extremely useful instrument for precise studies of the stars and our own solar system, free from atmospheric interference.

2.4 A Program for Astronomical Studies by Rocket-Borne Instruments

R. L. F. BOYD

UNIVERSITY COLLEGE, London, England

Interest at University College in the use of the techniques of space science for astronomical studies grew out of the realization that the measurements being made in the ionosphere would increase in value if they were associated with simultaneous studies of the sun. We sought, therefore, to devise simple means of observing the total solar flux in selected regions of the ultraviolet and X-ray spectra,* means which would make little demand on payload and telemetry capacity.

The sun, however, is an object of absorbing interest in its own right. Having, therefore, taken up the study of this star it was natural that our interest should soon be extended to others also.

Table I lists the experiments in which we are involved.

TABLE I

Experiments	Status
Solar X-radiation	
Emulsion detectors	Flown successfully; continuing
Proportional counters (rocket version)	Awaiting flight
Proportional counters (satellite version)	Awaiting flight
Scanning spectroheliograph	In preparation
Solar uv radiation	
Lyman-α ionization chambers	Flown successfully; continuing
Stellar uv radiation	
Photomultiplier sky scan ~1700 Å	Flown successfully; continuing
Photography ~1700 Å	Awaiting flight
(Large optics for satellite uv telescope)	Study with Edinburgh Observatory
Stellar X-radiation	
Reflection optics and discrimination against cosmic rays	Work started

* The X-ray work is done in collaboration with the Department of Physics, Leicester University, and some of the uv work in association with the Royal Observatory, Edinburgh.

FIG. 1. Emulsion detector.

Solar X-Radiation

Emulsion Detector

This instrument, which is illustrated in Fig. 1, has been developed for inclusion whenever possible in ionospheric payloads. It makes no demands on telemetry and may be recovered without damage to the record providing the aerodynamic stability of the round has been destroyed. Five foils of aluminum and beryllium make it possible to deduce the soft X-ray intensity and spectral slope from the blackening of the emulsion beneath.

At appropriate altitudes electric pulses from the master timer open and reclose a very strong shutter which thus not only determines the exposure but also protects the foils.

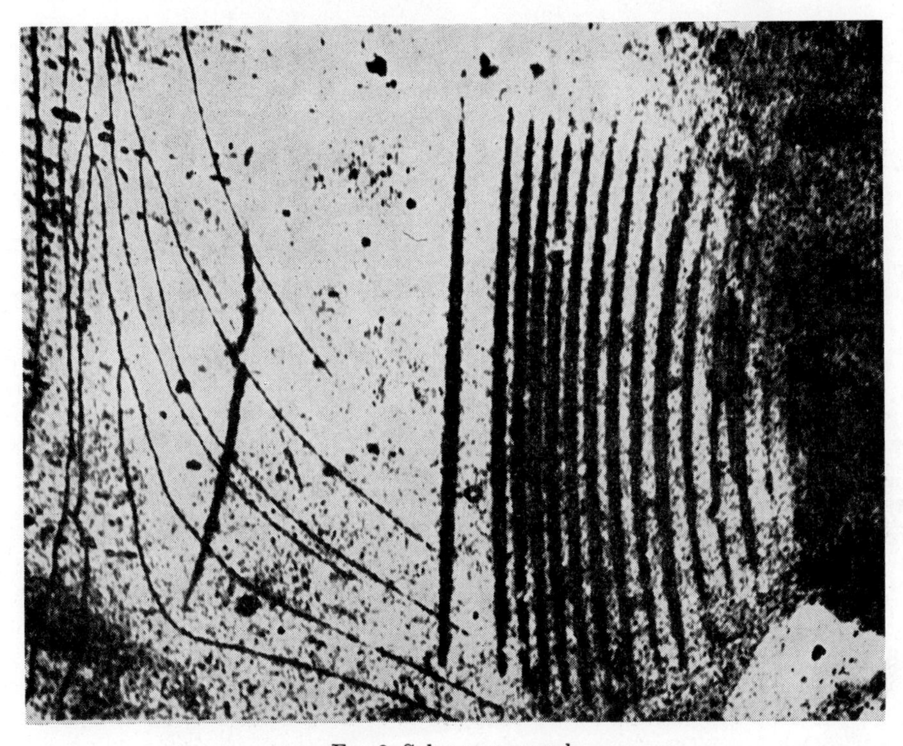

Fig. 2. Solar pass record.

Since these devices are used in unstabilized rounds some knowledge of the aspect history of the vehicle is required, so that the total exposure time may be found and corrections may be made for the variation in foil transparency with angle to the solar vector. A tiny pin-hole camera provides this information in the form of a record of solar passes (Fig. 2).

A Skylark rocket carrying this equipment was fired at Woomera, South Australia, on 1959 September 17^d 01^h 12^m, when the sun appeared from ground observations to be quiescent. The color temperature was found to be $1.7–1.9 \times 10^6$ °K, and the total energy in the 8–20 Å band was 2.3×10^{-2} erg cm^{-2} sec^{-1} outside the earth's atmosphere.

PROPORTIONAL COUNTER

In parallel with the Emulsion detector an electronic system has been developed, suitable where recovery is not available (most satellites) and also capable of greater accuracy in total flux and spectral slope. The central device in this system is a proportional counter yielding pulses whose height is a measure of photon energy. The resolution of such a system may be seen from the curve of Fig. 3.

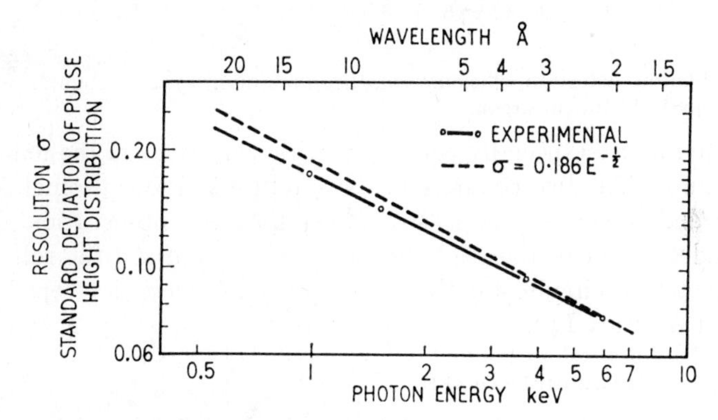

FIG. 3. Photon counter wavelength resolution (argon filling).

The counter made and filled by 20th Century Electronics Ltd. has been fitted with aluminum windows, with a 60° included angle field of view, for the Skylark (rocket) version of the experiment. The block diagram is shown in Fig. 4 and the detection efficiency in Fig. 5. This

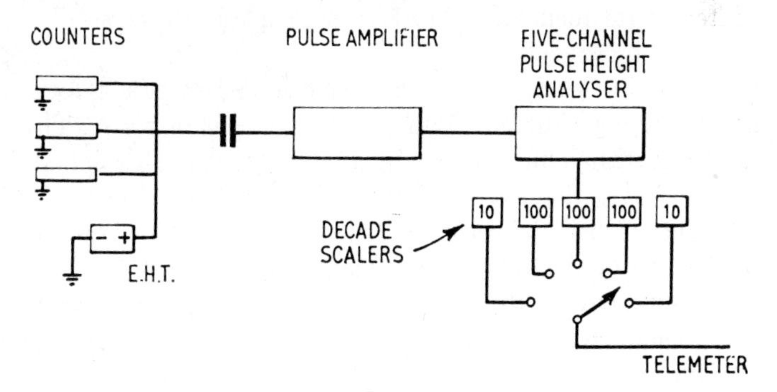

FIG. 4. Block diagram of instrumentation of X-ray counter.

response is suited to the flux from the quiet sun. For the U.K. 1 (satellite) version of the experiment a time sequence sampling of the spectrum is used, and by the use of beryllium windows with neon filling, the response is tailored to be appropriate to the hardening of the radiation under disturbed solar conditions. The associated ionospheric experiments

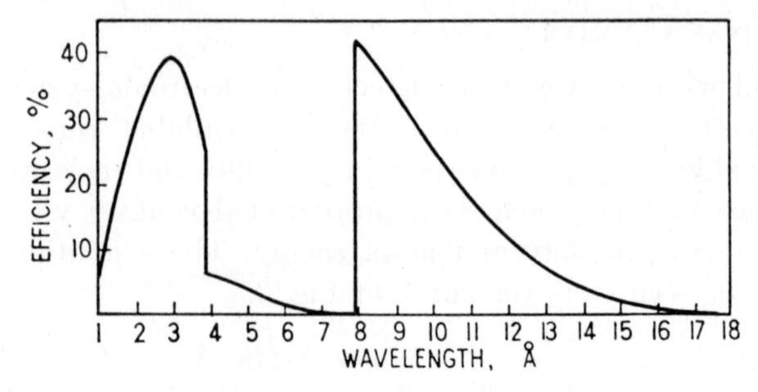

FIG. 5. Photon detection efficiency of the aluminum window counter with gas absorption path 2 atm-cm argon.

in the satellite are especially concerned with variations in the ionosphere at these times. The two counters in the satellite look out through several windows and a sky screen is so shaped that the observation time is almost independent of the angle between the ecliptic and the roll axis.

The electronic circuits for the satellite version were developed for us by Bristol Aircraft Ltd.

SCANNING SPECTROHELIOGRAPH

Soft X-rays striking a mirror at grazing incidence may be reflected with reasonable efficiency. After allowance for the photon detection efficiency of the counter, the over-all efficiency of a grazing incidence telescope for 12-Å radiation, using copper or gold with a maximum grazing angle of 2°, is about 10%. By using a telescope consisting of the frustrum of a very deep paraboloid of polished copper, with a proportional counter at its focus, a field of view of a minute or so of arc may be obtained.

A telescope of this kind, having an aperture of 3 cm and a focal length of 30 cm, is being constructed as an X-ray spectroheliograph. The equipment is to be installed in one of the currently available jet stabilized Skylark nose cones, the gyro reference having been replaced by sun sensors. The sensors will be set so as to operate the jets when the system has moved ½° from the solar vector, and the jet bursts so adjusted as to give a random scan of the solar disc at a rate of about one line scan per second. Telemetered signals from the sensors will give the pointing direction to an accuracy of order 1 min of arc.

The system as at present being engineered is suitable for the quiet sun and will use a proportional counter of the kind used for the total X-ray work with rockets, together with the electronics already developed. However, the interest in spectroheliograms of this type under disturbed solar conditions is such that the first opportunity will be taken to fly a satellite version of the experiment.

Solar Ultraviolet Radiation

Lyman-alpha

The rocket flights with nitric-oxide ionization chambers, and the instrumentation prepared for the first Anglo-American Scout satellite, use

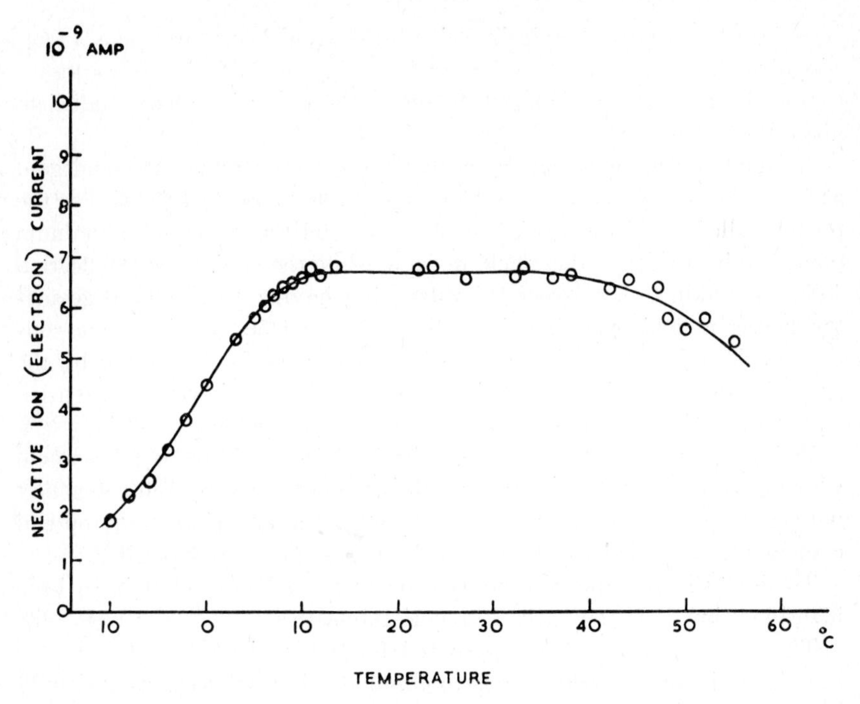

Fig. 6. Temperature response curve of iodine chamber. Collecting voltage, 46 volts; intensity of radiation, about 4 ergs/sec; 5% limits, 7°–45°C; 10-cm-long chamber with 1-mm gap between inner electrode and window.

chambers based on drawings very kindly supplied to us by Dr. Friedman. Anticipating an aging effect with these chambers as found by other workers, we also developed chambers using iodine vapor. Their sensitivity to temperature, owing to varying iodine vapor pressure (see Fig. 6), produces a severe thermal engineering problem if such chambers are included in a satellite payload. It was fortunate, therefore, that the expected deterioration of the nitric oxide chambers under continual irradiation was found not to occur in those made for us by 20th Century Electronics Ltd.

One rocket flight has been made with these chambers to date. It was entirely successful, though the limits to be set on the accuracy of the result are rather wide as the equipment had to be flown before adequate arrangements for calibration had been made. The value obtained for the Lyman-α flux from the sun was 4 erg cm^{-2} sec^{-1}.

Stellar Ultraviolet

Photomultiplier Sky Scan, λ1700 Å

On May 1, 1961, a Skylark rocket fired from Woomera gave a successful flight to the instrumentation shown in Fig. 7. As far as we know, this is the first occasion on which the southern sky has been studied in ultraviolet radiation.

Six photomultipliers, having synthetic fused quartz windows and gold cathodes giving a peak sensitivity around 1700 Å, scanned the sky as the rocket rolled and precessed. Five of the "telescopes" used aluminum honeycomb to restrict their field of view while the sixth used a reflection collimator akin to a Cassegrain system, but having a cylindrical geometry giving a field extending laterally $\pm\frac{1}{2}°$ and 50° in the plane containing the roll axis of the vehicle. In this way, sources detected by the five telescopes were interrogated to discover whether they were extensive or narrower than about 1°.

Redundancy of aspect data was obtained by installing a slit system which gave the angle between the roll axis and the lunar vector, together with a three axis magnetometer. (For the same purpose, an optical camera was installed but it has not been possible to recover it.)

To date signals from O and B type stars and the moon have been identified, but it is too early to report intensities.

The next firing now being prepared for will make use of Cassegrain optics on all the telescopes so as to eliminate the variation in sensitivity over the field of view which reduces the accuracy of the honeycomb arrangement. The logarithmic amplifier (see Fig. 8) will be replaced by a pulse counting system to improve the signal-to-noise ratio, which was rather marginal on the last flight.

Photography, λ1700 Å

Awaiting firing at Woomera at present is a Skylark carrying a camera in a jet stabilized nose cone. The stabilized system uses a gyro reference

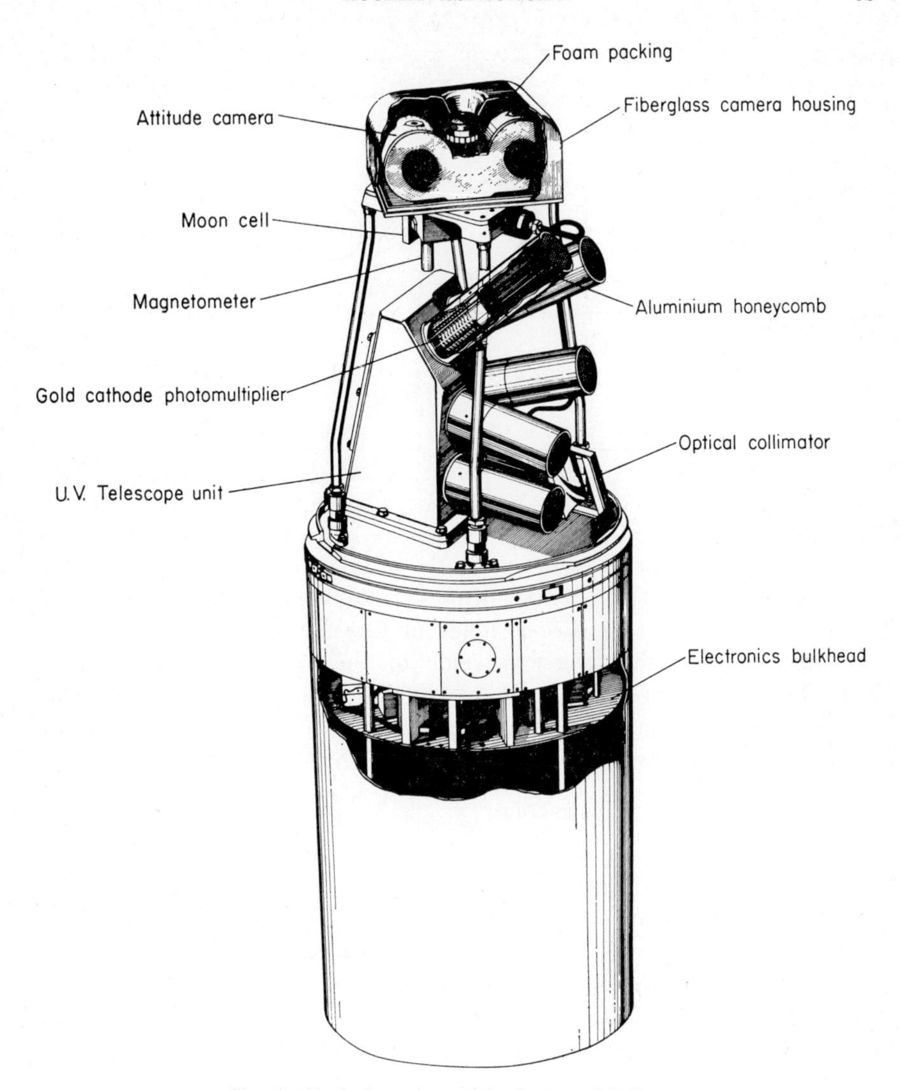

FIG. 7. Skylark rocket with photomultipliers.

and has an accuracy of only a few degrees. Nevertheless, it is reasonable to expect that for short periods during the flight the angular drift rate for the instrument may well be small enough to enable sky photographs to be obtained. The flight is part of the Skylark development program, but the opportunity has been taken to install a camera for ultraviolet photography as well as the visible light camera being used to monitor the round performance.

The camera installed uses a 55-mm film and takes 1-sec exposures

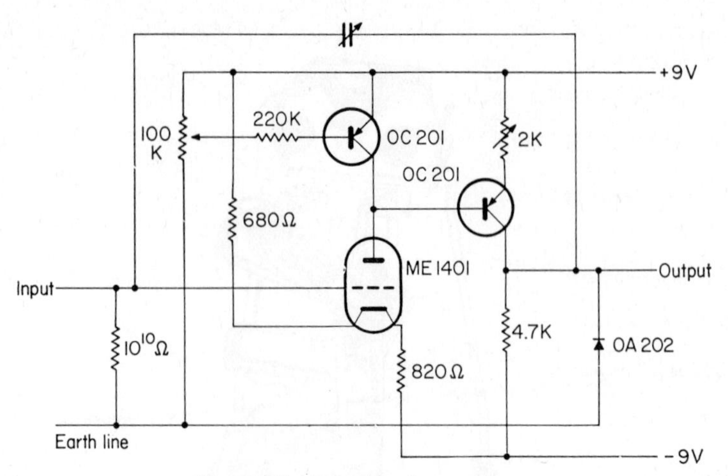

FIG. 8. The logarithmic amplifier.

continually. The lens is made of synthetic fused quartz (Spectrosil). It is a three-component anastigmat of focal ratio 3.5. There is a high degree of chromatic aberration. Use is made of this fact by focusing the lens for light just on the long-wave side of the short-wavelength cutoff (λ1700 Å). In this way, the stellar image halos may be expected to contain the information needed to give not only the ultraviolet intensity near λ1700 Å but also the spectral slope.

LARGE ULTRAVIOLET TELESCOPE

This is a project of the British National Committee for Space Research. The present author plays the part of a kind of godfather. Dr. Butler, Chairman of the B.N.C.S.R. working group for astronomy, is really *in loco parentis*. However, since we are associated with this interesting project a very brief account of it will be given here.

In the expectation that alone or in association with Europe, the British Government would develop a satellite launcher capable of orbiting a weight approaching a ton, it was decided to carry out a design study of a typical payload (this work was done by the Royal Aircraft Establishment). The primary experiment selected for this was an ultraviolet spectrometer employing a telescope of about 20-in. aperture. The telescope is about 4 ft long, having a rather large secondary mirror and a tertiary mirror providing uniaxial fine guidance to a precision of about 3 sec arc. Coarse guidance to a precision rather better than 1-min arc is obtained by a jet stabilized table carrying six star lock-on telescopes.

The whole system is stabilized in such a way that the main telescope and the solar cell array can rotate about an axis through the stabilized table normal to the ecliptic. Thus the solar paddles provide shade for the rest of the system and are kept pointing roughly at the sun. The telescope itself rotates about an axis at right angles to the solar paddles, that is roughly along the solar direction. In this way the entire sky may be studied in the course of a year.

A second experiment allowed for in the design is the stellar X-ray system referred to later in this paper. The X-ray telescope is mounted alongside the uv telescope and has an aperture of about 6 in.

Stellar X-Radiation

Anticipating that satellites capable of pointing to selected stars with a precision of at least 1° (and possibly many orders of magnitude better than this) may become available to us, a grant has been obtained and work has been started on systems capable of detecting the possibly very weak X-radiation from stars, in the presence of the background noise due to cosmic rays.

The conflicting effects of a probably falling flux intensity with energy in most cases, together with a rapid falling of interstellar absorption with energy, indicate that the spectral region we are already studying with proportional counters for the sun would be a good region for a first look at the stars. Optics of the kind already developed for the spectroheliograph would be satisfactory though it might be found worth while to use a number of very deep concentric parabolas. Most of the development effort must now go into the detection system to reduce to a minimum its sensitivity to cosmic rays. The use of the proportional counters already discussed together with adequate pulse-height discrimination would go a long way towards improving signal-to-noise ratio.

As a general principle however, the detector should be made as small as practicable to reduce the target for cosmic rays. It seems likely, therefore, that a scintillation detector or possibly even a semiconductor detector for soft X-rays may prove the best for the purpose.

While no flight is scheduled at present, development of the Skylark stabilized nose cone to use a sidereal reference is anticipated, and we expect to be ready to make use of this system as soon as it is available. Only in the case of sources having an absolute X-ray magnitude much greater than that of the sun could a rocket experiment expect to be successful. We are hopeful, therefore, that before long a suitable satellite may become available.

Discussion

DR. H. E. BUTLER: I am very interested in the possibilities of collecting data on stellar spectra in the region 3000–1200 Å by using a small Schmidt camera with an objective grating or prism—i.e., by doing conventional Schmidt photographic objective-prism photometry with a rocket-borne telescope. It appears that an instrument with an aperture rather less than 6 in., working at $f/2$ and having a 10° field of view, is practicable possibly using reflection optics exclusively. In a 1-min exposure, we should get very useful data on a minimum of one star per square degree.

The advantages of photography in the rapid collection of data cannot be overemphasized. There are many other simplifications—neither telemetry nor accurate trajectory data are required, and we carry out small programs at relatively short notice and cost. Needless to say, however, we have the very difficult task of constructing a good stabilization system having less accurate pointing control. To get the best data, stability of a few seconds of arc is needed during the exposure, although useful data could be collected less efficiently with less accurate stabilization. Although the difficulties of the problem should not be underestimated, there are several approaches that have not yet been properly explored and which might give the required answer.

CHAPTER 3

The Role of Balloon Techniques in Space Age Astronomy

JOHN B. ROGERSON, JR.

PRINCETON UNIVERSITY OBSERVATORY, Princeton, New Jersey

With the advent of the space age, the possibility exists to make those observations which have for so long been frustrated by the manifold effects of the earth's atmosphere. Optical measurements are no longer restricted to visible wavelengths but may be pushed both into the ultraviolet and into the infrared. Photographs may now be made with angular resolution limited only by the telescope or the photographic emulsion. The radio spectrum can be expanded to the limit of receiver techniques and particle radiations of all kinds become subject to direct measurement.

To make full use of these observational possibilities, however, the observing instrument must obviously be lifted completely out of the influence of the earth's atmosphere, and this requirement implies the use of a rocket. There are a sufficient number of difficulties associated with the use of rockets that it is pertinent to ask how much is gained by lifting the instrument to balloon altitudes of 15 to 20 miles.

Balloon altitudes help practically not at all in exposing the ultraviolet extension of the visible spectrum. One might expand the visible spectrum by some 50 to 75 Å into the ultraviolet and it may be possible to pick up some energy in the interval from 2000 to 2300 Å, but these gains are extremely marginal.

In the infrared, however, the situation is much more favorable. The atmospheric absorption in the infrared is dominated by water vapor and carbon dioxide, with water vapor blanketing the major portion of the spectrum. It is fortunate then that practically all water vapor absorption takes place in the layers below balloon altitudes. The carbon dioxide absorption, though materially reduced, is still present in important amounts in certain of the strong bands. In summary, it appears that for most infrared observations there is very little to gain by exceeding balloon altitudes.

High resolution photography has already been accomplished by the Princeton balloon-borne solar telescope. The results of this telescope strongly suggest that balloon altitudes suffice for the practical elimination of atmospheric seeing. Assuming then that sufficiently accurate guidance can be obtained for either a satellite or balloon-borne instrument, one would choose the satellite only to make use of the increased resolving power which is theoretically available with ultraviolet radiation.

There are also gains to be had for radio observations, particularly for wavelengths shorter than 10 cm, and observations of particle radiation are much more favorable at balloon altitudes than at sea level. However, the present paper will be restricted to optical observations, and no consideration will be given to the relative advantages of balloon and satellite altitudes for these types of observations.

It is clear then that of the three advantages bestowed on optical astronomy by the space age, namely, extension of the ultraviolet spectrum, extension of the infrared spectrum, and high resolution photography, the latter two are already available in important measure at balloon altitudes. For those experiments that can be performed equally well at balloon or satellite altitudes, it is interesting to examine some of the arguments which bear on the choice between the two.

(1) The stresses associated with a rocket launch are extremely severe, and it requires great ingenuity to get a delicate instrument both to survive the launching stresses and to arrive in orbit in good adjustment. On the other hand, the stresses associated with a balloon launch are quite mild and little special handling is needed to get an instrument safely to balloon altitudes.

(2) The expense of placing a satellite in orbit is at present so great that one is at least morally required to design his instrument to have both a fairly wide area of application and a long lifetime. With balloons, however, one may economically justify the launching of equipment which is highly specialized to best perform a specific task. Furthermore, a balloon experiment need only operate unattended for periods of the order of a day, so that there is no necessity to spend the time, money, and effort to make it failure-proof for long periods.

(3) For any experiment in which recovery is desirable, such as the recovery of exposed emulsions, one would certainly choose to use a balloon, at least for the present. Recovery techniques from satellites are being developed, but it may be some time before these techniques are routinely available for experimental packages. Recovery of image-

type data can even now be accomplished by substituting the television camera for the photographic camera, but one pays a substantial penalty in resolving power, field of view, or both. Image recovery through television techniques is under steady development, and it will no doubt become fully competitive with photography in the near future.

(4) There are some experiments for which large dimensions and/or unusual shapes may be necessary or desirable. In these cases, the nearly complete freedom of payload size and shape for balloon-borne equipment may prove a decisive advantage over the closely prescribed volumes available in satellites. The field of high resolution photography provides a good example of this problem. In order to use the resolution possible in the absence of seeing, a large optical magnification is necessary so that image details are not lost in the resolving power of the photographic or television camera. This requirement can be met with the best chance of preserving image quality through the use of simple optical systems and large focal lengths which consequently need long dimensions in the payload. To pack such an instrument in a small satellite volume would necessitate complex folded optics and possible consequent image degradation.

(5) Finally, for those experiments needing long night-time exposures, balloon techniques permit exposures of the order of 12 hours while satellites are restricted to about ½ hour per orbit. Thus a satellite instrument will take 3–4 times longer to accumulate a given exposure. This extra time required, aside from the inconvenience, may be a real limitation in studying time-dependent problems such as short period variable stars or binaries.

The foregoing arguments were presented to indicate that balloons have an important role to play in space age astronomy. In our great enthusiasm for the potentialities of satellite observations, we should be careful not to overlook some advantages offered by balloon techniques.

The Princeton Balloon Telescope Program

The Princeton University Observatory balloon-borne telescope program, Project Stratoscope, is an example of a program for which satellite altitudes have negligible observational advantage, while the balloon technique has a great cost advantage and numerous technical advantages, stemming largely from the gentleness of the balloon launch and simplicity of design as a result of freedom of size and shape. The aim of this program is the tackling of various astronomical problems which have hitherto been stymied by atmospheric seeing. The idea of a balloon-borne telescope was under discussion at Princeton in the early 1950's, and in 1957, under the direction of Dr. Martin Schwarzschild, this work

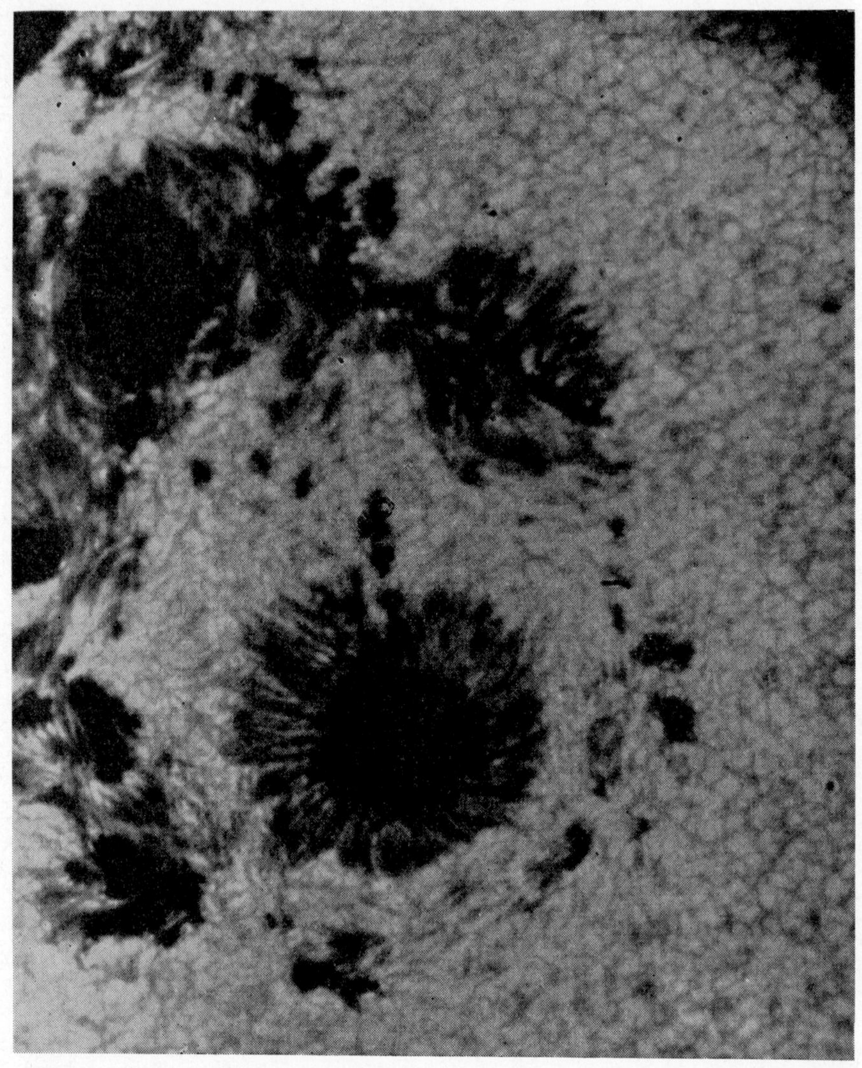

FIG. 1. Sunspot photograph taken by Project Stratoscope balloon-borne solar telescope.

resulted in a self-pointing telescope capable of taking high resolution photographs of the solar surface (see Fig. 1). With funds provided by both the Navy and the Air Force, a high quality 12-in. telescope with an effective focal length of 200 ft was designed by the Perkin-Elmer Corporation. For pointing the telescope, an enlarged version of a two-axis sun seeker was made by the University of Colorado, and the huge plastic balloon with the recovery parachute and instrument suspension system was developed by the General Mills Company. With this equipment one test flight and two fully instrumented flights were made in the summer and fall of 1957, resulting in a number of exceptionally high-definition photographs of the solar granulation and the solar limb (see Fig. 2).

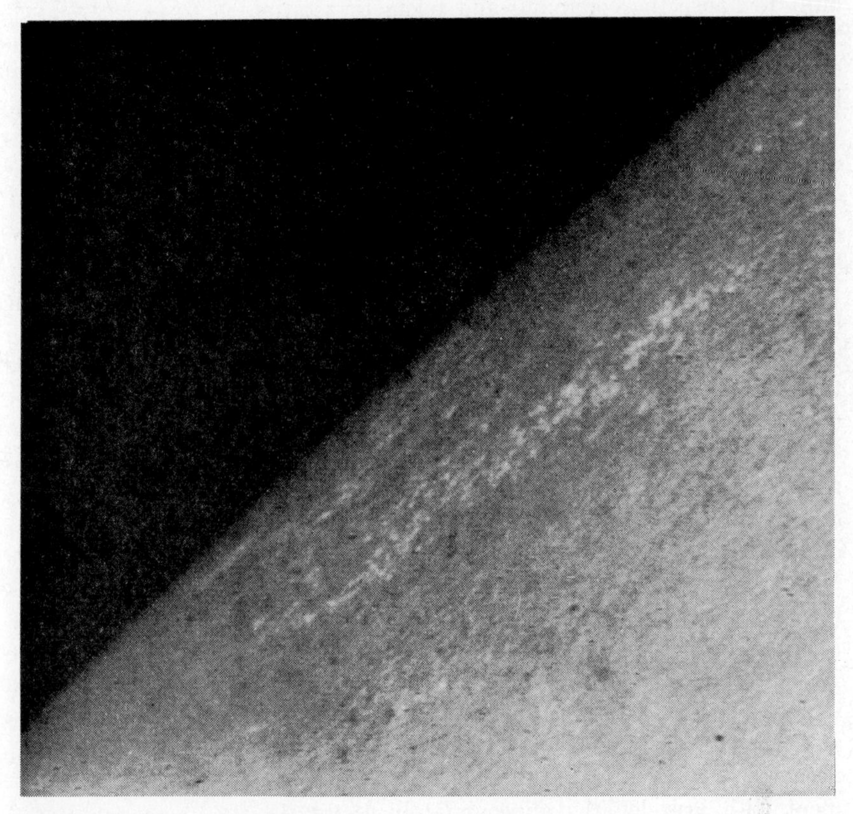

FIG. 2. Photograph of solar limb with a group of photospheric faculae taken by balloon-borne solar telescope.

Once the 1957 instrument was launched, it was completely out of ground control and only responded to the program of an internal timer. The successful operation of this equipment encouraged us to attempt a measure of radio control of the instrument during the next series of flights. Accordingly, a number of modifications of the instrument were made during 1958 under the sponsorship of the Office of Naval Research and the National Science Foundation. The guidance system was improved. In order to see on a ground monitor what the telescope was looking at, a vidicon television camera and transmitter were installed.

A radio command system was added to give us control over the telescope focus and pointing direction as well as control over some necessary adjustments of the television camera. A more sophisticated telemetry system permitted constant monitoring of the result of our commands as well as numerous diagnostic data. Finally, a mobile ground station was built to house the command and telemetry station.

The equipment thus modified was flown successfully during the summer of 1959. Among other results, these flights produced sequences of high-definition photographs of fixed areas on the solar disk permitting studies of the time variation of the granulation. Besides the astronomical results, which will not be discussed here, the flights demonstrated that our simple command scheme worked very satisfactorily. In barest detail, a switch thrown on the ground actuated a relay in the airborne equipment. The relay caused a motor to turn in a predetermined direction. A telemetry signal was taken from a potentiometer mounted on the motor shaft so that we could monitor the angular motion of the motor shaft. We could therefore turn off the switch when the shaft reached the desired angle. With this system, it seemed as simple to operate the telescope as if we were in physical contact with it.

The results of the six fully instrumental flights with the solar instrument proved that balloon altitudes (around 80,000 ft) are sufficient to eliminate the effects of seeing. It therefore seems desirable to make use of the high angular resolution possible in an attack on a number of night-sky problems which have been frustrated by the effects of atmospheric seeing. In pursuit of this goal, a very high quality 36-in. reflector is being built, which, it is hoped, will be diffraction limited (see Fig. 3). This project is under the joint sponsorship of the Office of Naval Research, the National Science Foundation, and the National Aeronautics and Space Administration. Various design requirements including the necessary optical magnification have resulted in a large L-shape instrument with arm lengths approximately 15 by 18 ft. (A model of this instrument was on exhibit during the symposium. It was loaned by the National Science Foundation.) To force such an instrument into available satellite volumes would undoubtedly imperil its optical quality. The instrument is to be capable of self-guidance with an accuracy of $1/30$ second of arc by deriving its guidance signals from two selectable guide stars in the focal plane of the telescope. By proper combination of the error signals from the two guide stars it is possible to control not only the direction of the optical axis, but the roll of the telescope around this axis.

The object acquisition proceeds as follows. The direction of gravity and the direction of magnetic north are sensed by the instrument. Using these data, the telescope can be pointed at the object with an accuracy of perhaps several degrees. This accuracy is sufficient to bring the object within the field of a 10° field television camera. This camera has separate optics, but is mechanically aligned with the main telescope. The ground observer is required to recognize the star field and correct the pointing

FIG. 3. Model of the 36-in. balloon-borne telescope to be used for night-sky objects.

to bring the object to the center of the field of this camera. At this time, the pointing will be sufficiently precise that the object, or at least the guide stars, may be seen by a second television camera which looks through the big telescope. Two movable pointing error sensors will have previously been commanded into such positions that when the guide stars are centered on their respective error sensors, the desired object is in the center of the field. The ground observer, looking at the fine television monitor, is therefore required to command the telescope pointing until each guide star is within the field of its sensor. At this point, the automatic guidance is commanded on, and it then centers the guide stars in their sensors and keeps them there. The telescope is focused in such a way as to maximize the gain of the guidance servo system. This condition requires the guide star image to have a minimum diameter which is equivalent to the condition of best focus. At this point, the photographic exposure may be started.

Altogether there are about 60 command functions, each with its telemetry feedback. These control telescope movement, balance adjustment, focus adjustment, photographic camera operation, television camera adjustment, automatic guidance adjustment, and balloon ballasting. The command and telemetry systems are fairly complex, and a moderate amount of redundancy has been built in to guard against the most likely failure modes. The success of this latest step in Project Stratoscope will be determined in May 1962, when the first flight is scheduled.

CHAPTER 4

Radiation Detectors

4.1 Image Tubes for Space Research

J. D. McGEE

IMPERIAL COLLEGE OF SCIENCE & TECHNOLOGY, London, England

Introduction

This paper is concerned with the recording of optical images in earth satellites and their conversion to signals suitable for transmission to a ground station.

The gains to be had from operating a telescope in a satellite are as follows:

(1) elimination of atmospheric light absorption and hence the opportunity for the first time to observe in the ultraviolet, and improved observing conditions in the infrared;

(2) elimination of disturbing effects due to the atmosphere, hence the ideal resolution of a telescope should be attainable in a perfectly stabilized satellite;

(3) elimination of part of the sky background glow, which at present limits the ability of large telescopes to detect faint or distant objects.

The disadvantages are as follows:

(1) The size of telescope will be severely limited, at least for some considerable time.

(2) Stabilization can not be expected to be perfect, and the spread of an image point due to lack of perfect stabilization may be comparable to that due to the disturbance caused by the atmosphere.

(3) The system must be operated by remote control, and all information collected by the telescope must be relayed to ground by television or telemetry techniques.

From these considerations it is clear that:

(1) The light collected by the telescope must be used as efficiently as possible. This requires the application of photoelectric devices as primary detectors, probably in the form of photomultipliers or image intensifiers so that the signal-to-noise ratio is determined only by the shot noise of the primary photoelectric conversion.

(2) Such devices must be capable of detecting ultraviolet light down, say, to 1000 Å, as immediate interest will be in the ultraviolet region. Later it will almost certainly be desired to use also the visible and near infrared to observe very distant objects.

(3) It will be necessary to integrate image information for considerable periods when more distant and fainter objects are studied. For this we require charge-integrating signal-generating electron tubes of a type that can be used repeatedly.

(4) The output of these photoelectronic devices must be in the form of an electrical signal which can be recorded, reproduced, and relayed by radio to earth.

As in ground-based astronomy, so we expect in satellite astronomy, a lot of work will be done by measuring the light flux from particular objects or spectral lines by means of photomultipliers. However, this aspect of the problem will not be dealt with here. This paper will be restricted to discussing the photoelectric recording of optical images, either in the one-dimensional form of spectra or as two-dimensional images of celestial objects.

Television cameras of the simplest form, that is vidicon cameras, have already been used in satellites (*1*) (e.g., Tiros I and II) for originating picture signals from optical images of the earth, and no doubt other objects such as the moon will soon be observed by such methods. The U.S.S.R. Lunik III recorded photographs of the far side of the moon (*2*) which were then developed and, at command some time later, these photographs were scanned to produce a television signal which was transmitted to earth. Such observations will, no doubt, be repeated and elaborated. Though they do call for a high degree of engineering and technical skill, they do not require anything very new in the photoelectronic systems themselves because they are required to operate only on objects of high brightness, for which the relatively insensitive vidicon is quite adequate, especially if the rate of scan is decreased and hence the realizable signal-to-noise ratio is increased for a given image brightness.

It seems that it would be most useful to discuss those methods of photoelectronic detection and recording of optical images which, one hopes, will ultimately lead to the most efficient use of the almost priceless photons captured by a satellite telescope. This may sound somewhat presumptuous when such devices may be said to be only in their infancy for use in ground-based telescopes. However, though it is early days, they are in use; and the pioneering work of Lallemand and co-workers (*3*) has shown that gains of several hundred, perhaps a thousand, times over conventional photography can be achieved. Moreover, he, Zavoiskii *et al.*, Wilcock *et al.*, and others (*4*) have shown that those single photons which liberate single photoelectrons can be detected individually, whether visually, photographically, or electrically. Thus the efficiency of detection of photons is the quantum efficiency of the photoemissive surface used. For the most efficient surface at the wavelength of greatest efficiency, this can be as high as 35%, and it can average more than 10% over the visible range. This compares with the corresponding efficiency of a fast photographic emulsion of ~0.1%. It is very approximately true that a 20 in. telescope using photoelectronic image detecting devices will give a performance comparable with that of the 200 in. using the most efficient photographic emulsions. It is also true that at present the photoelectronic devices are difficult to apply even in ground based telescopes, and none is known to me which could readily be used in a satellite-borne telescope. Nevertheless, the possibility is there, and it is obviously the function of this Symposium to consider the state of the art as it exists, and how it might be developed so as to provide instruments suitable for use in satellites.

It appears that the problem may be divided into the following three sections:

(1) those cases in which adequate image brightness is available and a conventional vidicon camera can be used;

(2) cases in which low intensity images must be observed. The vidicon may not be sufficiently sensitive without lag becoming objectionable. A television signal-generating tube of greater sensitivity, such as an image orthicon, might be used; but a possibly better solution might be an image intensifier coupled optically to a vidicon.

(3) In cases where the light intensity is very low, it may be necessary to make a long time-exposure. In this case, also, the image will be amplified by an image intensifier and then recorded on a charge-integrating signal-generating tube, from which it can be reproduced as a conventional television signal—though probably by slow scanning to give better signal-to-noise ratio and to reduce the necessary bandwidth.

The novel devices here are the image intensifiers and the charge-storage signal-generating tubes. It is about these that I propose to write as far as the state of development has gone in my own laboratories or is known to me.

Image Intensifiers

The quality of a recorded optical image is given by the expression (*4*)

$$s = \sqrt{\frac{I_0 TAPt\epsilon}{4F^2N^2a}},$$

where s is the ratio of the peak white signal-to-rms noise, I_0 the scene illumination, F the reciprocal of the numerical aperture of the lens, t the exposure time, P the number of photons per lumen, and ϵ the quantum efficiency, N the number of lines in the picture, and a the ratio of width to height of the picture; T is the light transmission coefficient of the lines and A the area of the image.

From this it follows that a picture of reasonable quality, such as a 500-line television picture of signal-to-noise ratio $\sim$20 db, can be recorded at very low light levels (of the order of 10^{-5} lm/sq ft provided each photon can be recorded quite definitely and with equal weight. The reason why photography does not reach this degree of sensitivity is that only about 0.1% of the incident photons result in the activation of a grain of silver halide. Photoelectric image detectors such as television signal generating tubes, which depend on a photocathode as primary transducer and which can have a quantum efficiency of 5 to 10%, do not reach the sensitivity that might be expected because their efficiency is limited by instrument noise, such as amplifier noise or scanning beam noise, and not by the shot noise of the primary photoelectric emission.

Several proposals (*5*) have been put forward for a television signal generating tube which will have the ultimate sensitivity, that is, its signal-to-noise ratio will be that determined by the shot noise of the primary photoemission; but to date no successful tube of this kind has been described.

The more usual approach (*6*) to this problem is to provide one or more stages of image intensification before integrating the electron stream as a charge image on a storage target. This is then discharged by scanning to produce the picture signal.

This method, so far as one can judge, has been only partially successful. The storage target of the image orthicon has a very limited capacitance, and hence if sufficient electron-image intensification is used to reach the ultimate sensitivity, the capacitance is already fully charged by too few primary photoelectrons.

Thus it would seem that it would be preferable to have as the signal generating tube a vidicon with a high target capacitance and to couple this optically with a straight image intensifier. It is very doubtful if it is worthwhile trying to put both devices in the same vacuum envelope, since this complicates the manufacture of the device while giving little worthwhile advantage.

Image intensifiers may be roughly divided into those in which the electron image is recorded by the direct action of high energy electrons on an electron-sensitive emulsion (*4*), and those in which the intensified image is formed on a fluorescent screen. The former have given very valuable results in astronomy, and no doubt will give still better results in the future; but they are unlikely to be of much use in satellite observations because of the fact that the record is on a photographic film which is difficult to deliver back to earth.

It is the latter that will be discussed in some detail here, since the output image may be optically coupled with the photocathode of a signal generating tube and the resulting signal may be transmitted to earth or recorded as required. There are three types that must be considered. These are:

(1) the transmission secondary-emission electron image multiplier,
(2) the cascade phosphor-photocathode image intensifier,
(3) the channeled electron-image multiplier.

The Transmission Secondary Emission Electron Image Multiplier

The first two of these devices are very similar and the general scheme is illustrated in Fig. 1. They differ in the mechanism of electron multiplication and this may be of significance in any particular application.

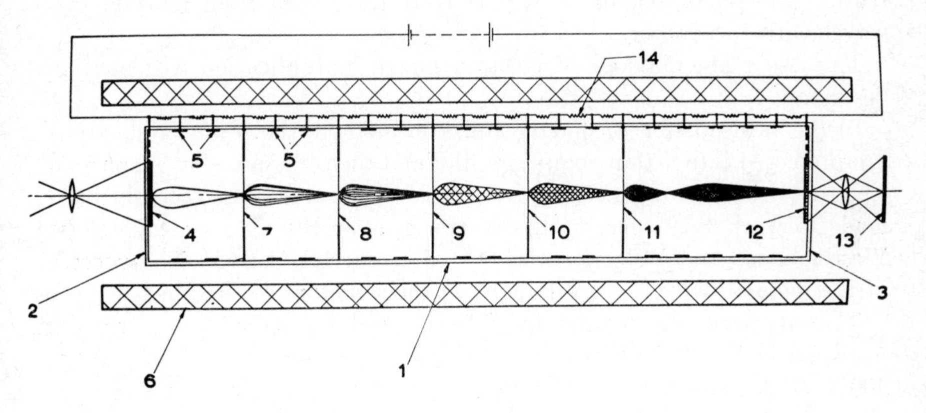

FIG. 1. Multistage electron image intensifier.

The optical image is cast on the transparent photocathode 4 formed on a transparent plate which may be the glass end–window 2 of the cylindrical vacuum tube 1. The photoelectrons liberated by the light are accelerated towards the first intensifying screen 7 in an electrical field, which is made as uniform as possible, and they are focused by a uniform axial magnetic field produced by a steady current in the solenoid 6. Photoelectrons which have small initial energies can be brought to a focus at the screen 7 by suitable adjustment of the accelerating electrical field and the axial magnetic field. Under these conditions the diameter of the circle of confusion of the electron image depends directly on the spread of velocities of the photoelectrons and inversely on the field gradient between the cathode and anode. In practice, with an electric field of $\sim 10^3$ volt/cm, and a magnetic focusing field of 100 to 200 gauss, photoelectrons can be focused to form an image with a resolution limit of about 100 line pairs/mm, which is good by optical standards.

The electrons of the image formed on the first screen produce a second generation of slow electrons from the opposite side of the screen, the number at any point being proportional to, but greater than, the number of incident primary electrons by a factor which may be between 5 and 100. These second generation electrons are then accelerated to, and focused on, the second intensifying screen 8 where a similar process takes place. After sufficient intensification at successive screens 9, 10, and 11 the electron stream is generally focused onto a final phosphor screen 12 at sufficient energy to give a bright fluorescent image which may be observed visually, photographed, or transferred optically to the photosensitive surface of a signal generating tube.

It should be noted that such a device has two functions: it may intensify an image, and/or it may convert the image from light of one wavelength to another.

The two main methods of electron image multiplication will now be described.

In the transmission secondary emission method, the primary electrons are projected into a thin composite film and then liberate slow secondary electrons from the opposite surface. This old idea (*7*) has recently been made to work very successfully by two groups: Sternglass *et al.* (*8*) of Westinghouse and Wilcock *et al.* (*9*) of Imperial College. The success of the method depends very largely on the structure of the films.

The composite films used by Wilcock and his collaborators are illustrated in Fig. 2. They consist of a thin aluminum oxide film A about 400 Å thick, supported at the edge on a soda-glass ring. Onto this is evaporated, first, a thin layer of conducting aluminum B about 200 Å thick, to form a conducting medium to maintain the dynode at a fixed potential; and then, on top of this, a layer of good secondary emitting material C, usually potassium chloride, about 400 Å thick. The aluminum oxide film is solely for mechanical support and is made as thin as is compatible with this function. The aluminum film is made thick enough only to be a reliable conductor while the potassium chloride must be thick enough to absorb the energy of the incident energetic primary electrons, so that few pass right through, but thin enough to allow as many as possible of the excited secondary electrons to emerge from the opposite surface.

It is found that with the film composition given above a secondary emission ratio δ of ~ 5 is attained for a primary electron energy of ~ 5 kev. In a typical tube such as that shown in Fig. 3, there are five

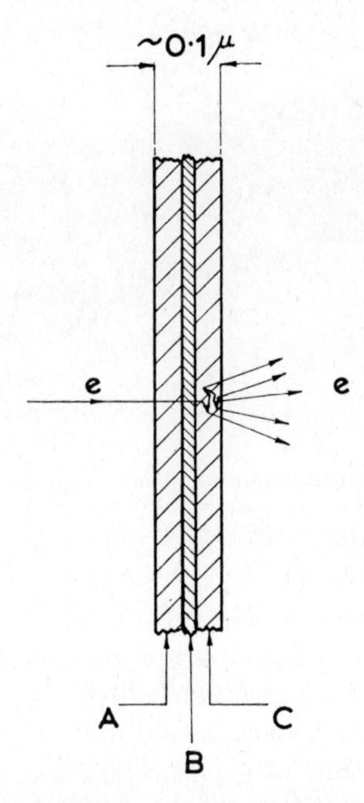

FIG. 2. Transmission secondary emission dynode.

stages of electron multiplication; they give an over-all electron gain of 3000 to 5000 at an over-all voltage of ~ 25 kv. This intensified electron stream is then accelerated by a high potential of ~ 15 kv in a longer, last stage and focused onto a phosphor screen on the inside surface of the end window of the tube. Hence the over-all voltage is about 40 kv and the axial magnetic field is about 150 gauss.

The phosphor is usually the most efficient blue ZnS(Ag), designated as P.11, and at the given energy an electron will excite 500 to 1000 photons which will emerge in the forward 2π solid angle with an approximately Lambertian distribution. Thus a single photoelectron produces a flash of blue light emitting between 1 and 5×10^6 photons, and if the same quality of blue light is used at the input to liberate the primary photoelectrons with a quantum efficiency of $\sim$10%, it follows that the light gain may be $\sim 10^5$ times. This figure is quite frequently realized in actual tubes.

The circle of confusion of the final electron image is the same as the circular spot of fluorescence produced by a bunch of electrons originating from one primary photoelectron. This has a diameter of $\sim 30\,\mu$ and the

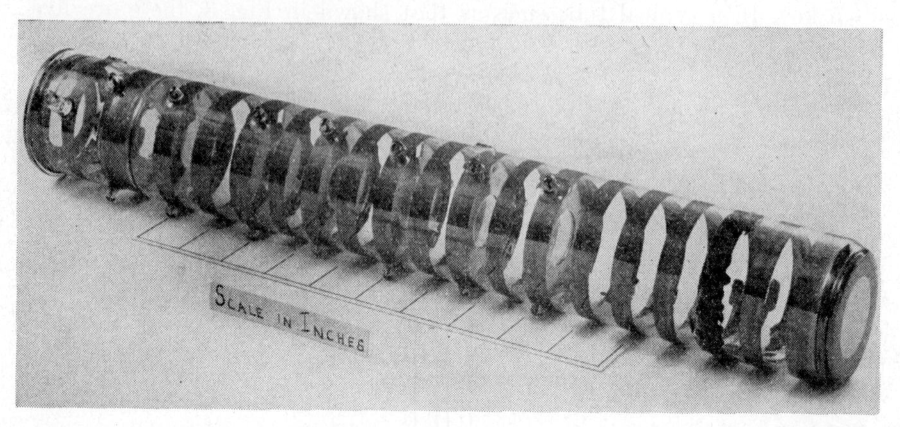

FIG. 3. Photograph of transmission secondary emission image intensifier tube.

limiting image resolution in the first model of tube was $\sim$15 lp/mm. These scintillations can be photographed with an efficient optical system and fast film and they can be seen clearly with an observing microscope.

Figure 4 shows a series of photographs of the output image reproduced by such a tube of a test pattern consisting of a fan of black and white lines. Figure 4a shows dark background only, and the number of scintillations recorded in the time of exposure, 0.2 sec, can be seen. In Fig. 4b, the image is very slightly illuminated, and some indication of its presence, though little information about its details, is apparent. In Figs. 4c–4e, the light is progressively increased and the image form becomes more clearly defined simply by a progressive increase in the number of recorded scintillations. It should be noted that the number of background scintillations outside the image area changes very little, and the small increase can be accounted for by scattered image illumination.

The effective image diameter in tubes made to date has been 20 mm and the magnification from input to output is unity. The image resolution is fairly uniform from center to edge of field and image geometrical distortion is quite small; both of these features depend on the uniformity of the electric and magnetic fields.

The thickness of the composite multiplying films is $\sim 0.1\,\mu$, and hence

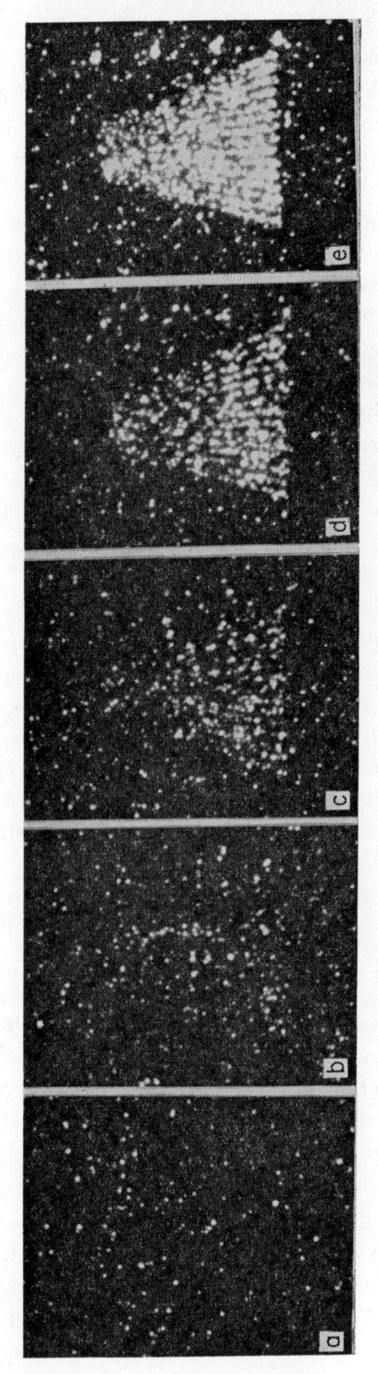

Fig. 4. Photographs of image intensified by transmission secondary emission tube.

transverse diffusion of the electrons in passing through the film can have but negligible effect on image definition. The main limiting factor is believed to be the rather large spread of energies of the emergent secondary electrons, which results in considerable "chromatic" aberration. However, the exact magnitude of this effect is not yet known.

Continuing work by Wilcock and his group has shown that the size of multiplying dynodes can be increased. They are already up to 33 mm effective diameter, and the resolution is better than 20 lp/mm. A diameter of 40 mm and a resolution of 25 lp/mm appears a reasonable target for the immediate future, and this represents an image of high quality.

The following characteristics of this type of tube should be noted:

(1) The energy of the electrons that impinge on a transmission secondary film must be held within fairly close limits in order to obtain the maximum secondary emission ratio, yet not have too many primary electrons passing right through with considerable residual energy and causing out of focus background in the next stage. Thus a ratio 5 at a stage voltage of 5 kv appears to be about optimum, and there is no obvious way in which this ratio can be increased.

The statistical law relating secondary to primary electrons is not known, but it is probable that the mean deviation from average is at least $\sqrt{5}$, as it would be if the relationship were Poissonian. Hence there is a big spread in the ratio for single electrons at the first multiplying dynode, and this spread is perpetuated throughout the rest of the tube. Hence the output pulses or scintillations have a wide spread in intensity, of at least 10:1. Clearly this will reduce the signal-to-noise ratio in the recorded image, especially if it is recorded on a detector which saturates readily, such as a photographic emulsion.

If recorded on a linear, i.e., an unsaturated, detector, the loss in signal-to-noise has been calculated by Baum and Wilcock (*10*) to be by a factor of about $\sqrt{2}$. However, it seems that it would be preferable if each primary photoelectron could produce a record of identical weight so that this loss of image quality could be avoided. This depends mainly on the multiplication ratio at the first stage, and there does not seem to be much chance of increasing this very much above 5.

(2) The composite films, though thin, are remarkably strong, and once mounted in vacuum they stand quite violent shocks given to the tube. It seems quite probable that they would stand the acceleration necessary in satellite launching. The Westinghouse experimenters have mounted their films on metal meshes which in effect take over the function of the aluminium oxide. Unfortunately, these meshes tend to appear as shadows, either individually or as moiré patterns, in the output image.

(3) The relation between the electric and magnetic fields in each

section must be carefully adjusted to ensure focus of slow electrons from one film onto the next. The relationship is given by the formula

$$d = Kn\sqrt{V}/B,$$

where d is the distance between dynodes, V the potential difference, B the magnetic induction of the focusing field, K a constant, and n an integer equal to the number of cycloidal loops performed by the electrons. In order to maintain electron image focus, stability of these fields to less than ½% appears to be necessary. Usually the magnetic field is fixed at approximately the correct value, and then the potential across each stage is adjusted to give focus. The magnetic field may be produced by a permanent magnet; this might be the better solution, especially for operation in space.

(4) The multiplying dynodes have the useful and important characteristic that they can be exposed to clean dry air for some considerable time without their efficiency being impaired. This is being made use of in vacuum ultraviolet spectroscopy, where it is necessary from time to time to admit air to the system, and where an exceptionally high vacuum cannot be maintained. Similarly, it may be useful in satellite observations which are concerned with the ultraviolet. In this case it would be convenient to dispense with a high vacuum tight window, or to have an easily removable window so that the ultraviolet can fall directly on the photocathode. This latter, of course, must also be such that it is unaffected by exposure to air; but this, in fact, is the case with most ultraviolet sensitive photocathodes which are also blind to visible light, such as the stable metals gold, platinum, tungsten, etc.

Ultraviolet Photocathode

One outstanding problem that has not been settled to my knowledge is a suitable form of primary ultraviolet sensitive transparent photocathode. This must be such that the ultraviolet light falls on one side and the photoelectrons leave from the other side. This is standard practice, of course, for conventional photocathodes sensitive to visible light, and it greatly facilitates the design of the tubes in which it is used. The transparent photocathode is bound to be fundamentally less efficient than an opaque one, but because the photoemission can be used so much more efficiently, it usually pays to use the former in actual devices.

Two possible forms of photocathode seem to be worth investigation for this purpose. These are illustrated in Figs. 5a and 5b.

The cathode illustrated in Fig. 5a is a fine metal mesh of 1000 meshes/in. and a shadow ratio of $\sim$50%, the bars of which have a cross section which is approximately triangular. Light falls on that surface of the

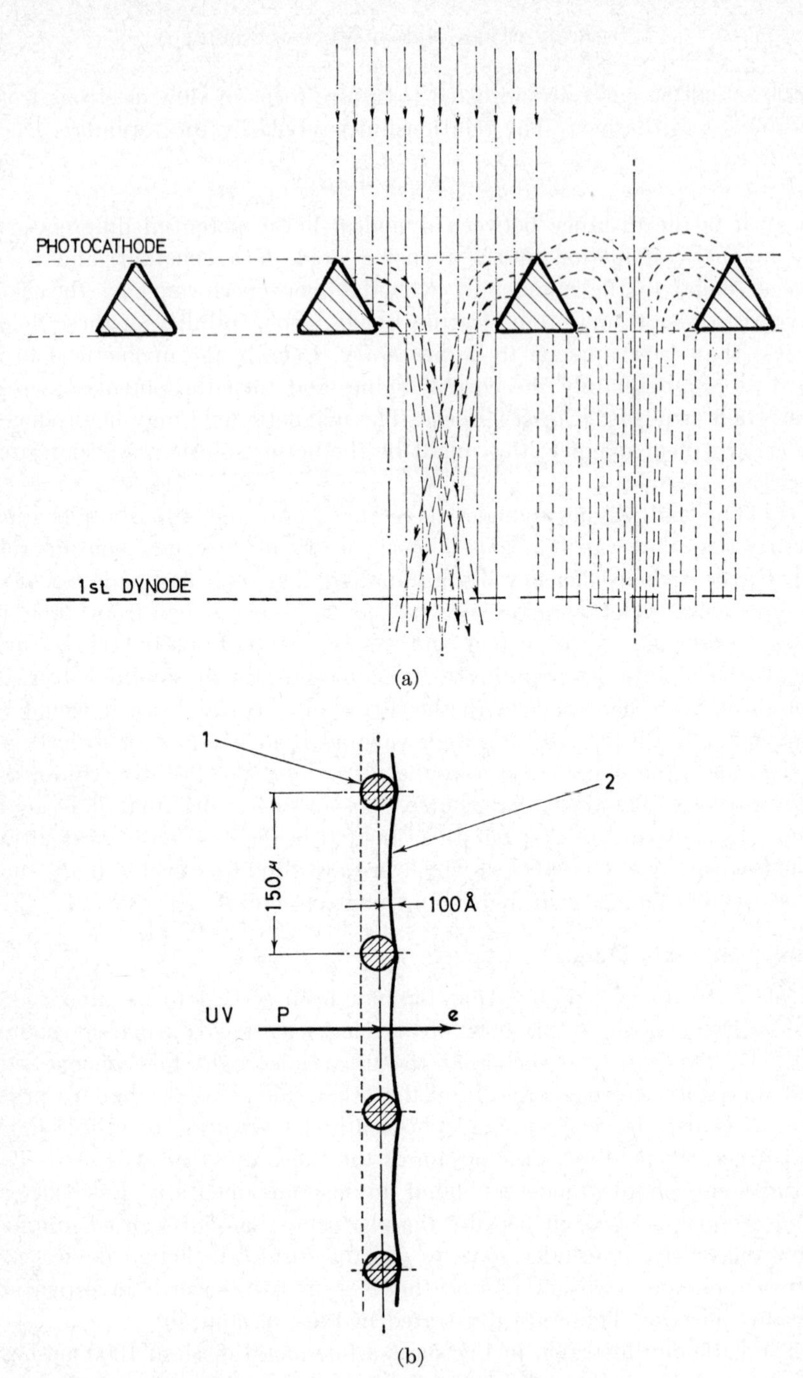

FIG. 5. Possible photocathode for ultraviolet sensitive image tube; (a) mesh, (b) thin metal film.

mesh comprising the ridges of the triangular bars. The surface may be prepared by evaporating onto it a suitable metal for the ultraviolet range required. If now a strong accelerating field is established between this mesh and the first dynode, it will penetrate through the apertures to such an extent that photoelectrons liberated from the sloping mesh surfaces will be pulled through the apertures and can be focused onto the first dynode. About 75% extraction of these photoelectrons can be achieved, which with 50% shadow ratio would give 37½% efficiency. However, there is the advantage that an opaque photoemitter is used which gives maximum photoelectric efficiency. On the other hand, the electron image definition is limited by the mesh structure and by the electron-optical distortion introduced by the minute electron lenses formed by the field penetrating through the mesh apertures.

In Fig. 5b another method is illustrated. A metal mesh of very low shadow ratio, say ~20%, but not necessarily very many apertures per linear inch, say 200, is stretched on a metal frame and a very thin film of the required photoelectric metal is mounted on it by one of the well-known methods. A quite transparent film of say, gold, about 100 Å thick, can be mounted in this way and it is possible that it can be made thin enough to enable ultraviolet light incident on one surface to liberate photoelectrons from the opposite surface. No attempts to use such an ultraviolet photocathode are known to the author, but if good transmission photoelectric emission efficiency could be achieved with this method it would have some advantages over the one previously described. The most important advantage probably would be the improvement in image definition, which would not be limited by the mesh pitch nor affected by the electron-optical action of the mesh apertures.

Cascade Image Intensifier

The second type of image intensifying screen is illustrated in Fig. 6 (*12*). It comprises a very thin transparent sheet A of mica or glass which carries on one surface a phosphor screen B backed as usual by an opaque aluminum film D, and on the other surface a transparent photocathode C. An electron *e* of an electron image formed on the phosphor screen B will excite photon emission from the screen which will pass through the transparent support sheet A into the photocathode C from which it will liberate photoelectrons. These photoelectrons are then accelerated by an electric field and focused by a magnetic field onto the next multiplying screen.

As is well known, the number of photons produced by each electron will depend on the energy of the electron provided the thickness of the screen is adjusted appropriately. Hence by increasing the voltage per stage, the light emission, and hence the gain per stage, can be increased almost linearly with voltage above a certain small threshold voltage. The phosphor is chosen for maximum efficiency and optimum matching of the energy distribution of its output light with the wavelength sensitivity of the photocathode. They are usually a ZnS[Ag] or P.11 phosphor, and an $SbCs_3$ or S.11 photocathode. If a high efficiency of screen and photocathode can be achieved, electron gains of something like 15, 30, and 100

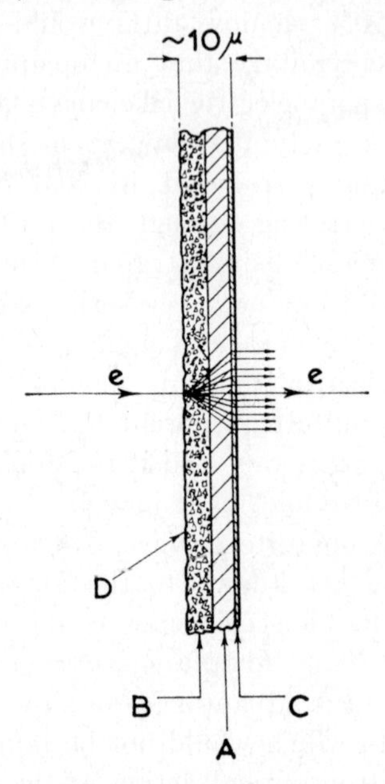

FIG. 6. Cascade phosphor-photocathode intensifier screen.

times can be achieved with electron energies of 6, 10, and 20 kev, respectively. Thus the gain per stage may be quite large if high voltage per stage can be used, and this should result in a more uniform gain for all primary photoelectrons. The high voltage per stage also helps to improve electron image definition and, because fewer stages are required to give the same over-all gain, less definition will be lost in the image transfer processes. On the other hand, if high voltage is to be used on each stage, a thicker phosphor layer is required to absorb the energy of the incident electrons; hence this tends to impair definition. Also, much greater care is necessary in the design of the accelerating electrode systems and in the processing of the tube, if high voltage per stage is to be used, in order to avoid a spurious background which increases rapidly with the stage voltage. At present there does not seem to be a clear cut decision between the two policies: few stages, each of high voltage and high gain; or many stages, each of low voltage and low gain. This is a question that awaits experimental evidence.

The most important factor limiting the definition in this type of intensifier is the transverse spread of light in the phosphor B and the supporting sheet A. The thickness of the photocathode C is so small by comparison that its contribution is negligible. The initial energy of the photoelectrons is so small, $\sim$1.0 ev, that its contribution to the loss of image definition is believed to be negligible compared with that due to the thickness of the screen.

Tubes of this type have been made by many workers in different countries, but the earliest successful tubes appear to have been those made by the Russian workers, Zavoiskii *et al.* The gain was sufficient to enable these workers to photograph scintillations produced by individual photoelectrons. The tubes had 5 or 6 stages with over-all light gains of $\sim 10^5$. The resolution appears to have been about 15 lp/mm; spurious background was troublesome unless the over-all voltage was reduced and hence also the over-all gain.

Similar tubes have been made in the U.S.A. and the U.K. Stoudenheimer (R.C.A.) reports the fabrication of two-stage tubes with a gain of $\sim$1000 times, and of three-stage tubes. However, again spurious background appears to be a serious problem at the operating voltages where high gain is achieved. In the author's laboratory, two-stage experimental tubes are under investigation, the object being to devise techniques by which adequate gain, definition, and image area can be achieved with, at the same time, a very dark background.

The type of intensifying screen described above cannot be exposed to air without serious damage to the photocathode. Hence the photocathodes must be prepared and kept in a very high vacuum. This is inconvenient from the point of view of space operation, since it would necessitate either the opening of a window after the device had reached a sufficient height or the provision of an ultraviolet transparent window. The reliable performance of the first of these alternatives is by no means easy and would probably lead to unnecessary complications. For the second alternative, there does not appear to be a suitable material that would be adequately transparent to ultraviolet and at the same time can be sealed to glass.

One way of overcoming this difficulty would be to make the light-input window, 2 in Fig. 1, either of thin mica or of fibre-optical glass. Both of these are now well established techniques. A thin layer of ultraviolet sensitive phosphor could then be deposited on the external surface and a transparent photocathode formed on the inner surface. The phosphor would transform the ultraviolet light into light of visible wavelengths, which could then pass through the thin mica or fibre-optical glass window to the internal photocathode.

It is understood that the efficiency of conversion of ultraviolet to blue light by suitable phosphors is quite high. More than half the light emitted by the phosphor would be lost since it would not enter the photocathode, but what did pass through the photocathode would be used fairly efficiently to liberate photoelectrons.

A possible objection to this device is that it would respond to visible light as well as ultraviolet; hence, when ultraviolet observations only are required, filtering of the visible light would be necessary. It is a convenience to be able to use an ultraviolet sensitive photocathode that is blind to visible light.

It may seem that this cascade intensifier is not so suitable for space operation, especially in the ultraviolet wavelengths, as the thin film transmission secondary emission multiplier. However, there is one aspect in which it may have an important advantage, that is, in the statistics of multiplication. As noted above, the gain per stage in this device may be 100 times or more, and if this is achieved in the first stage the mean deviation will be only 10%. This will be worsened a little by subsequent multiplying stages, but the effect is small compared with the spread from the first stage of the other type of multiplying screen. Hence the output signals from individual primary photoelectrons should be much more nearly identical; and these can be recorded with a better signal-to-noise ratio.

In other respects the probable characteristics of the two types of image intensifier seem to be very similar as regards light gain, image definition, image size, image geometry, spurious background. In both cases a high voltage (~40 kv) and a strong magnetic field (~150 gauss), both accurately stabilized, are necessary. These requirements would present considerable problems in space operation.

The Channeled Electron Image Multiplier

This approach to the problem (*11*) is worth brief consideration since it avoids the above-mentioned problems, though it has problems of its own.

The general principle of this method is illustrated in Fig. 7. Each dynode *D* consists of a large number of small, parallel, metal tubes close packed and welded to one another. Their ends are cut at an angle of 35° to their axes, from the same long bundle of tubes. They are then reassembled in the same relationship to one another but spaced apart by a small distance, to provide insulation from one another. Figure 7b shows a longitudinal section of the multiplier constructed in this way, while Fig. 7c is a transverse section. Figure 7a shows enlarged the electrical equipotentials and the approximate electron paths between two successive tubes in one channel.

There are other possible structures, notably that proposed by Burns (*12*), which have the requisite characteristics; but this arrangement, which is being used in the author's laboratory, will serve to illustrate the method.

In Fig. 7b the light image falls into the individual cells of dynode D_1, the walls of which are photosensitive. The liberated photoelectrons are then accelerated into the corresponding cells of D_2, and owing to the

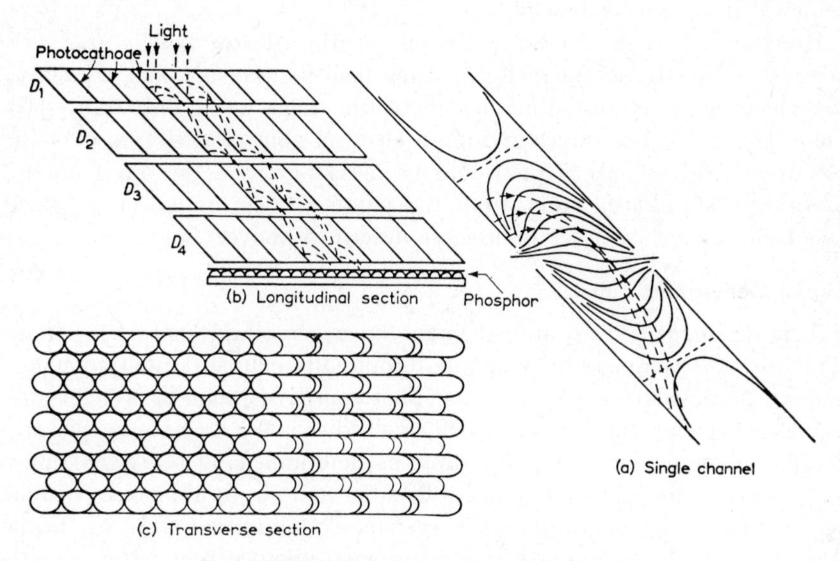

FIG. 7. Channeled electron image multiplier.

asymmetry of the field between these cylinders the paths of the photoelectrons are as illustrated in Fig. 7a. That is, slow electrons leaving the lower parts of the walls of D_1 are accelerated to and impinge on the lower parts of the walls of D_2, where they liberate secondary electrons. Here the secondary electrons find themselves in an electrical field which accelerates them on to D_3, where a similar process takes place.

There is an optimum relationship between the diameter, the length of the tubes, and the angle at which the surface is cut to give the correct electron trajectories. The walls of the dynodes are treated to make them good secondary emitters, and the primary electrons must land in an area from which slow secondary electrons will be extracted to the next stage. The multiplied output electron stream may fall on a fluorescent screen or on the charge integrating target of a signal-generating tube.

Electrons must be prevented from straying into adjacent channels, and so reducing definition, but no image detail is retained within individual channels. Hence the image detail that can be reproduced is limited by the fineness of structure of the dynodes. It seems likely that mechanical construction difficulties will probably impose a serious limit on the number of lp/mm that can be achieved. This may never be more than $\sim$2. However, the area of the dynodes might be increased, and it is considered possible that the final image quality might reach that of a 400- or 500-line television picture. This would not be adequate to take advantage of the high optical definition which it is hoped will be achieved in a space telescope.

However, there are several aspects of this device which are very attractive. Firstly, no magnetic focusing field is necessary and, secondly, the electrical potential difference between stages need only be $\sim$500 volts. Hence for ten stages giving an electron gain of $\sim 10^6$, an over-all electrical field of only 5 kv would be necessary, and this need not be accurately stabilized. Thus, from the point of view of power supplies, this tube is much simpler than those described above.

Signal-Generating Tubes

Having intensified an optical image by a very large factor, 10^5 times or more, it is comparatively simple to optically couple the output image on the fluorescent screen with the photosensitive input of a television signal generating camera tube, such as a vidicon. We are able in this way to obtain pictures in which the limit is determined by the signal/noise of the output image of the image intensifier and not by the noise peculiar to the television camera plus tube system. This limit is quite close to the shot noise limit determined by the primary photocurrent but is a little impaired by the nonuniformity of intensification for individual electrons. A further small reduction in signal-to-noise is due to the dark current, or background, of the image tube. This is at present very variable, for unknown causes; but in the best cases it is remarkably small, being of the order of 10 electrons cm^{-2} sec^{-1} from the photocathode. This corresponds to a very low light level, and would have an almost negligible effect on image quality.

In this way ultimate sensitivity limited by the shot noise of the primary photoemission can probably be achieved most conveniently. It is true that the image intensifier and television signal-generating tube might be married together in the same envelope, as for example RCA has done (*6*), but this seems unnecessary and undesirable. Both devices are complex and difficult to make and process, and these difficulties are increased enormously when all processing of both devices must be done in a single envelope.

Ultimately, it will be necessary, when observing very distant, faint objects, to increase the exposure time beyond that of which existing television camera tubes, e.g. a vidicon, are capable, which is of the order of 1 sec. For this purpose, a device such as that illustrated in Fig. 8 is proposed (*13*). This tube has been under experimental investigation in the author's laboratories, and it is believed to have the required characteristics.

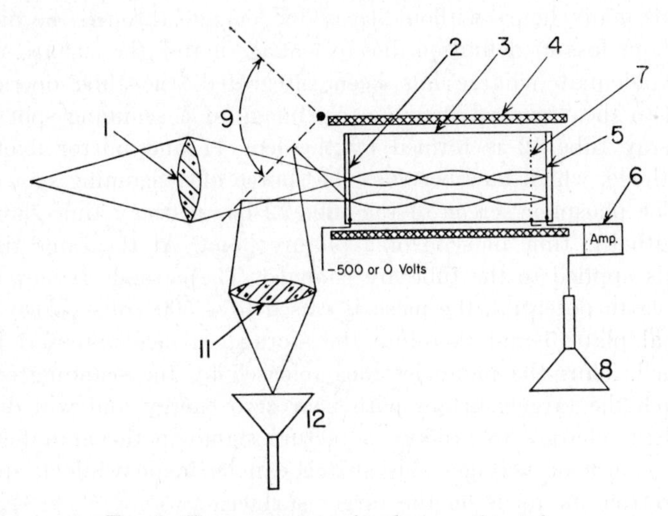

FIG. 8. Charge-storage, signal-generating tube.

This device consists of a glass vacuum tube 3 with a flat window at one end on the inner surface of which is formed a transparent photocathode 2. At the other end is a charge storage target 5, which is a metal plate with a thin layer 5–10 μ thick of some highly insulating, efficient secondary electron emitting material such as magnesium fluoride. The conducting signal plate of the target 5 is connected to the input of a suitable wide band amplifier 6 and the amplified signal can be displayed on a cathode-ray tube 8.

A fine, low shadow-ratio mesh 7 is positioned close to the surface of the storage target, and electrodes on the tube walls held at appropriate potentials enable suitable accelerating and decelerating fields to be applied between the electrodes 2, 7, and 5. A current in a solenoid 4 produces an axial magnetic field which can be adjusted to focus photoelectrons from the photocathode 2 onto the surface of the target 5.

In the charge-integrating, or "writing-on," regime the cathode 2 is held about 500 volts negative and the mesh 7 about 50 volts positive to the surface of the target 5. The magnetic field is adjusted to bring photoelectrons, released from the photocathode by an optical image formed by the lens 1, to an electron image on the surface of the target. As they arrive with considerable energy, $\sim$500 ev, they will liberate a fair number, say 5 to 10, secondary electrons, most of which will be collected on the mesh 7. So an amplified charge-image will be built up on the insulating surface of 5. On the capacitance formed by the layer of magnesium fluoride on the metal signal plate, these charges can be stored for many hours without decay by leakage through the dielectric and without loss of definition due to leakage across the surface.

When adequate charge has been integrated, the tube operation is changed to the "read-off" regime. An image of a scanning spot from a cathode-ray tube 12 is formed by the lens 11 and mirror 9 onto the photocathode, which now becomes the source of a scanning spot of electrons. The phosphor screen of the tube 12 has a decay time short compared with the time of scan of a picture point. At the same time, the potentials applied to the tube are changed. The cathode is now brought to near earth potential, the mesh is raised to $\sim$500 volts positive, while the signal plate 5 and therefore the storage surface potential remains unchanged. Thus the photoelectrons released by the scanning spot will now reach the target surface with near zero energy and will discharge the positive charges to produce a picture signal in the amplifier 6. By suitable choice of voltages this switch can be made while keeping the photoelectrons in focus on the target surface.

In this type of tube we have been able to obtain one stage of image amplification by secondary emission, a very high capacity charge-storage target, and storage for a very long time of the integrated charges. By slow scan-off the charges can be reproduced as picture signals with maximum efficiency as regards signal-to-noise ratio, and with a reasonably small bandwidth.

With such a device "writing on" and "reading off" must be done alternately. The "read off" will be done slowly to reproduce the charge image with optimum signal-to-noise ratio and to keep the bandwidth small. The frame period may be $\sim$1 sec instead of 1/25th or 1/30th sec as required with television. The "write-on" time will depend on the brightness of the image to be recorded. It seems that this time might be controlled automatically by integrating the current flow from the photocathode; when this has reached a predetermined amount, then the storage target would be charged to its optimum voltage level for an average, typical optical image. The scanning cycle would then be initiated automatically.

It should be practicable to set the image intensifier gain, the optical coupling efficiency and the photocathode sensitivity of the signal-generating tube so that in operation a single, primary photoelectron produces a signal larger than the noise level of the signal amplifier 6. Then when the target is discharged the noise that will limit the signal is that due to the shot noise of these photoelectrons. It is not possible to do better than this; all that can be done is to collect more photons and make photocathodes that will convert a larger proportion of them to photoelectrons.

Image Stabilization

It will be important to take advantage of the absence of the disturbing atmosphere to obtain the most perfect definition possible with the given optical system. No doubt every effort will be made to provide a stable platform. However, at this stage it should be borne in mind that if an electron image device is used for the purpose of image intensification, it can also provide a convenient means of fine correction of any wander in the direction of pointing of the telescope. This can be done as follows.

The fine control of the pointing of the satellite will probably be done by small telescopes directed at certain stars; from these telescopes electrical signals are derived which operate the control mechanism, such as a rotating sphere or gas jets. However, it might be more convenient to apply these correcting signals in the form of electrical currents through two sets of deflecting coils, of the type used to scan the beam in a television signal-generating tube, on the first section of the image intensifier. In this way the first electron image could be held quite accurately in the same position on the first dynode even though the optical image wandered across the photocathode. Because of the speed of action and absence of inertial effects, it might be more economical and effective to do the fine control by this means, leaving the coarse control to be looked after by mechanical means.

Summary

To summarize, it appears that the photons of an image can be converted to photoelectrons with at least 100 times the efficiency of photography, and that these photoelectrons can now be multiplied and the image intensified to a degree where the image quality is limited only by the shot noise of the primary emission.

Such an image can then be integrated, if need be over a long exposure period, as a charge image which can then be scanned to produce a picture signal which can be recorded and relayed back to earth to reproduce the original image. This should give a telescope of quite a small size a performance many times better than that achieved in conventional operation.

Considerable problems remain, chief of which seem to be the stabilization of the high voltage and the magnetic focusing field which are required to operate the image intensifiers, and the provision of a suitable ultraviolet-sensitive photocathode.

References

1. M. Neiburger and H. Wexler, Weather Satellites, *Scientific American* **205,** No. 1, 80 (1961).
2. A. A. Blagonravov, First Space Station Photography of the Moon, *in* "Space Research," (H. K. Kallman, ed.), p. 1109. North-Holland, Amsterdam, 1960.
3. A. Lallemand, M. Duchesne, G. Wlérick, R. Augarde, and M. F. Dupré, *Ann. astrophys.* **23,** 320 (1960).
4. J. D. McGee, *Repts. Progr. in Phys.* **24,** 167 (1961).
5. S. A. Ward and C. D. Robbins, Light scan camera tube, U.S.A.E.R.D.L. Image Intensifier Symposium, Fort Belvoir, Virginia, p. 171, October 1958.
6. G. A. Morton and J. E. Reudy, The low light level performance of the intensifier orthicon, *Advances in Electronics and Electron Phys.* **12,** 183 (1960).
7. L. J. Orvin, British Patent No. 455,156 (1934).
8. E. J. Sternglass, *Rev. Sci. Instr.* **26,** 1202 (1956).
9. W. L. Wilcock, D. L. Emberson, and B. Weekley, *Nature* **185,** 370 (1960).
10. W. A. Baum and W. L. Wilcock, Private communication.
11. J. D. McGee, E. A. Flinn, and H. D. Evans, An electron image intensifier, *Advances in Electronics and Electron Phys.* **12,** 87 (1960).
12. J. Burns and M. J. Neumann, "The channelled image intensifier," *ibid* **12,** 97 (1960).
13. J. D. McGee, *J. Roy. Soc. Arts* Vol. C, No. 4869, 329 (1952).

Discussion

Dr. A. J. Deutsch: Can Professor McGee say something about the photometric characteristics of the device? Is it linear?

Professor McGee: The signals reproduced from the charge storage device should bear a linear relationship to the integrated light input. The photoelectric effect is known to be very accurately proportional to the exciting light over several decades of intensity. It is known from experience with television signal generating tubes that the other two processes involved—namely, the charging by secondary emission and the discharging by a low velocity scanning beam—can also be very close to linear over at least two decades of intensity. Hence it is hoped that the signal output will be linear in relation to the integrated light input.

Dr. W. A. Baum: Let me first take this opportunity to comment that I have spent the past year with Professor McGee in London in connection with the work about which he spoke, and I think that this type of work is very important, not only for space research but for ordinary astronomy as well. It deserves all the support that we can give it.

Next I would like to comment on a satellite experiment which was proposed several years ago when the IGY programs were planned. At that time only very small payloads could be managed, and it was suggested that we might be able to get some useful information from a very simple multicolor photometer with a fairly wide field of view in a freely spinning satellite. A prototype of this instrument, designed and built with NSF support, included a mirror which would permit it to sweep out a series of cones and in the course of time survey the whole sky.

The purpose of this experiment would be to separate the contributions due to the zodiacal light, the light of the galaxy, the night air glow, and the extragalactic component. I proposed the experiment particularly because of interest in distinguishing the extragalactic component. It is hopeless to do so from the ground but it might conceivably be possible from a satellite.

Other people are going to talk at this symposium about much more advanced and much more elegant experiments, with oriented telescopes and so on, but it is perhaps still a good idea to "walk before we fly," and it might be wise to reconsider very simple experiments that require only a few pounds of payload. While I think the chance of separating out the extragalactic component is not very good, it is at least worth a try. If the amount of extragalactic light (amount of light received from outside our own Galaxy) is large enough to be recognized, its color distribution would give us an additional bit of information to help distinguish between various models of the universe.

4.2 *Techniques and Results of Extraterrestrial Radiation Studies from the Ultraviolet to X-Rays*

R. TOUSEY

U. S. NAVAL RESEARCH LABORATORY, Washington, D. C.

For the detection and measurement of radiation from the ultraviolet through the extreme ultraviolet and into X-rays, there are two principal techniques: photography, and photoelectric detection. Photography has many advantages. One of the most important is the capability of gathering an almost unlimited amount of detailed information, simultaneously, and rather quickly. The same information can be obtained photoelectrically, by scanning the image, but this requires a much longer time, and the various image elements are not recorded simultaneously.

The disadvantage of photography for space research is that the exposed photographic record must be recovered. From rockets at White Sands this has been routine for many years. It can now be accomplished from earth satellites, but from deep space probes it is not yet possible. However, in Lunik II the U.S.S.R. succeeded in developing the exposed film, and telemetering to earth the densitometer scan of the moon's image, with a high degree of success. Therefore, photography should not be dismissed as of little value, and as wholly superseded by the photoelectric record. Eventually, the advantages of both the photographic and the photoelectric scanning methods will probably be secured for the extreme ultraviolet with photoelectric image tubes, which combine the information storage capacity of the photographic film with the great convenience of electrical read-out and telemetry.

Let us now consider how photoelectric scanning devices and photographic emulsions compare from the points of view of sensitivity, and ability to gather information. The extreme ultraviolet, which is a spectral region of great interest for research from probes and satellites, will be discussed, since it can only be studied from altitudes above the earth's atmosphere.

Ordinary photographic emulsions become insensitive below about 2200 Å, because of absorption by the gelatin in which the silver halide grains are imbedded. Sensitivity can be restored by overcoating with a fluorescent material which acts as a transducer, converting the extreme ultraviolet into near ultraviolet and visible wavelengths to which the emulsion is sensitive. The same technique is used with ordinary phototubes (see, for example, Johnson *et al.,* 1951). This excellent method suffers from an inherent loss in the transducer. Much of the fluorescent light is lost and the effective quantum efficiency cannot easily be made greater than a few per cent.

The fluorescence sensitized type of detector is usually relatively nonselective. Sodium salycilate is one of the best sensitizing materials, because its quantum efficiency of fluorescence is not only large, but is also constant from 2000 Å or more, to 584 Å, and very likely beyond. Therefore, photographic film, or phototubes overcoated with sodium salycilate, are extremely useful, especially when it is necessary to know the sensitivity of the detector as a function of wavelength. However, the fluorescence sensitized detector is completely unsuited to applications where unwanted visible and near ultraviolet stray light is intense, because the spectral response range is not easily limited, except with external filters. For the same reason, this type of detector is not useful in designing narrow-wavelength-band, nondispersive systems.

Photographic emulsions that are sensitive to the extreme ultraviolet are made with practically no gelatin binder, following the process originated many years ago by Schumann (1901). At present, they are available from Eastman Kodak, Rochester, New York, and Kodak-Pathé, Paris. A similar emulsion, Ilford Q, is available in England. The most sensitive emulsion that we have seen is the Type SC-5, made by Kodak-Pathé, by means of the centrifuging and transferal process of Audran (1958). This material combines quite high resolving power with extreme speed. A density of 0.1 is produced by 5×10^{-3} erg/cm^2 at 1216 Å, according to measurements of J. D. Purcell of the U. S. Naval Research Laboratory (NRL), and the resolving power is several hundred lines per millimeter.

Photoelectric detectors for the extreme ultraviolet are relatively simple to produce. At least this is true of the cathode surface, because just about everything, including dielectrics, emits photoelectrons at short wavelengths. The metals are easiest to use, because one can easily make connection to the cathode. Tungsten is in most common use. Its photoelectric yield is shown in Fig. 1, which is the work of several different groups (Lukirskii *et al.,* 1960; Walker *et al.,* 1955; Hinteregger and Watanabe, 1953). On the long-wavelength side of 1600 Å, the yield is near zero, the actual values lying between 10^{-5} and 10^{-7}. A strong photoelectric effect sets in at wavelengths below 1300 Å. The efficiency rises rapidly, reaching about 15% at 700 Å. Photoemission continues, right on into the X-ray region; however, there appear to be no quantitative data between 113 and 475 Å. For tungsten, the yield is low near 100 Å, and here, nickel is a much better material, according to Lukirskii *et al.* (1960).

For extreme ultraviolet work, the metal photocathode is best built into a photomultiplier, of a type whose dynodes require no special activation procedure, and which are not damaged by repeated evacuation and exposure to air. The dynodes must also be nonresponsive to long-

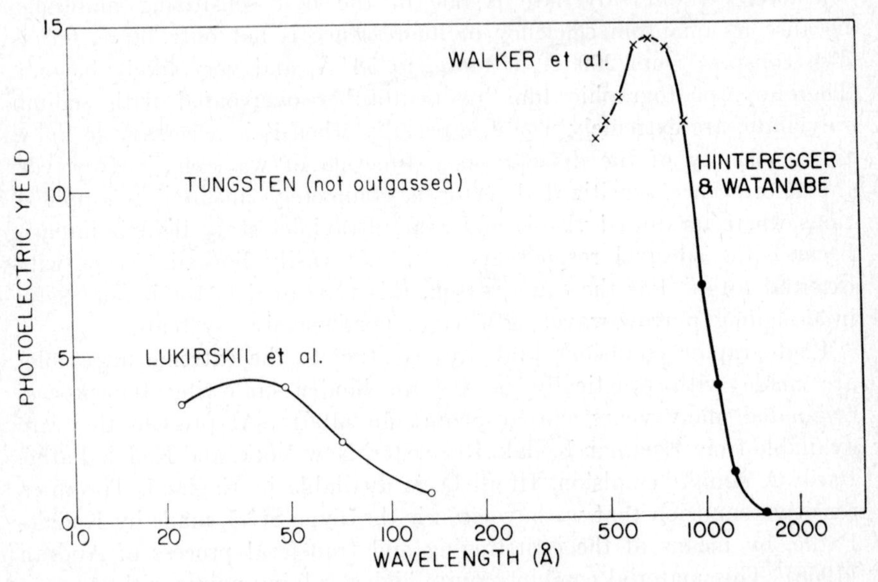

FIG. 1. Photoelectric yield of tungsten in the vacuum ultraviolet.

wavelength radiation. Allen type multipliers, with dynodes of Ag-MgO or Cu-Be are satisfactory. To this writer's knowledge, the only type of extreme ultraviolet photomultiplier used in space research as yet is the Bendix magnetically focused photomultiplier (Heroux and Hinteregger, 1960). This is shown in Fig. 2. Photoelectrons ejected from the cathode move in trochoidal paths through crossed magnetic and electric fields. The magnetic field is perpendicular to the screen, and the electric field lies in the plane of the screen. Multiplication takes place at each impact on the special dynode surface, and the electrons are collected by the plate at the end. The dark current can be reduced to the cosmic-ray background.

The present capabilities of the photographic and photoelectric scanning techniques will be illustrated by showing the best extreme ultraviolet solar spectra obtained by the two methods. Figure 3 presents a spectrum photograph, extending from 170 to 700 Å, and a solar curve.

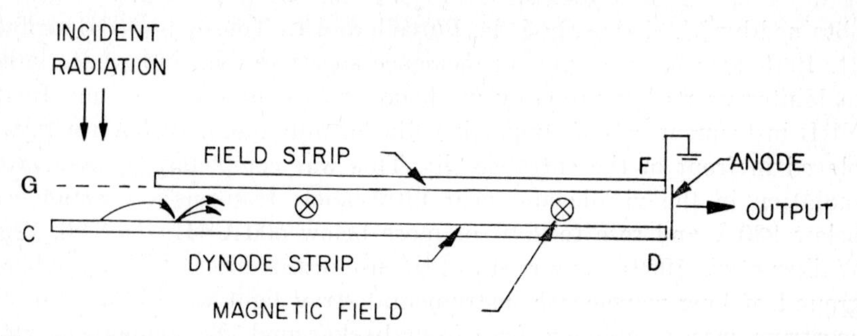

FIG. 2. Schematic diagram of the Bendix magnetic resistance strip photomultiplier. C, cathode, usually of tungsten; G, wire grid. The cathode, grid, and point D are maintained at about —1700, —800, and —155 volts, respectively, for a gain of 10^7.

The curve was obtained photoelectrically by Hinteregger (1960, 1961) at the Air Force Cambridge Research Laboratories (AFCRL) with a grazing incidence spectrograph. The spectrum was scanned with a Bendix

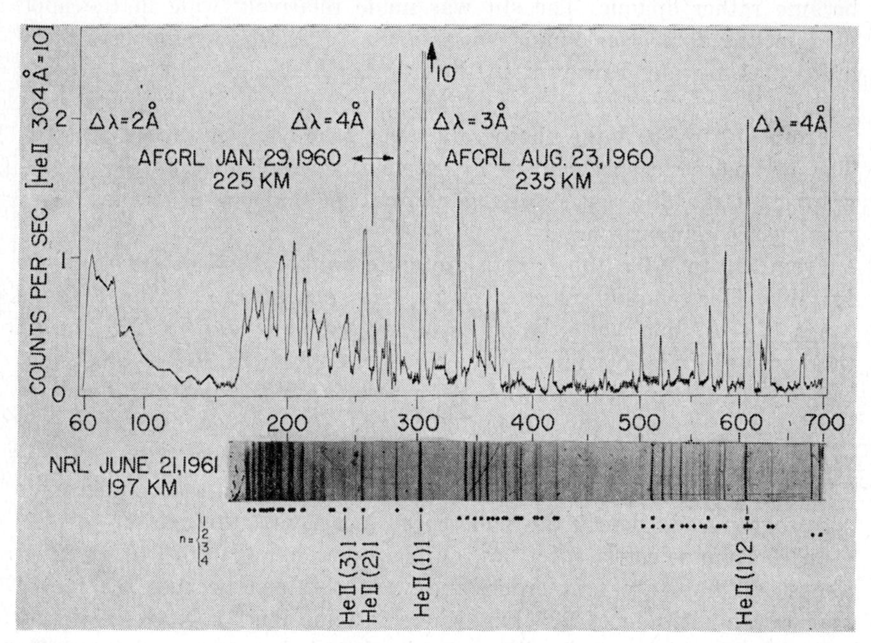

FIG. 3. The spectrum of the sun in the extreme ultraviolet. The photograph, obtained by Austin, Purcell, and Tousey of NRL, and the photoelectric trace, obtained by Hinteregger, were both made with grazing incidence grating spectrographs.

photomultiplier. Widely differing spectral regions should not be compared as to intensity, because the vertical scale is in counts per second, and has not been reduced to intensity. The photographic spectrum was obtained by W. E. Austin, J. D. Purcell, and R. Tousey of NRL on June 21, 1961, also using a grazing incidence spectrograph, somewhat similar to Hinteregger's but probably producing a less intense spectrum. In the NRL instrument, a self-supporting film of aluminum, 1000 Å thick, was placed in front of the entrance slit. This was completely opaque to all radiation in the visible and near ultraviolet; transmission commenced below 830 Å and rose to 20% or more below 500 Å (Hass *et al.*, 1957; Walker *et al.*, 1959). As a result of the use of this filter, the intense background of long-wavelength instrumental stray light was eliminated; the spectrum was completely free from background fog, which otherwise would have swamped all but the most intense features. In the photoelectric work, the suppression of stray light was accomplished by the tungsten cathode, which was relatively blind above about 1500 Å.

The photographic spectrograph was arranged to cover the wavelength range down only to 170 Å, the *L*-III edge of Al, below which the filter became rather opaque. The slit was made relatively wide in the hope of detecting some continuum emission. As a result, each line is of the order of 1 Å wide. However, in the original, the edges of the lines are sharp.

From 170 to 310 Å the photographic spectrum contains about 50 lines. The photoelectric spectrum is in excellent agreement with the photographic, if the different resolving powers are taken into account when making the comparison.

From 310 to 700 Å the spectra are quite unlike. There are two reasons for this. The photographic spectrum was obtained over the altitude range 178–197 km, while the photoelectric scan was made at 235 km. At the lower altitude, attenuation by N_2 is intense, from 310 to 700 Å, but is not severe from 170 to 310 Å. As a result, almost no first-order lines were photographed from 310 to 700 Å, and all the lines present in this region are second, third, and fourth orders of lines between 170 and 310 Å. They are strong because the diffraction grating used in the photographic spectrograph had nearly the same speed in orders 1 through 4.

In the photoelectric spectrum, on the other hand, from 310 to 700 Å almost all lines are first order, and were obtained because the rocket reached an altitude of 235 km, where attenuation by N_2 is relatively weak. A few higher order lines can be found, but they are extremely weak because the diffraction grating used in this instrument suppressed the higher orders.

Of the 50 lines present between 170 and 310 Å in the photographic spectrum, only a very few have as yet been identified, although the wavelengths have been determined to about 0.1 Å. Lyman-α of He II, 303.78 Å, is present in first and second orders. A line at 182.3 Å appears to be the first line of the Balmer series of C VI. Multiplet (4) of O VI, 173.08, 172.93 Å, is present as a weak line in second, third, and fourth orders. He II (2) is present, but is blended and He II (3) is present. He II (4) is absent, although He II (5) appears to be present.

An interesting possibility is that lines present at about 335 and 362 Å in the photoelectric spectrum are the resonance lines of Fe XVI, which correspond to the *D*-lines of sodium. The relative intensities are 2:1, as would be expected for the optically thin corona. The wavelengths of the lines, as extrapolated by Edlén (1936) are 336.17, 361.66 Å. Lines are present in the photographic spectrum close to these wavelengths but they are probably higher order lines.

It is possible to compare roughly the capabilities of the two methods from the point of view of spectral detail and wavelengths. The range 170–300 Å is the best to consider, because there the two instruments are probably more nearly equal in transmittance and the spectra were similar. Although the wavelength accuracy of the photographic spectrum of Fig. 3 is only 0.1 Å at present, the instrument is capable of a few hundredths of an angstrom precision when more standard lines are found and with improved adjustments. The wavelength precision of the photoelectric instrument is limited by the band pass, which is several angstroms in width. Thus the photographic spectrum potentially contains of the order of 100 times more wavelength information than the photoelectric. To obtain the same amount of wavelength information photoelectrically would require narrowing the slit and scanning more slowly, increasing the length of time by a factor of 100. Since the scan was made at a rate of 3 seconds for 100 Å, the time required would be 300 seconds per 100 Å. The photograph was made with an exposure of 110 seconds, but an exposure of 30 seconds would have given about the same resolution. One can conclude, therefore, that the photoelectric method requires about 10 times longer than the photographic to record the same amount of wavelength information in 100 Å, or 100 times longer per 1000 Å, for the case of these two particular rocket spectrographs.

Intensities are more easily and probably more precisely obtained with the photoelectric spectrograph. Changes of line intensity with altitude are much better measured photoelectrically, because a given line can be recorded in a time shorter by 100 to 1000 than the time required to build up a photographic image. This permits measuring the effect of attenuation by the atmosphere with much greater resolution in altitude.

To go more thoroughly into the matter becomes quite complicated but it is not difficult to find an upper limit for the time advantage of photography. Consider the number of photons required to give one bit of information. In a photograph, in principle, each blackened grain represents one such bit. For the photoelectric scanner, one photoelectron is one bit. The minimum number of photons required to produce a developable grain is not far different from the number of photons necessary to produce one photoelectron; in practice, however, it is frequently one to three powers of 10 larger. Therefore, grains and photoelectrons can be taken as very roughly equivalent. In a photographic emulsion the grains are spread over a large area and so give positional information automatically, and simultaneously. In photoelectric scanning, the photoelectrons come in one after another, and the scanning process gives the positional information. The photoelectric scan, therefore, requires a time that is longer than the photographic exposure by a factor which may be from one-tenth to one-thousandth the total number of grains in the photograph; the latter quantity may of course be very large indeed.

For deep space probe use, the photoelectric method is probably the only one that will be used to any great extent. Since the complexity and weight of developing and densitometric apparatus are great, photography can hardly be justified except when the simultaneous recording of a great deal of information is required.

Another field in which the photoelectric method has been extremely valuable is the study of radiation from the sun, the airglow, stars and nebulae by means of narrow-wavelength-band, nondispersive photometric systems. Many special types of photoelectric detector have been developed and used with great success in rockets. However, much remains to be done in this field. The subject of selective detectors cannot be treated without discussing filters, which form a part of the system.

In Table I are listed the principal photocathodes and filters, suitable for use in making selective phototubes and photomultipliers, arranged by spectral regions. The long-wavelength cutoff is generally a property of the photosensitive surface, while the short-wavelength cutoff is usually determined by the window, or filter.

The standard surface responding to 10,000 Å, or a little more, is Ag-O-Cs. The triple alkali surface responds to 8500 Å and has the very high peak quantum efficiency of 35% at 4000 Å. Cs-Sb reaches only 20% at 4000 Å, and cuts off at about 6500 Å. Cs-Te and Rb-Te are efficient solar-blind surfaces, peaking at 10% efficiency near 2000 Å; they cut off soon above 3000 Å; hence they are relatively blind to sunlight as it reaches us at sea level. The alkali halides form a valuable series of photoemitters with cutoffs ranging between 2100 Å for CsI and 1000 Å for LiF. They are useful all the way to X-rays; except for CsI, only a few experimental tubes have as yet been made with alkali halides. Metals, as described earlier, have cutoffs near 1500 Å. Thin aluminum, also mentioned earlier, provides a very useful long-wavelength cutoff filter for about 800 Å. Several other metals with useful cutoff wavelengths have been reported by Walker *et al.* (1959).

There are many short-wavelength cutoff filters; some common ones are shown in Table I. Glass cuts off anywhere from about 2200 Å up, depending on its composition. Silica in the purest form, transmits to about 1600 Å, sapphire to 1425 Å, CaF_2 to 1220 Å, the exact cutoff depending on its temperature, and good LiF to 1050 Å. Thin aluminum, as mentioned earlier, transmits to its L-III limit at about 170 Å.

TABLE I
VACUUM PHOTOTUBES AND PHOTOMULTIPLIERS

Long-wavelength cutoff		Short-wavelength cutoff	
λ(Å)	Photocathode	λ(Å)	Filters
10,000	Ag-O-Cs	2200–4000	Glasses
8500	Sb-K-Na-Cs	2000	KBr
6500	Sb-Cs	1600	Pure SiO_2
3500	Cs-Te, Rb-Te	1425	Sapphire
2100	CsI	1300	SrF_2
2100–1000	Various alkali halides	1220	CaF_2
1000	LiF	1050	LiF
1500	Metals	735	In, 800 Å thick
		510	Sn, 1020 Å thick
	Filters	500	Bi, 960 Å thick
1100	In, 800 Å thick	170	Al, 1000 Å thick
900	Sn, 1020 Å thick		
800	Al, 1000 Å thick		
700	Bi, 960 Å thick		

There is another type of detector, which is extremely useful, especially at very short wavelengths. This makes use of photoionization in a gas. These detectors can be made either in the form of photon counters, or ordinary ionization chambers. The spectral regions covered are shown in Table II. The long-wavelength cutoff is set by the ionization limit of the gas. Some of the more important gases are shown—ranging from xylene at 1500 Å to helium at 507 Å. One of the most useful is NO, whose cutoff comes just above Lyman-α, and which serves also as quenching agent in Geiger counters. Windows also provide a series of fairly good long-wavelength cutoffs. Besides those already shown in Table I, there are Glyptal and Mylar of different thicknesses, for 100 Å and 66 Å; Al, about 6 μ thick, transmits below about 18 Å, and 0.1 mm Be, below about 8 Å. For short-wavelength cutoffs, the same materials serve to provide limits at 170 Å, for thin Al at its L-III edge, 44 Å, the K-edge of carbon for Mylar and Glyptal, and 8 Å, the *K*-edge of Al. For a more complete survey of detectors see Friedman (1960).

Finally, we would like to mention another class of detectors which are very useful for hard X-rays. These are the proportional devices: proportional counters and scintillation counters. Here, the amplitude of the pulse is a measure of the energy of the absorbed photon. Hence these devices not only count photons, and so measure intensities, but also provide data on the spectrum of the incident radiation. By means of proportional and scintillation counters, flown in rockets during solar

TABLE II
PHOTOIONIZATION DETECTORS[a]

Long-wavelength cutoff		Short-wavelength cutoff[b]	
λ(Å)	Gas	λ(Å)	Filters
1500	Xylene	170	Al, 100 Å thick
1345	NO	44	Glyptal, 1.5 μ thick
1027	Xe	44	Mylar 6.0 μ thick
890	Kr	8	Al, 6.0 μ thick
791	Ar		
577	Ne		
507	He		
	Filters		
1220	CaF_2		
1050	LiF		
800	Al, 1000 Å thick		
100	Glyptal, 1.5 μ thick		
66	Mylar, 6.0 μ thick		
18	Al, 6.0 μ thick		
8	Be, 0.125 mm thick		

[a] Photon counters and ionization chambers.
[b] None for gases but the absorption becomes less as the X-ray region is approached.

flares, T. A. Chubb and H. Friedman and colleagues at NRL were successful in detecting hard X-ray emission. On September 1, 1959 during a Class-3 flare, a flux of 10^{-5} erg cm^{-2} sec^{-1} was measured in the wavelength range 0.41–0.14 Å, or 30–90 kev (Friedman, 1960).

Although it may appear that satisfactory detectors for the entire spectral range from the visible to X-rays are now available, there is still a great need for research in the field of photodetection. Many of the detectors, suggested by Tables I and II, have not yet been constructed although they would be of great use in experimentation from satellites and deep space probes. The next few years will undoubtedly see great advances in photodetection.

References

Audran, R. (1958), "Wissenschaftliche Phot.," p. 279. Verlag Dr. Othmar Helwich, Darmstadt.

Edlén, B. (1936), *Z. Physik* **100,** 621.

Friedman, H. (1960), *in* "Physics of the Upper Atmosphere" (J. A. Ratcliffe, ed.), Chapter 3. Academic Press, New York 1960.

Hass, G., Hunter, W. R., and Tousey, R. (1957), *J. Opt. Soc. Am.* **47,** 120.

Heroux, L., and Hinteregger, H. E. (1960), *Rev. Sci. Instr.* **31,** 280.

Hinteregger, H. E. (1960), *Astrophys. J.* **132,** 801.

Hinteregger, H. E. (1961), *J. Geophys. Research* **66,** 2367.

Hinteregger, H. E., and Watanabe, K. (1953), *J. Opt. Soc. Am.* **43,** 604.

Johnson, F. S., Tousey, R., and Watanabe, K. (1951), *J. Opt. Soc. Am.* **41,** 702.

Lukirskii, A. P., Rumsh, M. A., and Karpovich, I. A. (1960), *Optics and Spectroscopy* **9,** 343.

Schumann, V. (1901), *Ann. Physik* **5,** 349.

Walker, W. C., Wainfan, N., and Weissler, G. L. (1955), *J. Appl. Phys.* **26,** 1366.

Walker, W. C., Rustgi, O. P., and Weissler, G. L. (1959), *J. Opt. Soc. Am.* **49,** 471.

Discussion

Dr. A. G. Massevitch: Some results of solar X-ray measurements from Soviet spaceships and rockets are:

(1) Several measurements of solar X-ray radiation λ 10 Å–2 Å have been carried out in the U.S.S.R. by S. L. Mandelstam, Y. P. Tindo, B. N. Vasiljev, A. T. Shurigin, and Yu. K. Voronko during the flight of two geophysical rockets on the morning and evening of July 21, 1959 (at an altitude of about 100 km); during orbiting of the second spaceship, August 19–20 (perigee, 305 km; apogee, 320 km); the third spaceship, December 1–2, 1960 (perigee, 180 km; apogee, 249 km); and while launching a geophysical rocket into the moon's shadow during the solar eclipse on February 15, 1961.

Photon counters with windows made with beryllium and aluminum coverings were used. A special control was installed against interference from radiation belts for heights of 200 to 300 km at latitudes 30°S–35°N. The results of the measurements are the following:

(a) July 21, 1959: Energy fluxes (extrapolated to the boundary of the atmosphere of the earth) of 7.3×10^{-4} and 3.2×10^{-4} erg/cm^{2}sec. The corresponding electron temperature amounts to 4.5×10^6 °K.

(b) August 19–20, 1960: Mean energy flux of 7.6×10^{-4} erg/cm^{2}sec. A substantial increase of the flux was observed during a solar flare (2+).

(c) December 1–2, 1960: Mean energy flux of $\sim 2.4 \times 10^{-4}$ erg/cm^{2}sec (T_e 2×10^6 °K).

(d) Solar eclipse: Energy flux of 8×10^{-5} erg/cm^{2}sec; reduced to an unocculted corona, this corresponds to 4×10^{-4} erg/cm^{2}sec ($T_e = 1.2 \times 10^6$ °K).

All obtained energy flux measurements have a good correlation with the index of the green corona line ($\lambda = 5303$ Å), as shown in Table I. This seems to indicate that the X-ray radiation and the green line originate in the same coronal regions.

TABLE I

Date of measurement:	Aug. 19–20, 1960	Dec. 1–2, 1960	Feb. 15, 1961
(2–10 Å) (ergs/cm² sec)	7.6×10^{-4}	2.4×10^{-4}	4×10^{-4}
Index of the green corona line 5303 Å	91 88	51 47	65

It should be noted that these results are in good agreement with measurements made by H. Friedman and his collaborators, and with theoretical results obtained by G. Elwert [*J. Geophys. Research* **66,** 391 (1961)].

(2) A. T. Efremov, A. L. Podmoshenski, and O. N. Efimov made measurements of the ultraviolet radiation of the sun during orbiting of the second spaceship August 19–20, 1960. Photomultipliers with automatically changing filters of Cu; Be; Al; LiF; CaF_2; SiO_2; were used. Radiation of the quiet sun and during a flare was measured for $\lambda = 1\text{-}1500$ Å. The results are following: for the quiet sun, the energy flux corresponds to $T_e = 0.9 \times 10^6$ °K; during the flare, $T_e = 6.5 \times 10^6$ °K. No changes of the energy flux in the region 44–100 Å were noted during the flare as compared with the quiet sun. At $\lambda = 5$ Å, during the flare, the flux increased considerably. The intensity of *H Lα* changed about six times during the whole time of observation. During the flare the intensity seemed rather to decrease instead of increasing.

(3) From an experiment with the grazing incidence electrospectrophotometer mounted on the third spaceship (December 1–2, 1960), Bruns and Prokofiev found the mean value of 0.5 erg/cm²sec for the total flux in the He II (λ 304) line emitted by the solar chromosphere.

CHAPTER 5

Communications

EBERHARDT RECHTIN

JET PROPULSION LABORATORY, CALIFORNIA INSTITUTE OF TECHNOLOGY, Pasadena, California

Introduction

It goes without saying that, whenever possible, space exploration should be done from the surface of the earth. When atmospheric vagaries preclude effective exploration from the surface, the next logical choice is either high altitude balloons or earth satellites. Techniques for retrieving data from balloons or satellites are relatively well understood.

This talk is therefore aimed at the astronomer whose problems must be solved by sending spacecraft away from the immediate vicinity of the earth. The feasibility of certain kinds of exploration are strongly dependent upon the available communications. This report is intended to show the space scientist the kind of practical communications he might expect.

Illustrative Communication System Designs

There have been many studies made of conventional and unconventional techniques for communicating to and from the earth and the spacecraft. The most practical approach is now generally agreed to be direct communication using directional antennas at an operating frequency of several thousand megacycles per second. Typical spacecraft antennas are between 1 and 10 meters in diameter. Practical ground antennas are between 20 and 80 meters in diameter. Spacecraft radiated powers are on the order of tens to hundreds of watts. Practical communications systems designed within these limitations are shown in Table I. The first system, that of a weather satellite, provides a well-understood situation.

TABLE I
Illustrative Communication Systems

Parameter	Earth satellite	Lunar orbiter	Lunar lander	Mars orbiter	Space probe
Range (km)	4×10^3	4×10^5	4×10^5	4×10^8	4×10^{10}
Earth antenna gain	10^3	4×10^4	10^6	10^6	10^6
Vehicle antenna area (m^2)	0.05	7	2.5	100	100
System temperature (°K)	400	220	400	100	100
Vehicle radiated power (watts)	200	50	10	150	150
Bandwidth (cps) for $S/N = 10^3$ watts/watt	4×10^6	10^6	10^6	2.5×10^3	0.25

Weather Satellite

The weather satellite travels around the earth at a comparatively low altitude: 500–800 km. The slant range from the receiving antenna to the satellite varies considerably during any one pass with the maximum range occurring at the horizon. The satellite is seldom visible to the receiving station for more than 20 minutes at a time, and consequently, rapid acquisition of the signal and high-speed data transmission are essential. To simplify the station operation, the ground antenna beamwidth is comparatively broad (about 5°) with a resultant antenna gain of only 1000. To simplify vehicle operation, an omnidirectional vehicle antenna is chosen, resulting in a comparatively low frequency for transmission. For a variety of reasons, including the need to look close to the horizon, it will be difficult to use system temperatures much less than 400°K. To transmit high-quality coverage in the short times available would require about 4 Mc of bandwidth at a 30-db signal-to-noise ratio. The resultant radiated power of 200 watts would probably be supplied from rechargeable batteries using the sun as the prime source of energy.

Lunar Orbiter with Television

Real-time television can be sent from the moon with surprisingly little difficulty. In this system, the vehicle antenna is sufficiently broad in beamwidth to illuminate the whole earth (hence the vehicle antenna is not required to track a moving ground station) and the ground antenna is sufficiently broad in beamwidth to cover the circling orbiter while aiming the beam at the center of the moon's face (permitting a very simple antenna drive system needing information only from an almanac). About 10 frames per second could be transmitted at an acceptable signal-to-noise ratio. Because the television of the moon is a sufficiently unique problem, a special modulation system might be provided, using more efficient information coding (FM, PCM, digital telemetry, etc.). Most coding techniques achieve their greatest utility when used with signal-to-noise ratios of about 10 db. Applied to the lunar orbiter, coding bandwidths of 100 Mc could be used if desired.

Lunar Lander with Television

The surface exploration of the moon by instruments can be enormously more effective if an observer on the earth can watch the operation using a television camera mounted on a lunar automobile. The weight and power limitations on such automobiles, and the difficulties of keeping the automobile antenna pointed accurately at the earth, make it worthwhile to reduce the lunar vehicle capability and to increase the earth ground capability by increasing ground antenna gain. (Ground tracking is not as severe a problem for the automobile as for the orbiter.) The increased gain of the ground antenna also results in somewhat increased system temperature, since the antenna beam is completely concentrated on the lunar surface.

Mars Orbiter with Facsimile

Although the minimum distance between the earth and Mars is only about 80 million km, the communication distance to an orbiter of Mars is considerably greater for two reasons: efficient trajectories do not result in arrival at Mars when Mars is at a minimum distance; and it is desired to keep contact for at least one Martian year. The numerical values of the remaining parameters represent no particularly remarkable state of the art, with the possible exception of the vehicle antenna beamwidth. In this design, the Mars orbiter must keep its antenna pointed at the distant earth to within a fraction of a degree, a reasonable but not simple task for a space vehicle attitude-control system. If this task proves too difficult to perform on early flights, the probable tradeoff would be to reduce the antenna area, to increase the vehicle antenna beamwidth as a consequence, and to accept the reduced video bandwidth as a result. An alternate, but much more expensive, tradeoff would be to use a lower frequency of transmission, and then to require a larger ground antenna (but with the same gain) in order to retain the original system capability.

Space Probe

This communications system is essentially the same as that of the Mars orbiter, except that the increased distance to the probe is compen-

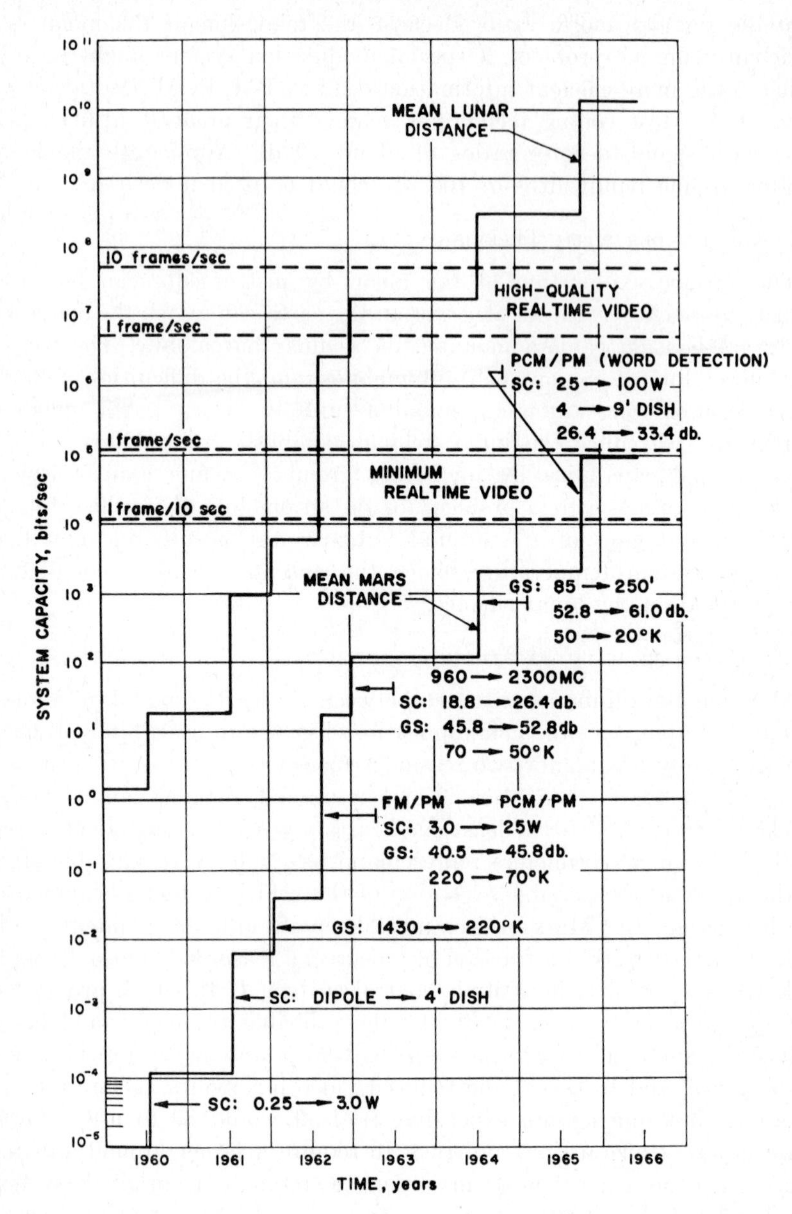

Fig. 1. Projected Deep Space telemetry system capacity. Initial conditions: 960 Mc, FM/PM; space craft (SC), 0.25 watt, +3 db (dipole); Goldstone (GS), 1430°K, +40.5 db (85 ft).

sated by a reduction in information transmission rate and quality. The resulting data are comparable to the cosmic-ray information from Pioneer IV obtained at the edge of the solar system instead of at the moon.

These illustrative communication systems can be varied within limits. If the antenna gain, vehicle antenna area, or vehicle radiated power is decreased, or if the system temperature is increased, the effect is a proportional decrease in the bandwidth or the signal-to-noise ratio of the received signal.

The communication capacity to deep spacecraft is also determined by the state of the art and the available facilities. A projection of the telecommunication capacity to deep space probes shows the system capacity in bits per second as a function of the time in years starting in 1960 and ending in 1966 (Fig. 1). In this figure we can see that there is an improvement in the capacity by almost a factor of 10^9 within a period of 5 years. The incremental improvements are labeled on the chart and they show such things as an increase in spacecraft power from ¼ to 3 watts, an improvement in the ground system temperature, changes in the diameters of the various antennas, and so forth. We can quite reasonably expect real-time, broadcast quality television from the distance of the moon, and slow-speed video from the planets; indeed, we can communicate approximately to the edge of the solar system with practical results. Communication outside of the solar system is not immediately practicable using known techniques.

The Deep Space Instrumentation Facility

The communication systems illustrated earlier would be meaningless unless there were appropriate instrumentation facilities being planned and installed according to these designs. The appropriate facilities of the United States are called the Deep Space Instrumentation Facility. The present facility consists of stations located around the world using 85-ft-diameter antennas such as are shown in Figs. 2 and 3 (receiving antenna, Goldstone, and transmitting antenna, Goldstone). There are three stations comprising the facility, one in California, one in Woomera, Australia, and one near Johannesburg, South Africa. They are capable of continuous coverage of a spacecraft within a latitude band of $\pm 30°$ and at all altitudes above 10,000 miles, as shown in Fig. 4. The sun, moon and the important planets are thus always accessible to observation.

The present and planned capabilities of the facility are shown in Table II. We plan to increase the number of stations. We intend to build still larger antennas. We will change our operating frequency from 960 to 2290 Mc in accordance with international frequency agree-

Fig. 2. Receiving antenna, Goldstone.

TABLE II
Deep Space Instrumentation Facility

Parameter	1961	Planned (1962–1970)
Number of stations	3	5
Longitude spacing (degrees)	120	120
Antenna diameter (meters)	26	26 and 70 (approx)
Listening frequency (Mc)	960	2295 ± 5
Listening system temperature (°K)	2000	<50
Transmitting frequency (Mc)	890	2113 ± 5
Transmitting power (kw)	10	10 and 100
Principal flight missions	Lunar unmanned	Lunar and planetary manned and unmanned
Typical communication service	Lunar slow-speed facsimile	Telephony, lunar television planetary facsimile

FIG. 3. Transmitting antenna, Goldstone.

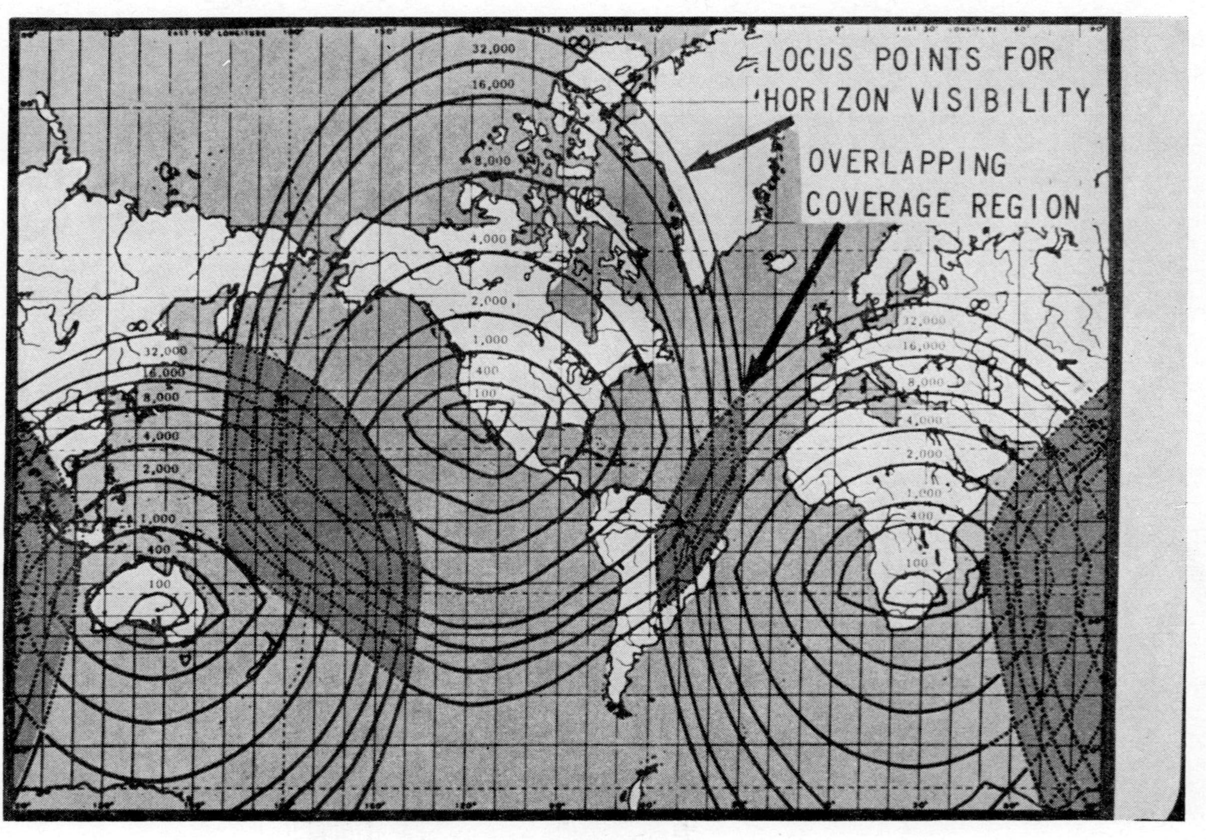

FIG. 4. World-wide station coverage.

ments. We propose to build considerably more sensitive listening systems at the higher frequency. We will change our transmitting frequency from 890 to 2113 Mc and increase our transmitting power from 10 to 100 kw. Our present principal flight missions are lunar unmanned missions, such as Ranger and Surveyor. We will almost immediately begin a planetary program and very shortly thereafter will do a manned lunar program.

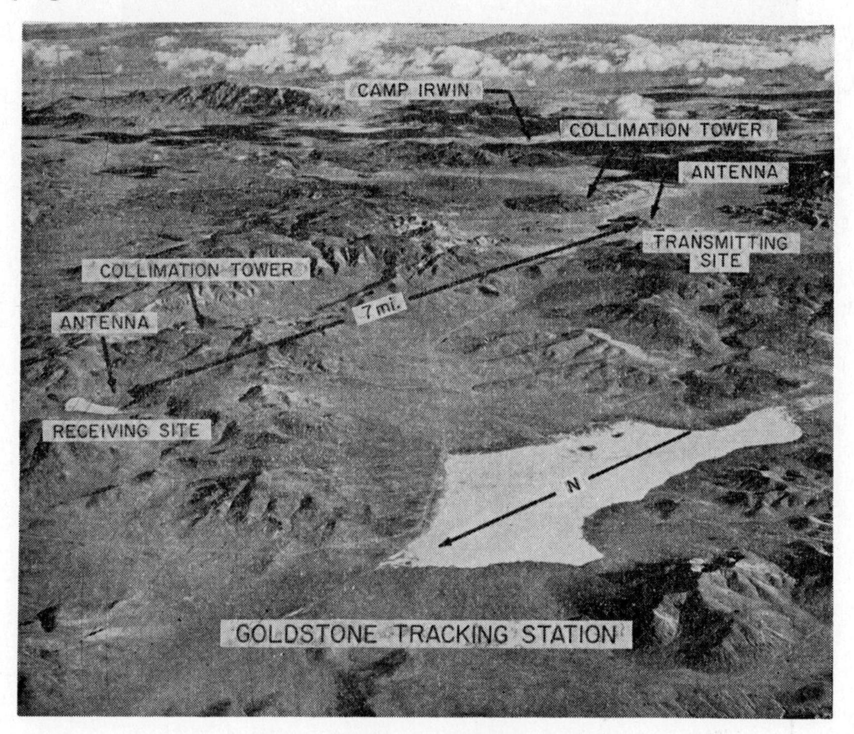

Fig. 5. Goldstone station coverage.

With transmitting and receiving facilities such as these, it is also possible to do quite worthwhile radar astronomy. By shifting the transmitting frequency and receiving frequency to a common value (2388 Mc has been used often), the Goldstone facility has participated in passive communications (Project Echo and voice moonbounce to Australia) and in Venus reflection studies. In the latter case, the astronomical unit was refined to a value of 149,598,500 $\pm$ 500 km and the rotation rate of Venus was observed to be slow enough that Venus probably keeps one side facing the sun. Similar observations of Mars, Mercury, and Jupiter are intended in the coming years. The unique isolation of the transmitter from the receiver at Goldstone (Fig. 5) permits bistatic CW

Fig. 6. Ranger RA-1 spacecraft.

radar operation, with a consequent ability to perform precision ranging, Doppler, and integrated Doppler measurements. The measurements are precise enought that, by observing small perturbations in the orbit of Venus, it might well be possible to detect moons of Venus or other planets in the solar system.

Typical Spacecraft

The experimenter must of necessity fit his equipment on to a spacecraft sized to the booster vehicle. For longer range communication spacecraft, the United States designs use directional antennas mounted on an attitude stabilized platform. Two typical spacecraft are shown. The first spacecraft is called the Ranger (Fig. 6) and is designed to go to the moon. The second spacecraft is called the Mariner (Fig. 7); it is designed

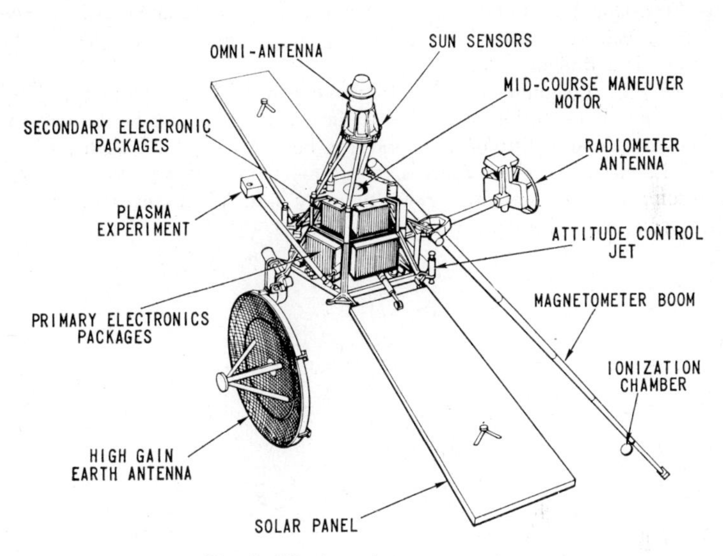

FIG. 7. Mariner A-1 spacecraft.

to go to the planets. Both of these spacecraft depend upon an Atlas vehicle as the first stage booster. We should expect a similar, but larger, spacecraft as boosters become larger. A typical weight of scientific exploration instruments aboard the present craft is on the order of several hundred pounds. In the near future this weight will increase to as much as a thousand pounds.

Some Suggestions to Prospective Explorers

There can evidently be very good communications from the spacecraft to the earth. But, in addition, the ability to communicate depends strongly upon the year in which the experiment is performed. The later the year, the more communications and weight will become available. The experimenter must carefully plan his own program to include all of the normal administrative, political, and technical delays which are common between the first idea and the final flight aboard a spacecraft. With proper planning, a considerably better experiment can be accomplished.

Discussion

Professor G. Righini: How certain are we about the rotational period of Venus?

Dr. Rechtin: As many of you know, there is presently a controversy underway. The measurements made by ourselves indicate that the rotation must be quite slow, measurements made by the U.S.S.R. indicate rotations perhaps of once every 9 to 11 earth days. Our measurements using a very stable continuous radio wave to the planet Venus indicate a rotational period of, say, 6 months or 225 days, but the measurement is a difficult one.

Dr. Z. Kopal: I should just like to make a very brief comment, that if the figures just quoted are to be taken at their face value, it would be difficult to reconcile them with an equality of temperatures between day and night, which have been established within a few degrees.

Dr. Rechtin: The significance of the day and night temperatures depends upon how you think the temperatures are created.

CHAPTER 6

Tracking

6.1 Optical and Radio Tracking of Satellites (and Interplanetary Probes)

A. G. MASSEVITCH

ASTRONOMICAL COUNCIL OF THE U.S.S.R. ACADEMY OF SCIENCES, Moscow, Russia

1. General Remarks

Optical tracking of artificial satellites form an important part of the general program of cosmic space exploration by means of rockets and satellites. For about 4 years a satellite-service—that means a network of more than 400 special tracking stations all over the world—has been in operation. Visual and photographic observations of satellites are carried out at these stations.

At present an immense collection of tracking data is available. Results of the observations obtained are regularly published in two main publications: in the Soviet bulletins "Results of Observations of Soviet Satellites" (*1*) (data on Soviet satellites) and in the *Smithsonian Astrophysical Observatory Special Reports* (data on U.S.A. satellites) (*2*). These data have led to important conclusions concerning the structure of the atmosphere, the correlation between air density variations and solar activity phenomena, and the figure and gravitational field of the earth.

One of the most important results obtained from satellite tracking data is the establishment of a correlation between air density variations and solar activity phenomena. This problem has now become very popular. Correlations with geomagnetic disturbances, solar flares, the 11-year cycle of solar activity in general, radio bursts from the sun on 10.7 cm, 20 cm, and even 143 cm have been found recently by several authors. Even astronomers, who for rather a long time ignored satellite observations almost completely, considering them something quite inferior to "real" astronomical observation, are now beginning to display interest in tracking data. But it is worthwhile to note that great caution has to be taken when establishing the above mentioned correlations. The variation of the mean motion of a satellite, related to the changes in its period of revolution, is a very irregular function. So are all the functions characterizing the activity of the sun. In principle it is almost always possible to correlate a peak in the "orbital" curve with one of the peaks in the corresponding "solar" curves. The problem really consists not so much in finding the correlated "solar" disturbances, as in eliminating very carefully the false correlations. As an example, Fig. 1 shows, according to Miss N. P. Slovokhotova (Astronomical Council, U.S.S.R. Academy of Sciences), the derivative n' of the mean motion of Sputnik III from May 1958 until February 1960 and the solar disturbances for the same time. In addition, curves characterizing the day-to-night variations and the elevation h of the perigee of the satellite over the surface of the earth are given.

If one takes into account those rather periodical or systematic variations which have nothing to do with solar activity, many of the original "orbital" to "solar" correlations can easily be eliminated. What remains looks like a more or less definitely established correlation of the irregularities on the mean motion of the satellite only with some (not all) very strong geomagnetic disturbances. No appreciable correlation with solar radio bursts seems to be left.

Optical tracking data have yielded several important conclusions concerning the figure and gravitational field of the earth. In fact, a new branch of gravimetry, astronomical gravimetry, has been developing recently. Its main aim is to build up a precise theory of the movement of a cosmic body orbiting close to the earth. In comparison to the methods used in geodetical gravimetry, new possibilities exist to determine the parameters of the earth's gravitational potential from the perturbations in the motion of satellites.

Interesting experience in precision optical tracking of satellites for geodesy has been recently obtained by the Smithsonian Astrophysical Observatory with the net of Baker-Nunn cameras distributed around the earth in the latitude zone from $-32°$ to $+36°$. This will be discussed in another chapter.

Last but not least, optical tracking data have been used continuously for ephemeris purposes. It should be noted, however, that the extensive data already obtained in the form of systematic tracking data have not yet been properly used. The published catalogs (*1, 2*) still contain basic material for many further interesting scientific papers, and it is very desirable that they should be used for scientific research more actively than they have until today.

The aims and possibilities of various tracking methods are now much better known than in 1957. One can clearly formulate what order of

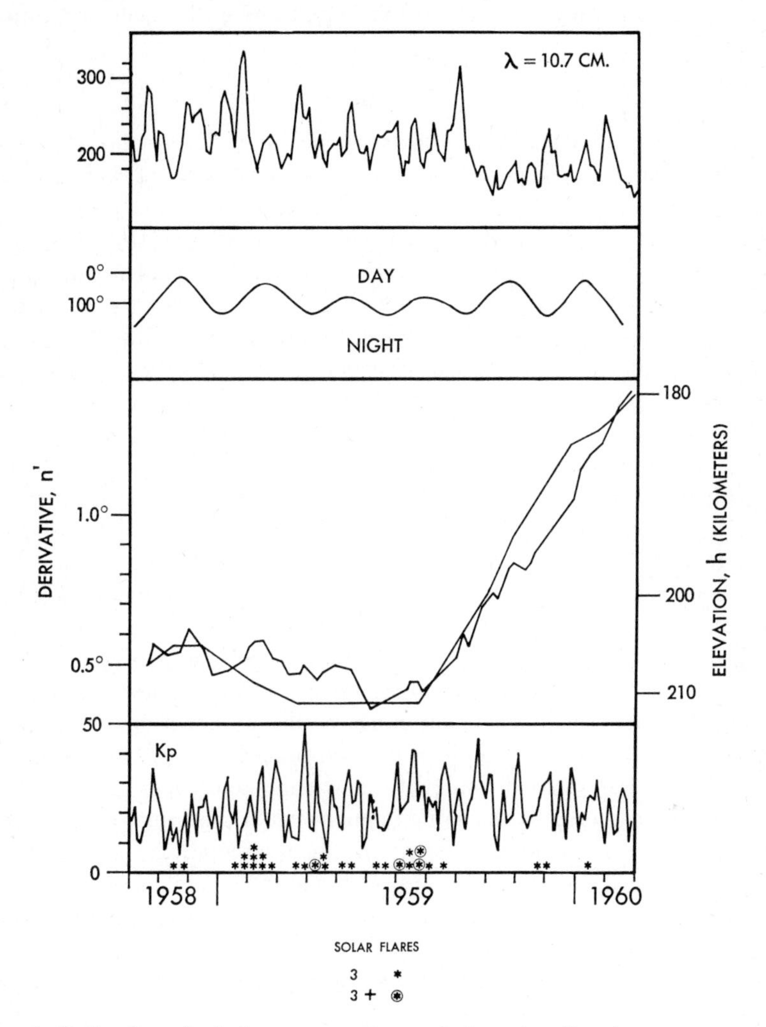

FIG. 1. Derivative n' of the mean notion and the solar disturbances of Sputnik III, May 1958 to February 1960.

accuracy of tracking data is necessary for different kinds of research problems. So, for example, to determine the density of the atmosphere and the oblateness of the earth (first-order perturbations), large quantities of good visual and visual-photographic tracking data can be used.

For determinations of irregularities in the density of the atmosphere and second-order perturbations in the earth's gravitational potential, exact photographic observations are necessary. And for geodetic purposes connected with the difference between ephemeris time and universal time, the required accuracy of tracking data has to be still higher (up to parts of seconds of arc).

2. Visual Observations

The accuracy of visual observations is not high. Experience shows that it is the timing that causes the greatest uncertainty. Practically, one cannot reach an accuracy in timing higher than 0.1 sec in visual observations. For a satellite moving with a velocity of 1°/sec, this corresponds to an accuracy in position of about 0.1°. Tracking stations with trained observers regularly obtain data with this and even higher accuracy, but certainly not every station. An extensive statistical investigation carried out recently at the Pulkovo Observatory shows that the mean personal error of an average observer in timing during visual observations is 0.067 sec (*3*).

Since the reduction is simple and fast, visual observations are most important for the ephemeris service; but they are also useful for several research purposes, and whenever the transmitters fail or have been exhausted.

It is possible to raise the accuracy of visual tracking data by improving instruments and methods of observation. This can be achieved in different ways: by using telescopes which automatically follow the satellite's motion, by taking into account the personal error of the observer, and—more effectively—by combining visual observations with photographic documentation. The latter method proceeds in the following way: Observations are carried out with a visual telescope mounted on a photographic camera. At the same moment when the faint satellite passes the cross-wire in the field of sight of the telescope, the shutter of the camera is opened and a photograph of the star field taken; because of its faintness the moving satellite leaves no track on the photograph. Then a bright object—a star or planet—is brought into the field of sight of the visual telescope and when it occupies the same position on the cross-wire as previously did the satellite, when the time was marked, a short exposure is made. Afterwards the position of this object relatively to the field stars is determined. It corresponds to the position of the satellite at the marked moment of time.

Such a photovisual method is successfully applied at the Potsdam Observatory, at the Pulkovo Observatory, and in several other places. It allows us to raise the accuracy in position determination to 2 minutes, but it is limited by the accuracy of timing, which, as in the usual visual tracking method, does not exceed 0.1 sec. This photovisual tracking method is very favorable for high satellites moving relatively slowly. In that case a timing accuracy of 0.1 sec corresponds to a higher accuracy in position determination, and the method can be employed to full advantage.

Photographs taken with small amateur cameras form another variation of the same method. The accuracy obtained in this case is entirely determined by the accuracy of timing the moment when the shutter is opened. Usually it corresponds to the accuracy of very good visual observations but has the advantage of documentation. There is a possibility to increase the accuracy of timing (up to 0.01 sec) with the help of an additional shutter, which marks on a chronograph the opening and closing. This method can be more favorably applied for bright close satellites.

As a counterpart to the photovisual method, the following can be recommended. Simultaneously with time marking, a shutter works automatically. The observer "remembers" at a rather precisely given time where the satellite was in the star field. As experience obtained at the tracking station of the U.S.S.R. Astronomical Council shows (V. Belenko) the personal error in this case is smaller than when marking the time during the passage of the satellite through a known stellar configuration, and the "weak point"—timing—becomes more exact.

One should keep in mind, however, that any attempt to raise the accuracy of visual observations has sense only so long as it does not affect the advantages of the method itself—its simplicity and quickness of reduction of the data. An automatic following telescope, photographs of the star field, etc., while improving the accuracy of the data, at the same time complicate the observations and lengthen the reduction time. Hence it is very important to calculate in advance what gain these improvements can really give. It is better, perhaps, to go over to photographic observation instead of making the visual observation too complicated, because from the scientific point of view a photograph is always of greater value than visual tracking data, even when improved.

In the U.S.S.R. visual tracking stations are attached to physical and mathematical departments of universities and teacher training colleges. The observers are mainly students. At present there are 74 visual stations. Soviet and American satellites are regularly observed. Since October 4, 1957, about 62,000 observations of Soviet satellites and more than 23,000 observations of American satellites have been made. The result of all the work done until July 1, 1961, is summarized in Tables I and II. There have also been several observations of the U.S.A. Dis-

TABLE I
OBSERVATIONS OF SOVIET ARTIFICIAL SATELLITES BY SOVIET STATIONS UP TO JULY 1, 1961

No.	Satellites	No. observations
1.	1957 α-1 Sputnik I (rocket)	1170
2.	1957 α-2 Sputnik I	119
3.	1957 β Sputnik II	4482
4.	1958 δ-2 Sputnik III	25191
5.	1958 δ-1 Sputnik III (rocket)	14303
6.	1960 ϵ-1 Sputnik IV (rocket carrier)	1454
7.	1960 ϵ-2 Sputnik IV (satellite	7227
8.	1960 ϵ-3 Sputnik IV (cabin)	7713
9.	1961 β-1 Sputnik VII	29
10.	1961 β-2 Sputnik VII (rocket)	25
11.	1961 β-3 Sputnik VII (detail)	26
12.	1961 γ-1 Sputnik VIII	17
13.	1960 λ-1 Sputnik V	163
14.	1960 λ-2 Sputnik V (rocket)	—
	Total:	61924

coverers, but they are not listed in Table II as we do not receive predictions or orbital elements for them from the U.S.A. Computing Center. All the tracking data on American satellites are immediately communicated by telegraph to the Smithsonian Observatory.

We receive many tracking data of Soviet satellites from 33 foreign countries. Up to July 1, 1961, about 46,000 results of observations from

TABLE II
OBSERVATIONS OF AMERICAN ARTIFICIAL SATELLITES BY SOVIET STATIONS UP TO JULY 1, 1961

No.	Satellites	No. observations
1.	1959 ι-1 Explorer VII	676
2.	1960 β-2 Tiros I (rocket)	577
3.	1960 γ-2 Transit I B (rocket)	281
4.	1960 η-1 Transit II A (satellite)	2334
5.	1960 η-3 Transit II A (rocket)	853
6.	1960 ι-I Echo	16185
7.	1960 ι-2 Echo (rocket)	12
8.	1960 ξ-1 Explorer VIII	293
9.	1960 π-1 Tiros II (satellite)	40
10.	1961 α-1 Samos II	990
11.	1961 α-2 Samos II (nose cone)	122
12.	1961 δ-1 Explorer IX	1242
	Total:	23605

foreign stations have been communicated to the U.S.S.R. Computing Center. A summary of results of observations received from foreign stations for all Soviet satellites is given in Table III.

Visual observations are carried out in the U.S.S.R. stations by means of "Moonwatch" telescopes (telescopes AT-I: $d = 50$ mm; magnification $\times 6$; field of sight, 11°) when observations are made in equatorial coordinates (α, δ), and by means of quite similar binoculars "TSK" with

TABLE III

OBSERVATIONS OF SOVIET ARTIFICIAL SATELLITES BY FOREIGN STATIONS UP TO JULY 1, 1961

No.	Satellites		No. observations
1.	1957 α-1	Sputnik I (rocket)	932—(114pg)
2.	1957 α-2	Sputnik I	16
3.	1957 β	Sputnik II	6226—(1394pg)
4.	1958 δ-2	Sputnik III	14793—(1754pg)
5.	1958 δ-1	Sputnik III (rocket)	12377—(2868pg)
6.	1960 ϵ-1	Sputnik IV (rocket carrier)	1314—(226pg)
7.	1960 ϵ-2	Sputnik IV (satellite)	4953—(434pg)
8.	1960 ϵ-3	Sputnik IV (cabin)	5002—(340pg)
9.	1961 β-1	Sputnik VII	17
10.	1961 β-2	Sputnik VII (rocket)	34
11.	1961 β-3	Sputnik VII (detail)	28
12.	1961 γ-1	Sputnik VIII	2
13.	1960 λ-1	Sputnik V	117—(18pg)
14.	1960 λ-2	Sputnik V (rocket)	5—(2pg)
		Total:	45818—(7150pg)

mountings for observations in horizontal coordinates (a, h). The latter observations are mainly carried out at northern stations. The observers themselves have made many improvements of the available equipment (*4*).

All results of observations received by the U.S.S.R. Computing Center are published in a special bulletin, "Results of Observations of Soviet Satellites," issued by the Astronomical Council of the U.S.S.R. Academy of Sciences. Until now there have appeared: (1) Sputnik II (1957 β), issues 1–3, 1958; (2) Rocket carrier of Sputnik III (1958 δ-1), issues 1–10, 1959; Sputnik III (1958 δ-2, issues 11–35, 1960–61); Sputnik IV (1960 ϵ-1, issues 36–45, in press).

3. Ephemeris Service and Orbit Calculations

Predictions for all Soviet satellites are regularly sent (2–3 days in advance) to all participating stations by telegraph. Orbit calculations are done at the Institute for Theoretical Astronomy in Leningrad. The method of deriving orbital elements evaluated at this Institute is given by Batrakov and Proskurin (*5*).

Observations are reduced for an interval of 10 to 20 days. Calculations of orbital elements are published in the "Bulletin of Soviet Tracking Stations" (*6*). In issue No. 7, 1961, besides the orbital elements for Sputnik III and its rocket carrier, a comparison of these systems with other available orbital elements for the same objects is made (*7, 8*). Orbital elements of Sputnik IV are published in issue No. 10 (*9*).

Attention should be drawn to the problem of the most effective distribution of tracking stations over the globe. The accuracy in determining the orbital elements of satellites, particularly the inclination i, eccentricity e, and the argument of perigee ω is the higher, the larger is the part of the orbit for which observations are available. In almost all systems of orbital elements already obtained on the basis of optical observations the elements e and i are determined rather poorly and have the greatest dispersion. This is a mathematical expression of the fact that there are by far not enough tracking stations in the Southern Hemisphere. It should be noted that the variations of e and i are very important for several scientific applications (the winds in the upper atmosphere, for example).

This problem has been the subject of a special discussion during the meeting of COSPAR in Florence in 1961. There is a great need for more active working tracking stations in the Southern Hemisphere.

4. Photographic Observations

Photographic observations of satellites exceed considerably the possibilities of radio tracking in the precision of coordinate determination. Photocinetheodolite observations are very valuable, but the highest precision can be obtained only by measuring a photograph of the satellite's track taken simultaneously with the background stars.

In different countries different cameras are used for photographic tracking of the satellites. The main efforts are directed to making the timing as precise as possible. At present, the highest accuracy is achieved with the American Baker-Nunn cameras (timing up to 2 msec; coordinates about 1 to 2 sec of arc).

The standard cameras operating in the U.S.S.R. ($d = 100$ mm, $f = 250$ mm) can be used for photographing bright satellites up to fourth magnitude; these make it possible to obtain an accuracy about 6 sec of arc in position and 2 msec in timing (with reference to the time standard of the U.S.S.R.). Twenty-seven photographic stations are operating regularly. Most of them are attached to astronomical observatories.

The accuracy of photographic tracking data can be raised by means of finding the most appropriate way of photographing and reducing the plate. As an example, the Soviet cameras were previously meant to give an accuracy in position about 1 min of arc. A new interpolation method of reducing photographic plates for determining positions of individual objects, worked out by A. A. Kiselev of the Pulkovo Observatory (*10*), has proved very efficient for rather small wide-angle cameras. It raises the attainable accuracy in position determinations about 10 times. This is achieved by taking into account very thoroughly the error in the position of the optical center, the distortion of the objective lens, and the refraction. As the main uncertainties, when reducing a photograph, are caused by chance errors in measuring the ends of the track of the satellite and the corresponding time marks, the satellite is photographed in such a way that about 10 separate tracks are obtained near the center of the field of sight. Smoothing 10 separate parts of the track for time and position errors practically removes these uncertainties.

The accuracy of photographic tracking data can be raised also by employing existing large astronomical telescopes, which, however, will have to be supplied with special timing devices. Long-focus telescopes can be used to obtain positions within 1 sec, but the corresponding timing problem remains to be solved. Rather encouraging work in this respect has been already done at the Potsdam Observatory by Dr. Güntzel-Lingner with the 12-meter focus refractor. Several ways in which existing astronomical telescopes have been made suitable for tracking faint satellites in the U.S.S.R. have been described (*11*).

In general, it may be stated that the present timing accuracy for photographic tracking data is behind the accuracy in position determination. This problem deserves more attention than it has received up to now.

5. Other Kinds of Optical Observations

Many tracking stations are also carrying out systematic photometric observations of the apparent brightness variations of satellites. In order to obtain certain results, a statistical reduction of a rather large amount of observational data (visual, photographic, photoelectric) is needed.

Photometric observations are carried out in the U.S.A., the U.S.S.R., Bulgaria, Germany, and other countries. For large satellites like Echo I, photometric data allow one to investigate in detail its surface conditions. For an elongated, cigar-like satellite, there evidently exists a correlation between the period of its rotation and solar activity. These interesting preliminary investigations should be continued.

For bright satellites, colorimetric observations can be carried out. Double astrographs of moderate size, available at astronomical observatories, could be used for this purpose.

Serious consideration should be given to the question how to use the

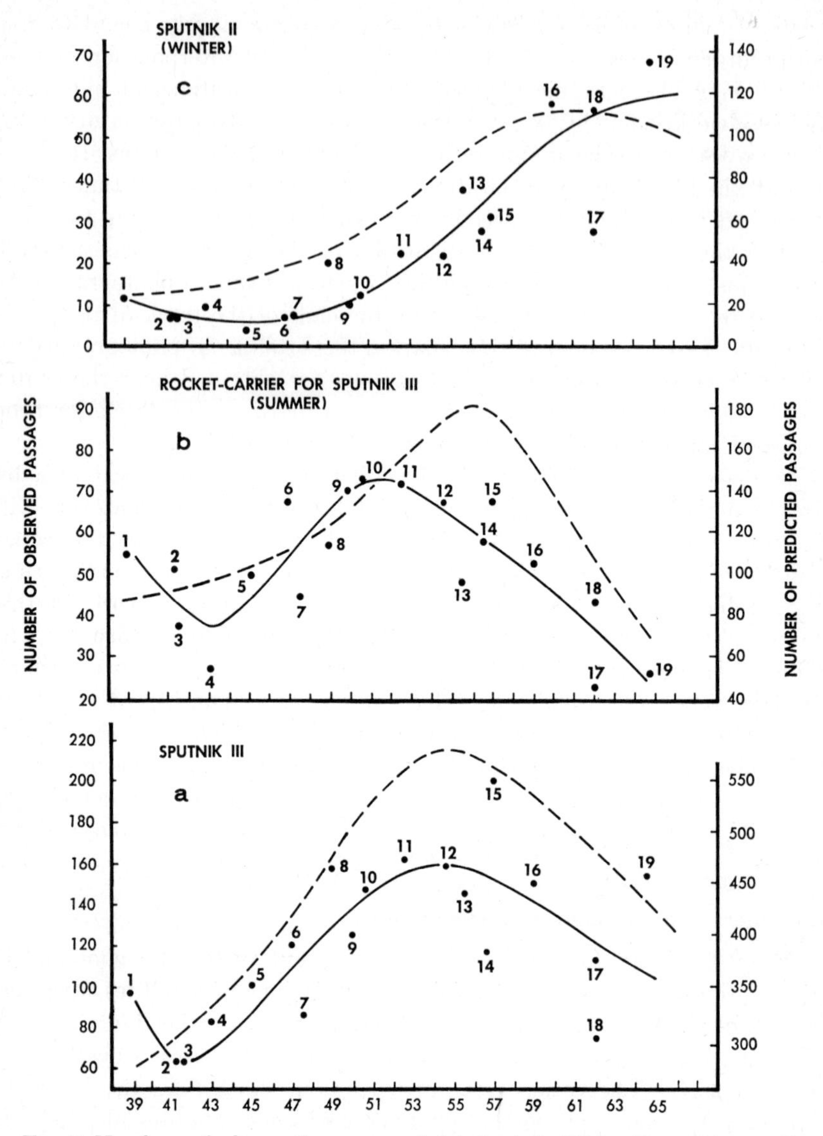

Fig. 2. Numbers of observed passages of (a) Sputnik III by 70 tracking stations during its lifetime, (b) Sputnik III during the summer months, (c) Sputnik II.

existing net of optical tracking stations for related astronomical problems that require statistical data. Even a rough analysis of the work of the tracking stations allows us to pick out those that have the best seeing conditions.

As an example, I consider some results of statistical work done by

Mrs. M. Lurie at the Astronomical Council of the U.S.S.R. Academy of Sciences on the basis of data from Soviet tracking stations. Figure 2a shows a plot of the number of observed passages of Sputnik III by 70 tracking stations, during its whole lifetime, aaginst the geographical latitude of the stations. For convenience, the stations are gathered into 19 groups. The dashed line represents the predicted number of passages (left scale). Figure 2b shows the same plot for the same satellite, but during summer months. One can clearly see here the maximum shifted to the left due to the "white nights" of northern latitudes. But, nevertheless, the number of observations for certain stations is systematically higher than for others located almost at the same latitude. Figure 2c represents the same data for Sputnik II during winter months. The same stations again show the best results.

There are other rather interesting observations that could be carried out at the existing tracking stations without much effort. Among them the following have been included in the recommendations of working Group 1 (on tracking and telemetering) of COSPAR during its meeting in 1961 in Florence: (1) continuous photographic observations of comets through specific narrow-band filters, in order to detect short periodic variations of brightness and structure; (2) world-wide observations of number densities in certain meteor showers in order to detect short periodic fluctuations in these number densities. We could also add observations of occultations of stars by the moon and planets and—a new and rather promising branch—by artificial satellites.

6. Radio Tracking

The main aims of radio tracking (besides ephemeris purposes) are investigations of the upper atmosphere and interplanetary space through analyses of the properties of radio waves transmitted from satellites and received at different points of the earth. This is an indirect method but has already proved to be very efficient. The following important measurements could be emphasized:

(1) Doppler effect measurements, including "rotational Doppler effect";

(2) study of the behavior of the amplitude of radio signals from a satellite;

(3) antipode effects and other phenomena of long-distance propagation of satellite radio signals around the earth;

(4) radio rise and radio setting of the satellite.

A rather full survey of results of ionospheric studies on the basis of radio tracking data obtained in the U.S.S.R. is given by Alpert (*12*). We should also mention here the interesting work done by V. P. Rozhin in the Antarctic (Mirnyi), where signals from Sputnik I were registered from the antipodes during three or four successive revolutions of the satellite. On October 6, 1959, signals from the antipodes were received four times in a row between 12^h 13^m and 17^h 10^m local time; on October 7, four times between 09^h 45^m and 17^h 05^m; and on October 8, three times between 10^h 43^m and 13^h 54^m.

Radio rise and radio setting observations of the first Soviet satellites have been successfully used by Alpert and collaborators (*13*) for the determination of electron concentrations in the ionosphere.

Cuperov (*14*) tracked signals of Sputnik III on Cape Tscheluskin. During the time of observation, from May 16 to June 6, 1958, it was possible to receive signals from distances up to 8500 km. It was noted that for propagation of radio waves over the continent, the distance did not exceed 4500–5000 km, while for propagation over the sea, it reached 8500 km. In propagation from a distance of 5000 to 8500 km, only one reflection from the surface of the earth took place. If the reflection point belonged to the continent, the signal usually did not reach the receiving station due to large losses at this frequency in the earth's solid crust. The probability of detecting signals from the satellite in the direct visibility region reached 94%. All cases in which no signals were tracked in the region of direct visibility corresponded to abnormally high absorption of radio waves, as noted by ionospheric stations in the Tixi Bay and Dixon Island during vertical soundings of the ionosphere.

Vitkevitch *et al.* (*15*) tracked signals from the second Soviet cosmic rocket in October 1959. An interferometer was used on 183.6 Mc/sec with a width of one fringe equal to 32 min. The radio interferometer was calibrated by using the cosmic radio sources Cygnus A, Taurus A, and Virgo A. The intensity of the received signal was found by comparison with the known intensity of Cygnus A. The characteristic periods of oscillations of the signal were evaluated from the variations of the intensity of the signal with time. On October 12, 1959, oscillations were observed with a short period about 45 sec and a long period of about 45 min, and on October 13, 1959, with a period of 10 to 13 min.

The characteristic change of the signal at the time of the collision of the rocket with the moon's surface was derived. Results of radio tracking also permitted a specification of the region of the landing of the container in the vicinity of the crater Archimedes (with an accuracy of ± 1 min).

7. Conclusions

In conclusion, it should be stressed that optical tracking data, especially photographic data, should be more and better used; and that a closer cooperation of the tracking station personnel with observing astronomers is needed, especially in regard to timing and reduction problems.

There is also a rather great need for better cooperation between the "orbital" people (celestial mechanics who do the evaluation of the orbital elements) and the observing staff (who supply them with observational data), on one side, and the astrophysicists and geophysicists (who utilize, or should, at least, utilize the calculated orbital elements for scientific research).

References

1. "Results of Observations of Soviet Satellites" (1958–1961). 1–3 (1958); 1–10 (1959); 11–35 (1960); 36–45 (1961) Moscow.
2. *Smithsonian Astrophys. Observatory Spec. Rept.* (1958–1961). 1–70.
3. B. A. Firago, *Bull. U.S.S.R. Optical Tracking Stations* No. 10, 9 (1961).
4. M. A. Lurie, *Astron. J. Soviet Union* **36,** 4, 36 (1959).
5. Yu. V. Batrakov and V. F. Proskurin, *Bull. Inst. Theoret. Astron.* **7,** (7), 537 (1960).
6. Yu. V. Batrakov and A. S. Sotshilina, *Bull. U.S.S.R. Optical Tracking Stations* (7), 3 (1961).
7. N. P. Slovochotova, *Bull. U.S.S.R. Optical Tracking Stations* No. 7, 14 (1961).
8. N. P. Erpilev, *Bull. U.S.S.R. Optical Tracking Stations* No. 7, 13 (1961).
9. Yu. V. Batrakov and A. S. Sotshilina, *Bull. U.S.S.R. Optical Tracking Stations* No. 10, 3 (1961).
10. A. A. Kiselev, *Astron. J. Soviet Union* **35,** No. 2, 34 (1959).
11. A. G. Massevitch, "Space Research" Vol. II, p. 102. Amsterdam, 1961.
12. Ya. L. Alpert, *Uspekhi Fiz. Nauk.* **71,** 369 (1960).
13. Ya. L. Alpert, F. F. Bobryakova, E. F. Chudesenko, and B. S. Shapiro, *Uspekhi Fiz. Nauk.* **65** (2) 161 (1958).
14. L. P. Cuperov, *Yskusstvennie Sputniki* **5,** 66 (1960).
15. V. V. Vitkevitch, A. D. Kuzmin, R. L. Sorotchenko, and V. A. Udaltsov, *Doklady Akad. Nauk. S.S.S.R.* **132** (7), 85 (1960).

Discussion

Dr. J. Siry: Dr. Massevitch, I was not sure from your manuscript whether you have also made radio observations of your satellites such as we do with minitrack or radar, for example.

Dr. Massevitch: There have been lots of radio observations made in the U.S.S.R. They do not have such a big net like the minitrack, but most of the results have been published.

Dr. J. D. McGee: I would like to ask Dr. Massevitch if image intensifiers have been used in tracking satellites, and, in particular if it is possible to record time very accurately?

Dr. Massevitch: We have tried to use image converters for tracking purposes. At the Sternberg Institute there have been several experimental photographs of bright satellites made. But the difficulty is, that the sky is too bright when you observe a satellite. For the proper use of image converters you need a very high satellite.

Dr. W. B. Klemperer: I would like to ask Mrs. Massevitch whether she would care to add a few words about tracking of the interplanetary, or Venus, probe.

Dr. Massevitch: We have tried to track the first three cosmic rockets with the big telescopes available in our country, but in all these cases we failed because the rockets were too faint. Now we have a big telescope that has been mounted in the Crimean Observatory which will be ready very soon. This is a 2.6-meter reflector. There is also a big Schmidt telescope at the observatory in Armenia. So we hope now to be more successful with the future tracking of the cosmic rockets.

As far as I know, the American astronomers tried to help us in this tracking, but they failed also because the objects were already too faint when they might otherwise have been first observed. But, of course, if big telescopes, like those of Palomar and Mount Wilson, could be available for tracking of cosmic rockets, even for a short time, it would be very helpful. I think it is worthwhile to spend some time on this because the results could be very interesting.

Dr. U. Güntzel-Lingner: Dr. Massevitch, at the Astrophysical Observatory in Potsdam we tried to track Explorer VII (1959 Iota 1) and Echo I (1960 Iota 1) with the photographic 80-cm lens of the Repsold double refractor.

The satellite was tracked with the parallel-mounted 50-cm telescope, which has a fine-divided vertical wire in the field of sight. Simultaneously a photograph of the star field was taken with the 80-cm objective lens. Another plate at the scale of the 80-cm lens and showing the image of the divided wire was superposed on the field photograph, and so the place of the satellite was fixed. The reduction of the plate was made according to A. Koenig (Heidelberg) with two field stars. The scale of the plates is 1 mm $=$ 16.98 sec of arc. The accuracy obtained is ± 3 sec of arc in the rectangular coordinates $x = \Delta\delta$, $y = \Delta\alpha \cos\delta$. The observations were usually carried out near the meridian.

With the use of a simple differential method, the given ephemerides were made more precise in advance, as the field of the telescope was rather small: about 20 min of arc.

This method can be applied to any astrograph or other astronomical telescope which can be made available for satellite tracking work.

Dr. E. Rechtin: I would like to echo some comments made by Dr. Massevitch concerning the importance of Doppler measurements and their utility.

Concerning the deep space probes, which are markedly different than the satellite, we have found that Doppler measurements coupled with reasonably continuous range measurement (integrated Doppler measurement) is a very powerful method of determining orbits of space probes. How well this works for satellites I would say is debatable, but for deep space probes it is possible for us to determine orbits to an order of a thousandth of a degree without too much difficulty. As a matter of fact, we are in the peculiar position that our Doppler and ranging information tells us the angular position of a probe more accurately than we can sense it with our antennas themselves.

The problem of determining orbits for space probes is quite different from that of satellites, principally because the number of perturbing terms are far fewer. The satellite problem is almost hopeless. As we continue to have more physics, more terms, more environments, and so forth, the equations are going to get out of hand.

6.2 *Geodetic Results from Precision Optical Tracking*

IMRE G. IZSAK

SMITHSONIAN ASTROPHYSICAL OBSERVATORY, Cambridge, Massachusetts

An important application of satellite observations is the determination of the coefficients in the expansion of the earth's gravitational potential. The coefficients J_2 and J_4 of the second and fourth zonal harmonics have been already determined with very high accuracy from the secular perturbations in the orbital elements ω and Ω. The coefficient J_3 has been found with considerable accuracy from the long periodic perturbations in the orbital elements e and ω. Concerning the value of the coefficient J_5, however, there is some disagreement among the determinations carried out by several authors. The necessity of a new simultaneous evaluation of the coefficients J_3 and J_5, using the orbits of satellites not considered before, is implicit. At the Smithsonian Astrophysical Observatory the Satellites 1960 $\beta 2$ and 1960 $\iota 2$, both high orbiting objects with small eccentricities, are being used for this purpose.

Investigations of the tesseral harmonics by the analysis of satellite orbits were started at the end of last year. This was made possible by the availability of a large number of precisely reduced Baker-Nunn observations, especially of satellites 1959 $\alpha 1$, 1959 η, and 1960 $\iota 2$. The preliminary results obtained thus far disagree vigorously. Nonetheless, there are good reasons to expect that the coefficients of several tesseral harmonics will soon be determined from satellite motions with much more reliability than was possible from the analysis of gravity measurements. The characteristic difficulties of the problem are illustrated and a description of a new approach to it is given, the mathematical formulation of which will be published in the *Smithsonian Astrophysical Observatory Special Reports.*

CHAPTER 7

Orbit Determination

7.1 Progress in Orbit Determination

JOSEPH W. SIRY

GODDARD SPACE FLIGHT CENTER
NATIONAL AERONAUTICS AND SPACE ADMINISTRATION,
Greenbelt, Maryland

The field of orbit determination for artificial satellites and spacecraft has evolved and progressed in a number of important ways since its beginnings early in the IGY. Orbit determination needs have become more exacting and complex as the objectives of the space programs have become more ambitious and sophisticated. The new requirements have stimulated the development of improved resources. Fresh results are continuing to flow from the program. In many important areas, the orbit determination needs appear almost invariant when stated explicitly. The effective orbit determination requirements relative to the resources at hand have varied considerably, however, with the relevant characteristics of the orbit, the environment, and the satellite itself. For example, the requirement for determining satellite position with a given accuracy was relatively easy to meet for one type of orbit, but difficult to meet for an orbit which was perturbed differently. The continual unfolding of orbit determination objectives, problems, and capabilities can be traced historically. The chronological order is also a logical one; hence it is fruitful to discuss the present and the projected future status of the field of orbit determination in terms of its evolution.

The objectives of the original Vanguard IGY orbit determination program were to determine the orbit of a spherical satellite of constant mass, which was to be launched into an orbital path having a perigee of about 200 miles, an apogee of about 1400 miles, and an inclination to the earth's equator of about 35°. During the initial fortnight, primary reliance for tracking was to be placed upon the Minitrack radio tracking system. Orbits determined using Minitrack data were to be used to generate predictions for the tracking and telemetry receiving systems at the Minitrack stations, as well as for the Smithsonian Astrophysical Observatory Baker-Nunn camera network. Precision optical tracking of the satellite for an indefinite period was to be accomplished by means of this latter network (*1–4*). The principal perturbations of the simple Keplerian orbit were expected to be those due to the earth's oblateness and the drag of the atmosphere, whose density was supposed to vary with height but not appreciably with latitude, longitude, or time. It was anticipated that it would be possible to derive measures of the atmospheric density near perigee, and of the earth's oblateness, from analyses of the satellite's motions.

In summary, then, the objectives of the original orbit determination program were to make predictions of the satellite's positions, to determine ephemerides for the use of experimenters whose instruments operated in the satellite, and to glean new geophysical information from the orbital data.

The first additional demands upon the original orbit determination program were made on October 4, 1957, when Sputnik I appeared in orbit, broadcasting on 20 and 40 Mc. There was, then, the immediate need for tracking on these additional frequencies. New tracking facilities were established on these frequencies at Minitrack stations almost literally overnight.

It soon developed that the effect of atmospheric drag was considerably larger than had been anticipated, by about a factor of 5. It was thought that this was possibly due to a previously undetected variation of high atmospheric density with latitude. In any event, here was the first of many surprises which nature had in store for the orbit determination programs.

The Sputnik I rocket carrier and the Sputnik II satellite brought with them for the first time the problems of the nonspherical tumbling satellites, whose projected frontal areas varied with time in ways that were not known. This same uncertainty about the projected area and hence the drag effect entered even more severely in the case of Explorer I, the first American satellite. The perturbation problem was of greater concern here, not only because of the very large length to diameter ratio of Explorer I and the fact that this pencil-shaped satellite, too, was tumbling in a manner not fully known, but also because this satellite was the first to be tracked by means of the 108-Mc precision Minitrack system. Thus, new orbit determination problems associated with the design of the satellite itself began to arise.

The next additional unscheduled extension of the demands upon the orbit determination system came in the form of the very low perigee height of the Explorer III orbit. Since the satellite dipped low into the dense atmosphere during each orbit, the drag effect was enormous, decreasing the period by a quarter of a minute or more per day (*5*). This effect was of the order of a thousand times larger than the drag effect on Vanguard I, for example. The problem was further complicated rather severely by the fact that the drag effect fluctuated considerably with time in a manner which was unpredictable. Thus the importance of the effects associated with the characteristics of the orbit itself began to be felt.

The next new orbit determination requirement came in the form of an increase in orbit inclination to more than 50°, with the launching of Explorer IV. This orbit swung well beyond the 75th meridian fence array of the Minitrack network, which was designed to cover the 35° latitude band of the Vanguard satellites. Here was the first example of the significant influence of the mission requirements upon the selection of the orbit characteristics and, in turn, upon the problem of orbit determination.

Analysis of the Vanguard I orbits determined on the basis of Minitrack data showed that the earth's oblateness was significantly different than had been supposed on the basis of presatellite geodetic and gravimetric data. Thus the magnitudes of both of the principal perturbing forces, those due to atmospheric drag and the earth's oblateness, differed from the presatellite conceptions by more than the estimates of their uncertainties.

The effect of the moon's gravitational field, negligible for close earth satellites, definitely had to be taken into account in connection with the Pioneer orbits. The first of these Pioneer probes achieved a distance of about 100,000 km from the earth on Columbus Day, October 12, 1958. It was launched under the direction of the Space Technology Laboratories. This organization also determined its orbit, using data from the Millstone Radar, the giant radio telescope at Jodrell Bank, a tracking dish at Hawaii, and Minitrack stations.

Lunik I and Pioneer IV escaped from the earth's gravitational field and went into orbit around the sun. The latter probe was tracked by the Jet Propulsion Laboratory by means of data obtained from the 84-ft dish antenna system at Goldstone Lake, California, and from a small mobile station located at Puerto Rico. The sun's gravitational field is the dominant one in determining the orbits of these two Pioneer spacecraft. The novel characteristics of these Pioneer orbits created additional problems. These were solved on the equipment side by using strategically located tracking dishes, usually of large size, to gather angular tracking data while these probes exhibited relatively rapid angular motions on the first leg of the escape trajectory. Appropriate numerical integration methods were brought into play to deal with the theoretical and computational aspects of the problem.

The Discoverer satellites, launched into polar orbits and often recovered in the Pacific Ocean area, posed another set of orbit determination problems.

Explorer VI furnished a new challenge in the form of an interesting combination of forces resulting from the space environment. The effects of a relatively large lunar perturbation were added to, and in fact coupled with, the effects of time-varying atmospheric drag. The lunar perturbation of this orbit was considerable, since the apogee height was about 40,000 km. Its principal effect was to vary the perigee height, which was initially about 250 km. This further complicated the already unclear picture of the variable atmospheric drag effect. This satellite was tracked by means of a new two-way Doppler system, developed and operated by the Space Technology Laboratories, and also by means of the Minitrack system. New mission characteristics again resulted in a unique orbit which brought with it its own peculiar orbit determination problems. Here, too, an important opportunity was provided for the comparison of two quite different types of radio tracking systems, a two-way Doppler system, and the Minitrack interferometer system.

The type of Doppler system applied in the Explorer VI program was also used in Pioneer V. This spacecraft reported back to earth from the greatest distance to which any man-made object had been tracked up to that time, some 35,000,000 km. The orbit determination program for Pioneer V yielded a new determination for the astronomical unit (*6*).

The next requirement to unfold was upon the theory rather than upon the data-gathering systems. It was planned to launch the Tiros satellite into a circular orbit. Accordingly, provision had to be made to handle this case, which was a special one from the standpoint of the general oblateness perturbation theory developed by Herget and Musen. The impact of space-project mission objectives upon the orbit determination program was thus felt anew.

Tiros was followed by the launching of Transit and solar radiation satellites into orbits having an inclination of 67°. This inclination, while not exactly the critical one, was close to it. Thus the possibility of precision radio tracking of orbits very near the critical inclination had to be reckoned with. This brought into sharper focus the problem of the critical inclination, and the difficulties associated with handling it by means of general theories such as those developed by Herget, Musen,

Brouwer, and others. Progress has been made in developing new theoretical methods designed to cope with this problem.

Perhaps the most challenging of the recent satellites from the orbit determination standpoint was Echo. The Echo orbit was the first to be perturbed significantly by radiation pressure. In addition, a large and variable drag effect was observed. Both these effects were further complicated by the fact that, for the first time, the mass of the satellite was not known accurately. The mass of the large Echo balloon varied in accordance with the rate of leakage of gas through its surface. This rate depended upon the rate at which micrometeorite punctures were sustained by the balloon. Since the relevant micrometeorite flux data were uncertain by large factors, there was considerable uncertainty concerning the satellite's mass. Finally, there was the most stringent prediction accuracy requirement imposed upon an orbit determination system, that of predicting with an effective accuracy of less than 0.15°. This effective accuracy had to encompass not only the uncertainties associated with the tracking data and the effects described above, but also any inconsistencies between the Goddard tracking and orbit determination system, and antenna systems such as the one at Goldstone for which predictions were made. Antenna prediction drive tapes generated by the Goddard orbit determination system agreed with Goldstone autotrack digital tape records within 0.15° in the case of the Echo satellite, and within 0.1° in the case of the denser Tiros I satellite. Tiros was not subject to significant radiation pressure effects, and was less subject than Echo to the vagaries of variable atmospheric drag. In a test of the Echo system using the Tiros I satellite, radio signals were transmitted from the Bell Telephone Laboratories antenna at Holmdel, reflected from the Tiros satellite, and received at the JPL Goldstone antenna system, while both the Holmdel and Goldstone antenna systems were being directed by drive tapes generated by the Goddard orbit determination system (7).

The satellite Explorer X probed the interplanetary magnetic field to a distance of about 280,000 km from the earth. It was planned to receive tracking data from this spacecraft only during the portion of its journey which took it out toward the moon's orbit. Hence, from the orbit determination standpoint, its characteristics were not unlike those of a space probe. This spacecraft was tracked on 108 Mc by the Minitrack system, the Deep Space Information Facility stations at Goldstone and Woomera, as well as by the stations at Jodrell Bank and Ascension Island. Once again, the characteristics of both the satellite and the orbit had a significant effect upon the orbit determination problem.

These, then, were among the new orbit determination requirements generated by the prolific space program. Some of the answers to the new problems have been sketched above. In addition, other important new orbit determination resources were brought into being in response to the growing needs.

The Minitrack network, for example, is being modified and further developed in several important ways. The 108-Mc Minitrack frequency was assigned for the IGY period only. Accordingly, a new network of stations employing 136 Mc has been put in place. In addition, the linear north-south fence along the 75th meridian has been supplemented by a kind of east-west tracking array, including stations at Winkfield, England; St. Johns, Newfoundland; East Grand Forks, Minnesota; Goldstone Lake, California; and Fairbanks, Alaska, as well as stations near the original locations in Australia and South Africa. This array of stations provides a capability for tracking polar and high inclination satellites. To better fit them for this task, ten of the stations are equipped with additional antennas whose beam patterns are oriented in the east-west direction, i.e., so as to be normal to the direction of motion of polar satellites. These are in addition to the north-south beam antennas which have been traditional with the Minitrack system. Automatic tracking data transmission facilities are also coming into use at the Minitrack stations.

A significant addition to orbit determination technology has been made by the Applied Physics Laboratory. A Doppler tracking network has been established and operated by APL as part of its program to apply orbit determination techniques to the solution of naval problems (*8*).

Perhaps the largest single addition to orbit determination resources on the equipment side is the Project Mercury global network of tracking radars linked by means of a high-speed communication system and real-time input and output equipment directly to the magnetic cores of a brace of IBM 7090 computers at the Goddard Space Flight Center. This system includes both FPS-16 and Verlort radars and acquisition aids, as well as related telemetry equipment.

Orbit determination computer hardware has also changed with the times. As just noted, the Mercury system at Goddard includes a pair of IBM 7090 computers. Other large computing systems such as the Sperry Rand Univac, the CDC 1604, and the Transac 2000 have also been used for orbit determination.

A number of significant theoretical contributions have been made to orbit determination resources. As a result, in addition to the modified Hansen theory developed by Herget and Musen in connection with the Vanguard IGY program, several additional alternatives to numerical integration are now available for use in solving certain classes of orbit determination problems (*9*). Among these are theories developed by Brouwer, Garfinkel, Kozai, and Vinti (*10–13*). The principal feature of these approaches is the achievement of a closed form solution to the problem of a satellite of an oblate primary. Vinti's solution, employing an ellipsoidal coordinate system, also represents directly the major portion of the effect of the fourth harmonic of the gravitational field. Some of these systems have been extended to include representation of additional perturbations. Brouwer's method, for example, has been developed to include the effects of the third, fourth, and fifth harmonics of the gravitational field, and certain effects of the atmosphere as well (*14*). Musen has modified and further developed the adaptation of Hansen's theory to include a number of additional perturbing effects (*15*).

Software developments are being pressed in an effort to keep abreast of advances in theory and hardware. At the Goddard Space Flight Center, for example, a new version of Hansen's method, Brouwer's method, a variation of parameters method, and a promising numerical integration method all have been programmed and used as part of an over-all differential correction system. These various orbit determination resources are currently yielding results of the following caliber.

Orbits adequate for nearly all prediction purposes are generated routinely on the basis of either Minitrack or Baker-Nunn observations. Prediction accuracy better than a tenth of a degree has been achieved for ordinary satellites on the basis of orbits determined from Minitrack observations. It was noted earlier, for example, that this was done in the case of the satellite Tiros I as part of the preparation for Project Echo.

Orbits for experimenters are also generated on the basis of Minitrack and Baker-Nunn data. Interim definitive orbits having arc lengths of a week, and standard deviations of fit less than 1 milliradian are obtained routinely. An uncertainty of one milliradian corresponds to an uncertainty of one kilometer at a topocentric distance of a thousand kilometers, which is typical. Minitrack orbits have been obtained which have standard deviations of fit of about half a milliradian, or about 100 sec of arc. Standard deviations of fit which are better than this have been achieved by the Smithsonian Astrophysical Observatory. The Applied Physics Laboratory group has used Doppler data to obtain orbits which are accurate to about a kilometer.

Numerous significant geophysical and astronomical results have been obtained by means of orbit determination programs. Among these are the discovery of relationships between high atmospheric densities and solar activity, both in terms of correlation with the 27-day solar rotation period, and in terms of correlation with particular solar flare events of certain types (*16, 17*). New values have been obtained for the oblateness coefficient in the harmonic expansion of the earth's gravitational potential (*18*). The earth was discovered to be pear-shaped on the basis of Vanguard I orbital information determined from Minitrack observations (*19*). Values for the fourth and fifth gravitational harmonics have been obtained from analyses of satellite orbital data (*20*). The ellipticity of the earth's equator has also been investigated by means of satellite observations (*21*). The effect of radiation pressure has been studied quantitatively in connection with the Echo satellite and also in connection with Vanguard I (*22*). These results have been obtained principally on the basis of Minitrack, Baker-Nunn, and Doppler observations. A determination of the astronomical unit was made by the Space Technology Laboratories using two-way Doppler data obtained in connection with the tracking of Pioneer V.

A number of new orbit determination developments are still in progress. It is anticipated that they will contribute to advancement in this field.

References

1. R. Porter, The United States IGY earth satellite program, *Ann. Intern. Geophys. Yr.* **6,** 276 (1958).
2. J. Mengel, Tracking the earth satellite, and data transmission by radio, *Proc. IRE* **44,** 755–767 (1956).
3. J. Hagen, Satellite launching vehicle—placing the satellite in orbit, *Ann. Intern. Geophys. Yr.* **6,** 284 (1958).
4. J. W. Siry, The Vanguard satellite orbit determination program, *Ann. Intern. Geophys. Yr.* **6,** 354 (1958).
5. J. W. Siry, Satellite orbits and atmospheric densities at altitudes up to 750 km. obtained from the Vanguard orbit determination program, *Planetary and Space Sci.* **1,** 184 (1959).
6. J. McGuire and L. Wong, A dynamical determination of the astronomical unit by a least squares fit to the orbit of Pioneer V, Space Technology Lab. Rept. 2301-0004-RO-000 (May 15, 1961).
7. J. W. Siry, Recent progress in orbit determination in connection with Projects Echo and Tiros, Paper presented at the XII Congress of the International Astronautical Federation, Stockholm, 1960.
8. W. H. Guier, Doppler tracking of Project Transit satellites, *IRE Trans. of Space Electronics and Telemetry Symposium,* September, 1960.
9. P. Herget and P. Musen, *Astron. J.* **63,** 430 (1958).
10. D. Brouwer, Solution of the problem of artificial satellite theory without drag, *Astron. J.* **64,** 378 (1959).
11. B. Garfinkel, Orbit of a satellite of an oblate planet, *Astron. J.* **64,** 353 (1959).
12. Y. Kozai, Motion of a close earth satellite, *Astron. J.* **64,** 367 (1959).
13. J. Vinti, New approach in the theory of satellite orbits, *Phys. Rev. Letters* **3,** 8 (1959).
14. D. Brouwer and G. Hori, Theoretical evaluation of atmospheric drag effects in the motion of an artificial satellite, *Astron. J.* **66,** 193 (1961).

15. P. Musen, Motion of a satellite in an asymmetrical gravitational field, *J. Geophys. Research* **65,** 2783 (1960).
16. L. Jacchia, *Nature* **183,** 1662 (1959).
17. L. Jacchia, *J. Geophys. Research* **65,** 2775 (1960).
18. M. Lecar, J. Sorenson, and A. Eckels, *J. Geophys. Research* **64,** 209 (1959).
19. J. O'Keefe, A. Eckels, and R. K. Squires, The gravitational field of the earth, *Astron. J.* **64,** 245 (1959).
20. Y. Kozai, The gravitational field of the earth derived from motions of three satellites, *Astron. J.* **66,** 8 (1961).
21. I. Izsak, A determination of the ellipticity of the earth's equator from the motion of two satellites, *Astron. J.* **66,** 226 (1961).
22. P. Musen, Influence of the solar radiation pressure on the motion of an artificial satellite, *J. Geophys. Research* **65,** 1391 (1960).

7.2 Differential Orbit Improvement with the Use of Rotated Residuals

IMRE G. IZSAK

SMITHSONIAN ASTROPHYSICAL OBSERVATORY,
Cambridge, Massachusetts

Introduction

In analyzing precisely reduced Baker-Nunn observations of satellites, we usually find different mean residuals in right ascension and in declination. For satellites of low inclination, the larger residuals occur in right ascension; for satellites of high inclination, those in declination are dominant. The ratio of the mean residuals in the perpendicular directions of right ascension and declination can be as high as 5:1 or as low as 1:5. In reality, the ratios might be even more striking, since, without proper weighting, the least-squares procedure of differential orbit improvement tends to distribute the deviations uniformly between the two components.

Both irregular changes in air drag, which simple formulas cannot account for, and errors in the time of observations affect the position of the satellite primarily in the orbital plane; in the direction perpendicular to the orbital plane, these effects are much smaller.

The residuals of the observations, in addition to the two factors—air drag and errors in time—are affected by others: small errors in the station coordinates; tesseral harmonics in the gravitational potential of the earth; inaccuracy of constants used in the computations and by other causes not sufficiently well known. If, therefore, we wish to concentrate on the correction of station coordinates, for example, it is desirable to minimize where possible the effect of other influences on the residuals. Fortunately, the effects of irregular changes in air drag and of errors in time of observations can be eliminated simultaneously by projecting in a uniquely determined direction the customary residuals in right ascension and declination. This modification in computation of orbits stems from a suggestion advanced by Whipple and Hynek (1957) and recently presented in a paper at the COSPAR meeting in Florence (Veis and Whipple, 1961). They called the procedure the "Sumner plane" method and emphasized repeatedly its importance for application of satellite observations to geodesy. For orbital and geodetic research, this procedure improves the usefulness of observations that have a high degree of accuracy in angular position, but, for some reason, not in timing.

Basic Equations

To find the distinctive direction in question, we need look only into the structure of the basic equations of differential orbit improvement. These are given in the literature in various forms (Bauschinger, 1928; Herget, 1948; Brouwer and Clemence, 1961). For our present purposes, the following vectorial formulation seems best adapted.

The geocentric and topocentric position vectors $\mathbf{r}$ and $\boldsymbol{\varrho}$ of the satellite, and the (geocentric) station vector $\mathbf{R}$ of the observer are connected by the relation

$$\boldsymbol{\varrho} = \mathbf{r} - \mathbf{R}.$$

For corrections to these vectors, the analogous relation

$$d\mathbf{r} - d\mathbf{R} = d\boldsymbol{\varrho} \tag{1}$$

holds true.

If the position of the station is given in the geodetic rectangular coordinate system, we have

$$d\mathbf{R} = \mathbf{e}_X dX + \mathbf{e}_Y dY + \mathbf{e}_Z dZ, \tag{2}$$

where the unit vector $\mathbf{e}_X$ lies in the intersection of the equator with the meridian of Greenwich; $\mathbf{e}_Z$ points toward the north pole; and $\mathbf{e}_Y$ is perpendicular to both of them.

The vector $d\boldsymbol{\varrho}$ can be resolved in the topocentric direction of the satellite, and in the directions of right ascension and declination as

$$d\boldsymbol{\varrho} = \mathbf{e}_A\, d\rho + \mathbf{e}_B\, \rho \cos \delta\, d\alpha + \mathbf{e}_C\, \rho d\delta. \tag{3}$$

The correction $d\mathbf{r}$ results from the corrections to the familiar orbital elements M, a, e, ω, Ω, I, and can be written in the simple form

$$\begin{aligned} d\mathbf{r} = (\dot{\mathbf{r}}/n)dM + (\mathbf{r}/a)da + \left\{(\mathbf{e}_N \times \mathbf{r}) \frac{a/r}{\sqrt{1-e^2}} \sin E - \mathbf{a}\right\} de \\ + (\mathbf{e}_N \times \mathbf{r})d\omega + (\mathbf{e}_Z \times \mathbf{r})d\Omega + (\mathbf{e}_K \times \mathbf{r})dI. \end{aligned} \tag{4}$$

The only symbols here that call for explanation are the unit vectors $\mathbf{e}_K$ and $\mathbf{e}_N$: they point to the ascending node and to the pole of the orbit, respectively; and the vector $\mathbf{a}$, which is $a\mathbf{e}_P$, $\mathbf{e}_P$ being the unit vector in the direction of perigee. For completeness, we also introduce the unit vectors

$$\mathbf{e}_L = \mathbf{e}_N \times \mathbf{e}_K \qquad \text{and} \qquad \mathbf{e}_Q = \mathbf{e}_N \times \mathbf{e}_P.$$

Five of the coefficients in Eq. (4) have a graphic meaning; the coefficient of de, however, is derived by a short computation. In the case of a perturbed motion, as in that of artificial satellites, the letters M, a, e, ω, Ω, I stand for mean orbital elements. They are usually expressed by polynomials and long-periodic trigonometric functions of time. The exact definition of these elements is given only by the particular perturbation theory used in the orbit computation, and the precise relation between the semimajor axis a and the anomalistic mean motion n is also defined by the theory.

In the SAO Differential Orbit Improvement Program as developed by G. Veis and C. H. Moore, we use

$$\begin{aligned}
M &= M_0 + M_1(t - t_0) + M_2(t - t_0)^2 + \ldots, \\
n &= \dot{M} = M_1 + 2M_2(t - t_0) + \cdots, \\
a &= \sqrt[3]{\frac{\mu}{n^2}}\left\{1 - \frac{J}{3p^2}\sqrt{1 - e^2}\,(1 - \tfrac{3}{2}\sin^2 I)\right\}, \\
da &= -\frac{2}{3}\frac{a}{n}\,dn = -\frac{2}{3}\frac{a}{n}\{dM_1 + 2(t - t_0)dM_2 + \cdots\},
\end{aligned}$$

with the constants

$$\mu = 3.986135 \times 10^5\ \text{km}^3\,\text{sec}^{-2}, \quad J/a_e^2 = 1.624 \times 10^{-3}, \quad a_e = 6378.388\ \text{km}.$$

For satellite orbits of very small eccentricities, let us say, $e < 0.03$, the formulation given in Eq. (4) becomes disadvantageous, because the perigee on an almost circular orbit cannot be well determined. In such cases, it is better to combine the conventional orbit parameters into

$$L = M + \omega, \quad D = E + \omega, \quad u = v + \omega, \quad \epsilon = e\cos\omega, \quad \eta = e\sin\omega.$$

Then an elaboration of the expression

$$\frac{\partial \mathbf{r}}{\partial e}(\cos\omega\, d\epsilon + \sin\omega\, d\eta) + \frac{1}{e}\left(\frac{\partial \mathbf{r}}{\partial \omega} - \frac{\partial \mathbf{r}}{\partial M}\right)(-\sin\omega\, d\epsilon + \cos\omega\, d\eta)$$

leads to the alternate form

$$\begin{aligned}
d\mathbf{r} &= (\dot{\mathbf{r}}/n)dL + (\mathbf{r}/a)da \\
&\quad + \left\{(\mathbf{e}_N \times \mathbf{r})\left(\frac{a/r}{\sqrt{1 - e^2}}\sin D + \eta_*\right) - a(\mathbf{e}_K - e\eta_*\mathbf{e}_Q)\right\}d\epsilon \\
&\quad - \left\{(\mathbf{e}_N \times \mathbf{r})\left(\frac{a/r}{\sqrt{1 - e^2}}\cos D + \epsilon_*\right) + a(\mathbf{e}_L + e\epsilon_*\mathbf{e}_Q)\right\}d\eta \qquad (5) \\
&\quad + (\mathbf{e}_Z \times \mathbf{r})d\Omega + (\mathbf{e}_K \times \mathbf{r})dI,
\end{aligned}$$

where

$$\epsilon_* = \frac{\epsilon/\sqrt{1-e^2}}{1+\sqrt{1-e^2}}$$

and

$$\eta_* = \frac{\eta/\sqrt{1-e^2}}{1+\sqrt{1-e^2}}.$$

The Method of Rotated Residuals

Returning now to our original subject, we have to project the vector $d\boldsymbol{\varrho}$ onto some directions in the plane perpendicular to the line of sight, because optical observations yield only angular residuals. In the usual procedure, we project onto the directions of the unit vector $\mathbf{e}_B$ and $\mathbf{e}_C$; such a projection amounts to a scalar multiplication, by these vectors, of the Eqs. (4), (2), and (3), which are connected through Eq. (1). Then, dividing by the approximately known topocentric distance ρ, we obtain the equations of condition in $\cos\delta\, d\alpha$ and $d\delta$; they are affected by all the corrections to the orbital elements.

It is clear, however, that both the errors in the time of the observations and the irregular changes in air drag can essentially be thought of as "wrong corrections" to the mean anomaly. Hence, if we eliminate dM from the equations of condition, the new residuals will not be contaminated by these two effects, that is, to the first order. But the vector coefficient of dM in Eq. (4) is $\dot{\mathbf{r}}/n$, a vector lying in the orbital plane. Therefore, the desired projection of $d\boldsymbol{\varrho}$ is obtained if we execute the scalar multiplication of Eq. (1), by the unit vector

$$\mathbf{e}_W = \frac{\mathbf{e}_A \times \dot{\mathbf{r}}/n}{|\mathbf{e}_A \times \dot{\mathbf{r}}/n|}.$$

The resulting equation of condition is

$$\begin{aligned} O\cdot dM &+ \frac{1}{\rho}(\mathbf{e}_W\cdot\mathbf{r}/a)da + \frac{1}{\rho}\mathbf{e}_W\cdot\left\{(\mathbf{e}_N\times\mathbf{r})\frac{a/r}{\sqrt{1-e^2}}\sin E - \mathbf{a}\right\}de \\ &+ \frac{1}{\rho}[\mathbf{e}_W\cdot(\mathbf{e}_N\times\mathbf{r})]d\omega + \frac{1}{\rho}[\mathbf{e}_W\cdot(\mathbf{e}_Z\times\mathbf{r})]d\Omega + \frac{1}{\rho}[\mathbf{e}_W\cdot(\mathbf{e}_K\times\mathbf{r})]dI \\ &- \frac{1}{\rho}(\mathbf{e}_W\cdot\mathbf{e}_X)dX - \frac{1}{\rho}(\mathbf{e}_W\cdot\mathbf{e}_Y)dY - \frac{1}{\rho}(\mathbf{e}_W\cdot\mathbf{e}_Z)dZ = dw, \qquad (6) \end{aligned}$$

where

$$dw = -\sin\psi\cdot\cos\delta\, d\alpha + \cos\psi\cdot d\delta,$$

with $\cos \psi = \mathbf{e}_W \cdot \mathbf{e}_C$ and $\sin \psi = -\mathbf{e}_W \cdot \mathbf{e}_B$. The geometry of the equations can be visualized by the representation of the relevant unit vectors on a unit sphere in Fig. 1.

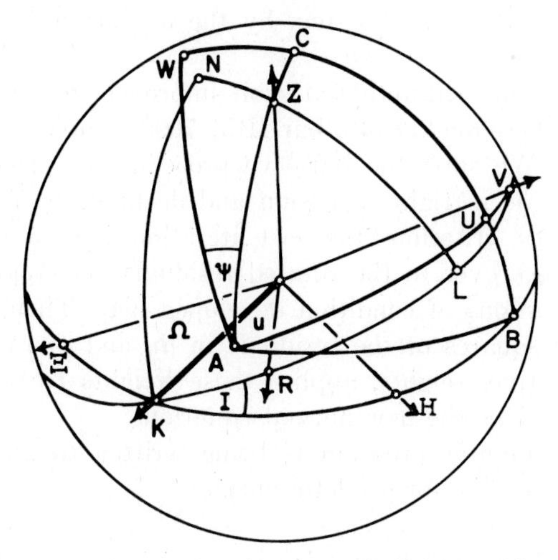

FIG. 1. The geometry of rotated residuals. Ξ, H, Z is the sidereal coordinate system; the points R and V indicate the directions of the geocentric position and velocity of the satellite.

The procedure followed does not imply discarding the other component of the residuals, especially if our concern is with orbit improvement proper rather than with the correction of station coordinates or the detection of tesseral harmonics. In general, the coefficient of the unknown da in Eq. (6) is relatively small, a fact that will result in ill-conditioned normal equations. That is why we prefer to determine the semimajor axis via the mean motion; the latter quantity entering in dM is multiplied by $t\text{-}t_0$, but disappears in Eq. (6). Also, to study air drag or to check on the accuracy in timing observations, we are concerned with residuals in a direction as close as possible to that of the velocity vector $\dot{\mathbf{r}}$.

With only optical observations at our disposal, this direction is given by the unit vector

$$\mathbf{e}_U = \mathbf{e}_W \times \mathbf{e}_A.$$

The corresponding equation of condition is obtained from Eq. (6) by changing the index W to U and adding the term $1/\rho(\mathbf{e}_U \cdot \dot{\mathbf{r}}/n)\ dM$. The residual in question will be

$$du = \cos \psi \cdot \cos \delta\ d\alpha + \sin \psi \cdot d\delta.$$

All observations thus furnish us with two equations of condition, one in dw and one in du. Because they are not equally reliable, we multiply the second type of equation by the square root of an appropriate relative weight and solve the whole system by the method of least squares for the unknowns sought.

This modification of differential orbit improvement has been incorporated by E. M. Gaposchkin into our IBM-7090 computer program in the following way: We start the iterative procedure of orbit improvement using the residuals in right ascension and declination. When, according to a convergence criterion, the last iteration has been reached, the computer switches over to the rotated residuals and applies with equal weights the equations of condition developed here. Then, by comparing the sum of the squares of the residuals in du and dw, it computes the appropriate relative weights, applies these weights to the equations of condition, and solves the new normal equations.

A separate computer program is being written to analyze the final residuals in du and dw for geodetic purposes.

Appendix

In order to utilize Eqs. (2), (3), and (4), we need the components of the relevant vectors in some coordinate system. Choosing the coordinate system defined by the unit vectors $\mathbf{e}_K$, $\mathbf{e}_L$, $\mathbf{e}_N$, we have

$$\frac{\mathbf{r}}{a} = \frac{r}{a}\begin{bmatrix} \cos u \\ \sin u \\ 0 \end{bmatrix}, \qquad \frac{\dot{\mathbf{r}}}{n} = \frac{a}{\sqrt{1-e^2}}\begin{bmatrix} -(\sin u + \eta) \\ (\cos u + \epsilon) \\ 0 \end{bmatrix},$$

$$\mathbf{e}_A = \begin{bmatrix} \cos\delta \cos(\alpha - \Omega) \\ \sin I \sin\delta + \cos I \cos\delta \sin(\alpha - \Omega) \\ \cos I \sin\delta - \sin I \cos\delta \sin(\alpha - \Omega) \end{bmatrix},$$

$$\mathbf{e}_B = \begin{bmatrix} -\sin(\alpha - \Omega) \\ \cos I \cos(\alpha - \Omega) \\ -\sin I \cos(\alpha - \Omega) \end{bmatrix},$$

$$\mathbf{e}_C = \begin{bmatrix} -\sin\delta \cos(\alpha - \Omega) \\ \sin I \cos\delta - \cos I \sin\delta \sin(\alpha - \Omega) \\ \cos I \cos\delta + \sin I \sin\delta \sin(\alpha - \Omega) \end{bmatrix},$$

$$\mathbf{e}_X = \begin{bmatrix} \cos(\theta - \Omega) \\ \cos I \sin(\theta - \Omega) \\ -\sin I \sin(\theta - \Omega) \end{bmatrix} \mathbf{e}_Y = \begin{bmatrix} -\sin(\theta - \Omega) \\ \cos I \cos(\theta - \Omega) \\ -\sin I \cos(\theta - \Omega) \end{bmatrix} \mathbf{e}_Z = \begin{bmatrix} 0 \\ \sin I \\ \cos I \end{bmatrix},$$

where θ denotes the sidereal time at Greenwich.

References

Bauschinger, J. (1928), "Die Bahnbestimmung der Himmelskörper," 2nd ed. Verlag von W. Engelman, Leipzig.

Brouwer, D., and Clemence, G. M. (1961), "Methods of Celestial Mechanics." Academic Press, New York.

Herget, P. (1948), "The Computation of Orbits." Edwards Brothers, Ann Arbor, Michigan.

Veis, G., and Whipple, F. L. (1961), *in* "Proceedings of the COSPAR Space Symposium," North-Holland, Amsterdam. Experience in Precision Optical Tracking of Satellites for Geodesy.

Whipple, F. L., and Hynek, J. A. (1957), *in* "Proceedings of the VIIIth International Astronautical Congress, Barcelona, 1957. Springer Verlag, Wien. Optical and Visual Tracking of Artificial Satellites.

Discussion

DR. A. G. MASSEVITCH: I have mentioned in my paper that orbital elements of satellites derived by several authors in England, the U.S.A., and the U.S.S.R. are in good agreement to the first order. For ephemeris service and even for simple theoretical interpretations such an agreement is quite sufficient. But for evaluation of the fine structure of the atmosphere (irregularities in density variations) and for determination of the earth's gravitational field one has to be careful when using orbital elements derived by different authors. The fact is that each system of orbital elements is derived from tracking data assuming a certain theory of the motion of artificial satellites. The constants (or corresponding initial values of the elements) in these theories do not coincide and may differ from each other by terms of higher order in small parameters depending on the internal structure of the earth.

These differences are negligible when perturbations of the first order are calculated but become significant in the case of second-order perturbations. They lead to rather different forms of the coefficients of the secular motion of the node Ω' and the perigee ω', which are especially important when determining the parameters of the earth's gravitational potential, for example.

A simultaneous utilization of orbital elements, or a comparison of results obtained on the basis of elements, derived by different computing centers requires an evaluation of formulas giving the analytical relations between constants of the implied theories. Since this is not always realized, unnecessary discussions sometimes arise in the comparison of results of calculations. The matter deserves more attention than it has been given up until now. Very desirable would be an appendix to publications of orbital elements, giving not only the details of the theory employed (in a generally understandable way for use not only by celestial mechanics specialists but especially for geophysicists), but also several formulas specifying the relations between the constants of this theory and those of analogous investigations.

SECTION II

Desiderata for Future Astronomical Observations from Stations in Space (Solar, Interplanetary, Galactic, and Extragalactic Phenomena)

CHAPTER 8

Solar Physics

8.1 Photosphere and Chromosphere

A. UNSÖLD

INSTITUTE FOR THEORETICAL PHYSICS AND ASTROPHYSICS, UNIVERSITY OF KIEL, Germany

This introductory paper will explain some of the general ideas underlying modern solar physics, then show what we know and what we do not know, and finally indicate where the use of rockets or space vehicles might contribute to the solution of still open problems.

I. General Principles

The structure of the solar atmosphere is, in principle, determined by: (a) one equation describing the *energy transfer*—by radiation, convection, conduction, mechanical or magnetic energy; (b) the *hydrostatic equation* or, more generally, the basic equations of hydrodynamics or magnetohydrodynamics; and (c) the *chemical composition;* H:He: metals* (Mg, Si, Fe, . . .) = 1:0.15:5 $\times$ 10^{-5} by numbers. In the higher layers the free electrons originate almost exclusively from the latter. Moreover, we must know the surface gravitation, g = 2.736 $\times$ 10^4 cm $\sec^{-2}$; and the effective temperature, T_e = 5780°K, determining the total energy flux per cm^2 of the solar surface.

II. The Outer Layers of the Sun

1. Photosphere

The photosphere, i.e., the layers which produce the continuous and most of the Fraunhofer line spectrum, is in radiative equilibrium; the

* The light elements (C, N, O, Ne) having higher ionization potentials are not so important in the solar atmosphere.

energy transfer is by radiation. Over an element dl the intensity I of the radiation at frequency ν experiences a decrease by absorption $-I_\nu \times \kappa_\nu \rho \times dl$ (κ_ν being the mass absorption coefficient) and an increase by emission which we write under the assumption of local thermodynamic equilibrium (LTE) as $+\kappa_\nu \rho \times B_\nu(T)\ dl$, where $B_\nu(T)$ means the Kirchhoff-Planck function for the local temperature T.

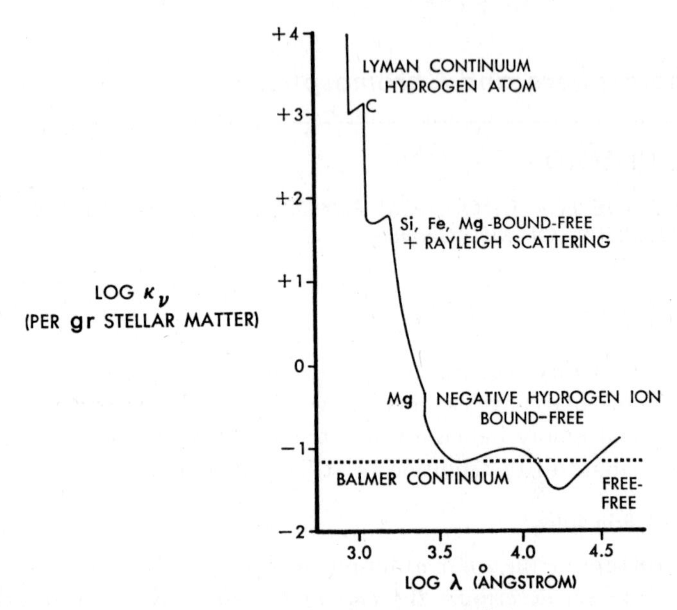

FIG. 1. Continuous absorption coefficient.

For describing various layers of the solar atmosphere we often use, instead of the geometrical depth t as measured from some arbitrarily defined level downwards, the so-called optical depth $\tau_\nu = \int_{-\infty}^{\tau} \kappa_\nu \rho\ dt$. Our range of sight, looking perpendicularly into the atmosphere, i.e., observing at the center of the solar disk, goes down to $\tau_\nu \approx 1$. Farther out on the disk, looking at an angle θ to the normal to the atmosphere, we can see down to $\tau_\nu \approx \cos\theta$.

As an illustration, let us describe in more detail that layer of the photosphere, $\tau_\nu \approx 0.1$, where the Fraunhofer lines of the neutral metals are chiefly produced. (The ν refers to wavelengths near $\lambda_0 \approx 5000$ Å.) Here the temperature is $T = 5040°$K, or the often used $\theta = 5040/T = 1.00$. The electron pressure (dynes/cm²) is given by $\log P_e = 0.45$, the total gas pressure by $\log P_g = 4.79$. Their ratio $P_e/P_g \approx 5 \times 10^{-5}$ nearly corresponds to the abundance of the metals relative to hydrogen. The absorption coefficient κ_ν per gram of solar matter and its origin are indicated in Fig. 1. At the right side we have also marked the average value of κ_ν over the whole spectrum, the so-called Rosseland *opacity* $\bar{\kappa}$, which determines the total transfer of radiative energy.*

2. Hydrogen Convection Zone

From the deeper photospheric layers downward, i.e., from $\log P_g \approx 5.1$ and $T \approx 6500°$ to (very roughly) $\log P_g \approx 12$ and $T \approx 10^6$°K, the solar atmosphere is convectively unstable. Above that layer the hydrogen is roughly neutral, within it partly ionized, below it totally ionized. So the following happens: if a volume element of partly ionized gas rises, the hydrogen begins to recombine and for every atomic recombination 13.6 ev (75.8 kT at 10,000°K, e.g.) are added to the thermal motion. Because of this, the effective ratio of the specific heats c_p/c_v approaches unity, and the adiabatic temperature gradient becomes so small that our rising volume element becomes hotter than if it were in radiative equilibrium and so it continues to rise. This effect is still more favored by the influence of ionization on the competing radiative temperature gradient, and so we obtain a zone with convective motion. In the range $\log P_g \geqslant 5.3$ practically the whole energy transfer is by convection, radiative transfer being unimportant over the indicated range of pressures and temperatures.

This hydrogen convection zone is a thermodynamic machine, and it is the source of all the mechanical and hydromagnetic energy which is available at a level of high negative entropy in the solar atmosphere. In the photosphere it produces the granulation, more or less turbulent convection in which we observe cells of about 0.6 to 2 sec (400–1500 km) diameter and with temperature differences of a few hundred degrees. The corresponding motions of $\sim$0.8 to 1.5 km/sec produce an important contribution to the Doppler width of the lines, the purely thermal velocity of neutral atoms being $\sim$2 km/sec. These motions—for historical reasons—are usually called "photospheric turbulence," though the analogy with aerodynamical turbulence is only a rather partial one. While the granulation is—aerodynamically speaking—a "small scale phenomenon," in which the Coriolis force of solar rotation is unimportant, this is not the case with sunspots, etc., which evidently are influenced by solar rotation. The low temperature within sunspots is most probably due to the convective energy transfer being impeded by their magnetic fields; but the details of the mechanism are still rather obscure. What is primarily needed is further development of the—extremely difficult—basic theory of convective motion.

* The "average transparency" $1/\bar{\kappa}$ is defined as an average of $1/\kappa_\nu$, over the whole spectrum with a suitable weight function.

3. Chromosphere

At the edge of the solar disk the continuum radiation drops off sharply where the tangential optical depth is ≈ 1, corresponding to $\tau_{5000} \approx 0.006$. This is usually defined as "the solar limb." Farther out we observe, at a total eclipse or to some degree also just with a suitable solar telescope, the emission lines of the chromosphere, the so-called flash spectrum. The lower chromosphere may be characterized roughly by $\tau_{5000} \approx 0.003$, T $\approx$ 4000°K, $\log P_e \approx -0.7$, $\log P_g \approx 3.9$. The scale-height H, over which by definition the number density decreases by a factor e, increases from about 120 km in the low chromosphere to the order of 600 km at a height of 4000 km above the solar limb. The strongest chromospheric lines, Ca II H and K, can be seen up to heights of $\sim$10,000 km. The increasing scale heights as well as the Doppler widths of chromospheric lines indicate violent motions increasing from $\sim$12 km/sec in the low chromosphere to $\sim$15 km/sec in the middle and high chromosphere. This "chromospheric turbulence" is a kind of continuation of the already mentioned photospheric turbulence. Since for $T = 4000$°K and an effective molecular weight $\mu = 1.5$ the velocity of sound is 6 km/sec, the velocities in the higher chromosphere—even assuming higher temperatures—must in any case be comparable to that of sound.

The heat energy dissipated by the "turbulent" velocity ξ is of the order of magnitude ξ^3/H ergs/gm sec, where H again means the scale height. Comparing this with the amount of radiative energy emitted, namely $\kappa \times 4\sigma T^4$ ergs/gm sec (where $\bar{\kappa}$ is the Rosseland average absorption coefficient, σ the Stefan-Boltzmann constant, and T the local temperature), it is noticed that for $\log P_g \leqslant 2.5$ to 3 the transfer of mechanical energy becomes comparable in importance with that by radiation. The higher layers of the chromosphere therefore become increasingly hotter. These phenomena become both more complicated because of the high degree of temperature and density inhomogeneity of the chromosphere. These chromospheric inhomogeneities are most likely connected, somehow, with the granulation elements of the photosphere; but possibly *not* in one-to-one correspondence. We shall come back to this point later.

4. Transition Layer and Solar Corona

As the "turbulent" motions approach the velocity of sound another dissipative process becomes important (besides ordinary "viscous" dissipation), which increases with a high power of the Mach number: while the usual incompressible turbulence of the velocity field $\mathfrak{w}$ is characterized by div $\mathfrak{w} = 0$ and curl $\mathfrak{w} \neq 0$, sound waves are produced now for which on the contrary div $\mathfrak{w} \neq 0$ and curl $\mathfrak{w} = 0$. As these waves propagate outwards into layers of smaller density ρ, their velocity amplitudes (neglecting dissipation for the moment) increase $\sim \sqrt{1/\rho}$ and they steepen up to become shock waves—or, if there is a magnetic field, some type of magnetohydrodynamic waves—carrying energy in their turn into higher layers. As long as the density is sufficiently high, the dissipated energy can be radiated away, just by increasing the temperature somewhat. With increasing temperature and decreasing density, however, this becomes more and more difficult. The solar atmosphere now turns to the more efficient mechanism of thermal conduction by free electrons. The temperature as a function of height rises first so steeply that the amount of energy carried as mechanical energy into the zone of greatest dissipation can be largely returned downward as a conductive heat flux $-K dT/dh$, where $K = \text{const} \times T^{5/2}$ is the thermal conductivity of the coronal plasma. Only a small fraction of the energy, corresponding to the relatively small outward temperature gradient, is conducted outward into space. This is the well-known explanation of the solar corona.

Let us designate as the solar "transition layer" that part where the temperature rises with height from about 4 to 8×10^3 °K to 1 to 2×10^6 °K, over only 1 to 3×10^4 km.

The preceding principles explain also why, in places with increased mechanical energy flux, the temperature of the corona rises comparatively little while the electron density goes up by a considerable factor ($\sim$5 to 10). This produces the so-called coronal condensations, and streamers extending outward from centers of activity. Also the strange temperature stratification in solar *faculae* or *plages faculaires*—hotter in high layers and cooler than the surroundings in deep photospheric layers—is probably due to mechanical transfer of energy partly replacing that by radiation.

We do not yet understand how the strong magnetic fields in sunspots reduce the convective transfer and thereby the total energy flux, while the weaker magnetic fields in faculae favor the mechanical transfer of energy leaving the total flux almost unchanged.

We should be aware that *all* the superthermal phenomena in the solar atmosphere are ultimately fed by mechanical energy at high negative entropy derived from the "motor" of the hydrogen convection zone. Moreover, only a very small fraction, 0.003% or less of the total energy flux πF (6.32×10^{10} ergs/cm^{2}sec), is sufficient to heat the outermost extension of the solar atmosphere to $\sim 2 \times 10^6$ °K, compared with the temperature somewhat less than 4000°K which would occur in radiative equilibrium.

Summarizing, we may describe the solar atmosphere by the data given

TABLE I
SOLAR ATMOSPHERE

Height h (km)	Solar radii	Temp. (T °K)	Gas pressure (dynes/cm²) $\log P_g$	Electron pressure (dynes/cm²) $\log P_e$	Electrons/cm³ $\log N_e$	Turbulent velocity ξ_t (km/sec)	Layer	Main energy transfer
1,400,000	3.0	$2 \cdot 10^6$	−3.8	−4.1	5.5		⋮	
700,000	2.0	$2 \cdot 10^6$	−2.8	−3.1	6.4			
350,000	1.50	$2 \cdot 10^6$	−2.1	−2.4	7.2		Corona	Thermal conduction
42,000	1.06	$2 \cdot 10^6$	−0.9	−1.2	8.4			
20,000	1.03	$2 \cdot 10^6$	−0.8	−1.1	8.5		↓	
		↕ Very inhomogeneous				~15	Transition layer	Mechanical energy
3000		~4–6000	0.2	−1.7	10.5		↑	
2000	***	~4–6000	0.5	−1.4	10.8	12	Chromosphere	Radiation
1000		~4–6000	1.2	−0.9	11.3	7		
	Opt. depth τ_{5000}							
Solar limb: 0	0.005	4090	4.1	−0.5	11.7	1–2	↓ ↑	
	0.01	4295	4.3	−0.3	12.0			
	0.05	4855	4.6	+0.2	12.4			
	0.1	5030	4.8	+0.4	12.6		Photosphere	Radiation
	0.5	5805	5.1	1.2	13.3	2	↓ ↑	
−260	1.0	6400	5.2	1.8	13.8			
	2.0	7180	5.3	2.4	14.4		Hydrogen	
−280	***	10^4	5.3	4.0	15.86	2	convection zone	Convection
	Solar radii							
−16,000	−0.02	10^5	9.4	9.1	20.0	0.3	↓	
−140,000	−0.2	10^6	12.3	12.0	21.9	0.0		Radiation

in Table I. Though the table is based on our most recent evidence, some entries may well require later revision.

III. Solar Radiation—What We Know and What We Do Not; Possible Observations from Space Vehicles

1. Solar Constant

The solar constant S gives the total flux of solar radiation at 1 astronomical unit distance and outside our atmosphere. Using S we can easily calculate the energy flux πF through 1 cm² of the solar surface and define by $\pi F = \sigma T_e^4$, the effective temperature T_e, which is one of the fundamental constants in solar physics. "Most probable" numerical values are:

$$S = 1.961 \text{ cal cm}^{-2} \text{ min}^{-1} = 1.368 \times 10^6 \text{ ergs cm}^{-2} \text{ sec}^{-1}$$
$$\pi F = 6.32 \times 10^{10} \text{ ergs cm}^{-2} \text{ sec}^{-1} \quad \text{and} \quad T_e = 5780°\text{K}.$$

But, measuring S involves more or less "theoretical" corrections for the unobserved infrared and ultraviolet parts of the spectrum, recent estimates being 4.78 and 3.89%, respectively. The present uncertainty of S probably amounts to ± 2 to 3%. Measurements of S from rockets have been attempted by A. L. Quirk (1953); it would surely be important to measure S outside our atmosphere with improved accuracy.

2. Continuous Spectrum

The integrated continuous spectrum of the solar disk at a frequency ν is produced, on the average, at an optical depth $\tau_\nu \approx 2/3$. Figure 1 shows that, for $\lambda < 3000$ Å, the continuous absorption coefficient is expected to go up by several powers of 10 due to the bound-free continua of the metals (whose calculation is still rather unsatisfactory) and Rayleigh scattering of hydrogen atoms. In fact, the opacity becomes so great that the continuous spectrum for 912 Å $< \lambda <$ 3000 Å mostly originates in chromospheric layers, where the temperature as well as the temperature fluctuations are but poorly known. An accurately measured absolute energy distribution curve for this range of the continuum appears, therefore, very desirable to obtain. Near λ2080 Å existing spectra seem to indicate a "step" in the energy distribution. This his been tentatively attributed to Al, but the main series lines, which should precede such a series limit, are not there.

3. Lyman Continuum and Lines of Hydrogen

Because of their very large absorption coefficients, the Ly continuum and the Ly α line originate in layers which may be called "high chromosphere" or "lower transition layer." Absolute intensities give indications as to the temperature distribution in this, not yet very well-known, part of the solar atmosphere. Ly α is emitted in an optically thick layer and broadened largely by Doppler effect. Spectrally resolved profiles also of some of the higher members of the Lyman series would give us the velocities ("turbulence," important for heating of the corona) and the amount of matter. The energy distribution in the Ly continuum is rather directly connected with electron temperature.

The emission lines which dominate the solar spectrum more and more for $\lambda < 1800$ Å are produced in the transition layer. Using L. Oster's model, C. W. Allen (Liège Symposium 1960) was able to account fairly well for the existing measured (or rather estimated) intensities. More accurate absolute measurements would increase our knowledge of the temperature and density distributions in the transition layer by answering the question, "How much matter is there in the temperature range T to $T + \Delta T$?" Measurements of line widths for Doppler effects would be most interesting too, but extremely difficult. (Similar problems arise in connection with continua and lines in the X-ray region; these originate in the corona and are dealt with by E. Schatzman, see Chapter 8.2).

4. Angular Resolution. Far Ultraviolet "Spectroheliograms"

The geometrical and aerodynamic or magnetohydrodynamic structure of the solar atmosphere is characterized by features of different orders of size:

(a) *Granulation* (photospheric convection) and chromospheric granulation as well as the "spicules" (seen, e.g., in $H\alpha$) extend from the limit of telescopic resolving power to a few seconds of arc (1 sec = 725 km). The physical connection between low and high level features is *not* sufficiently clear. It is sometimes forgotten that the spicules also share many properties with the larger prominences. Both can be interpreted as cooler condensations ($\sim$10 000°?) in the corona ($\sim 2 \times 10^6$ °) stabilized by magnetic fields.

(b) *Flocculi,* a network of some 10,000-km mesh width best seen on the well-known calcium and hydrogen spectroheliograms.

(c) The large *"plages faculaires,"* or *facular areas* over centers of activity and connected with extended magnetic fields of a few hundred gauss. In the transition layer and at least the lower corona, these regions are sometimes characterized by electron densities increased by factors from 3 to 10, and (temporarily) also by increased temperature (coronal condensations and streamers). These areas are mainly responsible for the emission of Ly α, the whole X-ray region and the enhanced radio frequency radiation in the centimeter and decimeter range.

A more detailed interpretation of the solar spectrum should obviously take into account the high degree of inhomogeneity of the outer solar atmosphere. Any quantitative information about the emission within and outside of the mentioned features (stray light!) for lines as well as continua from λ 3000 to the X-ray region would be highly interesting. Could one get quantitative observations of prominences (on and outside the solar disk) in Ly α and the Lyman continuum?

5. Some Remarks Concerning Corpuscular Radiations

Since we do not yet know how particles on the sun are accelerated to superthermal energies, we begin by stating how much matter would have to be penetrated going upward from various layers. Above the base of the photosphere there are $\sim$4 gm/cm^2, above that of the chromosphere, $\sim$0.25 gm/cm^2, above that of the corona $\sim 6 \times 10^{-6}$ gm/cm^2. One has the impression that most theoretical developments consider high velocity phenomena only in terms of shock waves. One should, however, also remember that what have been observed so far are rather long-stretched prominences or clouds of matter, sometimes escaping from the sun with velocities up to $\sim$700 km/sec, corresponding to $\sim$2.6 kev per proton. Further discussion of these matters, however, definitely belongs in the following paper.

General References

(Without any claim for completeness; pointing out some recent summarizing books or articles and a few relevant recent papers)

Colloque International d'Astrophysique: "Astronomical Spectra in the Far Ultraviolet." Université de Liège, 1960.

Flügge, S. (ed.) "Handbuch der Physik" Vol. 52; Astrophysik III. Springer-Verlag, Berlin, 1959, contains:

L. Goldberg, The photosphere of the sun.

C. de Jager, Structure and dynamics of the solar atmosphere.

Greenstein, J. L. (ed.), "Stellar Atmospheres" Vol. 6, Stars and Stellar Systems. Univ. of Chicago Press, Chicago, 1960.

Kallmann, H. (ed.), "Space Research," Part IV, Solar Radiation. North-Holland, Amsterdam, 1960.

Liller, W. (ed.), "Space Astronomy." McGraw-Hill, New York, 1961.

Thomas, R. N., and Athay, R. G., "Physics of the Solar Chromosphere." Interscience, New York, 1961.

Unsöld, A., "Physik der Sternatmosphären. Mit besonderer Berücksichtigung der Sonne," 2. Aufl. Springer-Verlag, Berlin, 1955.

Athay, R. G., Thomas, R. N. with Matsushima, S., Menzel, D. H., and Pecker, J. C., The thermodynamic structure of the solar atmosphere I–V, *Astrophys. J.* **111,** 165 (1950); **112,** 337 (1950); *Astrophys. J. Suppl. Ser.* **1,** 479, 491, 505 (1954/5).

Böhm, K. H., Die Temperaturschichtung der Sonnenatmosphäre im nichtgrauen Strahlungsgleichgewicht, *Z. Astrophys.* **34,** 182 (1954).

Goldberg, L., Müller, E. A., and Aller, L. H., The abundances of the elements in the solar atmosphere, *Astrophys. J. Suppl. Ser.* **5,** 1 (1960).

Jager, C. de, The interpretation of hydrogen spectroheliograms. Temperature-variation and turbulence in the low chromosphere, *Bull. Astron. Inst. Netherlands* **13,** 133, 275 (1956/7).

Oster, L., Das Strahlungsfeld der Übergangsschicht Chromosphäre-Korona, *Z. Astrophys.* **40,** 28 (1956).

Unsöld, A., Aufbau und Variationen der Sonnenkorona, *Z. Astrophys.* **50,** 57 (1960).

Weidemann, V., Metallhäufigkeiten, Druckschichtung und Stossdämpfung in der Sonnenatmosphäre, *Z. Astrophys.* **36,** 101 (1955).

Discussion

DR. Z. SUEMOTO: It is well known that any of the current chromospheric models like that of Athay and Menzel give too much intensity in decimeter and centimeter radio wavelength ranges if one wishes to give right intensities to the helium lines, and vice versa. Moriyama of the Tokyo Astronomical Observatory showed that this is due to the circumstance that in a model like this the radio energies in these wavelength ranges are supposed to be emitted more or less uniformly from the whole disk. He then proposed an inhomogeneous distribution of the radio as well as helium emitting regions over the disk. If we assume a certain per cent coverage over the disk, the optical thickness $N_e^2 T_e^{-3/2} H$ in radio waves of the layer at a certain temperature, 20,000°, e.g., comes out to be much larger than is expected from the simple proportionality relation, because we are dealing with an optically thick atmosphere here. He found in this way that with 10% coverage we can get a good agreement between radio and helium emissions.

After this work had been done, I calculated the intensities of extreme ultraviolet lines, which turned out to be again much stronger than expected from radio intensities. It was seen that this time again 10% coverage is just about right to give an agreement between these two intensities. Moreover, the whole thickness of the transition layer turns out to be only a few hundred kilometers. We are thus led to think of a sheath-like structure of the transition layer enveloping each spicule, the interspicule regions being the corona itself above the height, say, 1500 km.

8.2 *The Solar Corona*

E. SCHATZMAN

INSTITUT D'ASTROPHYSIQUE, Paris, France

There is a perfect continuity from the chromosphere to the corona and interplanetary space. Consequently, the definition of the corona is conventional. We shall say that the solar corona is made of a hot gas, at a temperature of about one million degrees. This definition is a little restrictive, as the transition region between the corona and the chromosphere is at a lower temperature; the interplanetary gas is also at a lower temperature. Such a definition excludes the prominences which, however, appear in the corona.

Before considering the problems of the corona which can be studied with the help of space research, it is necessary to consider the physical properties of the coronal plasma.

I. The Plasma in the Corona

Many questions can be raised concerning the coronal plasma. We shall consider these questions in the order of rising difficulty.

1. Density

The determination of the density of the coronal plasma follows directly from measures of the intensity of the polarized light scattered by the electrons. Though simple in principle, this method leads to great difficulties, for the light scattered by the sky adds to the light coming from the corona. Despite the presence of large inequalities (coronal streamers), the results of the observations have to be analyzed by the assumption of spherical symmetry in order to resolve the integral equations giving the intensity of the radial and tangential components of the polarized radiation (van de Hulst, 1953). The measures of the diffracted light would be considerably improved if they were made above the earth's atmosphere.

2. Temperature

Values of the temperature are deduced from the observation of a great variety of physical phenomena. Various methods consider:

(a) Ionization and excitation:

(1) ionization of iron,
(2) intensities of the red line (Fe X) and green line (Fe XIV),
(3) intensity of the X-ray spectrum.

(b) Temperature of the radiation in the meter band.
(c) Hydrostatic equilibrium.
(d) Width of the spectral lines:

(1) profile of the red line,
(2) profile of the green line.

The values which are obtained by these methods do not agree.

Methods (a) and (b) yield the temperature of the electrons; (c) implies equal temperatures for electrons and ions; and (d) gives the temperature of the ions.

The temperature deduced from the intensity of the radio waves is probably the one which is the least dependent on the knowledge of the microscopic quantities. However, it depends greatly on the absence of nonthermal radiation.

The interpretation of ionization and excitation requires a knowledge of the ionization and excitation cross sections; it implies a Maxwellian velocity distribution function for the electrons; and it may depend on the solution of a radiative transfer problem.

It is naturally very important to know the exact value of the coronal temperature. However, to discuss the physical conditions in the corona, it is quite sufficient to know the order of magnitude of the temperature.

At a distance of 40,000 km above the solar limb, the density is of the order of 3×10^8 electrons/cc, and the temperature is of the order of $10^{6\circ}$.

3. Physical Conditions

At such a temperature hydrogen is fully ionized, as is helium. The heavy atoms retain only a few electrons. One can deal with the coronal plasma as with a fully ionized plasma. To a first approximation, it is possible to deal with this gas as if it had only one constituent, hydrogen. However, as shown by S. Chapman (1958), there are cases where this approximation is not satisfactory (transport problem in ionized gases).

To each density there corresponds a plasma frequency. Waves at lower frequency cannot propagate in gas at that density. This property defines precisely the interest of extraterrestrial radio astronomy for the study of the outer layers of the corona. The ionosphere absorbs almost all radiation below 10 Mc (which corresponds to the plasma frequency at 1 solar radius from the surface of the sun). A value of 2 Mc ($\lambda = 150$ meters) is reached by the plasma frequency at 5 solar radii.

This critical frequency is modified by the presence of a magnetic field, the ordinary wave propagating more deeply inside the corona than the extraordinary wave. The difference is small, except for large magnetic fields. Observations of radio waves of low frequency, only possible in space, would provide valuable information on the outer corona.

4. Thermal Equilibrium

The corona radiates; therefore, at each point of the corona there is a balance between the energy brought into the corona and the energy radiated. According to Allen and Woolley (1948) 10 times more energy is radiated in the lines than in the continuous spectrum.

Free-bound and free-free transitions per cm³ of pure hydrogen will produce continuous radiation at the rate

$$\epsilon_{\rm H} = 5.45 \times 10^{-22} N_e^2 T^{-1/2} + 1.44 \times 10^{-27} T^{1/2} N_e^2.$$

In the corona, the line radiation arises from other ions. Let us call ϵ the actual rate of emission per cubic centimeter. The thermal evolution of a given volume of hydrogen is given by

$$3N_e k(dT/dt) = W - \epsilon$$

where W is the balance of all kinds of energy, except radiation. It represents the energy deposited by heat sources (waves, particles) or by thermal conductivity.

If W were to vanish suddenly, the corona would start cooling. The time scale of the cooling can be calculated. For pure hydrogen at $T = 3.8 \times 10^5$°K, with $N_e = 3 \times 10^8$ cm^{-3}, the time scale of the cooling would be $t_r \simeq 0.7$ sec. Taking into account the line emission by the other ions, the rate of cooling would be at least ten times faster. We can conclude that changes in the thermal balance of the corona are immediately followed by changes in its temperature.

A most important property of the corona is its high thermal conductivity. For coronal values of density and temperature, we can calculate, according to Spitzer (1956), a coefficient of thermal conductivity $K \simeq 10^{-6} T^{5/2}$. K is therefore very large: for $T \simeq 10^6$, we have $K \simeq 10^9$.

In the presence of a magnetic field, the conductivity is not isotropic any more, and it becomes a tensor. Spitzer (1956) has estimated the conductivity in a direction perpendicular to the magnetic field. He finds that it is reduced by a factor $(1 + \omega_c^2 t_c^2)^{-1}$, where ω_c is the cyclotron frequency of the electrons and t_c is the collision time of the electrons. Also,

$$\omega_c t_c \simeq 10^{6.9}(BT^{3/2}/N_e).$$

With $B \simeq 1$ gauss and $T \simeq 10^6 K$, the reduction factor $(\omega_c t_c)^2$ therefore looks very large, even for relatively high densities ($N_e \simeq 3 \times 10^8$ cm^{-3} and $K \simeq 10^{-9.2}$ $(\omega_c t_c)^2 \simeq 10^{18.2}$. For such a value of the conductivity, the time of relaxation of the temperature is 1 year over a distance of 4 meters. We see that the coronal plasma is remarkably unable to transport heat across the lines of force, unless the magnetic field is extremely small ($B \simeq 10^{-6}$ gauss, for example).

Differences in temperature from point to point are to be expected. However, those which have been found can probably be explained, as will be shown later, by the effects of other mechanisms (radiative transfer, turbulence, etc.).

It is suggested that the study of the corona with high resolving power and long exposures could provide a test of the possible differences of temperature in the corona.

5. Nature of the Thermal Equilibrium

Heat is deposited in the corona by various dissipative mechanisms, by radiation, and by conduction. The velocity distribution function of the electrons naturally depends on the mechanism of heating and dissipation. The matter has been discussed by Seaton (1960), who had found in the interstellar medium cases of temperature differences between the electrons and the ions, or between the electrons and the atoms.

Spitzer (1956) has also considered the problem in the case of fully ionized gases. We follow here an argument different from that of Bhatnagar *et al.* (1955).

If $D(\rho,T,z)$ is the rate at which energy is locally dissipated into heat at height z, the energy balance is

$$D = \epsilon - \frac{2}{7} K_0 \frac{d^2 T^{7/2}}{dz^2}. \tag{1}$$

It is quite likely that in the lower corona the three terms are of comparable importance, and that higher up D is negligible. At greater heights, it should be necessary to take into account the kinetic energy of the corona; this question will be considered later in connection with the problem of the solar wind.

It is usually accepted that the heating mechanism is due to the dissipation of the kinetic energy of compression waves. Since this energy is carried essentially by the ions, it is quite natural to think that the ions are hot and that they heat the electrons which radiate. In the equation written above, the terms on the right-hand side represent energy carried by the electrons. The left-hand side represents the energy brought to the electrons by the ions. If T_1 is the temperature of the ions and has the same order of magnitude as T, it can be shown that

$$T_1 - T \simeq \frac{6 \times 10^{16}}{N_e^2} T^{3/2} D.$$

Let us consider the right-hand member of Eq. (1). For $N_e \simeq 3 \times 10^8$ cm^{-3}, ϵ can be of the order of 3×10^{-6} cgs (continuous and ultraviolet lines). Near the temperature maximum, with $z \simeq 10^4$ km, the conductivity term is positive and of the order of 3×10^{-4}. Therefore, conductivity dominates the energy loss, and we find that $T_1 - T \simeq 2 \times 10^5$°K. This is too small to explain the differences which Billings (1957) has observed between electron and ion temperatures. In the region where T is increasing outwards (lower corona), or decreasing outwards (outer corona), the conductivity term gives a much smaller contribution, so that the difference between electron and ion temperature should be smaller also. If the observed difference in temperature between electrons and ions is confirmed, it will require further explanation.

6. Heating Mechanism

This is not the place to discuss the details of the heating mechanism. A discussion was given in Varenna by Kaplan and Schatzman (see Schatzman, 1960) and Osterbrock (1961).

However, the following remarks have to be made. In the regions of high magnetic field, where the Alfvén waves have a velocity V_A much greater than the velocity V_S of sound, compression waves generated by the turbulence of the convective zone give rise to fast waves which propagate isotropically with the velocity of Alfvén waves. These dissipate energy very differently from ordinary compression waves (Fig. 1), and they can deposit energy in higher layers of the corona. We shall especially consider the strength of the shock wave $\eta = (\rho_1 - \rho_0)/\rho_0$, and its variation during its propagation (Osterbrock, 1961). The strength decreases very rapidly in the high chromosphere, and the shock wave becomes practically an acoustic wave in the corona.

Very important differences in the heating process are certainly present in magnetic regions. We should notice that, in the region where $V_A \gg V_S$, the fast wave leaves behind two waves of small amplitude, both propagating along the magnetic field: a transverse wave propagating with velocity V_A and a longitudinal wave propagating with velocity V_S.

The latter wave is certainly related to the presence of a density gradient and a magnetic field gradient (Grad, 1960).

Let us consider the structure of the solar magnetic fields. We have measurements of the longitudinal field (Severny, 1958, 1960; Leighton, 1959), but very few results concern the transverse field (Michard, 1961). The observations of Leighton show the remarkable identity between the calcium plages and the magnetic regions. The magnetic fields measured by Leighton, with the help of the line λ6102.7 of Ca I, reach 100 to 200 gauss. The horizontal extension of the coronal arches, above the plages, shows that the extension of the magnetic field above the solar limb is similar to its surface extension.

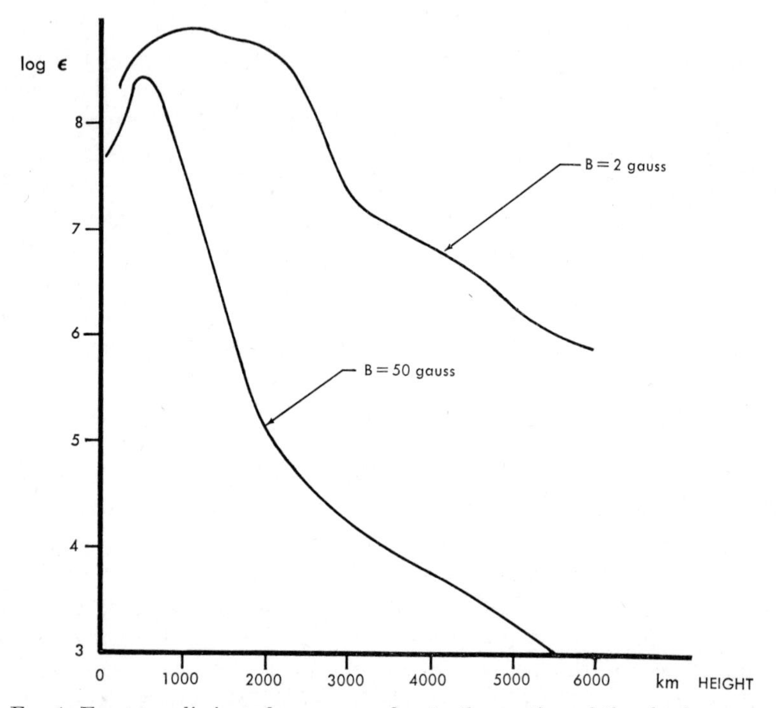

FIG. 1. Energy η dissipated per gram, due to the motion of the shock waves.

Observation shows a correlation between bipolar regions and coronal activity. As an example, we reproduce a figure given by Waldmeier, according to which the excitation of the line λ 5694 of Ca XV is related to a bipolar magnetic (B.M.) region.

Filaments near faculae seem to be determined by magnetic fields. Filaments often mark the limit between two regions of opposite polarity in a bipolar magnetic region, or they lie at the boundary of the region.

The appearance of filaments corresponds to a perturbation either in the heating mechanism or in the heat balance, or both.

7. Accelerating Mechanism

It is possible to develop here a suggestion of Hoyle (1960) concerning the production of fast particles in shock waves.

Consider a shock with the magnetic field perpendicular to the direction of propagation. Beyond the shock front, the magnetic field is larger. A particle will be accelerated if, after entering region (2) behind the shock front it can escape and come back to region (1) ahead of the shock, despite the motion of the shock front. Let us consider a coordinate system moving with the matter in the region behind the shock front. When the particle returns to the region ahead of the shock front it experiences an increase in velocity. If V_2 is the particle velocity, and U_2 the shock front velocity, the condition for acceleration is $V_2 > 1.38\, U_2$. For weak shocks and a strong magnetic field, $U_2 = V_A$ (Alfvén velocity). As mentioned by Parker (1958a,b), particles are not trapped by the shock, and their energy changes with the magnetic field. However, due to scattering by the irregularities of the magnetic field, some particles can keep going with the shock and can be accelerated for a long time. Such particles, moving with a shock of strength η in a magnetic field B, over a distance L, obtain a high kinetic energy. For protons the energy is

$$W_{\mathrm{ev}} \simeq 4 \times 10^{-6} \eta^2 L^2 B^2,$$

and for electrons

$$W_{\mathrm{ev}} \simeq 8 \times 10^{-4} \eta^2 L^2 B^2.$$

If such a process is at all possible, the electrons gain more energy than the protons as they come across the shock front 1843 times more frequently than the protons. It should be noted that these results have been obtained neglecting collision losses; they represent a large overestimate especially for electrons, which can radiate much energy.

For $\eta = 10^{-3}$ (Fig. 2), $B = 50$ gauss, and $L = 10^9$ cm, we find for protons $W \simeq 10^{10}$ ev. By including the relativistic effects, and taking into account the synchrotron radiation, it is possible to find that electrons are accelerated to an energy

$$(W_{\mathrm{ev}})_{\mathrm{lim}} = 10^{12.88} \eta^{1/2} N_e^{-1/4}.$$

For $N_e = 10^8$ cm^{-3} and $\eta = 10^{-3}$, this gives $(W_{\mathrm{ev}})_{\mathrm{lim}} = 2 \times 10^9$ ev.

Although it is probable that only a small number of particles can be accelerated, this calculation leads to two important conclusions which are probably valid, despite the approximations which have been made:

(1) this heating mechanism can accelerate particles in the regions where the magnetic field is perpendicular to the direction of propagation, especially in the presence of strong shocks; and (2) the particles can be accelerated to very large energies.

It seems possible to explain in this way the presence of the line λ 5694 of Ca XV, which has an excitation potential of 814 ev, above the B.M. regions, where the magnetic field is roughly parallel to the surface of the sun (Waldmeier, 1956) (Fig. 3).

This mechanism cannot act if the shock is longitudinal. It may be possible to explain in this way the correlation between the line λ 5694 of Ca XV and the B.M. regions.

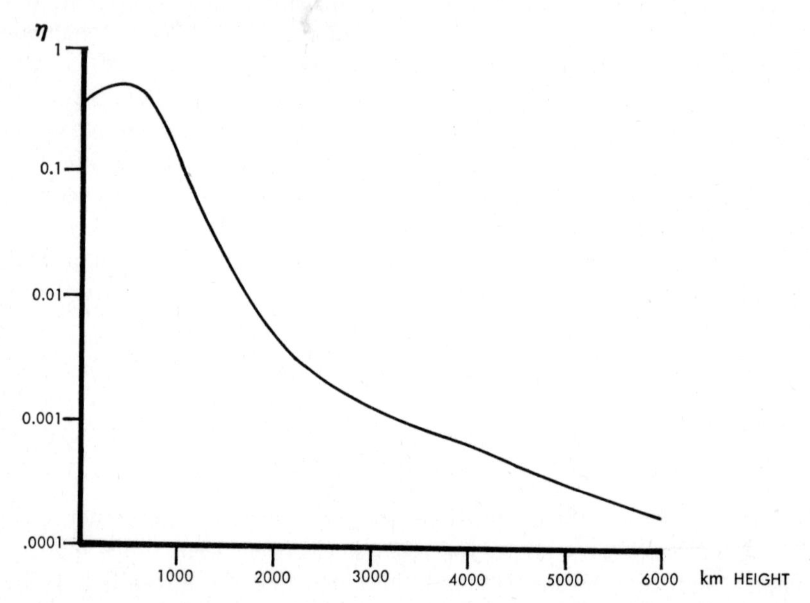

FIG. 2. The strength of the hydromagnetic shock wave, according to Osterbrock.

The centers of activity (C.A.) are complex magnetic regions where it may well be possible to have production of a stream of fast particles arising from a field of perpendicular shocks. It will be necessary to see how this wind of fast particles changes during the evolution of a C.A. The only visible signs of the *M* regions of the geophysicists are the filaments of the old C.A. and the coronal streamers. However, Mustel (1961) seems to have demonstrated the existence of a strong correlation between magnetic perturbations and activity centers. A test for the existence of these fast streams could be obtained by space observation.

Departures from the Maxwell distribution function of the velocities,

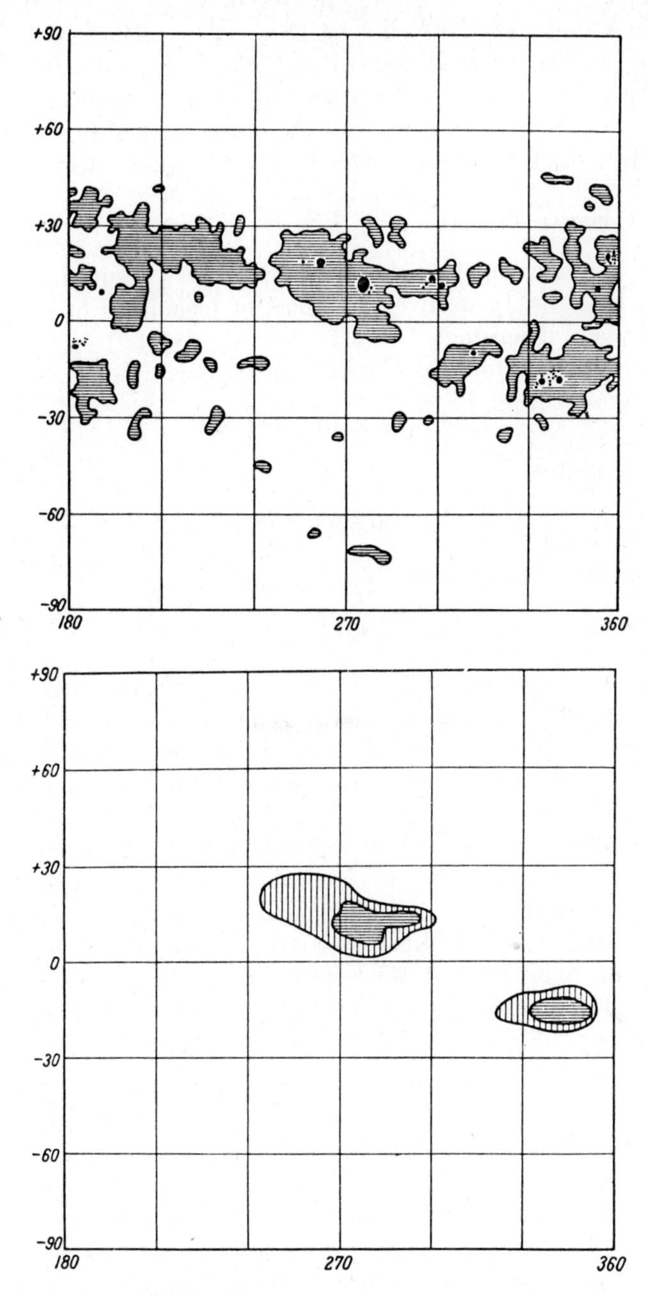

FIG. 3. According to Waldmeier, a map of the sun, showing the plages and the great B.M. groups and the place where the 5694 line of Ca XV is intense. It is possible to note the coincidence between these two regions.

due to the running shocks, could be observed as abnormal excitation above B.M. regions, or as streams of fast particles. Abnormal excitation and efficient heating would be a normal feature of coronal condensations. It will be necessary to examine whether this accelerating mechanism could produce electromagnetic waves by the Cerenkov effect.

8. The Coronal Plasma

In order to study the other phenomena which can occur in the coronal plasma, it is necessary to give the orders of magnitude of several important physical quantities.

The collision time interval between electrons is

$$t_{ce} = 1.32 \times 10^{-2}(T^{3/2}/N_e),$$

and between protons

$$t_{cp} = 0.57(T^{3/2}/N_p).$$

The equipartition time between protons and electrons is

$$t_{eq} = 24.6(T^{3/2}/N_p).$$

In typical conditions ($T = 10^{6}\,^\circ K$, $N_e = \frac{1}{2} \times 10^8 \mathrm{cm}^{-3}$, height of 10^5 km), $t_{ce} = 0.3$ sec, $t_{cp} = 12$ sec, and $t_{eq} = 500$ sec. Lower in the corona these relaxation times are much shorter. Any electromagnetic phenomena of shorter period can produce an anisotropy in the velocity distribution function. Two possibilities are a rapid evolution of the magnetic field, and the various waves which heat the corona.

If we consider, especially, perpendicular shocks, we can see that a phenomenon very similar to magnetic pumping is going on; but as waves follow one another at intervals of the order of magnitude of the relaxation time, an anisotropy of the velocity distribution function can be generated. This would be possible in the corona, but not in the chromosphere.

9. Viscosity

A work of Knoff (1960) on transport phenomena in plasmas leads to the following results. If ω is the gyro frequency and τ the average time between collisions, then in the case $\omega\tau \gg 1$ the tensions are given by

$$P_{11} = P_{22} = -(\mu)_1(\mathring{e}_{11} + \mathring{e}_{22}) = (\mu)_1\mathring{e}_{33}$$

$$P_{33} = -2(\mu)_1\mathring{e}_{33}, \qquad P_{ij} = 0, \qquad i \neq j$$

where $\mathring{e}_{ij}$ is the rate-of-strain tensor

$$\mathring{e}_{ij} = \frac{1}{2}\left(\frac{\partial u_i}{\partial x_j} + \frac{\partial u_j}{\partial x_i}\right),$$

and where (u_1, u_2, u_3) is the velocity of matter. The components of the magnetic field are $(0, 0, B)$, and $(\mu)_1 = \frac{2}{3}\, p\tau$ is the first approximation of the coefficient of viscosity, where p is the pressure.

It is readily seen that when the gas is moving in the direction of the magnetic field, the velocity is $(0, 0, u)$ and the rate-of-strain tensor vanishes if $(\partial u/\partial x_3) = 0$, which is true as a first approximation. In a motion perpendicular to the lines of force, one finds, as expected, that the matter is carried by the lines of force.

10. Instabilities

The plasma can present various kinds of instabilities.

Let us remark first that the anisotropy of the velocity distribution function (Jensen, 1959) makes the plasma paramagnetic or diamagnetic.

Let us call E_r and E_l the kinetic energy of particles associated with their motions, respectively parallel and perpendicular to the magnetic field. If $E_r - 2E_l > 0$, the plasma is diamagnetic and it is pushed towards regions of lower magnetic field; if $E_r - 2E_l < 0$, the plasma is paramagnetic and it is pulled towards regions of higher magnetic field.

Jensen believes that certain motions in the corona, especially in the formation of prominences, are due to the diamagnetic properties of the plasma.

Aside from these macroscopic instabilities, a great variety of microscopic instabilities can appear. It is certain that they are not all known.

(a) When a jet of charged particles moves across a plasma, plasma oscillations are excited. If the velocity of the jet is larger than a critical value, plasma oscillations amplify the oscillations of the particles in the jet, and instability appears.

(b) In the presence of a strong magnetic field, and if the velocity distribution is anisotropic, a certain kind of free waves experience a negative damping. This problem has been considered by Akiezer and Pargamanik (1948 and later), and by Parker (1958b).

It is known that instability phenomena are observed in plasmas and are associated with radio emission. However, they are still poorly understood. Therefore, it is not yet clearly seen how the solar radio emission can be related to these kinds of instabilities.

We can conclude this section by drawing attention to further study of the motions in the corona. The recent study of Athay and Moreton

(1961), on the disappearance of filaments following a flare, is an indication of how much has still to be done. Motions in the outer corona can be permanently studied only in space.

II. Coronal Phenomena

11. Prominences

There exist quiescent prominences and active prominences, but we do not know the mechanism of formation for any of them.

Quiescent prominences seem to hang in the magnetic field, either between sunspots or around sunspots. The theory of Schlüter and Kippenhahn (1957) explains how the magnetic field can be deformed to carry the weight of the filaments.

The question of the thermal equilibrium of prominences is not properly solved. It is certain that prominences are colder than the surrounding coronal medium. But they are heated very efficiently by the coronal ultraviolet and by hot electrons which are guided by the lines of force.

The mechanism of condensation is unknown, although cooling has the correct time scale (Kleczek, 1957).

12. Coronal Condensations

Several coronal phenomena are associated with activity centers. It should be particularly noted that there is a strict correlation between $\lambda 5694$ of Ca XV with the active spot areas. We have seen, in connection with the acceleration of particles in shock waves, the nature of this association. On the other hand, according to Waldmeier (1956), coronal condensations are coronal phenomena related to the maximum development of the activity center. These are extended regions above A.C.; their density is higher, and also, as far as we know, their temperature: the width of the lines gives 2 to 6×10^6 degrees. The excitation of $\lambda 5694$ Ca XV also implies a high temperature.

Is the temperature of the coronal condensation really so high? Radio emission at decimeter wavelengths and the intensity of X-rays are in agreement with a temperature of 10^6 degrees. It is not certain whether a small scale turbulence could explain the difference. The radio emitting region covers an area equal to the area of the calcium plages, but its height is between several thousand and hundred thousand kilometers. These radio emitting regions are identical with the X-ray emitting regions (Chubb *et al.*, 1960).

Is the X-ray emission of the coronal condensations mainly in the lines (Elwert, 1958) or in the continuum (Kazachevskaya *et al.*, 1959)?

These problems must be solved. New space observations could provide the answers.

13. Radiation from the Corona

The problem of radiation from the corona is now a classical one, which has been recently broadened by new studies of eclipses and by the observation of the uv spectrum from rockets. As an example, and in order to show some of the problems which have to be solved, I would like to describe some of the results due to C. Pecker, and to C. Pecker and R. N. Thomas.

A study of the levels of Si X (belonging to the isoelectronic sequence of C II, N III, etc.) leads one to predict the presence of a certain number of permitted transitions. Pecker gives the data shown in Table I.

TABLE I
Permitted Transitions

Upper level $2s2p^2$	ev	Wavelength for transition to the ground level $^2P_{1/2}{}^0$	$^2P_{3/2}{}^0$	Observed (Rense)	
$^2D_{3/2}$, $^2D_{5/2}$	35.7	347.4	356.1	344.7	354.9
$^2S_{1/2}$	45.6	272.0	277.3	272.3	276.8
$^2P_{1/2}$	48.2	256.6	261.3	257.1	261.8
$^2P_{3/2}$	48.7	253.8	258.3	—	257.1

The classical problem of the ratio of the intensities of the red and green coronal lines takes a new aspect when the transfer problem is included. In the two levels $^2P_{3/2}{}^0$ (ground) and $^2P_{1/2}{}^0$ of Fe X, the population is governed not only by collisions but also by permitted transitions which start from the level $3p^6\ ^2S_{1/2}$, of excitation potential 29 ev. These transitions correspond to two intense lines near λ345 Å. Measurements of these two lines would permit one to solve with certainty the radiative transfer problem, as estimates of the optical thickness show that it is not negligible. Therefore, the calculation of the intensity of the red line cannot be done without taking into account the radiation field in the uv lines of Fe X. A similar correction has to be made for Fe XIV, which shows a series of lines in the region $\lambda\lambda$250–350 Å. Therefore the "temperature of ionization," as deduced from the ratio of the intensities of the red and green lines, depends on the geometry of the ultraviolet radiative transfer.

Pecker and Thomas conclude that the electron temperature in the corona is almost uniform, the differences in intensity being essentially due to the variations of density.

14. Flares and Coronal Phenomena

Flares are chromospheric phenomena, occurring in the lower layers above the photosphere (16,000 km according to Warwick, 7300 km according to Giovanelli and McCabe). The main phenomenon is a rapid brightening ($\Delta \log I = 0.5$ in less than 5 min). The flare spreads over a region of considerable area, and it lasts a few hours.

In a flare, an ejection of matter can take place (surge) about 4 min after the beginning of the flare. There is a rapid motion of matter outward, the biggest extension (60,000 km) being reached in about 10 min. In projection on the solar disk, the surge is seen in absorption. The velocity of the ejected particles is much larger, about 1000 km sec^{-1}, at the beginning of the flares, in the fast motions that Giovanelli calls puffs. Radio bursts of type III are associated with these puffs, but the source velocity is still larger (10^5 km/sec).

In the same way, it seems that the surges, which begin later, are associated with the outbursts (type II radio bursts). There again, the source velocity of the type II burst is much larger than the velocity of the surge.

In both cases, the processes associated with the optical phenomena generate in the corona a powerful accelerating mechanism. Moreover, the type II eruption is followed by strong radio emission which lasts for a long time (10 min to several hours) and presents a wide continuum (type IV bursts of Boischot). This last emission comes out of a cloud of very great dimensions, which rises in the corona with a speed of about 1500 km/sec, and then stops at large altitudes (4 to 5 solar radii) and disappears on the spot.

The continuous spectrum of the type IV eruptions is probably due to cyclotron radiation. It is due to electrons which are trapped in a magnetic field which lasts for a sufficient length of time. In the meantime, the flare ejects the lines of force of the magnetic field, and the shock front acquires a wake of fast particles which can radiate.

Flares, surges, and puffs are followed by an emission of corpuscular radiation, including cosmic rays and slower particles. Their direct observation, before interaction with the earth's magnetic field, could help to explain the solar accelerating mechanism. It seems indeed that the optical phenomenon is much slower than the phenomenon which gives birth to the radio emission. The flare itself is consequently due to a process underlying the optical and the radio phenomena and producing both.

15. The Solar Wind

The problem is the following: Are the outer regions of the solar corona expanding? To discuss this problem, we shall consider the work done by Parker (1960b, 1961) and by Chamberlain (1961). We shall first note, with Parker (1960a), that the hydrodynamic equations apply to the corona and that, at least in first approximation, the tensor of the pressure is isotropic.

If we assume that this is true, then two fundamental questions arise:

(1) What is the total energy input to the corona?

(2) What is the hydrodynamic model of the expansion?

In the outer regions of the corona, it is reasonable to assume the adiabatic relation between temperature and density ($r > 20R_\odot$). In order to examine the energy input to the solar corona, we shall adopt the model of Parker. An isothermal region extends from a distance a to a distance $b > a$, b being larger as the energy input increases; and an adiabatic region extends from b to some finite distance, or (eventually) to infinity. If the energy input is very small, the corona has a finite size; the density decreases very fast beyond b and vanishes at a finite distance. When the energy input increases, b increases, the whole size of the corona increases, and, for some critical value, it extends to infinity. The flow is then subsonic at infinity.

If the energy input increases still further, a shock front appears; this separates an inner region, where the flow is supersonic, from an outer region, where the flow is subsonic (Fig. 4). Clauser (1960) has shown the importance of a stationary shock front for the solution of this problem. The position of the shock moves outwards until the supersonic solution extends to infinity. The corona at infinity has a finite velocity of expansion and a vanishing density. From the subsonic flow to the supersonic flow Parker gives an energy input going from 0.14×10^2 to 8×10^{28} ergs/sec.

For still larger energy input, one finds the same supersonic solution, but with a larger flow of matter outwards and a nonzero velocity at infinity. Parker (1961) has considered the case when the shock is very far from a star, and he has studied the effect of a stellar wind on the interstellar matter. It is quite evident that at large distances from a star the problem does not accept a stationary solution. Deutsch (1960) has considered the interpretation of the observations of stellar spectra in the theory of the stellar wind.

Considering this hydrodynamic picture, it seems that the only theoretical difficulty in supposing that there exists a solar wind consists in the existence of the isothermal zone between a and b, which can result only from the presence of strong energy sources in the corona. However, it is quite obvious that the existence of the solar wind can be proved only by observations. Physically, its existence depends on the energy input in the corona.

Chamberlain (1961) takes conduction into account, but in the outer corona conduction is negligible, and he obtains the adiabatic solution. However, his adiabatic solution is chosen in such a way that both the

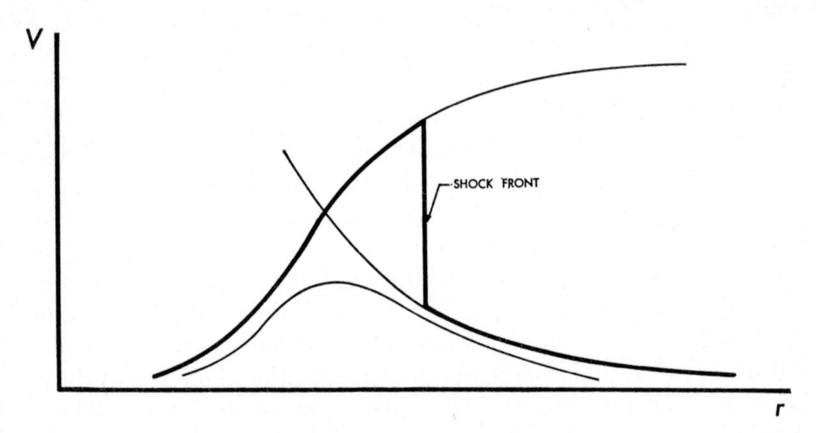

FIG. 4. The velocity as a function of the distance to the sun, in the intermediate case.

velocity and the density vanish at infinity; this result can be obtained only by making a special choice in the constants of integration, defined by the conditions at infinity, and not by the conditions near to the sun. With this solution, the temperature varies at large distances like r^{-1}, the density like $r^{-3/2}$, and the velocity like $r^{-1/2}$.

In Parker's model, the temperature varies like $r^{-4/3}$, the density like r^{-2}, and the velocity is constant. If one asks whether these differences can be observed, he is led to consider the degree of ionization of the outer corona, which varies essentially like $N_e^2 T^{-1/2}$ (radiative captures). This product varies like $r^{-14/3}$ in Parker's theory, and like $r^{-7/2}$ in Chamberlain's theory. Chamberlain's theory leads, then, to a larger abundance of interplanetary hydrogen in the vicinity of the earth. However, Brandt (1961), in considering the absorption by $H\alpha$, finds that the neutral hydrogen which is between the sun and the earth has an optical thickness of 0.03 or 0.04 in the core of Hα, which gives a vanishing contribution to the line profile.

16. Interplanetary Medium

The corona at its bottom rotates with the sun. How far out is the corona carried by the solar rotation? Lüst and Schlüter (1955) supposed that the corona rotates with the sun up to a distance of 50 to 100 solar radii. Is it necessary to take into account the rotation to calculate the equilibrium of the outer corona? The only test of the density of the matter in the vicinity of the earth has heretofore been the zodiacal light.

We can compare the theoretical results of Chapman (1959), Parker (1960a,b), Chamberlain (1961), for the region at 1 a.u., and the recent observations of Blackwell and Ingham (1961a,b) as shown in Table II.

TABLE II

Chapman	Parker	Chamberlain	Blackwell
N_i 600	24–35	30	120
V —	265–550 km sec^{-1}	20 km sec^{-1}	—
T 10^5	10^6–10^4 °K	2×10^4 °K	—

The most important test is naturally the measurement of the velocity of the particles, as the different theories can equally well explain the observed density.

References

Allen, C. W., and Woolley, R. v. d. R. (1948), *Monthly Notices Roy. Astron. Soc.* **108,** 292.

Athay, R. C., and Moreton, G. E. (1961), *Astrophys. J.* **133,** 935.

Akiezer, A. L , and Pargamanik, L. E. (1948), *Uchenye Zapiski, Khar'kov Gosudarst. Univ. im. A.M. Gor'kogo* **25,** 75.

Bhatnagar, P. L., Krook, M., Menzel, D. H., and Thomas, R. N. (1955). *Vistas in Astron.* **1,** 296.

Billings, D. E. (1957). *Astrophys. J.* **125,** 817.

Billings, D. E. (1959), *Astrophys. J.* **130,** 961.

Blackwell, D. E., and Ingham, M. F. (1961a), *Monthly Notices Roy. Astron. Soc.* **122,** 129.

Blackwell, D. E., and Ingham, M. F. (1961b), *Monthly Notices Roy. Astron. Soc.* **122,** 143.

Brandt, J. C. (1961), *Astrophys. J.* **133,** 688.

Chamberlain, J. W. (1961), *Astrophys. J.* **133,** 675.

Chapman, S. (1958), *Proc. Phys. Soc.* (*London*) **72,** 353.

Chapman, S. (1959). *Proc. Roy. Soc.* **A. 253,** 462.

Clauser, F. (1960), *4th Symposium on Cosmical Gas Dynamics. Intern. Astron. Union Symposium,* No. 12.

Chubb, T. A., Friedman, H., Kreplin, R. W., Blake, R. L., and Unzieker, A. E. (1960), *Liège.*

Deutsch, A. (1960), *4th Symposium on Cosmical Gas Dynamics. Intern. Astron. Union Symposium,* No. 12.
Elwert, G. (1956), *Z. Astrophys.* **41,** 67.
Elwert, G. (1958), *Z. Astrophys.* **44,** 112.
Grad, H. (1960), *Revs. Modern Phys.* **32,** 830.
Hoyle, F. (1960), *Monthly Notices Roy. Astron. Soc.* **120,** 338.
de Jager, C. (1961), *Bull. Astron. Inst. Netherlands* **16,** No. 510, p. 71.
Jensen, E. (1959), *Astrophys. norveg.* **6,** No. 9.
Kazachevskaya, T. V., and Ivanov-Kholodny, G. S. (1959), *Astron. Zhur.* **36,** 1922; *Soviet Astron.* **3,** 937, 1960.
Kleczek, J. (1957), *Bull. Astron. Inst. Czechoslov.* **8,** 120.
Knoff, J. B. (1960), *Publ. Inst. Teoret. Astrofys., Oslo.* In press.
Leighton, R. B. (1959), *Astrophys. J.* **130,** 366.
Lüst, R., and Schlüter, A. (1955), *Z. Astrophys.* **38,** 190.
Michard, R., Mouradian, Z., and Semel, M. (1961), *Ann. Astrophys.* **24,** 54.
Müstel, E. R. (1961), *Astron. Zhur.* **38,** 28.
Osterbrook, D. E. (1961), *Astrophys. J.* **134,** 347.
Parker, E. N. (1958a), *Phys. Rev.* **109,** 1328.
Parker, E. N. (1958b), *Phys. Rev.* **109,** 1874.
Parker, E. N. (1960a), *Astrophys. J.* **132,** 175.
Parker, E. N. (1960b), *Astrophys. J.* **132,** 821.
Parker, E. N. (1961), *Astrophys. J.* **134,** 20.
Schatzman, E. (1960), *4th Symposium on Cosmical Gas Dynamics. Intern. Astron. Union Symposium,* No. 12, p. 209.
Schlüter, A., and Kippenhahn, R. (1957), *Z. Astrophys.* **43,** 36.
Seaton, M. J. (1960), *4th Symposium on Cosmical Gas Dynamics. Intern. Astron. Union Symposium,* No. 12.
Severny, A. B. (1958), *Contribs. Crimean Astrophys. Obs.* **29,** 22.
Severny, A. B. (1960), *Contribs. Crimean Astrophys. Obs.* **24,** 12.
Spitzer, L., Jr. (1956), "Physics of Fully Ionized Gases." *Interscience,* New York.
van de Hulst, H. C. (1953), in "The Sun" (G. P. Kuiper, ed.). Univ. of Chicago Press, Chicago, Illinois.
Waldmeier, M. (1956), *Z. Astrophys.* **38,** 219.

8.3 *Interplanetary and Solar Magnetic Fields*

LEVERETT DAVIS, JR.

CALIFORNIA INSTITUTE OF TECHNOLOGY, Pasadena, California

The region discussed in this paper is the space in the solar system that is outside the sun, outside the planetary magnetic fields, and inside the region where one encounters the galactic magnetic field. The magnetic field in this region is our topic; however, it is also necessary to consider the plasma, or conducting gas, that fills the space and makes its properties so different from the absolute vacuum that is often tacitly assumed. The plasma can slide along the field lines but any transverse relative motion is virtually impossible because of the high conductivity. Any information on the motion of the plasma thus tells us how the magnetic field is being deformed. It is also necessary to give some attention to the galactic and solar cosmic rays; that is, to the relativistic particles that come to us continuously from other regions of the galaxy and intermittently from the sun. The motion of these particles is governed by the magnetic field and much information on its large scale structure can be deduced from the way the particles are on occasion blocked out of or trapped in certain regions. Thus the observations that are needed to understand these phenomena are observations of the strength and direction of the magnetic field, observations of the density, velocity, and perhaps temperature of the gas or plasma, and observations of the flux of relativistic particles. All these quantities vary with time, and we need to learn how they vary with position in the solar system.

You may wonder why the title of this paper contains the phrase "solar magnetic fields" when consideration of the sun itself is discussed in other papers. This choice of the region to discuss seems appropriate to this symposium since photospheric fields can be observed from the surface of the earth by means of the Zeeman effect and some tentative deductions on solar fields can be made from the shape of coronal streamers and other solar structures. It is the interplanetary region that can, and must, be explored by space vehicles which cannot approach the sun proper. Nevertheless, it appears very likely that the interplanetary magnetic field arises from the solar field, being produced by the interaction with the solar field of the plasma coming from the sun. Thus the study of the interplanetary field is also a study of the solar field, and the study of the interplanetary region is solar astrophysics in that it tells what is the output of the sun in plasma, in relativistic particles, and in magnetic fields. Knowledge of this output for the sun and other stars is certainly important in astronomy.

It is appropriate to note that this interplanetary region may be regarded as the "weather" in which the planets and their magnetic fields are immersed. The variations of the geomagnetic field, the aurora, the level of ionization in parts of the ionosphere, the density of particles in the outer Van Allen zones are all influenced by this environment. Much indirect information on the interplanetary magnetic field can be obtained from a study of these related phenomena; but the interpretation of this information is likely to remain obscure until we have available a considerable body of direct observations made outside the geomagnetic field. For the geomagnetic field responds in a very complicated way to the pressure, to the winds and breezes, of the plasma in which it is immersed. We need very badly direct, long continued observations of the causes outside the geomagnetic field that produce the effects we observe inside it. Incidentally, such comparisons may well yield new and important knowledge of plasma physics.

Let us now summarize what is known about the interplanetary magnetic field and what appear to be the most important questions to be answered. If one excludes indirect observations, the summary of what is known is very brief. Pioneer V, in the spring of 1960, measured the component of the magnetic field approximately normal to the earth-sun line out to distances of more than 10 million miles. When magnetic conditions at the earth were disturbed, there were disturbances at the space probe, and field strengths from 10 to 40 γ were observed ($1\ \gamma = 10^{-5}$ gauss). The disturbances at the earth were too great to be due directly to the interplanetary field and must be due to the plasma in which it is imbedded. When there were no disturbances, the field component observed was remarkably constant, usually at about 2.5 γ. Incidentally, this last observation seems inconsistent with nearly everything we thought we knew about the plasma and fields in interplanetary space. Field strengths less than 2.5 γ seem to be very rare indeed: a very surprising result.

Explorer X, in the spring of 1961, measured the vector magnetic field rather near the earth at a disturbed time, and a preliminary report indicates that fields were found in the range 10–30 γ approximately along the earth-sun line. Plasma measurements have been made by several of the Russian space probes and by Explorer X. It is my impression that these are mostly consistent with a solar wind of a few hundred km/sec outward from the sun and a particle density in the range 10–100 cm^{-3}; but this statement should not be regarded as a summary of the observations. A discussion of indirect methods of getting information on these quantities leads at once to argument and controversy. To avoid this, and in an effort to be brief, let us regard the indirect methods as equivalent to questions to be answered by direct observations. Among these questions are:

(1) Is there a solar wind of plasma coming out from the sun? What is its velocity and density? How does it vary with time? What does it do to the interplanetary and planetary magnetic fields? The importance and difficulty of answering these questions is obvious.

(2) What is the structure of the interplanetary magnetic field in quiet times? Is it merely the galactic magnetic field? Is it due to a solar dipole or ring current? Is it a radial field combed out by the solar wind and then made spiral by the solar rotation? What is the connection of the field with the rotating sun? Is it just a chaotic mess produced by stirring up the interplanetary plasma?

(3) Is the apparent trapping of solar cosmic rays and the partial exclusion of low-energy galactic cosmic rays, as observed in coincidence with some magnetic disturbances, due to the production of gigantic loops of magnetic field lines extending outward from the sun; or is it due to shock waves or turbulence in the interplanetary field? What is the scale of these structures, particularly in solar longitude? What is the effect, if any, at the earth of flares and other disturbances on the back side of the sun?

(4) What is the effect of the interplanetary "weather" on the planetary magnetic fields?

(5) What is the nature of the transition between the interplanetary and the galactic magnetic fields?

Finally, how does one go about making space age measurements that will help provide answers to these questions? Observations from the surface of the earth are the easiest and should be the most extensive. But they are indirect and difficult to interpret with assurance. Observations from satellites above the atmosphere and ionosphere, but within the geomagnetic field, eliminate some complications, but they are still indirect. Real progress requires vehicles that go well outside the geomagnetic field, preferably to 200,000 km or more. These should measure the vector magnetic field down to about $\frac{1}{2}\,\gamma$ or so, as well as the plasma density and velocity. It will be helpful to make such measurements from any vehicles that happen to enter this region, just as in early oceanography it was helpful to have reports from anyone who happened to cross the ocean. But real progress in understanding the changing and complicated interplanetary medium will almost certainly require an observatory that sends back the relevant data continuously. It should be far enough away so that we can be assured that there is no perturbation in its observations due to the geomagnetic field. It should not be located on the moon until we have verified that this introduces no perturbations. On the other hand, the ideal first interplanetary observatory should not be sent to distances of tens or hundreds of millions of kilometers; it should remain close so that copious data may be transmitted easily and so that the observations will give the outer boundary conditions for the geomagnetic field. If we really wish to undertake an adequate program of observing the environment which determines the phenomena in the geomagnetic field, we should plan to continue such observations over a solar cycle. Intermittent observations are likely to be as frustrating as they would be in meteorology. A real interplanetary program is more than just an incidental supplement of a planetary program.

In addition to these observations made just outside the geomagnetic field, it would be very valuable to have observations made at some distance along the earth's orbit, in order to determine the scale of the various disturbances and to monitor the phenomena on the back side of the sun. On the average they will, of course, be exactly the same as on the front side; but we would like to know, for example, if the Forbush decrease in cosmic ray intensity occupies a spherical region, a hemispherical region, or a small segment about the sun. We would like to know if flares on the back side of the sun produce solar cosmic rays here. In the beginning such observations can well be made from probes sent toward Venus or Mars, since they will also go to solar longitudes very different from that of the earth. Eventually we may well decide that special probes are needed to explore interplanetary space, just as special vessels are needed for a complete study of oceanography. It requires only a relatively modest effort to send a probe in an orbit whose perihelion or aphelion distance is not quite 1 a.u., and which therefore goes nearly along the earth's orbit but eventually to very different longitudes. Ultimately a patrol maintained by several well spaced probes may seem necessary.

At first sight it would seem desirable to extend our survey to cover a range of distances from the sun. But if there is any regular flow outward, we can do a great deal by converting measurements in time at one radius into a description of the variation with radius. We should be able to command enough theoretical technique to make this fairly reliable. Sometime we shall wish to send probes to explore the plasma and magnetic fields at distances from the sun of 1/10 or 1/20 a.u., where there may well be essential differences from the behavior near 1 a.u. Quite possibly somewhere between 3 and 30 a.u. from the sun, perhaps depending on the phase of the solar cycle, the transition to the galactic magnetic field may be found. However, relatively powerful rockets will be needed for these missions, and for missions out of the plane of the ecliptic. It seems unlikely that we shall attempt them until our immediate neighborhood has been explored. When this has been done, we shall doubtlessly have had so many surprises, and have increased so much our knowledge of interplanetary and solar magnetic fields, that my discussion this morning will seem very naive and primitive.

Discussion

DR. J. RING: The papers have shown that a critical test of these solar wind theories would be provided by a measurement of coronal temperature at 3 solar radii. It is difficult to do this from earth during an eclipse because of the faintness of the corona at this radius and the short time that is available. In a satellite, however, an artificial eclipse can be generated by an occulting disk in front of the optics, and an interferometer would provide a simple way of obtaining high spectral resolution. A long integration time would permit the use of a small optical system. Care must be taken to measure the widths of lines originating from elements of very different atomic mass, thus separating Doppler from turbulence broadening effects.

DR. A. J. DEUTSCH: I think a similar decision could be made from a measurement of the temperature of the medium at 1 a.u. Have attempts been made to obtain the kinetic temperature of the interplanetary gas outside the geomagnetic field at about one astronomical unit?

PROFESSOR R. B. LEIGHTON: I would like to ask one question of Professor Davis. How much more information would one get from two space probes at some distance from the earth—fired as a piggyback package, say—each measuring the magnetic field, than could be obtained from a single one?

DR. L. DAVIS: If the two space probes are fired piggyback, separated by hundreds or thousands of kilometers, one might, with very good timing, find out something about the propagation of plasma waves and other disturbances, the velocities of propagation, and the scale of disturbances, all of which might be interesting. However, a more interesting experiment which I would have liked to include in my discussion would be to arrange for two probes quite widely spaced along the earth's orbit, so that they look at the sun from different longitudes 30°, 60°, 90°, or even 180° apart, to find out what is the longitudinal scale of these disturbances which come out from the sun.

Answering another question, I do not know explicitly of planned experiments to measure the temperature of the gas in the neighborhood of the earth. There are a number of experiments planned to measure properties of the plasma. These may give the temperature too, but they will certainly give the velocity of the plasma in the neighborhood of the earth, and this velocity differs as drastically on the two theories as the temperature does. It may provide an answer, conceivably within months, to this question.

8.4 The Vacuum Ultraviolet Solar Spectrum

BENGT EDLÉN

FYSISKA INSTITUTIONEN, Lund, Sweden

Professor Schatzman and Professor Unsöld have stressed the importance of spectroscopic observations of the sun in the vacuum ultraviolet; this paper will comment briefly on the problem of the identification of this spectrum.

From observations made so far, we know that the spectrum consists essentially of bright lines. The continuum has disappeared from about 1600 Å down. We know, especially from the observations by Dr. Tousey and his colleagues, of a great number of lines in the region down to about 500 Å, the majority of which have been identified. They are mainly the resonance lines of light elements ($Z \leqslant 16$), in different stages of ionization from the lowest stage up to quite high stages. For instance, the O I resonance lines at 1300 Å are a strong feature, as are the resonance lines of O VI at 1031 Å. A conspicuous feature is the sequence of resonance doublets of the Li I-like spectra C IV, N V, O VI, Ne VIII, Mg X, and Si XII, with wavelengths from 1550 Å to about 500 Å. All these doublets have been clearly observed and identified. The appearance of this wide range of ionization stages shows that the light we observe comes from different layers of the sun; the low ionization stages from the chromosphere, presumably; the intermediate stages from the transition layer, in the terminology of Dr. Unsöld; and the highest stages from the corona. This mixture of very different excitation conditions causes a special problem in the interpretation of the spectrum.

The recent observations reported by Dr. Tousey, of the spectrum from about 170 Å up to about 350 Å, pose a new problem of identification. Apart from the resonance series of ionized helium and one or two more lines, the bulk of the new lines observed is still unidentified. When trying to determine the probable origin of these lines, we should, for abundance reasons, first search among the light elements in high ionization stages. Then we meet a spectral structure consisting essentially of two well-separated groups of lines, one due to transitions from the high configurations $2s^r2p^{k-1}\ nl$ with $n \geqslant 3$, to the low configurations $2s^r2p^k$ ($r = 0$–2, $k = 0$–6); and another group consisting of transitions of the type

$2s^{r-1}2p^{k+1} \rightarrow 2s^r2p^k$. The wavelengths of the first group ($\Delta n \geqslant 1$) decrease asymptotically as Z^{-2}, while those of the second group, ($\Delta n = 0$), which includes the resonance lines, decrease as Z^{-1}. It appears from a study of the isoelectronic sequences that the wavelengths of the first group will, already for moderate ionization stages, fall below 170 Å. They cannot explain more than one or two of the observed lines, the only probable identification being that of a faint line at 173 Å as O VI. On the other hand, the lines of the second group, representing the $2s$–$2p$ transitions, fall in the relevant wavelength region for the elements and ionization stages that one would expect to be abundant. As contributors to the observed solar spectrum below 500 Å, we may thus search among the following spectra: (Mg IV–X), Si VI–XII, S VIII–XIV, Ar X–XVI, Ca XII–XVIII. As already mentioned, the resonance doublets of Mg X and Si XII have been found by Tousey as prominent lines. They have not been observed in the laboratory, and their identification is based on predicted values obtained by extrapolation along the isoelectronic sequence. It is evident that we must rely to a great extent on extrapolations for the further identification of the solar lines. The method of extrapolation may be illustrated by the following formulas for the resonance doublet of the Li I-like spectra:

$$2p\,{}^2P_{3/2} - 2s\,{}^2S_{1/2} = 15393\zeta + 6053 - 19752(\zeta + 2)^{-1} + 0.4565(Z - 1)^4 - \tfrac{1}{4}({}^2P_{3/2} - {}^2P_{1/2}), \qquad {}^2P_{3/2} - {}^2P_{1/2} = \frac{R\alpha^2}{16}(Z - s')^4,$$

$$s' = s - \frac{5\alpha^2}{32}(Z - s')^3, \qquad s = 1.720 + 0.782(Z - 0.4)^{-1}.$$

The indicated level differences are here expressed in cm^{-1} as functions of the nuclear charge Z or of the net charge of the atomic core, $\zeta = Z - 2$. The Rydberg constant is R; α is the Sommerfeld fine-structure constant. The accuracy of this formula was recently confirmed by a measurement of the Ne VIII doublet on spectrograms obtained by Hughes, Bockasten, and Hallin (*1*) from the hot plasma of Sceptre IV at Aldermaston, England. The data are given in Table I.

TABLE I

Ne VIII	Extrapolated	Observed
${}^2P_{3/2} - {}^2S_{1/2}$	129,802 cm^{-1}, 770.40 Å	770.41 Å
${}^2P_{1/2} - {}^2S_{1/2}$	128,148 cm^{-1}, 780.35 Å	780.33 Å

In this connection let us call attention to the promising possibility of obtaining more of the wanted spectroscopic data on highly ionized atoms by using as light sources the hot plasma machines now in operation at several places.

For the further interpretation of the far ultraviolet solar spectrum we have next to consider the isoelectronic sequences beginning in the second short period, in particular the transitions $3s^{r-1}\,3p^{k+1} \rightarrow 3s^r 3p^k$, which are analogous to the transitions $2s^{r-1}\,2p^{k+1} \rightarrow 2s^r\,2p^k$ of the first short period already discussed. With regard to the known relative cosmic abundance of the elements and to the stages of ionization to be expected, we find that in all these isoelectronic sequences the most prominent lines should be produced by iron in various stages of ionization from Fe X to Fe XVI. It was suggested by Dr. Tousey that two prominent lines appearing in the photon-counter tracings obtained by Dr. Hinteregger might be identified with the resonance doublet of Fe XVI. The intensity ratio is correct and the wavelengths correspond closely to the wavelengths calculated from the approximate level values given in Moore's "Atomic Energy Levels" (*2*). A more precise prediction of the position of these lines can be obtained by the following extrapolation formula (*3*):

$$3p\,{}^2P_{1/2} - 3s^2S_{1/2} = 16213.3\zeta + 13832.1 - 60077(\zeta + 3.53)^{-1} + 0.8(\zeta + 5)^3, \qquad {}^2P_{3/2} - {}^2P_{1/2} = \frac{R\alpha^2}{54}(Z - s')^4,$$

$$s' = s - \frac{31\alpha^2}{192}(Z - s')^3, \qquad s = 4.5526 + 11.083(Z - s)^{-1},$$

where the symbols have the same meaning as in the analogous formula for $2p$–$2s$ already quoted. The formula gives for Fe XVI the wavelengths 360.3 and 335.0 Å, which agree with the observed values to the accuracy with which they can be deduced from Hinteregger's tracing. Dr. Tousey's identification of the resonance doublet of Fe XVI is thus strongly supported and may give the clue to the further interpretation of the far ultraviolet solar spectrum.

References

1. T. P. Hughes, K. Bockasten, and R. Hallen, (1961), private communication.
2. C. E. Moore, "Atomic Energy Levels."
3. B. Edlén, "Encyclopedia of Physics," Vol. 27, pp. 159, 169. Springer-Verlag, Heidelberg, in press.

Discussion

Dr. Leo Goldberg: I wonder if Professor Edlén has attempted to look for lines in the intermediate stages of iron between, say, Fe II and Fe X. For example, shouldn't there be lines of Fe VIII and IX in the ultraviolet region of the spectrum that we have been discussing?

Professor Edlén: I have not looked especially into that possibility. Of course, there will be stages from iron X to iron XVI represented in about the same region, or at slightly shorter wavelengths. The situation with regard to the spectral structure of these ions is similar to the one for the first short period for which I showed a complete diagram. Iron is, of course, one to two orders of magnitude more abundant than any other element beyond calcium, so these ions of iron would be the thing to look out for. I have not done that in detail yet.

8.5 Hydrodynamic Aspects of the Corona

JOSEPH W. CHAMBERLAIN

YERKES OBSERVATORY, Williams Bay, Wisconsin

This paper will comment on three points concerning the hydrodynamic aspects of the corona.

Point one deals with the expansion velocity of the solar corona. In my opinion Dr. Parker's solution is entirely correct, mathematically and physically—provided, of course, one assumes his boundary conditions. I emphasize this remark, because in the past I have questioned whether his solution was appropriate. I believe that the low-velocity solution that I offered is also correct and that the choice between these solutions depends on the conditions in the corona. Although I agree with Professor Schatzman that it is difficult to see how the conditions at infinity might feed back and affect the corona, it is not necessary to raise this question at all. Both the high-velocity and the low-velocity solutions that are of physical interest give a vanishing pressure at infinity. We are talking here, of course, about a corona surrounding a star that is in otherwise empty space.

In regard to Professor Schatzman's paper, it is important to point out that there is no such thing as an atmosphere with a finite top. Certainly one can construct a finite atmosphere mathematically by adjusting appropriately the polytropic index, but this is a mathematical fiction. In a real corona the conduction will always smooth the effective polytropic index, which specifies the temperature in terms of the densities, until it reaches the adiabatic value of 5/3, which gives an atmosphere extending to infinity.

The low-velocity solution, incidentally, is roughly equivalent to thermal evaporation of an atmosphere by the escape of fast particles on the tail of the velocity-distribution curve. The coefficient of conductivity gives the information, in effect, about the distribution function of velocities. We shall return to the relationship between these two solutions in a moment.

Point two deals with the densities in the corona. Pottasch (1960) has analyzed the density measurements on the assumption of hydrostatic equilibrium. He found a temperature distribution that was nearly constant out to 3 solar radii. One of Professor Unsöld's figures showed that the temperature was 2,000,000 degrees out to 3 solar radii. If the temperatures at that distance are indeed that high, then there is no escaping from Dr. Parker's high-velocity solution. However, as soon as one admits an outward expansion of the corona, even a slow one, then the temperatures derived from this hydrostatic analysis become invalid. The analysis by Dr. Pottasch was one of the two justifications that Dr. Parker offered for the high-velocity solution being the appropriate one. The other justification for a high velocity of material from the corona was, of course, Professor Biermann's analysis of the comet tails.

As Professor Schatzman stated, both Dr. Parker's model and mine give an acceptable fit with the observed electron densities. But this is not surprising, since in both approaches to the problem there is an undetermined parameter that one can use to force the computed densities to fit the observed ones. Consider the three ways of analyzing the coronal densities. The first case is that of Dr. Pottasch, the hydrostatic model. One sets the expansion velocity equal to zero and uses the density to derive the temperature. In the case of the high-velocity solution, the undetermined parameter is the distance from the sun at which heat is fed in. Thus, with this model we can also think of the temperature in the corona as being undetermined, and we are able to adjust it by analysis of the electron densities.

In the case of the low-velocity solution, which would apply to a corona heated only near the chromosphere, one might think that, with the temperature and density determined at the base of the corona, the whole problem is uniquely determined. At first sight it would appear there is nothing left to adjust, since an integration constant that appears in the problem is uniquely determined to be zero for this solution. However, we still have the thermal conductivity which can be adjusted. The low-velocity solution does not in fact give a good representation of the coronal densities unless one arbitrarily reduces the thermal conductivity by a factor of 3 to 8. In summary, then, the electron densities are of no value in deciding which model of the corona is the more appropriate. The temperature gradient, if it can be determined more directly, would be of value, and some preliminary results by Dr. Billings indicate that the gradient of the temperature in the corona is compatible with the low-velocity expansion.

Point three deals with the thermal conduction. As mentioned, with the low-velocity solution the thermal conductivity appears to be reduced in the corona from the values one would derive for near-Maxwellian velocity distributions. There are two possible ways in which this could occur. First, if there are magnetic fields in the corona then the motions of the individual particles are constricted and the flow of heat outward is reduced. Even a fast thermal particle will not escape from the sun if a weak magnetic field is constraining it. A second possibility is that the distribution function of velocities has significant departures from a Maxwellian distribution, which is used in computing the ordinary coefficient of conductivity. The individual particles that can readily escape from the sun may be depleted, and the tail of the Maxwellian distribution would then be largely missing. It takes quite a number of collisions for a particle that is below the velocity of escape to work its way out on the Maxwellian tail and fill in the distribution.

It is the coefficient of conductivity that gives us the distribution function of particles in the hydrodynamic treatment and relates, therefore, the hydrodynamic theory of expansion to the evaporative theory of escape. There is nothing in the equation of motion or in the equation of continuity that involves a knowledge of the velocity-distribution function. But as soon as we insert a coefficient of thermal conductivity in the first law of thermodynamics, we tacitly assume that the distribution function is known. If the expansion of the corona is thus regarded as the escape of the high-velocity particles from the atmosphere, then it appears quite likely that the tail of the Maxwellian function is partially truncated, or, in terms of the conductivity, the coefficient is reduced. Incidentally, the possibility of a partially truncated distribution function in the corona has not received as much attention as it deserves in relation to the discrepancies between the ion and the electron temperatures. An excitation temperature might give high weight to the tail of the electron distribution function, whereas a Doppler temperature would weight the mean energy of the particles more.

Reference

Pottasch, S. R. (1960), *Astrophys J.* **131,** 68.

8.6 Nonthermal Emission of the Sun

L. BIERMANN

MAX-PLANCK-INSTITUT FÜR PHYSIK UND ASTROPHYSIK, Munich, Germany

A large part of the desired observations of solar and interplanetary phenomena concerns the various aspects of solar activity, particularly the nonthermal radiative and corpuscular emissions of the sun. In this connection a knowledge of the flux of nonthermal energy as a function of time and of position on the sun's surface would be important; hence a concerted attack on these problems, e.g., the role of plage areas as sources of corpuscular and radiative nonthermal emissions, would be desirable. The problem of the flares might be approached from the same point of view, i.e., by investigating the connection between the stationary and the nonstationary nonthermal fluxes of energy. In addition to observations of the solar corpuscular radiation (its direction, density, velocity, and connected magnetic field, all as functions of position and time), continuous direct observations of the solar corona from satellites or space probes would be desirable. The velocity of corotation with the sun of coronal and interplanetary matter is of special interest in this connection.

The problem of the state of the interplanetary plasma should be approached as far as possible using different techniques simultaneously. In addition to those already referred to, these techniques should include observation of comets (if present) and of artificial plasma clouds, say, of barium or carbon monoxide, to be emitted from space probes, in quantities of the order of one or a few kilograms. These measurements might well supplement each other. If, by means of space probes guided towards a comet, the mechanism of interaction between the solar corpuscular radiation and the cometary gases—nonionized and plasma—could be cleared up, the comets themselves could be used more efficiently than is possible today as probes for the physical conditions in interplanetary space.

Discussion

PROFESSOR K. WURM: I would like to make some remarks concerning the corpuscular theory of cometary tails published by Dr. Biermann. In a discussion with him, I learned that he has recently modified his original theory.

In his original theory he had considered only the collision interaction between the solar protons and the cometary particles, other forces being only vaguely mentioned. In order to explain the observed rather high acceleration of cometary tails, he had to assume fairly high proton densities. My arguments against this first form of Biermann's theory are mainly based on the statement that certain cometary phenomena do not allow us to postulate solar proton streams with a density as high as 100 particles/cc.

Dr. Biermann is now trying to explain the acceleration of the tail ions on the basis of a hydromagnetic effect. As he informs me, on this basis it seems to be unnecessary to assume corpuscular densities of the order of a 100 or higher. There remains, however, one essential point about which we have very different opinions.

Dr. Biermann is inclined to attribute the ionization in comets (which leads to the formation of the gas tails) to a charge transfer between the solar protons and the cometary neutral particles. I have found recently that such an assumption leads to difficulties. With the low proton densities of the solar streams the rate factor for ionization proves to be much too low. I have come to the opinion that the ionization is not caused at all directly by an outer influence, and that we are forced to attribute the ionization to conditions within the comet.

I intend to discuss my arguments extensively at the International Astronomical Union at Berkeley.

PROFESSOR BIERMANN: We have two problems, as Dr. Wurm mentioned, the ionization of the gas which then forms a plasma tail and the acceleration of the tails.

As to the acceleration, in my theory it is ascribed to the influence of solar corpuscular radiation. In several papers I discussed three different mechanisms of momentum transfer from the solar corpuscular radiation to the tail plasma: the first is kinetic interaction, and the second magnetic coupling; as a third possibility, plasma effects connected with certain types of plasma instability were proposed.

The first two were mentioned already in my first paper of 1951; the magnetic interaction was later also discussed by Professor Alfvén. In 1951, some observational data suggested a density of the solar plasma of several 10^2 cm^{-3}. The theory of the kinetic interaction could be brought into a quantitative form. As to the magnetic interaction it did not appear necessary to describe it quantitatively because it could obviously lead to higher acceleration than the first.

The third possibility was mentioned in a lecture which I gave at the National Academy of Sciences early last year [*Revs. Modern Phys.* **32,** No. 4, p. 1008 (1960)]. A new assessment of the observational position, which has changed in important respects, was also given there.

As to the ionization, I ascribed this, in 1953, to charge transfer between the solar protons and cometary CO molecules. However, it was found some years later, and it came to my attention only still later, that the cross section of this process is as high as 3×10^{-15} cm^2, whereas originally I had assumed only 1×10^{-15} cm^2. As a consequence there is a certain discontinuity in figures which are found in the literature on the subject. Now we assume a range of solar particle intensity of from 10^9 protons/cm^2 sec up to 10^{11} in magnetic storms. These figures are compatible with the recent evidence from zodiacal light observations. I still have to study the new work of Dr. Wurm to which he made reference here. Until then I do not wish to express any opinion at this stage as to the conclusions one should draw from it.

CHAPTER 9

Stars and the Galaxy

9.1 Stellar and Interstellar Observations

LEO GOLDBERG

HARVARD AND SMITHSONIAN OBSERVATORIES,
Cambridge, Massachusetts

Introduction

The advantages of astronomical observations carried out above the earth's atmosphere have already been widely quoted and require only brief mention here. First, there will be a substantial reduction in the brightness of the sky background once one gets above the airglow generated in the upper atmosphere of the earth. The three principal contributors to the brightness of the night sky are (1) the airglow, (2) the zodiacal light caused by the scattering of sunlight by interplanetary dust, and (3) galactic and extragalactic radiation from faint stars and nebulae. The brightness of the airglow is time dependent, the variations being both irregular and correlated with the sun spot cycle; the brightness also increases strongly from zenith to horizon. The spectrum of the airglow consists of both lines and continua, but even when the lines are eliminated by filtering techniques, the visual brightness in the darkest parts of the sky still averages about the equivalent of 150 to 200 tenth-magnitude stars per square degree. The amount of extraneous skylight that will still be seen from above the earth's atmosphere is difficult to estimate because the brightness of the zodiacal light in directions away from the ecliptic has not been determined. Estimates range from 5 to 50 tenth-magnitude stars per square degree, but these are hardly more than guesses.

The second factor limiting ground-based astronomical observations is the turbulence of the earth's atmosphere. The theoretical resolving power of a 50-in. telescope is about $\frac{1}{10}$ sec of arc for visible light and proportionately better for larger telescopes, but star images observed through the earth's atmosphere are rarely smaller than ½ sec of arc, even under the best conditions. The limiting magnitude of the faintest stars that can be observed with a telescope of a given size is determined by the size of the image and the brightness of the background. A reduction in image size by a factor of 5 would result in a gain of between 3 and 4 magnitudes, and a further gain of from 1 to 3 magnitudes would result from the lowered sky brightness. The possibility of observing extremely faint stars is of fundamental importance to stellar astronomy.

The third and undoubtedly most important advantage to be gained from astronomical observations in space is the elimination of the earth's atmosphere as an absorbing medium for all but a few very narrow regions of the electromagnetic spectrum. The entire high energy portion of the spectrum, including γ-rays, X-rays, and most of the ultraviolet are hidden from view on the ground; so also is a large fraction of the infrared radiation, to which the earth's atmosphere is only partially transparent in a few relatively narrow spectral regions between 1 and 24 μ.

Infrared Observations

Most of the astronomical observations discussed in this paper will be concerned with the short-wave end of the spectrum, but there are also a few points to make in connection with the infrared. The first is that a great deal in the way of infrared observations from the ground, or better still from balloons, still remains to be done through a number of fairly transparent windows in the earth's atmosphere in several spectral bands between 1 and 11 μ. In the past, the chief limitation upon observation in this spectral region has been the insensitivity of energy detectors. However, although there have been important advances in instrumentation in recent years, very few applications have been made to planetary and stellar astronomy after the early work of Kuiper, chiefly prior to 1950. At wavelengths greater than 2 μ the available detectors are still not comparable in sensitivity with those at shorter wavelengths and no suitable imaging devices have yet been developed. However, astronomers have not yet made full use of available instrumentation, and, in particular, the use of a Michelson interferometer with Fourier analysis of the signal has not been fully exploited.

Table I lists a number of classes of typical objects that may be expected to emit richly in infrared radiation, together with their temperatures and corresponding wavelengths of maximum emission. The first category includes late-type stars of Population II, whose visible radiation is almost completely obscured by interstellar dust. The second group comprises ordinary late-type stars whose temperatures are difficult to evaluate from the visible spectrum, which is weak and strongly mutilated by molecular band absorption. The third and fourth groups include hypothetical exceptionally cool stars whose radiation has not yet been detected, since the peak intensities fall between 1.5 and 6 μ. These include very faint, cool stars at the extreme lower end of the main sequence; cool, giant stars like the invisible component of ϵ Aurigae, dying stars which have passed the white dwarf stage, and newly formed protostars which

TABLE I

Typical objects	Temp. (°K)	Wavelength (μ)
Obscured type II gK	4000	0.7
Ordinary cool stars	3000	1.0
Extraordinarily cool stars	2000–1000	1.5–3.0
Protostars, etc.	500	6.0
Interstellar dust	100	30

are still radiating by gravitational contraction and have not yet reached the main sequence. Finally, measurements at extreme infrared wavelengths, in the neighborhood of 30 μ, might reveal the thermal radiation from interstellar dust clouds, although the detection of this very feeble radiation is far beyond the capability of existing detectors.

It is possible that the first four groups of objects in the table could be detected from the ground through one or another of the atmospheric windows, but probably most of the objects will be so faint that they could be detected only from above the airglow.

Observation of Ultraviolet, X-Rays and γ-Rays

Bad seeing is eliminated at altitudes above about 60,000 ft; at altitudes between 80,000 and 100,000 ft, the absorption of infrared radiation by the atmosphere is relatively weak. It seems reasonable therefore, to carry out both infrared experiments and those requiring high angular resolution from balloons, and to assign the first priority in satellites to observations at the high energy end of the spectrum. Since the nature of stellar and nebular radiation at wavelengths below 3000 Å is almost completely unknown, it is difficult to plan detailed observational programs until at least a preliminary reconnaissance has been carried out to obtain an ultraviolet map of the sky, of the type being planned for the first orbiting astronomical observatory by Whipple and Davis at the Smithsonian Astrophysical Observatory. Such surveys, and others concerned with γ- and X-rays are almost certain to open up new fields of investigation in the domain of high energies; but it is also possible, in the light of present astronomical knowledge, to plan a whole series of important experiments concerned with problems that have already been defined by ground-based observations. Before proceeding to describe a few of the typical experiments that have been proposed, we must realize that there will still be two inherent limitations to observation from observatories in space. The first has already been mentioned, namely, the elevation of the sky brightness by the scattering of sunlight by

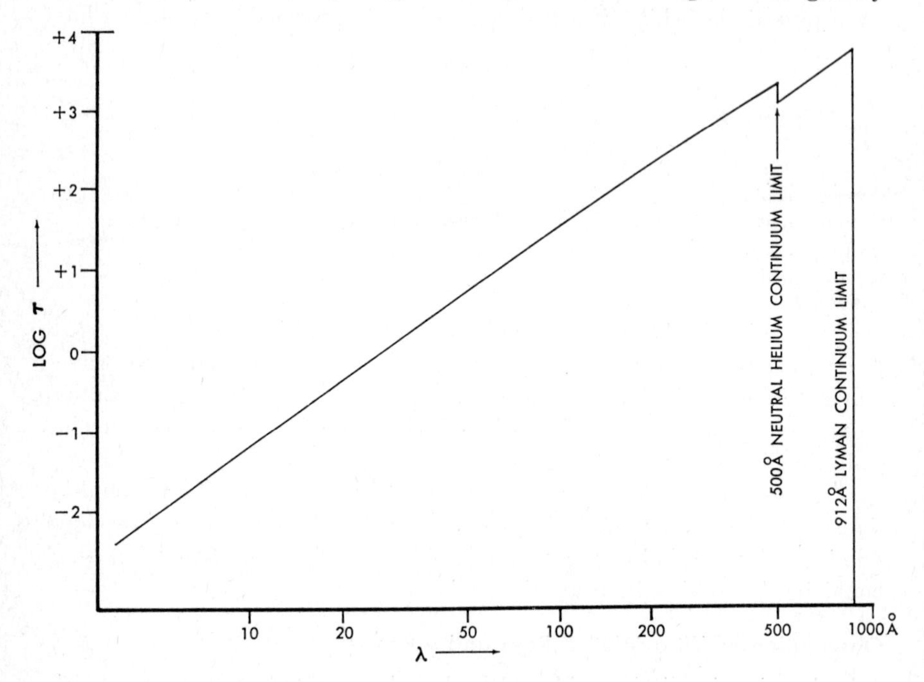

FIG. 1. Absorption by interstellar hydrogen and helium.

interplanetary dust. In theory, this limitation could be removed by orbiting an observatory about the sun in a plane highly inclined to the ecliptic. The second limitation is much more fundamental, since it arises from the absorption of ultraviolet radiation by gas in the interstellar medium.

The density of the interstellar gas is exceedingly low, averaging about 10^{-24} gm/cc, or about one hydrogen atom per cubic centimeter. However, the line of sight distances to individual stars and nebulae are enormous. For example, the number of neutral hydrogen atoms in the line of sight between the earth and the Orion nebula is 10^{21} cm^{-2}; there are also about $\frac{1}{7}$ as many helium atoms and a much smaller number of all other elements combined. It has been shown by Aller (1959) and others that the absorption by hydrogen and helium alone is sufficient to extinguish all radiation from the Orion region of wavelengths between 912 and

30 Å (see Fig. 1). More recently, Strom and Strom (1961) have shown that when the X-ray absorption of the heavy elements in the interstellar medium is taken into account, the transmission of radiation from Orion

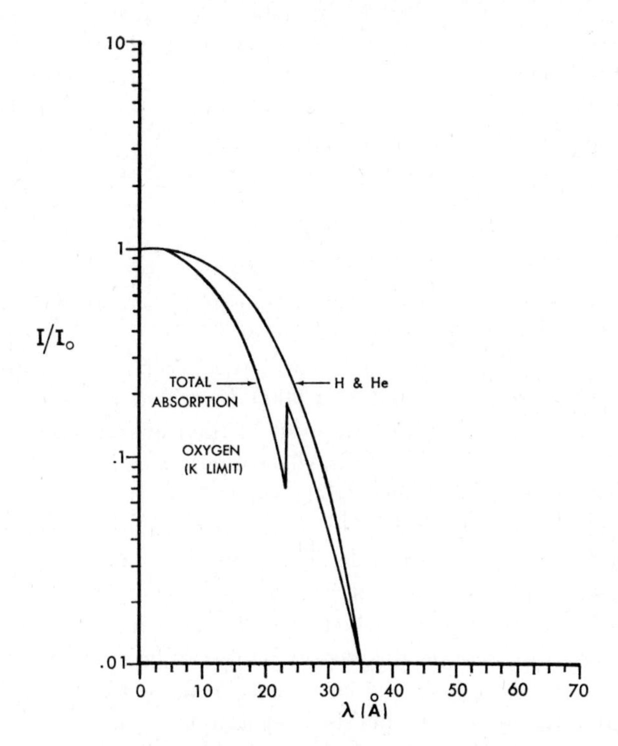

FIG. 2. Interstellar absorption of soft X-rays.

is still only 50% at a wavelength of 15 Å (see Fig. 2). Thus, we shall probably not be able to observe ultraviolet radiation short of 912 Å from any but the nearest stars, although the possibility that there will be a certain number of holes or windows where the density of the interstellar medium is very low cannot be ruled out.

I. EXTRAGALACTIC LIGHT

The distribution, brightnesses, sizes, and red shifts of external galaxies are the basic observational data which can prove or disprove current theories of the structure and origin of the universe. It turns out that the observational differences predicted by different theories become substantial only at very great distances and, as has been pointed out by Sandage (1961), it is marginal as to whether observations made at the limit of even the 200-in. telescope will be sufficiently discriminatory. At the very largest distances, approaching the radius of curvature of the universe, individual galaxies become too faint and numerous to be observed, but are merged together to constitute a feebly glowing background which is far too weak to be detected against the airglow. It is possible, however, that the color and brightness of the extragalactic light and its distribution over the sky could be measured from a satellite. Such an experiment has been proposed by Baum and others. The equipment needed would be of light weight and simple design, consisting of a photometer with filters to isolate a number of relatively broad spectral bands.

II. Ultraviolet Radiation of Hot Stars

The distribution with wavelength of the energy radiated by a star is a fundamental quantity from which one may deduce the effective temperature of the star and the structure of its outer layers. Stars with effective temperatures in the range 4000° to 9000°K, which represent the great majority of those observed, radiate most of their energy in regions of the spectrum that can be observed from the ground. This is not the case with the very hottest stars of spectral classes O and B, with temperatures between 20,000° and 50,000°K, which radiate only a very small fraction of their total energy in the visible. The situation is illustrated in Fig. 3, which has been taken from an article by Code (1960). The region bounded by the vertical lines, which is observable from the ground, contains only the tail end of the energy curve of a star of temperature 25,000°K. The main part of the curve has been calculated theoretically, but since the theoretical model is based upon such a minor fraction of the star's radiation, its validity is extremely doubtful. In fact, some very recent rocket observations, by Stecher and Milligan (1961) at the Goddard Space Flight Center, of the ultraviolet spectra of five O and B-type stars would indicate that the theoretical models are grossly in error. It is found, for example, that observation and theory are in good agreement only to a wavelength of 2400 Å. At this point, the observed curve turns down steeply, until it departs from the theoretical curve by an order of magnitude at 2000 Å. These observations must be repeated and confirmed, but if they are correct they overturn completely our present notions about the structures of the atmospheres of hot stars and illustrate the kinds of surprises that are in store in the near future.

If observations of the ultraviolet energy distributions of hot stars should prove present models of their atmospheres to be incorrect, we shall also be forced to revise our notions of the chemical abundances in their atmospheres, since the abundances derived from atomic line spectra are

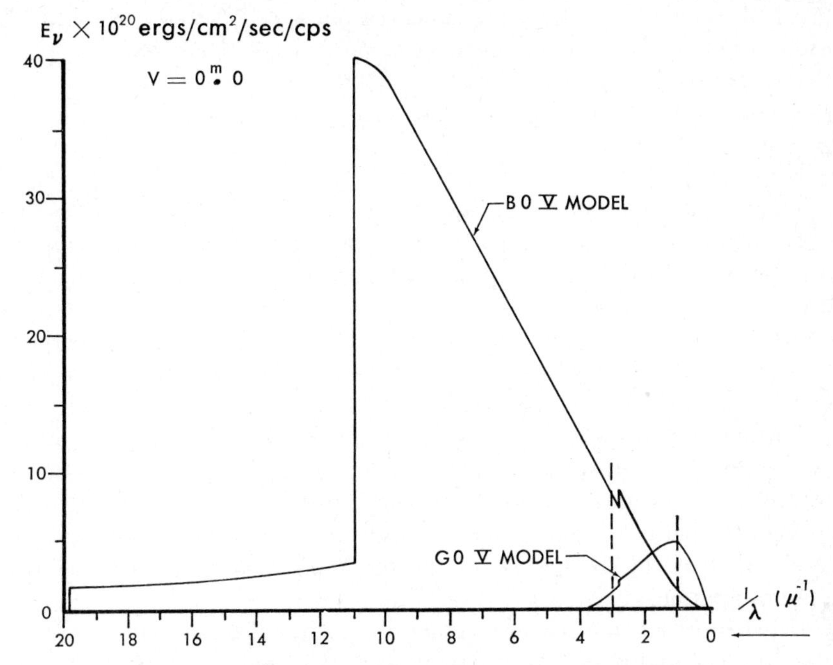

FIG. 3. Spectral energy distribution for main sequence stars.

very critically dependent upon the assumed model. This is a very important point because very hot stars are also relatively young, and modern theories of stellar evolution predict that their chemical abundances should be appreciably different from those of cooler, older stars. Furthermore, calculations of the physical state of the interstellar medium require knowledge of the ultraviolet radiation field which comes chiefly from the high temperature stars.

III. CHEMICAL ABUNDANCES

Accurate chemical abundances are of the highest importance in all theories of stellar evolution. For this reason, a large amount of effort has been expended in deriving abundances from the observed intensities of lines in stellar spectra. For many elements, especially the light gases such as hydrogen, helium and other inert gases, carbon, nitrogen, oxygen, and the halogens, the lines that occur in the visible part of the spectrum are not the ones best suited for abundance determinations, because they originate from excited levels, and it is not possible to transform line intensities into abundances without frequently doubtful assumptions as to the physical state of the stellar atmosphere. This difficulty can be greatly reduced by using lines that originate from the lowest energy state in which most of the atoms are concentrated. In the spectra of relatively cool stars like the sun, the ultraviolet spectrum is so crowded with lines that accurate measurements will be all but impossible, and therefore such abundance studies can best be performed for the hotter stars.

IV. Stellar Chromospheres and Coronas

The visible radiation of the sun is emitted from an atmospheric zone about 300 km in thickness, at the upper boundary of which the temperature is about 4500°K. Above this boundary, astronomers distinguish two layers: the *chromosphere,* which is about 20,000 km in thickness, and the *corona,* which extends to very great distances from the sun, perhaps, as suggested by Chapman (1959), beyond the orbit of the earth. Both of these layers are essentially transparent to visible light, but their faint radiations can be easily observed when the sun is eclipsed. A new era in solar physics began in 1941 when Edlén proved that the temperature of the corona is on the order of 1 million degrees. The transition from low to high temperature takes place abruptly in the chromosphere, probably as a result of the dissipation of the mechanical energy associated with the granulation.

It is important to discover whether other stars also have chromospheres and coronas, and if so, whether they are limited only to stars like the sun or whether they are characteristic of other types of stars as well. The answer can be found by observing stellar ultraviolet spectra. The normal, low temperature component of the sun's radiation is a continuous spectrum crossed by dark absorption lines, which extends through the visible and near ultraviolet spectral regions, but fades out very rapidly at shorter wavelengths. Rocket observations show that beginning at about 1700 Å the spectrum consists chiefly of bright emission lines characteristic of the high temperature gases in the chromosphere and corona. Stars possessing similar high temperature envelopes would also exhibit bright emission lines in their far ultraviolet spectra.

Such stars might be revealed by the Smithsonian survey, but in searching for them we can also make use of existing information which identifies certain classes of stars as more promising than others. One such group of stars, which has been studied extensively by Wilson (Wilson and Bappu, 1957), consists of objects of type G or later which show bright emission reversals in the central cores of their Ca II absorption lines. Several lines of evidence indicate that the presence of the emission reversals is connected with the existence of a chromosphere and probably also a corona. A remarkable feature of the emission reversal is that its width is closely correlated with the intrinsic luminosity of the star over a total range of 16 magnitudes. This suggests that far ultraviolet emission spectra may be most conspicuous in some of the brightest stars in the sky, such as Aldebaran, Betelgeuse, Antares, and Arcturus. It also goes without saying that stars with such high temperature envelopes are likely to be sources of intense X-ray emission.

Other stars from which intense ultraviolet emission is to be expected are the so-called recurrent novae, such as RS Ophiuchi, T Pyxidis and T Coronae Borealis, all of which have displayed forbidden coronal lines from highly ionized atoms during their outbursts. In fact, any star displaying bright emission lines in its visible spectrum is probably a powerful emitter of ultraviolet radiation.

V. The Interstellar Medium

The value of a space observatory for the investigation of the interstellar medium has been particularly emphasized by Spitzer (1960). Of special importance would be the precise determination of chemical abundances to verify or disprove current ideas on stellar evolution, which suggest that stars condense out of the interstellar medium and replenish it by ejection in later stages after converting hydrogen and helium into heavy elements. Of very great significance would be the discovery of interstellar lines of the hydrogen molecule at $\lambda 1108$ and $\lambda 1008$ Å, for which Spitzer plans to search with a high dispersion spectrograph in the Orbiting Astronomical Observatory. In spite of the very great abundance of atomic hydrogen in the universe, H_2 has never been found outside of the solar system, probably because it radiates only very weakly in visible wavelengths. On the other hand, there is indirect evidence that it may be present in interstellar space in very large quantities. The most compelling argument comes from attempts to account for the mass of our Milky Way galaxy, as deduced from its rotation, and from the density of material in the neighborhood of the sun as derived from the observed motions of stars in the direction perpendicular to the plane of the Milky Way. It has been found by Oort, for example, that the total density of matter in the neighborhood of the sun is about 10^{-23} gm/cc, which is the equivalent of 0.15 solar masses per cubic parsecond. The stars in the solar neighborhood account for only 38% of this density, and therefore the balance must be found in the interstellar medium and in the form of stars too faint to be observed. Now atomic hydrogen, in the interstellar gas, can account for only 2% of the remainder, and the amount of dust is insignificant. Therefore about half of the total mass in the neighborhood of the sun has not been discovered, and it is possible that a large fraction of it could be in the form of molecular hydrogen. Spitzer has also pointed out that at present the only interstellar absorption lines strong enough to permit an accurate measurement are those of neutral sodium and ionized calcium. Extension of the spectrum to the ultraviolet would permit measurements on more abundant atoms such as carbon, nitrogen, oxygen, magnesium, and iron.

VI. X- and γ-Rays

Many objects in the galaxy may be expected to emit X-radiation with high intensity. It is known that X-radiation from the sun is greatly enhanced in active regions (Chubb *et al.*, 1961) and there is no reason why many stars may not have solar-type activity on a scale much greater than that of the sun. The so called flare stars, for example, display activity which is much more conspicuous than flare activity on the sun. Friedman has also recently shown that a map of the sun in X-rays looks hardly different from one made in radio radiation at 10 cm. This suggests that galactic and extragalactic radio sources may also be powerful X-ray emitters. Gamma rays in the energy range 50–200 Mev are expected to result from collisions between high energy cosmic rays and the interstellar gas. Within our own galaxy, γ-ray emission might be found in objects like the Crab nebula and outside the galaxy from external and radio sources such as Cygnus A. Gamma-ray emission from intergalactic matter is also an intriguing possibility, especially if it results from the interaction of matter and antimatter.

References

Aller, L. H. (1959), *Publs. Astron. Soc. Pacific* **71,** 324.

Chapman, S. (1959), *Proc. Roy. Soc.* **A253,** 462.

Chubb, T. A., Friedman, H., and Kreplin, R. W. (1961), *Mém soc. roy. sci. Liège* **4**(5), 216.

Code, A. D. (1960), *Astron. J.* **65,** 278.

Sandage, A. (1961), *Astrophys. J.* **133,** 355.

Spitzer, L. (1960), *Astron. J.* **65,** 278.

Stecher, T. P., and Milligan, J. E. (1961), *Astron. J.* **66,** 296.

Strom, S. E., and Strom, K. M. (1961), *Publs. Astron. Soc. Pacific* **73,** 43.

Wilson, O. C., and Bappu, M. K. V. (1957), *Astrophys. J.* **125,** 661.

Discussion

Dr. D. Menzel: Several speakers in this symposium have mentioned a discrepancy between theory and observation in the distribution of light in the Lyman ultraviolet. Dr. Goldberg referred to Code's work. In my opinion, this discrepancy results from the rather naive theory on which the spectrum is calculated. Code's theory and similar conventional theories usually take into account only the opacity resulting from the bound-free and free-free continua. The Lyman continuum alone will produce a sharp drop in intensity beyond the sun's limit. However, it is quite clear that the Lyman lines themselves must be very broad in these early type stars. The higher members will overlap and produce a pseudo-continuum that grades imperceptibly into the real continuum. The lower members may well be several hundred angström units in breadth, and thus extend effective continuum absorption almost up to 3000 Å. I think this overlapping is responsible for the low intensity observed in the ultraviolet spectra of these stars.

DR. J. GREENSTEIN: I agree very strongly with what Dr. Menzel has said. I have no computations for a hot star; the ionization of hydrogen and the possible existence of other weak sources of opacity might make the problem difficult. But I have computed the case of the sun. Here, the longer wavelength wing of Lyman α contributes more opacity than does the continuous absorption coefficient of H^- at around 1100 Å from the center of the line; i.e., at 2300 Å the two sources of opacity are equal. I think that the atomic data may be available for the hot stars from the work on the contribution of atomic lines to the opacity, which has been done for the AEC and other organizations. What is required is the amount of transition probability in the lines as we approach the various series limits that one would find in the hot stars.

DR. D. MENZEL: May I say that Lowell Doherty and I made such calculations for the sun, which we presented last year at the Liège Symposium. We agree completely with the statement that was made.

DR. L. GOLDBERG: It does not seem to me, however, that extensive wings of Lyman α could account for the very steep drop in the spectral intensity between 2400 and 2000 Å, as recently observed by Stecher and Milligan in the spectra of early-type stars.

9.2 *High Energy Phenomena in Stellar Astronomy*

JESSE L. GREENSTEIN
MOUNT WILSON AND PALOMAR OBSERVATORIES
Pasadena, California

Introduction

Only the most significant type of novel experiments can justify the cost and effort of extra-terrestrial observations. These must be connected with features of the universe which cannot be observed from the ground, from rockets, or from balloons. Thus it is likely that the "high energy" components accompanying astronomical phenomena will in the future provide the most striking new information. We are already familiar with the high temperature outer envelope of the sun, and its emission of X-rays. But γ-rays could represent different types of even more fundamental phenomena, since they correspond to transitions between energy levels of nuclei, rather than of atoms. The range of energy expected for γ-rays from common nuclei is 1 to 6 Mev; collisions resulting in capture in higher nuclear energy levels often result in cascading emission of several different γ-rays. In all cases the nuclear processes give narrow lines; laboratory techniques permit identification of the nucleus from the energy of the transition. Continua are emitted by such processes as bremsstrahlung, the violent deceleration of a high energy electron on capture. Another continuum is emitted by the decay of mesons, where two γ-rays share the decay energy, so that all energies up to a fixed maximum value can be emitted.

Typical nuclear reactions in stellar interiors produce γ-rays with energies from 1 to 10 Mev, in various energy-production cycles, but these are degraded into lower energy photons as the radiation is absorbed and re-emitted during its passage outwards. Since absorption cross sections are relatively high, it is unlikely that γ-rays will be observable from stellar layers buried under more than 100 gm/cm^2 of material. Thus only those nuclear reactions occurring at or near the surface of the stars will be directly detectable. Thermal γ-rays from stellar surfaces are negligible, since the highest stellar temperatures, near 10^6 °K, correspond only to 100 ev. Thus all the stars together can produce only a negligible γ-ray flux at the earth unless novel high energy phenomena occur.

But it is this very fact, that high energy phenomena do indeed occur, that makes γ-ray astronomy so difficult. Cosmic rays—fast moving nuclei of H, He, and other elements—are emitted by the sun, fill most of the galaxy, come from peculiar stars and nebulae, and carry energies measured in Bev (and even up to 10^{19} ev). The cosmic-ray background renders γ-ray detection difficult, making it necessary to use complex detectors and circuitry to discriminate between the γ-rays and the cosmic rays. But even worse, the cosmic rays create their own γ-rays by nuclear collisions, either in interstellar space or in our atmosphere. Thus a γ-ray detector carried in a balloon will encounter from 0.001 to 0.2 γ-rays $cm^{-2}sec^{-1}$ steradian^{-1} as it rises through the atmosphere. Even at the maximum heights attainable in a balloon, the upward (albedo) γ-radiation is about 0.02 units. Computations also indicate that outside the solar system, in interstellar space, the gas density is sufficient that cosmic-ray collisions will produce an equilibrium count of γ-rays in the range 10^{-5} to 10^{-3} $cm^{-2}sec^{-1}$, dependent on galactic latitude. (This is based, of course, on the assumption that the cosmic-ray density is the same in the galaxy as in the solar system). Absorption of γ-rays is negligible in either a galaxy or intergalactic space. Even if we assume the relatively high density of 10^{-28} gm cm^{-3} for intergalactic space, absorption would require a path length of 10^{30} cm, or 10^{12} light years, (about 100 times the radius of the universe). Even at large redshifts, until $dE/E \rightarrow 1$, γ-ray energies would still be observed by a stationary observer to be high. Nevertheless, this lack of absorption and the propagation in straight lines—apparent advantages over cosmic rays—cannot as yet be fully utilized because there are no real γ-ray telescopes.

Other fundamental difficulties of γ-ray astronomy are:

(1) lack of focusing devices of large collecting area to increase counting rates.

(2) Lack of pointing accuracy required for detection of small sources. Collimation is provided only by the geometrical arrangement of shielding components. Acquisition of, and lock-on to, small sources will be very difficult.

(3) The discrimination between photons and charged particles requires simultaneous use of various sensors, together with coincidence and anticoincidence circuits.

None of the difficulties are insuperable, and the first γ-ray telescope has already been orbited, although no results are yet available (August 1961). Balloon observations have already provided significant results. Cline (*1*) finds an upper limit to the γ-ray flux near the top of our atmosphere 7×10^{-3} cm^{-2} sec^{-1} sr^{-1}. This limit is only 10 times the probable γ-ray flux from the interstellar gas, and already restricts the possibility of the "steady-state" theory of creation of matter (see below).

Possible Astronomical γ-Ray Sources

(a) The enormous concentration of high energy in a solar flare suggests that the conversion of energy from magnetic fields into high energy nucleons and electrons will provide high γ-ray fluxes. Approximately 10^{-6} of solar energy appears in all forms of high energy phenomena, which is about 10^{12} ev $cm^{-2}sec^{-1}$ at the earth. *If only 10^{-6} of the high-energy component of solar radiation were γ-rays, (i.e., 10^{-12} of total energy), the counting rate would be 1 γ-ray cm^{-2} sec^{-1}*, an already excluded value. However, balloon observations during a solar flare are still needed.

Magnetic stars and flare stars of the dMe and T Tauri types represent stellar sources in which magnetic-discharge phenomena might far exceed their solar intensity. However, the inverse square law would reduce fluxes at the earth by a factor of 10^{-12} or more compared to the solar distance.

(b) Enormous energy concentrations of relativistic electrons exist in all nonthermal radio sources, such as the Crab nebula (2000 pc distant) and extragalactic objects like NGC 5128, Cygnus A, M 87 (distances 10^7 to 10^8 pc). Recent improvements in our knowledge of the size and distance of these objects show that up to 10^{61} ergs must be contained in the form of magnetic fields, relativistic electrons, and protons, if the radio noise is assigned to synchrotron emission in a magnetic field. If the energy in protons is a large fraction of the total, all radio sources must be powerful γ-ray emitters. Assuming a reasonable power law, the mean energy per proton is about 10^{-3} ergs, and the total number of protons in the source is of the order of 10^{63}. If these decay by collision in 10^7 years, the expected flux of γ-rays is 10^{-4} cm^{-2} sec^{-1} even for the distant source Cygnus A. The sources subtend relatively small angles, and γ-ray telescopes with high angular resolution should discriminate very clearly between them and the nearly isotropic galactic or extragalactic γ-rays. Some years ago this writer suggested that collisions of large masses of gas, such as would occur when galaxies collide, might provide a source of monochromatic γ-rays from such nuclear collisions as $D^2(p,\gamma)He^3$, if deuterium exists in the interstellar gas.

(c) The total radio emission of our own galaxy is about 10^{-7} that of the strong radio sources such as Cygnus A. The largest fraction of galactic radio noise comes from the galactic center, at a distance of 10^4 pc. The inverse-square factor for Cygnus A, compared to the galactic center, is 10^{-8}, so that our own galactic center should be stronger than

Cygnus A in total flux, but of lower specific intensity because of its large size.

(d) A most speculative but possibly very important goal of γ-ray astronomy would be the detection of proton-antiproton annihilation radiation. If nature is symmetrical, we might speculate that protons and antiprotons (or neutrons and antineutrons) are created in equal numbers, but are somehow segregated in separate galaxies. Then, the possibility exists that proton-antiproton annihilation would occur subsequently. There could be exchange of matter between galaxies, due to evaporation from stars and from the halo of interstellar gas; there could be collisions of galaxies. Or, the steady-state universe, with creation of matter at a constant rate, might result in antiprotons appearing in interstellar space in our galaxy. The collision cross section is large, 10^{-25} cm^2 at high energy and much larger at low energy because of the attractive force between the oppositely charged particles. The $p + \bar{p}$ collision yields a π^0 meson, whose decay gives γ-rays of a wide spectrum and average energy 10^2 Mev. Thus, the annihilation process in matter even at very large distances, with a red shift $\Delta E/E \approx 0.99$, would radiate photons which we would detect as γ-rays in the Mev range. The entire observable universe would then contain γ-ray sources.

The consequences of steady-state antimatter creation would be serious in our own galaxy. At the usually adopted steady-state-cosmology figure of 10^{-22} pairs cm^{-3} sec^{-1}, the annihilation of the new antiprotons by the old interstellar protons would produce about 10 times the maximum possible counting rate found by Cline in a balloon flight. Since the γ-rays come in straight lines, experiments with good angular resolution, freedom from terrestrial γ-rays and longer duration (possible from satellites) should delimit the interstellar gas, if some antiprotons are being created in it.

If only a very low γ-ray flux exists, it is possible that steady-state cosmology might be able to postulate that antimatter is for some reason not created in the presence of normal matter. Then the expected flux from collision and interchange of gas between systems can be searched for.

To end on a lighter note, let us compute the expected γ-ray flux on the assumption that (1) the steady-state theory is correct, (2) protons and antiprotons are produced in equal numbers, (3) antigravity does not exist, and (4) each galaxy condenses with one form of matter (or antimatter) as a result of chance fluctuations only. The last assumption requires that if a system contain N atoms, it is the residue of an original N^2 atoms, all but N of which have been destroyed by annihilation collisions. Since a galaxy contains 10^{68} atoms, 10^{136} atoms had to be produced and 10^{136} γ-rays emitted. The latter number is so large that even if the galaxy took 10^{9} years to condense and formed at the edge of the observable universe, 10^{10} light years distant, the flux at the earth is 10^{63} γ-rays cm^{-2} sec^{-1}, more than sufficient to blow the universe apart.

Résumé

The existence of high energy phenomena in the stars and interstellar space has already suggested an enormously wide field of theoretical interpretation and speculation. Cosmic rays have led to deep insights not only in high energy physics but in astrophysics. But little is yet known about the high energy photons from the astronomical environment. Starting with the geophysical and interplanetary environments, γ-ray astronomy should provide new data on phenomena not accessible to ground-based observation. Balloons are a first step, orbiting satellites are next, and large orbiting laboratories should follow. New devices to provide large collecting area and collimation are badly needed. There exists a fundamental difficulty, γ-rays of cosmic-ray origin; but perhaps γ-rays will contribute to the study of cosmic rays, for example, to the question as to whether cosmic rays ultimately decay in the disk or in the halo of our galaxy. Once successful discrimination between this background and the astronomical sources becomes possible, a new field of astronomy should be opened to fruitful study.

Reference

1. T. L. Cline, *Phys. Rev. Letters* **7**, 109 (1961). See also W. L. Kraushaar and G. W. Clark, *ibid.* **8**, 106 (1962).

CHAPTER 10

Structural Problems of Galaxies in the Light of Lyman-α

GUIDO MÜNCH

MOUNT WILSON AND PALOMAR OBSERVATORIES, Pasadena, California

1. Introduction

The fundamental importance of the information that might be derived from Lyman-α observations of stars and nebulae has long been realized. From the literature on the subject, however, it does not appear that a proper discussion has been carried out of the conditions under which meaningful observations might be obtained. Thus, for example, it has been said (*1*) that "there is almost no hope at all of getting any observations on the Lyman series of gaseous nebulae." At the other extreme, it also has been said (*2*) that "Lyman-α quanta will be successively scattered *less inelastic* encounters until they finally escape from the fringes of the Galaxy." Both statements are incomplete, as they do not contain an evaluation of the processes through which Lyman-α radiation is converted into other frequencies (true absorption). We propose to discuss here briefly the problem of Lyman-α scattering and absorption in the interstellar medium. On this basis, the kind of observations that should be attempted, to derive information about the structure of our galaxy and other stellar systems, will be pointed out.

From the start, it will be supposed that the Lyman-α illumination of the geocorona or the interplanetary medium can be eliminated through the use of sufficiently high spectral resolving power. The half-width of the geocoronal Lyman-α is quite small (around 5 km/sec or 0.02 Å). Outside this range, then, we would not expect much interference. The width of interplanetary Lyman-α would be considerably larger on account of Keplerian Doppler shifts, but its intensity would be low, at least in directions off the ecliptic.

2. The Lyman-α Sources

The sources of Lyman-α radiation are to be found in stellar chromospheres and in the regions of the interstellar medium where hydrogen is predominantly ionized. The solar luminosity in Lyman-α, according to Hinteregger (*3*), amounts to

$$\mathfrak{L}_\alpha(\odot) = 2 \times 10^{28} \text{ ergs/sec} = 5 \times 10^{-6} L_\odot. \tag{1}$$

Assuming that all stars with spectral types later than G0 emit the same fraction of their luminosity in Lyman-α we find, in consideration of the stellar luminosity function, that the stars will emit around $\eta(\odot) = 10^{26}$ ergs/sec pc^3. This amount should be compared with the flux beyond the Lyman limit from main-sequence OB stars (around 10^5 $L_\odot$) multiplied by their mean number per unit volume (10^{-8} pc^{-3}) or η (OB) $= 10^{30}$ ergs/sec pc^3. In the large, then, the early-type stars are the predominant sources of Lyman-α radiation. Their mean mutual distance, however, may exceed the mean free path of a Lyman-α quantum before absorption, as we shall show. The energy density in Lyman-α, thus, would be expected to vary over large ranges. In any case, it would appear logical to begin our discussion with the problem of the absorption of Lyman-α inside an H II region.

3. Absorption of Lyman-α in H II Regions

In an H II region free of dust, the process through which Lyman-α quanta are lost is by the emission of two photons from the $2S$ level of hydrogen, collisionally mixed with the $2P$ level, which in turn is excited by resonance absorption. Symbolically, we describe this process through the reactions

$$\mathrm{H}(1S) + L\alpha \rightarrow \mathrm{H}(2P), \tag{2}$$

$$\mathrm{H}(2P) + \begin{Bmatrix} e^- \\ p \end{Bmatrix} \rightleftarrows \mathrm{H}(2S) + \begin{Bmatrix} e^- \\ p \end{Bmatrix}, \tag{3}$$

$$\mathrm{H}(2S) \rightarrow \mathrm{H}(1S) + 2h\nu. \tag{4}$$

Let the optical depth of the H II region at the center of Lyman-α be τ_0 and let it be supposed that there are no random mass motions or systematic expansion. A typical galactic H II region would have $\tau_0 = 10^6$ (*4*). If the scattering of L_α were a strictly coherent process (frequencies of incident and scattered quanta exactly the same), the number of scatterings that a Lyman-α photon would suffer before diffusing out would be τ_0^2. The $2h\nu$ conversion process has the probability

$$\lambda = \frac{C(2P \rightarrow 2S)}{A(2P \rightarrow 1S)}, \tag{5}$$

where $C\ (2P \rightarrow 2S)$ is the collisional transition rate of the process (3) and $A\ (2P \rightarrow 1S)$ is the Einstein probability coefficient for spontaneous emission from the $2P$ level of hydrogen. With the values of $C\ (2P \rightarrow 2S)$ calculated by Seaton (*5*), one finds for a temperature $T = 10^4$ °K,

$$\lambda = 10^{-13} N_e, \tag{6}$$

where N_e is the electron number density in cm^{-3}. Absorption in an H II region with $\tau_0 = 10^6$ would be then complete if $N_e \approx 10$ if the scattering were coherent.

Actually, the frequency shifts produced by the relative thermal motions of the scattering atoms considerably increase the probability of Lyman-α diffusion. Let the scattering process be supposed completely noncoherent, the frequency distribution of a scattered photon being independent of the exciting one, and reflecting only the velocity distribution of the scattering atoms. If frequency shifts from the center of Lyman-α are measured in units of the Doppler width

$$\Delta\nu_D = \frac{\nu_0}{c}\left(\frac{2kT}{m_H}\right)^{1/2}, \tag{7}$$

the probability $p(x)\Delta x$ that a photon is scattered in the range (*6*) $\nu = \nu_0 + x\Delta\nu_D,\ \nu + \Delta\nu = \nu_0 + (x + \Delta x)\ \Delta\nu_D$ is

$$p(x)\Delta x = \frac{1}{\sqrt{\pi}} \exp{(-x^2)}\Delta x. \tag{8}$$

Every time a photon is scattered, then, there is the probability

$$W(x_1) = 2\int_{x_1}^{\infty} p(x)dx = 1 - \text{erf}\ (x_1) \tag{9}$$

that its frequency will be shifted from the rest frequency an amount greater than x_1, at which the optical depth of the nebula is unity or less:

$$x_1 = (\ln \tau_0)^{1/2}. \tag{10}$$

The mean number of scatterings suffered by a photon before it escapes from the nebula is thus

$$Q = 1/W(x_1). \tag{11}$$

For $\tau_0 = 10^6$ as before, $x_1 = 3.72$ and $Q = 7 \times 10^6$. The conversion of Lyman-α into a $2h\nu$ continuum would then be negligible.

We see, thus, that a calculation of the escape of Lyman-α from an H II region depends critically on the proper study of the transfer problem involved. Actually the assumption of complete noncoherence is not correct either, especially for the case of very large τ_0, when the exact form of the scattering cross section must be taken into account. If a is the natural damping constant in units of the Doppler width, we should write for the absorption coefficient at the frequency x

$$k(x) = k_0 \frac{a}{\pi} \int_{-\infty}^{\infty} \frac{\exp(-y^2)dy}{(x-y)^2 + a^2} \tag{12}$$

where k_0 is the absorption coefficient at the center of the line for vanishing damping. It is noticed that the transition frequency x_g from the Doppler core to the damping wings occurs in Lyman-α at $x_g = 3.27$, when $T = 12{,}000°K$. The noncoherent transfer of radiation in the wings must be taken into account, then, whenever $\tau_0 > \tau_g = \exp\{x_g^2\} = 4 \times 10^4$. For $T = 120°K$ the corresponding numbers are $x_g = 2.85$ and $\tau_g = 3.3 \times 10^3$.

A general solution to the transfer problem involved has not yet been obtained. Because cases of practical interest have very large τ_0, it is appropriate here to indicate the nature of its complexity. The probability that a photon with frequency x', before scattering, has frequency x after scattering has been written by Unno (*7*) in the form

$$g(x,x') = \frac{\epsilon(x,x')}{\int_{-\infty}^{\infty} \epsilon(x,x')dx'} \tag{13}$$

where

$$\epsilon(x,x') = \frac{1}{\pi^{3/2}} \int_{(\bar{x}-\underline{x})/2}^{\infty} \exp(-\xi^2) \left(\tan^{-1} \frac{\xi - \bar{x}}{a} + \tan^{-1} \frac{\xi + \underline{x}}{a} \right) d\xi \tag{14}$$

where $\bar{x}$ is the larger and $\underline{x}$ the smaller of the pair $|x|$ and $|x'|$. The solution of the transfer equation with a redistribution function of the form (13) offers, however, difficulties not yet solved in general. For scattering within the Doppler core, Field (*8*) has given an instructive solution to the problem of following in time the frequency distribution of a thermal Lyman-α photon. His results agree fairly well with those obtained under the hypothesis of complete redistribution. Unfortunately, they may not be applied for $\tau_0 > \tau_g$, as mentioned above. An attempt to take into account the partially coherent scattering in the damping wings has recently been made by Osterbrock (*9*), who approaches the problem by approximating the redistribution in frequency in the damping wings by a one-dimensional diffusion process (in frequency space). This assumption is mathematically equivalent to approximating the redistribution function (13) in the damping wings by an expression of the form

$$p(x,x) = \frac{1}{2l} \exp\left\{-\frac{|x - x'|}{l}\right\}, \quad (15)$$

where l is a properly adjusted "mean free path." According to Osterbrock (*8*), asymptotically for large τ_0

$$Q = 6 \times 10^{-6}\tau_0^2, \quad (16)$$

uncertain within factors of order unity. For an H II region with $\tau_0 = 10^6$, then, there would not be appreciable Lyman-α conversion to two photon continuum, but for $\tau_0 = 10^8$ strong absorption would occur.

4. Absorption of Lyman-α in H I Regions

The decay of Lyman-α by $2h\nu$ emission in H I regions per hydrogen atom is less than in H II regions by an amount corresponding almost entirely to the decreased collisional mixing of the $2P$ and $2S$ levels. The effect of collisions of neutral H atoms may somewhat increase the degree of mixing over the extent determined by the free charges. On the other hand, the Doppler width decreases on account of lower temperature, with the result that the scattering cross section at the center of Lyman-α increases by an order of magnitude. For a kinetic temperature of 120°K and density N_H of hydrogen atoms, the linear absorption coefficient at the line center is

$$k_0 = 5.4 \times 10^{-13} N_H \text{ (cm}^{-1}\text{)}, \quad (17)$$

and since according to Seaton (*4*)

$$\lambda = 0.6 \times 10^{-13} N_e \quad (18)$$

for $N_e = 3 \times 10^{-4}\, N_H$, it would appear that the decay of Lyman-α by $2h\nu$ emission while traversing the galaxy in the direction of its pole ($N_N L = 4 \times 10^{20}$ cm^{-2}) is negligible. In H I regions in the galactic plane the absorption by dust particles most likely competes with $2h\nu$ losses. The interstellar particles are not expected to be pure dielectrics, but rather to have a refractive index

$$\mu = n - m\sqrt{-1} \quad (19)$$

with a nonvanishing imaginary component. The actual value that m may have is very uncertain. Van de Hulst (*10*) has considered a value $m = 0.10$ and has shown that in this case the cross section for absorption is of the order of the geometrical cross section πr^2 for $2\pi r > \lambda$, with λ the wavelength of the radiation. For a linear absorption of $a = 0.9$

$\times 10^{-22}$ cm^{-1} (which corresponds to an extinction of 0.3 mag/kpc) the mean square displacement L of a Lyman-α quantum before it is absorbed by dust is

$$L = \tau_0/aQ. \tag{20}$$

For coherent scattering then

$$L = L_0 = (a\sigma_0)^{-1/2} = 0.050 \text{ pc} \tag{21}$$

for a linear scattering coefficient at the center of Lyman-α $\sigma_0 = 5.4 \times 10^{-13}$ cm^{-1} (unit N_H). For complete noncoherence [cf. Eqs. (10) and (11)]

$$L = (\tau_0/a)W(\ln \tau_0)^{1/2} \tag{22}$$

while in the asymptotic case we have

$$L = 400L_0 = 20 \text{ pc} \tag{23}$$

for the value of σ_0 adopted above. The meaning of this distance is that of the mean free path of a Lyman-α quantum before it is absorbed by dust, and it would refer to some frequency $x < x_1 = (\ln \tau_0)^{1/2}$. Actually, for distances L greater than a few parsecs, the $\Delta\lambda_D$ should be computed not with the thermal rms velocity, but with that of the random mass motions, around 8 km/sec. This would decrease σ_0 to 9×10^{-14} cm^{-1} and increase the value of L to about 50 pc.

In any case, the corresponding τ_0 would be large enough for the asymptotic case to apply. Considering the uncertainties affecting the description of the process of noncoherent scattering, it would seem that under some conditions of practical interest the processes of $2h\nu$ emission and dust absorption may both have to be considered. Evidently a more rigorous treatment of the problem is needed.

5. Conclusions and Predictions

On the basis of the preceding discussion we may infer that the existence of an observable diffuse field of Lyman-α radiation is quite possible. The problem of predicting its characteristics is similar to that of the diffuse galactic light, with the difference that their respective solutions depend on the distribution of interstellar matter at quite different distances from the observer. In order to make an estimate for the order of magnitude that might be expected in the intensity of the diffuse galactic Lyman-α, we shall suppose that the distribution of interstellar gas and dust is uniform. Let it be assumed, further, that the Lyman-α sources are distributed also uniformly within a spherical volume of characteristic radius 50 pc, the distance found above for the mean distance traveled by a Lyman-α quantum before it is absorbed by dust. If the specific emission of solar type stars in Lyman-α is $\eta(\odot)$, we have for the intensity I_0 of the direct illuminating Lyman-α

$$I_0 = \frac{\eta(\odot)L}{4\pi(\Delta\nu)_0}, \tag{24}$$

where $(\Delta\nu)_0$ is the frequency width of the stellar Lyman-α. Adopting the width of the solar Lyman-α as typical ($1\ \text{Å} \simeq 2 \times 10^{12}\ \text{sec}^{-1}$), with the value of $\eta(\odot)$ given before we find

$$I_0 = 2 \times 10^{-24}\ \text{erg/cm}^2\ \text{steradian}. \tag{25}$$

The intensity of diffuse radiation in a medium of large optical depth scattering isotropically with albedo ϖ_0 is

$$I_d = \frac{\varpi_0}{1 - \varpi_0} I_0 \simeq QI_0 \tag{26}$$

because of the meaning given before to Q. Since τ_0 ($L = 50$ pc) $= 1.4 \times 10^7$, from Eq. (16) it follows that $Q = 1.2 \times 10^9$ and then

$$I_d = 2.4 \times 10^{-15}\ \text{erg/cm}^2\ \text{sr}. \tag{27}$$

This intensity would be essentially constant within the width

$$(\Delta\nu)_d = (\ln \tau_0)^{1/2}\Delta\nu_D = 2.7 \times 10^{11}\ \text{sec}^{-1}. \tag{28}$$

The net surface brightness of the diffuse Lyman-α radiation would thus be

$$S_d = (\Delta\nu)_d I_d = 6.4 \times 10^{-4}\ \text{erg/cm}^2\ \text{sec sr}. \tag{29}$$

It should be kept in mind that the basic information entering into the calculation of this surface brightness is very uncertain. Especially the assumption of a uniform distribution of the interstellar matter is quite unrealistic, for it is known that even within 10 pc from the sun fairly dense clouds of interstellar matter may be found (*11*). The point we wish to emphasize is that an intensity as large as S_d can be measured without any difficulty by means of devices already used in rocket flights. An attempt to measure S_d would have to face the problem of eliminating the local Lyman-α glow, which has about the same surface brightness. Probably the most straightforward way of achieving this would be through the use of existing broad-band detectors (nitric oxide ion chambers with filters of lithium and calcium fluoride) aboard a probe in a deep excursion off the ecliptic. With the propulsion systems that will be used in the 1962 fly-by missions to Mars and Venus, a scientific payload of about 100 lb could be sent to a height above the ecliptic of the order of 10^7 km.

An observation of the diffuse field of galactic Lyman-α radiation would provide information regarding the unknown distribution of interstellar hydrogen at very small distances from the sun. The preceding estimate of S_d was carried out, by the way of an illustration, on the assumption that the whole characteristic volume is an H I region. Actually this may not be the case. Nearby B-type stars, such as α Virginis and η Ursae Majoris, may provide large sources of Lyman-α radiation, which could contribute appreciably to the local surface brightness in an amount depending on the distribution of neutral hydrogen in their neighborhood. The same remark applies to the large extended southern H II region excited by γ Velorum and ζ Puppis (*12*). Because of its irregular boundary and apparent large extension ($30° \times 60°$), it is not known how close to the sun this H II region may approach; in fact, the possibility has been suggested (*13*) that the whole solar system may just be inside this H II region. If this were found to be the case, the whole complexion of the problem of interpreting the diffuse radiation field of galactic Lyman-α would radically change.

Important problems related to the structure of galaxies in the large could be studied through their emission in Lyman-α. The stellar systems to be considered are those with red shifts large enough to be unaffected by galactic hydrogen extinction. Since the mean thickness of the galactic hydrogen slab is around $\tau_0 = 4 \times 10^7$, for an rms velocity of 8 km/sec, it follows that the local galactic interstellar medium has optical depth less than unity for wavelength shifts $\Delta\lambda$ such that

$$\Delta\lambda < \left(\frac{a\tau_0}{\sqrt{\pi}}\right)^{1/2} \Delta\lambda_D = 4.1\ \text{Å}, \tag{30}$$

an amount which is independent of the Doppler width. An extragalactic source of Lyman-α with a red shift larger than 1000 km/sec is thus essentially free of local absorption in the direction of the galactic pole, if there is no intergalactic neutral hydrogen. Now, it is known that the nuclear regions of some galaxies are extended H II regions not surrounded by neutral hydrogen, but gradually merging into tenuous coronas or halos where the matter is highly ionized (*14*). It is suspected that such regions are essentially dust free. Under these conditions the losses from $2h\nu$-decay and dust absorption are negligible, and there can be no doubt that the Lyman-α radiation produced in local recombinations will escape the galaxy of its origin. Because of the very great strength that would be expected in this line, it should be expected that in Lyman-α we could reach more distant objects than we can from ground. This is assuming, again, the absence of intergalactic hydrogen. In fact, either the observation of Lyman-α, or the failure to detect it in a system expected to show this line from its optical characteristics, would provide a basis for establishing narrow limits for the density of intergalactic hydrogen.

Acknowledgment

I am indebted to Dr. D. E. Osterbrock for providing me a copy of his paper in advance of publication. My thanks are also due to Prof. A. Unsöld for discussions on the problem of Lyman-α transfer.

References

1. L. H. Aller, Publs. Astron. Soc. Pacific **71,** 324 (1959). *10th Liège Symposium,* p. 535 (1961).
2. A. B. Meinel, "Science in Space," Chapter VIII, p. 29. Natl. Acad. of Sci., Washington, D. C., 1960.
3. H. E. Hinteregger, *10th Liège Symposium,* p. 111 (1961).
4. S. R. Pottasch, *Ann. astrophys.* **23,** 749 (1960).
5. M. J. Seaton, *Proc. Phys. Soc.* **A68,** 457 (1955).
6. H. Zanstra, *B.A.N.* **11,** 1 (1949).
7. W. Unno, *Publ. Astron. Soc. Japan* **4,** 100 (1952).
8. G. Field, *Astrophys. J.* **129,** 551 (1959).
9. D. E. Osterbrock, *Astrophys. J.* **135,** 195 (1962).
10. H. C. van de Hulst, *Rech. Astr. Utrecht Obs.* **11,** Part 2, 27 (1949).
11. G. Münch and A. Unsöld, *Astrophys. J.* May 1962.
12. C. Gum, *Observatory* **72,** 151 (1952).
13. C. Gum, *Observatory* **76,** 150 (1956).
14. G. Münch, *Astrophys. J.* **131,** 250 (1960).

CHAPTER 11

Relativity and Cosmology

H. P. ROBERTSON*

CALIFORNIA INSTITUTE OF TECHNOLOGY, Pasadena, California

Space age astronomy opens up unparalleled vistas for the testing of theories of gravitation, of cosmogony, and of cosmology. These possibilities group themselves under two principal aspects, those offered by (1) our increasing capability of direct instrumental exploration of the gravitational, inertial, and energetic fields at significant distances from the surface of the Earth, and (2) our ability to place facilities, for collecting information on celestial objects, outside the obscuring curtain of the terrestrial atmosphere.

Einstein's special theory of relativity and his geometrical theory of gravitation—inappropriately called "the general theory of relativity"—are the most completely formulated and tested of the extensions of classical mechanics to macro- or microscopic phenomena, encompassing, on the one hand, relative motions at a significant fraction of light velocity and, on the other, the gravitational interaction of bodies at great (stellar, galactic, or extragalactic) distances. As such, these theories form a norm against which to test supplementary or alternative hypotheses—such as those attempting more adequately to explain the origin of inertia, and the "continuous creation" theory. In this spirit, then, this discussion will be couched in terms of the Einstein theories, being concerned with the testing of the predictions of these theories, alert at the same time to possible deviations from them.

The Special Theory of Relativity

So far as the special theory of relativity is concerned, there is a plethora of evidence of its validity from terrestrial experiments; its

* Deceased August 26, 1961.

major predictions are at the present time hardly open to doubt. But from the standpoint of the logic of science, there do perhaps remain points whose elucidation is worthwhile. One such is the problem of deriving the Lorentz transformations by induction from experiment; analysis shows that to do this three independent tests are required. Since the theory arose as an extension of the Newtonian principle of relativity from mechanical to electromagnetic phenomena, it would be most satisfactory to exploit the latter to the full. The analysis shows, however, that only two of the data are obtainable from measurements on light alone; these have been supplied by the Michelson-Morley (1886) and Kennedy-Thorndike (1932) experiments. The third datum must involve in some way temporal phenomena on a material body, and this was first satisfactorily obtained by the Ives-Stilwell (1938) experiment on the "transverse" Doppler effect of light from an atomic beam. Of these three the least satisfactory is the Kennedy-Thorndike, for the attainment of an accuracy comparable to the others requires far more rigorous experimental procedures—the constancy of an interferometer pattern through hours, or preferably months.

There is little reason, however, to look to extraterrestrial experiments to strengthen the foundations of the special theory—unless there are some reasons not now apparent for suspecting that confinement to the earth's surface may have serious effect on the fundamentals of electromagnetic theory. There are, indeed, special relativistic effects to be expected in satellite experiments, due mainly to the relative velocity of the satellite and an observer on the earth. But these effects are more simply and more directly tested in terrestrial experiments, uncomplicated by other comparable effects attributable to difference in gravitational potential. Satellite observations can then be reduced with the aid of the special relativistic theory, leaving the residual to be accounted for by gravitational or other effects.

The Theory of Gravitation

The theory of gravitation, either Einstein's or one of its less completely formulated rivals, does on the other hand yield predictions which can best be tested by extraterrestrial observations. It is in this field that observations on or from the platforms we are beginning to put up offer promise of more significance for the theory. So far as the "classical" predictions are concerned—the redshift of light due to difference of gravitational potential, the deflection of light on passing the sun, and the perihelion motion of a planet—we are now in a pretty good position to say that they are quite decisively favored over the Newtonian predictions. Even so, in some cases greater accuracy may be required, as a test between Einstein's and other hypotheses, and in others new observations or experiments are desirable to distinguish between rival predictions. It is in this area that we may look for advances from space age astronomy.

From the gravitational field of a static, spherically symmetric body, preliminary analysis shows that the Einstein theory requires again three independent observations to determine those effects which go beyond the special theory. In order clearly to trace the source of these effects, we introduce the leading terms in the space-time metric for such a field in the form

$$ds^2 = \left(1 - \frac{2\alpha m}{r} + \frac{2\beta m^2}{r^2} + \cdots\right) dt^2$$
$$- \frac{1}{c^2}\left(1 + \frac{2\gamma m}{r} + \cdots\right)(dx^2 + dy^2 + dz^2)$$

where α, β, and γ are three numerical parameters, whose Einsteinian values are all $+1$, and m is the "mass" GM/c^2 in length units of the central body of gravitational mass M (G being Newton's universal constant of gravitation, and c the velocity of light *in vacuo*). The theory is based upon the hypotheses (1) that for $ds^2 > 0$, ds is the time interval measured by a natural "clock" between two events, and for $ds^2 < 0$ that $c\sqrt{-ds^2}$ is the spatial distance; and (2) that the trajectory of a free particle is a geodesic of the space-time (and of a beam of light, a geodesic for which $ds = 0$).

First, the parameter α. If the geodesics are to give the Newtonian trajectories in the first approximation $m/r \ll 1$, then α must be $+1$. [For the geodesic condition $\delta \int ds = 0$ reduces in this approximation to

$$-\frac{1}{c^2}\,\delta \int \left(\tfrac{1}{2}v^2 + \frac{GM}{r}\right) dt = -\frac{1}{c^2}\,\delta \int (T - U)dt = 0,$$

i.e., the Hamiltonian principle of classical mechanics.] The real issue here is then whether *measured* time near the event is given by ds, and to test this requires resort to the empirical. This leads to the familiar prediction that light of initial wavelength λ_1 will, on traversing a variable gravitational field, be found by an observer at rest relative to the emitter to have a wave length

$$\lambda_2 = \lambda_1(1 + \Delta U/c^2),$$

where ΔU is the difference of gravitational potential between the receiver and the emitter. Thus light emitted from the sun will be observed at the earth to have a shift $\lambda_1 m/R$, where m is the mass of the sun (1.47 km, in length units), and R is its radius. The establishment of this effect is of great interest in principle, and could—as has often been proposed—be carried out with the aid of an artificial satellite; this requires that we be able to compare the satellite clock with one on the earth with an accuracy of 1 part in 10^{11}.

Within the past year, however, the urgency of this experiment has been considerably reduced, due to the work of Pound and Rybka at Harvard. Using the Mössbauer effect—the most important physical tool discovered during the past decade—they were able to test this hypothesis by observing the change in frequency of light over a distance of 75 ft in the earth's gravitational field. In spite of this excellent confirmation, it would still be of interest to check this effect, and the associated special relativistic effect due to motion, by a pickaback device on a satellite.

In yet another way, space age astronomy can lead to a direct astronomical check of this prediction, by observation of the dwarf components of such systems as Sirius and 40 Eridani. As pointed out by Dr. Heckmann at the recent NASA symposium in Stanford, the ability to record spectra of these faint companions of bright stars outside of the deleterious influence of the earth's atmosphere, should enable such a check on the theory or, if you prefer, on our theories of stellar constitution.

The second of the effects predicted by the general theory—the deflection of light, through 1.75 sec of arc at the limb of the sun—is now the least accurately tested of the three. In terms of the parameters introduced above, this effect is

$$2(\alpha + \gamma)m/R;$$

for the Newtonian theory, $\alpha = 1$, $\gamma = 0$, leading to just one-half of the Einsteinian prediction. That the observations do favor the Einsteinian value is the opinion of most competent judges, but the accuracy is admittedly less than desired. Here space age astronomy can be called upon in two ways—firstly, by direct observation of the star field around the sun, and secondly, by a rather sophisticated test of the behavior of the inertial space-time framework around a satellite.

This second possibility requires more detailed explanation. One of the consequences of the general theory of gravitation is that the inertial frame in the vicinity of a freely moving body will, because of the curvature induced by the central gravitating body, exhibit a precession, when viewed in terms of our conventional Galilean concepts. For a satellite of a central body of mass m, this precession amounts to

$$\tfrac{1}{2}(\alpha + 2\gamma)(m/a)$$

per radian traversed. For a satellite just skimming the earth, the Einsteinian value of this precession is 8.3 sec of arc per year; it varies inversely with the 5/2 power of the radius a of the orbit. This effect should be exhibited by a free gyroscope flown in a satellite. Professor Schiff and his colleagues at Stanford are convinced that this is a practicably demonstrable effect, and have submitted a proposal for carrying it out. It is important that this proposal be pursued with vigor, for it should lead to a direct check on the parameter γ and hence to one independent of the deflection of light.

Finally, the best confirmed of the classical tests is that of the precession of the major axis of a planetary orbit. This is given by

$$[2\alpha(\alpha + \gamma) - \beta](m/p)$$

per radian, and amounts for the planet Mercury to 43 sec of arc per century. That this is accurately confirmed is beyond any reasonable doubt, for the probable error is around ½ sec. We have here a most satisfying situation—a discrepancy known quantitatively for decades before its explanation as a by-product of an extensive theory set up on totally different grounds. It may be of interest to quote from Simon Newcomb's article on Mercury in the 11th edition of the "Encyclopaedia Britannica," published in 1911:

> A perplexing problem is offered by the secular motion of the perihelion of Mercury. In 1845 Leverrier found that this motion, as derived from observations of the transits, was greater by 35 per century than it should be from the gravitation of all the other planets. This conclusion has been fully confirmed by subsequent investigations, a recent discussion showing an excess of motion to be 43″ per century. It follows from this either that Mercury is acted upon by some unknown masses of matter, or that the intensity of gravitation does not precisely follow Newton's law. . . .

Clemence's most recent value hardly changes this figure, while decreasing the estimate of probable error. It would appear that Newcomb's alternative—that gravitation does not precisely follow the Newtonian law—is realized in Einstein's theory.

From all of the above, it is clear that $\alpha = 1$ (the Einsteinian value) with very great accuracy, and that with quite good certainty $\beta = 2\gamma - 1$. The results on the deflection of light are not as comforting, although easily good enough to decide in favor of the Einsteinian value of 1.75 sec as against the Newtonian 0.87 sec. In order to clean this up, as well as to test directly the effect of curvature on the inertial frame, it would seem very desirable to carry out the gyroscope experiment in an artificial satellite, as proposed by Schiff.

There is yet another effect involved in the gyroscope experiment—the effect of rotation of the central body on the inertial field carried by the satellite, as predicted by Lens and Thirring in the early days of the general theory. This gives rise to a precession similar to the geodetic effect described above; but here the angular velocity involved is that of the rotation of the earth about its axis, rather than of the satellite in its orbit—which introduces a factor of about 1/16 for a low orbit. The exact amount (and even the sign) varies with the inclination of the orbit to the earth's axis; for a direct equatorial orbit it reduces the predicted geodetic effect of 8.3 sec per year by about ½ sec. It is to be regretted that this effect is so small, for it may have an important bearing on Mach's hypothesis concerning the origin of inertia.

Cosmology

It is clear that all the advantages which may accrue to cosmology in space age astronomy result from the second of the two facets with which this discussion was begun—our ability to collect information on celestial objects, freed from the obscuration of our own atmosphere.

For the problems of cosmology, the two most important observables are the apparent magnitude m of a nebula and its red shift $z = \Delta\lambda/\lambda$. These are followed closely in importance by number counts $N(m)$ out to various limiting magnitudes m. At some time in the future it should be possible to record the magnitudes, in various spectral regions, free from the differential absorption and scattering in the atmosphere. In addition to giving us better estimates of the true bolometric magnitudes as a test of cosmogonic theories, these will act as check points for the calibration of surface-bound observations.

The observable m is most closely related to the distance parameter r involved in the mathematical models. But it alone does not suffice for the determination of r, as this reduction involves the red shift z—the more involved the more distant is the object considered. If, then, we are to develop criteria for distinguishing between various models—such as the "big bang" models of conventional relativity and the "steady state" model of the continuous creation theory—we must also seek ways of increasing our knowledge of red shifts, especially for those objects near the limits of observation. Having expressed the great importance of these for the theory, we must look to our observational colleagues for an evaluation of the prospects for achieving this knowledge from the space platforms which may become available.

Finally, the number counts $N(m)$ out to given limiting magnitudes m, in various spectral regions, should be of great value in deciding between rival hypotheses. Here we are on somewhat more shaky ground, for it will be difficult to decide which observed gross nonuniformities are due to general cosmogonic or cosmological effects (such as curvature), and which are to be attributed to true irregularities in the distribution of matter composing the cosmos.

Discussion

DR. ZWICKY: Some of the fundamental problems relating to cosmology which can only be solved (or far more easily be solved) by the use of rocket-borne telescopes or telescopes mounted on the moon are as follows:

With terrestrial telescopes, the universal red shift has been observed out to a cluster of galaxies whose symbolic velocity of recession is about 140,000 km/sec. Because of the scarcity of spectral lines whose large red shifts can definitely be recognized it seems unlikely that symbolic velocities of recession greater than 200,000 km/sec can be observed with the conventional methods. Observations of the red shift of the hydrogen Lyman-α line would allow a far greater range. Shifts of the Lyman-α line into the visible red would indeed correspond to symbolic velocities of recession $V_s = c\,\Delta\lambda/\lambda \sim 5\,c$ or 1,500,000 km/sec. Observing ever more distant galaxies, the increasing shift of Lyman-α to the red could be observed if instruments were carried aloft by rockets. Lyman-α is a most easily recognizable intense line and, because of its displacement toward the red, it would not be absorbed by galactic interstellar hydrogen; it would thus arrive as the best tell-tale messenger from very remote galaxies. Observations of this sort promise thus to give us more information about the distribution and evolution of matter in the universe than any data so far available.

It has recently been shown [*Astron. J.* **65,** 504 (1960)] that nuclei of galaxies are very characteristic bodies which, because of self-destructive effects can reach only a certain size and mass (about equal to 10 million suns). So far only the nucleus of the great nebula in Andromeda could be resolved, having dimensions of 2.5″ by 1.5′ of arc. Because of poor seeing conditions on earth it will be necessary to use rocket-borne (or perhaps balloon-borne) telescopes which may easily achieve a resolving power of one-tenth of a second of arc to measure the apparent size and luminosity of a few hundred nuclei of the nearest galaxies. Such measurements will enable us to establish a reliable cosmic distance scale. For this purpose it will be particularly important to compare the sizes of the nuclei of nearby galaxies with the nucleus of the Milky Way. To gauge the size of the latter, however, it will not only be necessary to observe outside of the Earth's atmosphere, but the observations must be made in some suitable range of wavelengths, namely $10\,\mu < \lambda < 1000\,\mu$, since light in all other wavelength ranges is absorbed and scattered by the dispersed interstellar matter between us and the nucleus of our galaxy.

The use of either the Mössbauer effect or of lasers has been considered for the determination of the rest mass of the gravitons and of the nature of the universal red shift of light from distant galaxies. In a recent report to the Astronomical Society of the Pacific (meeting of June 12–14, 1961, at the University of Southern California) I have discussed both cosmic and terrestrial (or better interplanetary) tests for the determination of the rest mass of gravitons. Two of these "local" tests are based on either the Mössbauer effect or on the use of special lasers; the experiments visualized are, however, hampered by certain peculiar difficulties if carried out on the earth itself. As far as we know at the present time, they are only feasible from rockets or on the moon. This rather remarkable fact, that certain fundamental tests of the type mentioned cannot be successful on the earth at all, should be properly emphasized in all discussions about the scientific value of experimentation in interplanetary space or on the moon.

Finally, I wish to comment on the problem of the possible existence of matter and antimatter which has been brought up in previous reports, especially that by Dr. J. L. Greenstein. Curiously enough, this problem is not new but actually has been settled long ago. In a paper entitled "Where Can Negative Protons be Found?" [*Phys. Rev., Letters* **48,** 169 (1935)], I showed that if terrene and contraterrene matter existed either in the Milky Way system or in extragalactic space, γ-rays between 10 and 200 Mev as well as γ-rays up to 10^{18} ev would have to be found in the primary cosmic radiation in very high intensity, an expectation which was flatly contradicted by the balloon observations available in 1935 and contradicted still more decisively by recent observations with rockets.

CHAPTER 12

Large Orbital Telescopes and Their Guidance Problems

12.1 High Resolution Optical Space Telescopes

A. B. MEINEL*

KITT PEAK NATIONAL OBSERVATORY,† Tucson, Arizona

There are quite a few practical problems of considerable difficulty that one faces in designing a large space telescope. For the purpose of definition let us classify as large telescopes those of aperture approximately 1 meter or larger. "High resolution" systems are defined as those requiring resolution of 1 part in 10^5 or 2 sec of arc or better. We will not dwell upon the eventual astronomical requirement for high resolution. It is true that the initial space experiments deal primarily with the properties of the radiation collected by the telescope rather than its spatial distribution, but one can be assured that as space astronomy develops we will constantly be pushed to increase the resolution that the telescope can yield.

There is a touch of amusement among the general astronomical community when we talk about pointing accuracies and resolutions of tenths and hundredths of a second of arc. They are very much entitled to that view since it is difficult on earth under rather favorable conditions to obtain second-of-arc performance. And much human effort lies behind the superb results produced from our largest terrestrial telescopes.

General Considerations

We shall deal first with some general questions of space telescope design and later expand these within the specific design framework of the NASA OAO-2 36-in. telescope.

* Now at Steward Observatory and Lunar and Planetary Laboratory, University of Arizona.

† Operated by the Association of Universities for Research in Astronomy, Inc., under contract with the National Science Foundation.

The boundary conditions which apply to a space telescope are as follows:

I. Passive

A. Dimensional and weight limitations of the spacecraft

B. Physical properties of materials

(1) Mechanical strengths
(2) Thermal expansion coefficient
(3) Thermal conductivity
(4) Reflectivity of materials
(5) Scattering of surfaces

II. Dynamic

A. Launching environment

(1) "*g*" forces and vibration
(2) Shroud heating
(3) Pressure change

B. Space environment

(1) Thermal variations
(2) Vacuum
(3) Induced torques

As far as the space telescope is concerned, the principal problems are produced by the vibration at launch and by the fluctuating thermal environment in orbit. Design studies to date have concerned the optical elements and the collimating structure, since they are the vital parts of the telescope. It is desired for reasons of simplicity—hence reliability—that the collimating structure should also support the optics during launch. There is, however, serious doubt that large vitreous optics could be "hard" mounted because of their fragility. Metal optics do appear promising; a 36-in. flat and a 28-in. aluminum spherical mirror have been polished at Kitt Peak.

Metal mirrors have, in general, large thermal expansion coefficients. Aluminum, for example, has $24 \times 10^{-6}/°C$ while fused silica has $0.6 \times 10^{-6}/°C$. Invar has a low coefficient, but it is ruled out as being magnetic and consequently causing large torques—although this objection does not hold for high orbits (24 hr or higher orbit).

In the use of a metal, such as aluminum, one must approach the telescope design with a different philosophy. It is a well-known theorem that the focus position of an optical system is invariant with temperature, if the entire system is of the same material and is isothermal. In metals this property is important because the thermal conductivity is high and thermal equilibrium is rapidly achieved.

The thermal equilibrium of the spacecraft in orbit is determined by

FIG. 1. Several silica lightweight mirror types developed by Corning Glass Works for space and airborne applications. (Courtesy Corning Glass Works.)

many variables. For practical considerations, however, the thermal properties of the telescope inside the spacecraft are determined only by the impedance to heat flow of the walls of the experiment can and the infrared flux from the earth entering the aperture of the telescope. As to the thermal impedance, the low value possible with a metal mirror will result in a low gradient across the mirror even for rather significant differences (∼30 °F) between the two sides of the spacecraft. In regard to the movement of the earth in and out of the field of view, the high conductivity of aluminum for the optics and collimating structure will permit the system to come smoothly to a new equilibrium temperature. Although numerical quantities should be given, the necessary computations are quite tedious and incomplete at this time. However, a thermal response time of 5 min appears likely. While this thermal arrangement

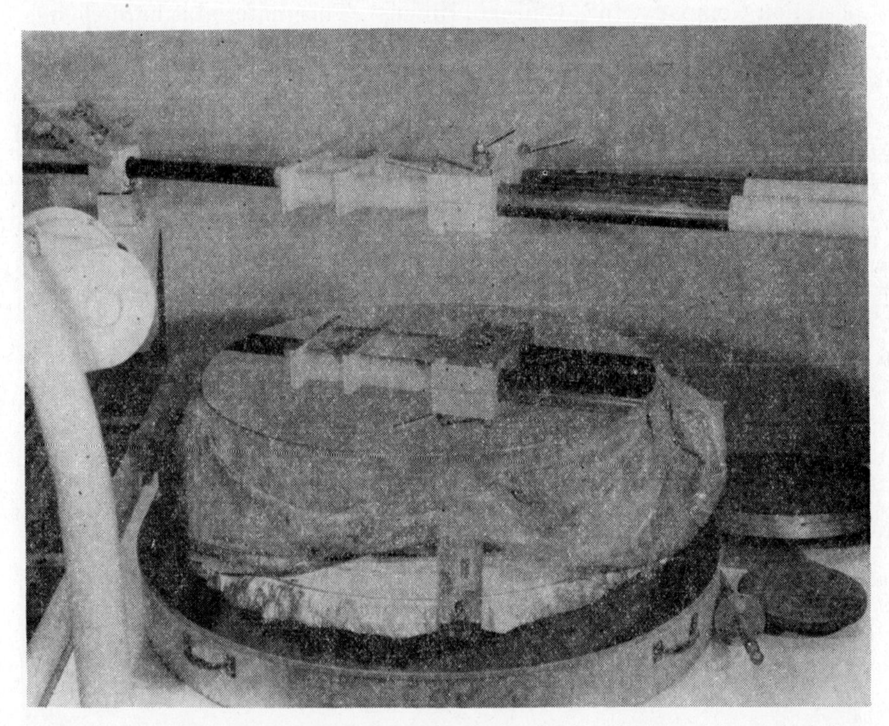

FIG. 2. The 36-in. aluminum-Kanigen flat during final polishing at the optical shop of the Kitt Peak National Observatory.

appears quite satisfactory for the OAO-2, telescope where images of 100 μ diameter are acceptable, the use of the same approach for future telescopes of higher resolution will depend upon the results and experience with this spacecraft.

Figure 1 shows several experimental mirrors of fused silica. While weight reductions to 35% of an equivalent solid shape are possible, the problem of mounting such structures in the 36-in. size class has not been satisfactorily solved.

Figure 2 shows the Kitt Peak 36-in. aluminum flat during final polishing. This mirror, completed 9 months ago, has been thermally cycled by ITEK with no detectable change in its optical figure. As a result we feel that aluminum is sufficiently stable to yield high resolution mirrors where a lifetime of a few years is sufficient. However, aluminum in its usual state is too soft to take an optical polish. The standard procedure is to overcoat the aluminum disk in its fine ground state with 5 to 10 thousandths of an inch of an amorphous nickel-nickelphosphide compound known by the trade name Kanigen (General-American Transportation Company, Inc., Chicago, Illinois). This material is hard enough

FIG. 3. The 28-in. prototype space telescope mirror shown mounted on the shake table adaptor. The mirror is mounted kinematically at three points.

(Rockwell 50–60) to take an excellent polish and shows surface scattering of light comparable with that from polished optical glass. Measurements have been made at Lyman-α by NRL of the scattering from an aluminum mirror overcoated successively with Kanigen, evaporated aluminum, and MgF.

Figure 3 shows a 28-in. diameter $f/2$ aluminum-Kanigen mirror. This mirror has a weight factor of 15%. The mirror is shown attached to a shake-table adapter. This mirror will be shake-tested to determine if any figure change occurs. Before shaking, the mirror figure is good to better than ¼-wave over the entire surface, even though the mirror face is only ¼ in. thick. The ribs are also the same thickness. In contrast to honeycomb structure, heavy sections are used to keep the conductivity high while still keeping the weight low. The mirror as shown is mounted with a three-point kinematic support which represents both the launch and collimating structure.

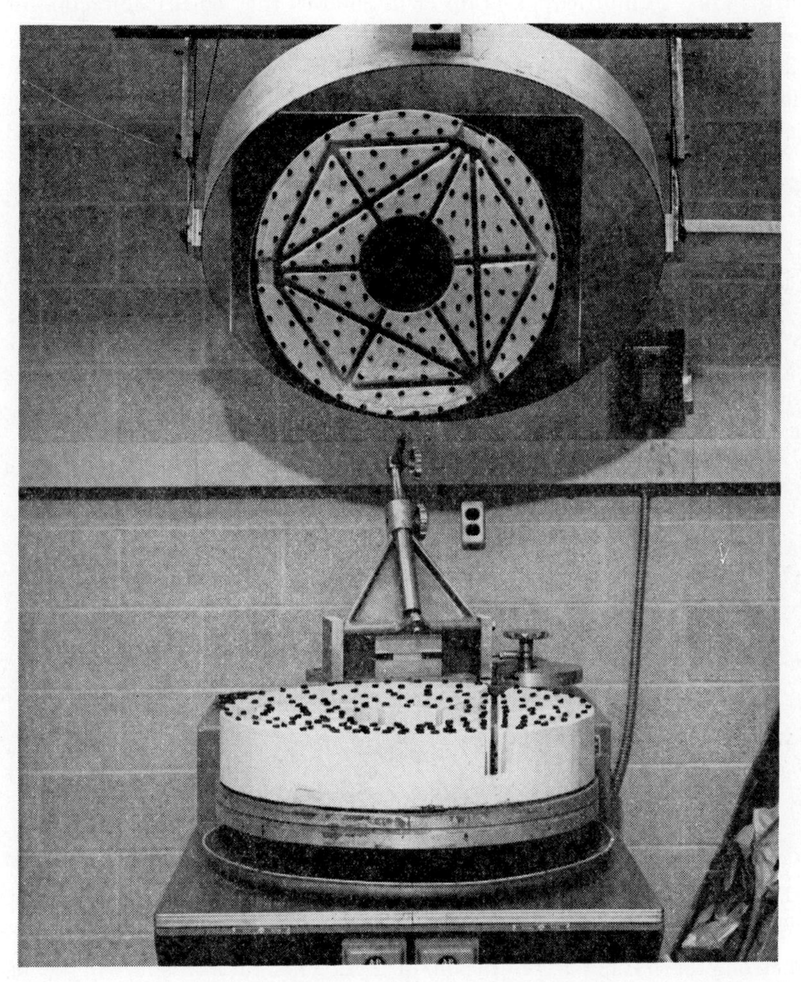

FIG. 4. Mounting surface for polishing the 28-in. aluminum-Kanigen mirror. Note the recesses to receive the ribs shown reflected in the 36-in. aluminum-Kanigen optical flat mounted over the polishing table.

Figure 4 shows the jig used to support the mirror during optical working. The numerous pitch balls actually float the mirror in an unstressed state but provide support during the polishing process. The top view of the jig is shown reflected in the 36-in. aluminum-Kanigen test flat.

The NASA OAO-2 36-in. Telescope

In Fig. 5 the instrument container is shown at the side of the spacecraft. This cylindrical section will house the 36-in. telescope and spectrometer.

Figure 6 shows an outline of a configuration developed as part of a study with the Goddard Space Flight Center. The OAO-2 telescope system will consist of a telescope of approximately 36-in. aperture and a

FIG. 5. Structural mock-up of the Grumman Aircraft Company Orbiting Astronomical Observatory. The telescope-experiment container is shown on the right.

spectrometer having a resolution of 2 Å. This instrument will be used for the spectroscopic study of stars to approximately 12th magnitude (ultraviolet), as well as for the brighter extended celestial objects. The provision for slit combinations of 2, 8, and 64 Å would permit the observation of the energy distributions of stars perhaps as faint as main sequence K and M stars within the region from 3800 Å to as far as 1050 Å. No provision is yet planned for observations at wavelengths shorter than 1050 Å, partly because of detector problems and partly because very little starlight of shorter wavelengths is expected to reach

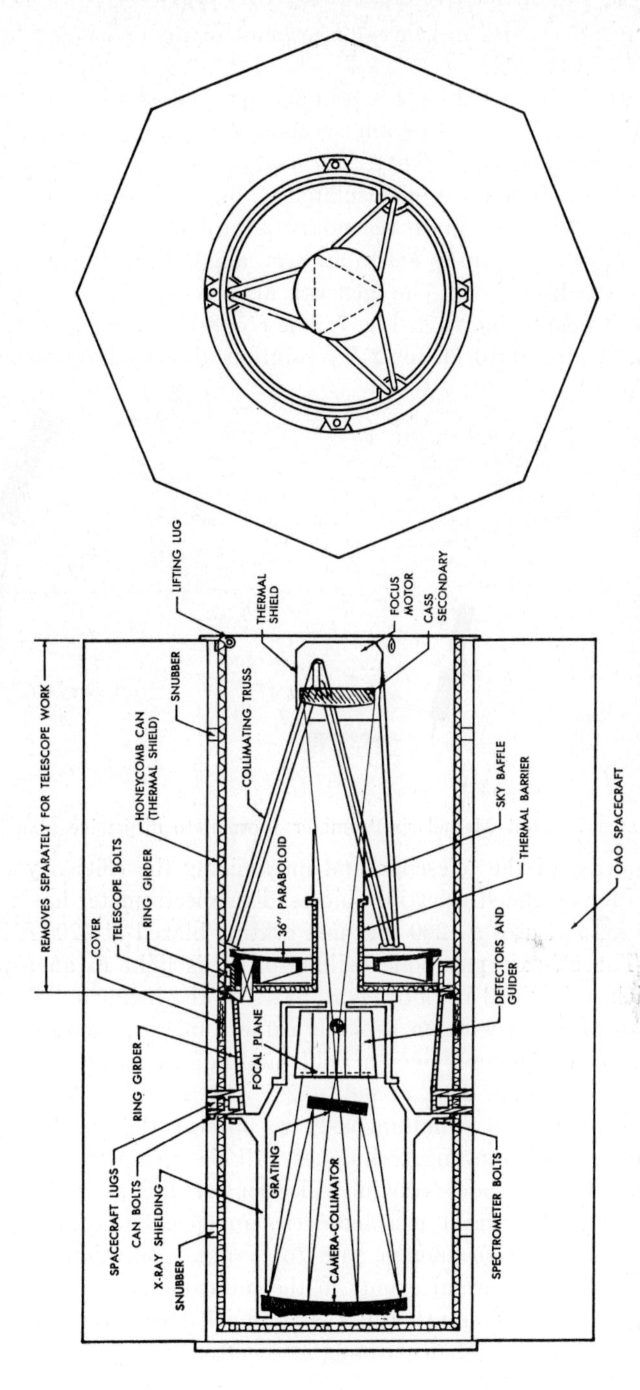

FIG. 6. Line drawing of a design configuration for the Goddard Space Flight Center 36-in. telescope and spectrometer utilizing a metal-Kanigen ribbed mirror.

the earth over interstellar distances on account of the opacity of atomic hydrogen.

The design shown uses an $f/1.8$ primary paraboloid yielding an $f/5$ Cassegrain system. The Cassegrain secondary is supported by a six-legged tripod for torsional rigidity. The collimating structure is consequently separated from the well-insulated walls of the experiment can. Focus motion of the Cassegrain secondary is provided.

The $f/5$ Cassegrain beam is fed to an 8-in. aperture grating spectrometer without predispersion. The general arrangement of one of the spectrometer designs is shown in Fig. 7. The $f/5$, 8-in. design was adopted to yield a slit width of 10 in. for 2 Å resolution, thereby minimizing the

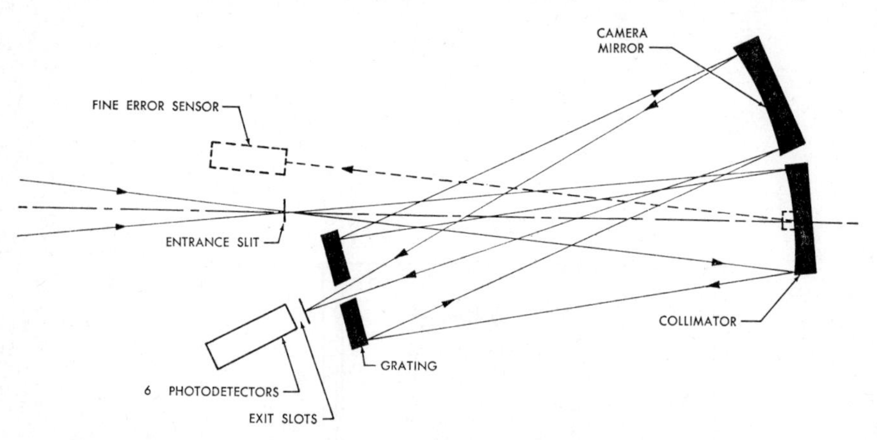

FIG. 7. General layout Meinel spectrometer (normal to dispersive plane).

guidance required of the telescope and maximizing the efficiency of the spectrometer for extended celestial objects. The spectrometer has a focal length of 40 in. and uses a 1200 line/mm grating blazed at 1200 Å in the first order. The off-axis parabolic collimator feeds light to an aspheric grating, which is inclined in both coordinates to the incident light. This arrangement, combined with an aspheric camera mirror, produces excellent and achromatic images over a field angle of 24° at $f/5$. Residual aberrations are less than 25 μ, or only 0.2 Å.

Six detectors are used simultaneously to observe the spectrum with 100% overlap. Pulse counting techniques will be used with diode pre-image stages. These diodes provide selection of the desired spectral sensitivity and dark current characteristics independent of the photomultiplier; they give also enough gain to permit separation of photo-initiated events from thermal events in the multiplier.

The telescope design illustrated in Figs. 6 and 7 derives an error signal for fine centering and guidance from the spectrometer. A small section of the collimator beam is diverted to an error sensor. If the slit jaws are transparent to long wavelengths where the experiment detectors are insensitive, then the error sensor can generate an error signal and center the object in the wide (10 in.) slit without changing the mode of operation. In the case of extended objects the telescope does not provide a meaningful error signal, and the astronomer must rely upon the dead-reckoning accuracy of the star trackers.

This concludes the brief description of the OAO-2 telescope. This spacecraft will provide us with our first opportunity for a large space telescope and a chance to learn how to make the larger and better space telescopes that the future of space astronomy will require.

12.2 *Stabilization and Orientation Control of Large Orbital Telescopes*

RUSSELL A. NIDEY

KITT PEAK NATIONAL OBSERVATORY, Tucson, Arizona*

The high resolution space telescopes as described in Chapter 12.1 by Dr. Meinel foreshadow the major telescopes of the future. The primary space telescopes will not only be large and as nearly diffraction-limited as possible—they will also be in orbit around the earth. They will be in orbit not only to avoid the absorption and poor seeing occasioned by our atmosphere but also because of the extreme accuracy of stabilization required. An accuracy of 0.1 to 0.01 sec of arc necessitates a new design philosophy.

If a telescope is attached to an unstabilized platform, such as the earth, the moon, or a space station, explicit gimbals must be used to counter the motions of the platform. The stiction in the bearings of these gimbals will intolerably perturb the telescope especially in space, where lubricants either cannot be used or become relatively ineffective. In free-fall, however, bearing noise can be largely obviated by causing the telescope to be rotated about its center of mass on implicit gimbals, gimbals with mathematical rather than physical axles. In addition to being in orbit, to enhance the accuracy of stabilization the space telescope must also be remotely controlled.

The involuntary motions of a man (including the cardioballistic motion of his blood) preclude direct physical contact between the observer and the telescope. Hence, the control of the telescope executed by the observer must be accomplished by remote sensors and actuators. If then, as must be the case, the control is to be effected from a padded isolation cell, the cell should be on earth.

The orbit radius must be sufficient to ameliorate the geoperturbations, as well as to avoid the Van Allen radiation belt, yet not so great as to compromise the telecommunication system required for remote control. A radius in excess of $6a$ (a=earth radius =6378 km) is indicated by the

* Operated by the Association of Universities for Research in Astronomy, Inc., under contract with the National Science Foundation.

former requirements, and no more than 10 times as great, corresponding to a hundredfold increase in telemetry power, by the latter.

The high precision, remotely controlled, earth orbiting telescope will be used not as a survey instrument but rather to study in greater detail the spectral and spatial characteristics of unusual galactic and extragalactic objects discovered by the smaller survey instruments. These objects will range from first magnitude stars to nebulae. The corresponding observation times will range from a fraction of a minute to several hours.

Control Operations

The observer on earth must thus be able to orient the telescope toward the object to be observed essentially at random anywhere on the celestial sphere (restrained primarily only by the sun), must then be able to direct the light bundle into the angular field of the instrument, and finally must invoke an automatic stabilization system to maintain the light bundle within the field for the duration of the observation. These operations are coarse orientation control, fine orientation control, and stabilization, respectively.

Because of the vast ranges in brightness and angular size as well as observation time, the telescope must be stabilized about all three principal axes by using a pair of offset guiders. A single guide star can be used to determine rotations in only two of the three angular degrees of freedom. Hence, a second guide star must be invoked to sense error about the third axis. The second or subordinate guide star should ideally be orthogonal to the first or principal guide star. If the stabilization is equally precise about all three axes, and if due compensation is made for the differential aberration,* both guide telescopes can be grossly offset from the primary. Indeed, it is highly desirable to use a single guide star pair such as Arcturus (Alpha Boötis) and Achernar (Alpha Eridani) for an extended period of time. Beyond $6a$ the earth subtends less than 0.09 steradian; hence, many appropriate guide star pairs, including Arcturus and Achernar, can be nearly continuously observed. Thus, a celestial reference system can be established to continuously

* The difference in the aberration of light as seen by either of the guide telescopes and the primary telescope, when these point in different directions. (The aberration is occasioned by the orbital velocity and consequently shares the orbital period. The aberration caused by the motion of the earth around the sun may be as great as 20.5 sec whereas that due to the motion of the satellite around the earth may be as great as 2.0 sec at $6.6a$. The latter aberration varies as the inverse square root of the orbit radius).

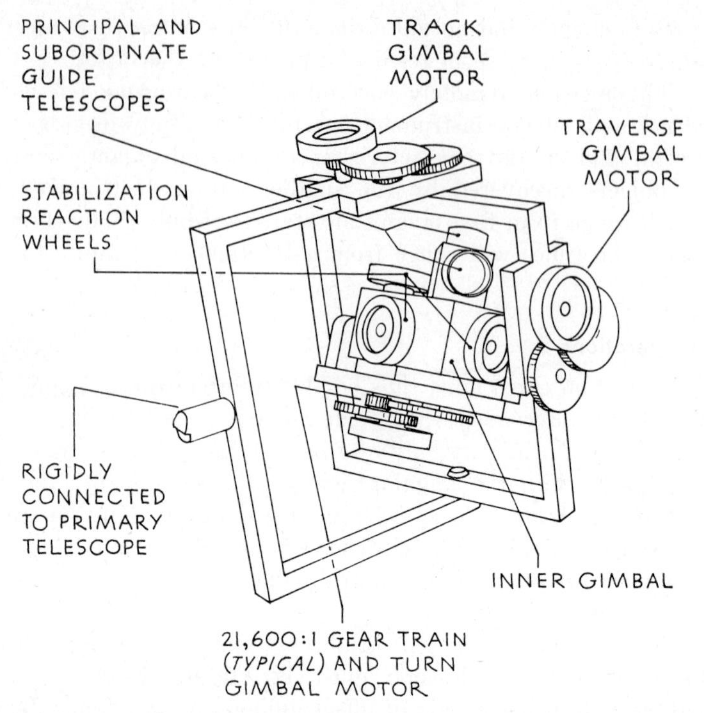

FIG. 1. Schematic illustration of the astroguider to be used for stabilization and orientation control of the orbiting telescope.

provide not only the stabilization signals but also precise celestial aspect information.

The astroguider (*1*) under development at the Observatory is such a bistellar reference system. It is shown in schematic form in Fig. 1.

The Astroguider

The two orthogonal photoelectric guide telescopes are situated on the inner gimbal of a triaxial gimbal system. Three gimbal axes are required not only to avoid gimbal restraint but also to provide control of the orientation of the celestial image in the focal plane of the primary telescope. As shown in the illustration, proceeding from the inner gimbal outward, the axes are turn, traverse, and track. Obviously it is immaterial whether this or an alternative set of gimbals will be used.

By placing the stabilization actuators, in this case three orthogonal reaction wheels, in the frame of reference of the guide telescopes (as on the inner gimbal), the transformation of signals from one coordinate system to another is avoided. This assures greater reliability and precision. In addition, cross-coupling from one control axis to another, by precessional effects during slewing motions of the primary telescope, is obviated without the use of the more sophisticated reaction sphere.

Two error signals are derived from the principal guide telescope and are immediately and locally amplified to drive the two reaction wheels with axes normal to the optical axis of this telescope. Thus, the principal guide telescope is continuously and automatically aligned to the principal guide star. Similarly, a third signal from the subordinate guide telescope drives the third reaction wheel to align the subordinate guide telescope to the subordinate guide star. In this manner the inner gimbal and the primary telescope (through the explicit gimbal system) are both servo-stabilized to the celestial frame of reference. The implicit gimbal axes are thus parallel to the axes of the reaction wheels but, of course, pass through the center of mass of the satellite.

To avoid upsetting the stabilization loops while slewing the primary telescope from one object to the next, the explicit gimbal drive motors should also be used as reaction wheels. This can be done if the gear-train ratio is nearly equal to the ratio of the moment of inertia of the satellite as a whole to that of the rotor, and if the rotor motion has the same direction as the corresponding gimbal motion (as with a spur gear train with an even number of reductions, as illustrated).

Coarse orientation is thus accomplished by commanding appropriate motions of the three explicit gimbals (as monitored by corresponding transducers). Since the position relative to the known star pair of all celestial objects can be readily computed in terms of the three explicit gimbal angles, the object of interest can be immediately placed in the field of view of the primary telescope.

However, to center the image precisely within the angular field of the instrument, a fine orientation control signal obtainable only from the primary telescope is required. This is particularly true because of the thermal deformation produced by solar insolation of the reference gimbal relative to the optical axis of the primary telescope. This signal will undoubtedly be transmitted to earth, interpreted at the control center, and transformed as required before retransmission to the satellite to drive the fine gimbals. The fine gimbals will probably be used to rotate plain parallel plates set in the convergent beams of the two guide telescopes, for then a single set of fine controls will suffice for a number of instruments. The fine system will also be used to compensate for the cyclic differential aberration mentioned earlier, as well as for the deformation and random mechanical drifts.

To effect the fine orientation control the observer must obviously be in intimate contact with the telescope. This can be realized only if the communication is bidirectional and immediate. The delay introduced by the signal transit time is of no consequence out to $60a$, but it would be if the satellite were not in line-of-sight of the control center, necessitating undue intermediate storage of the telemetry signals and/or commands. Hence, if the mission is not to be compromised, no less than three ground stations will be required.

Communication

The length of the communication day (transmission path within 60° of local vertical) from an equatorial control center to a satellite in a circular equatorial orbit, as a function of orbit radius, is shown in Fig. 2.

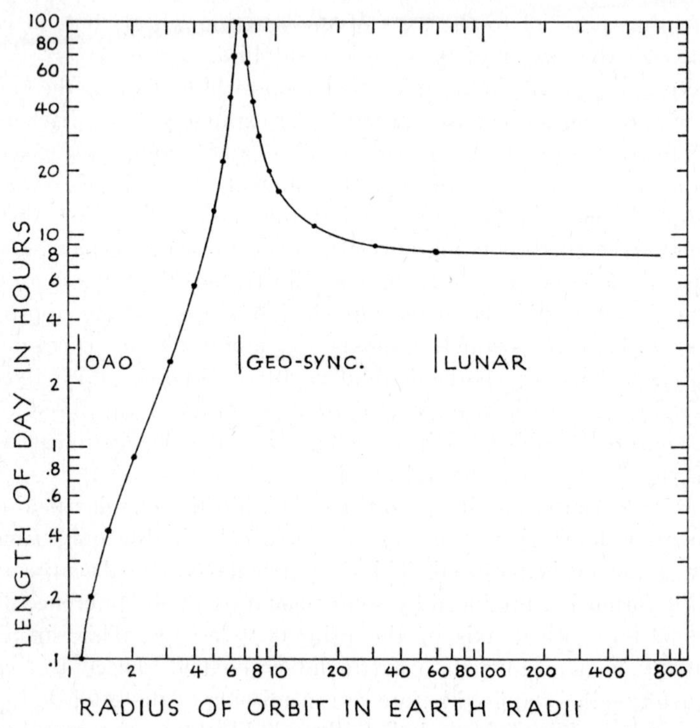

FIG. 2. Length of the communication day of the orbiting telescope as a function of the orbit radius.

An orbit of 8 to $9a$ radius, corresponding to a communication day of 28.7 to 19.6 hours, is particularly appropriate for the space telescope. At this altitude the maximum slant range is not excessive and, consequently, neither is communication power. Specifically, 1 watt of isotropically radiated power at 2000 Mc/sec will conveniently telemeter 3000 bits of information per second with less than one error per million bits, assuming PCM transmission and a 60-ft receiving antenna with a maser preamplifier.

Perturbations

Furthermore, at this altitude the external torque exerted on the satellite by the gravitational field of the earth is some 100 times less than in the orbits below the Van Allen belt, permitting the maximum tolerable difference in the principal moments of inertia of the satellite to be increased to one part in a hundred without compromising the stabilization system. The corresponding tolerance on the coincidence of the center of solar radiation pressure and the center of mass is ½ in. The remaining external perturbations, such as electrostatic, magnetic, and aerodynamic, are negligible by comparison. A combination of solar vanes and shiftable counterweights will undoubtedly be necessary, not only to null the two major perturbations but also to intentionally invoke external torque to reduce, as required, the instantaneous angular momentum stored in the reaction wheels.

Accuracies

The accuracy of stabilization is limited only by the size of the guide telescopes and the fineness of the reaction wheels. A 4-in. photoelectric telescope using a conventional photomultiplier at room temperature on a first magnitude star can theoretically resolve 1 msec of arc in less than 50 msec of time. Allowing 2 orders of magnitude degradation for practical difficulties, no less than 0.1 sec of arc should be realized.

The accuracy of coarse orientation control is determined primarily by the size of the encoders which can be incorporated on each of the explicit gimbals. With 16-bit encoders, 20 sec of arc is currently practical. If the field of view of the primary telescope is at least 1 min of arc, as anticipated, this accuracy is more than adequate.

The accuracy of fine orientation control is limited only by the ability to sense absolute error in the primary telescope. Gradual differential deformations can readily be sensed and predicted by observing a relatively bright star in the immediate vicinity of the object of interest for several minutes prior to offsetting to an object which is too faint or diffuse to produce suitable integral signals. Hence, even in this extreme case, an accuracy finer than 0.1 sec of arc is feasible over an offsetting range of a few minutes of arc.

Concluding Remarks

In conclusion consider the following five more or less categorical statements: (1) The large, high resolution space telescope of the future must be in a distant orbit around the earth. (2) It must be unmanned. (3) It must be stabilized about all three principal axes with a fully automatic, offset, bistellar guidance system. (4) The fine orientation of such a telescope must be remotely controlled by an observer on earth. (5) The communication between the observer and the telescope to effect the orientation control must be bidirectional and immediate.

The author affirms that such a space telescope not only can, but will, ultimately be added to the roster of instruments used by space age astronomers to extend and refine our knowledge of the universe.

Reference

1. Russell A. Nidey, *in* "Space Astrophysics" (William Liller, ed.), Astrostats for Astrophysical Research in Space. McGraw-Hill, New York, 1961.

Discussion

Dr. U. Güntzel-Lingner: An important field of work of a high resolution space telescope will be to observe relative positions of the components of close double stars of rapid orbital motion. For these stars we are now unable to determine the relative orbits and, consequently, the periods, the dimensions of their orbits, and the masses of the components. Our observations with ground-based telescopes are limited by atmospheric turbulence; the separation which can be resolved with a 36-in. refractor under best conditions is about 0.2 sec visually or 1.8 sec photographically. If a long-focus space telescope is in orbit, and if the guidance of the optical axis is of high precision, we can hope to obtain excellent photographs of the undisturbed diffraction images of the components. The formula $\delta = 1.22\lambda/D$ allows us to compute the diffraction limited resolution; we find $\delta = 0.14$ sec for an aperture D of 36 in. and for visible radiation at about λ 550 mμ. This would be good enough for the measurement of the positions of more than 100 bright and close double stars with unknown orbits.

CHAPTER 13

Extraterrestrial Radio Telescopes

13.1 Satellite Measurements of Cosmic and Planetary Radio Noise

A. E. LILLEY

HARVARD UNIVERSITY, Cambridge, Massachusetts

Introduction

A new era of astronomical research has begun with the launching of radio telescopes into space. This paper will review some of the scientific objectives and experiments which may be carried out, provided one has the opportunity of transporting radio telescopes into space. The basic features of such radio telescopes, although they will differ considerably in appearance, will be an antenna and a radiometer, with the radiometric output delivered to the observer via a telemetry system. We shall exclude two additional classes of radio experiments which will ultimately be performed in space: firstly, radar experiments of the type envisioned for a spacecraft radar transported to the immediate vicinity of a planet, and secondly, we shall also exclude that class of experiments involving radio transmitters dropped to a planetary surface. By excluding these two categories of experiments, we exclude the radar investigations of planetary surfaces and Doppler investigations of rotation rates; and in the second category we exclude new techniques for the investigation of planetary ionospheres and rotation rates.

Restricting the discussion to passive radio observations in space, it is worthwhile to explore criteria employed for selecting space radio experiments. Selection criteria for space radio experiments are no different from those in optical and hard particle experiments, and the basic criterion is certainly that of uniqueness. Radio experiments will be conducted in that part of the electromagnetic spectrum where observations are rendered impossible from ground locations because of the earth's atmosphere and ionosphere. An additional category of experiments will result in those cases where the radio intensity of the solar system source is too weak to be measured from the earth. The possibility of close proximity observations to planets enables modest equipment to obtain resolutions which are impossible to achieve on the surface of the earth. All three of the cases mentioned satisfy the criterion of uniqueness.

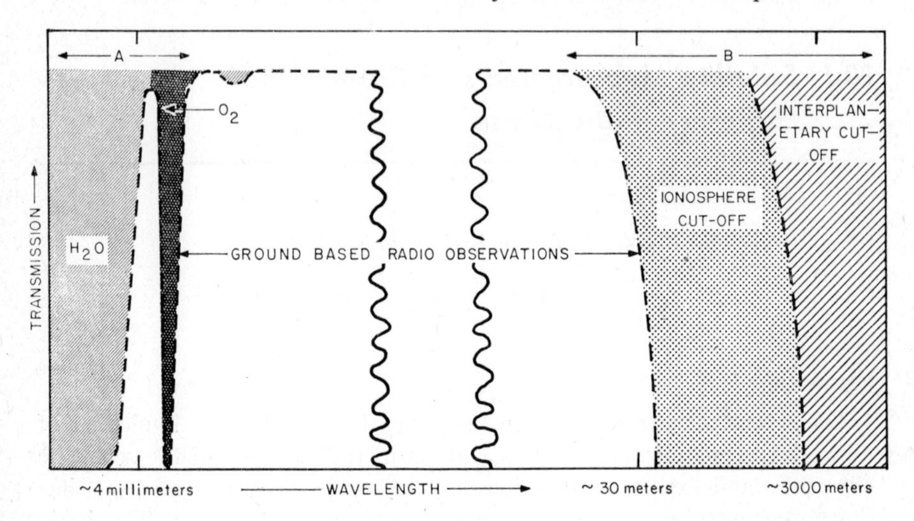

FIG. 1. Radio transmission spectrum of the earth's environment. From the millimeter to the decameter wavelength domain, the earth's atmosphere and ionosphere permit the conduct of ground-based radio observations. Additional limited observations are possible within the small window evident at a wavelength near 4 mm. The atmospheric constituents of water vapor and oxygen are responsible for terminating propagation at the millimeter wavelength end of the spectrum. At the right-hand side of the diagram the electron content of the F_2 layer terminates the long wave radio propagation. The wavelength intervals for millimeter and very long wave space radio telescopes are the regions marked A and B. It is in these regions that radio telescopes are flown in earth satellites and deep space probes.

The major portions in the electromagnetic spectrum where experimentation has been performed or is in the active stage of preparation may be visualized by examining the transmission spectrum of the earth's environment for radio waves. In Fig. 1 the transmission of the earth's environment is shown as a function of wavelength throughout the radio spectrum. On the left side of Fig. 1, transmission of centimeter and millimeter waves is terminated by the combined actions of water vapor and oxygen. Resonant transitions in the millimeter region blend by virtue of pressure broadening to render the atmosphere completely opaque to

TABLE I
EXPERIMENTAL OBJECTIVES OF SPACE RADIO TELESCOPES OPERATING BELOW FREQUENCIES OF 10 MC

Objective	Experimental technique
Galactic and extragalactic radio emission mechanisms	Multichannel radiometric observations of the flux distribution of cosmic noise between 10 Mc and 100 kc
Dynamic solar radio spectra	Multichannel and sweep frequency radiometric observations of the dynamic spectra of solar radio outbursts
Ionized component of the interstellar medium (measurement of low "emission measures")	Precision determinations of the brightness temperature of interstellar space in the frequency interval between 100 kc and 1 Mc
Investigations of the interplanetary medium	Multichannel radiometric observations of the cutoff of low frequency cosmic radio noise at times of solar disturbances. Time-average determinations of the lowest frequency of propagation possible in the interplanetary medium
Planetary radio noise	Close proximity observations of planetary radio noise sources due to sporadic disturbances, nonthermal spectra, and radio noise sources in regions of the Van Allen type
Planetary ionospheric experiments	Modulation of multichannel reception of cosmic noise in the frequency range between 100 kc and 10 Mc, produced by a changing electron density environment. Requires a satellite in an eccentric orbit about a planetary ionosphere

wavelengths shorter than about 2 mm. Moving toward longer wavelengths, the last completely opaque line is the 5-mm blend of oxygen. The last line of any measurable consequence exists at 13.5 mm where the absorption is due to water vapor.

From a wavelength of several centimeters extending to longer wavelengths, the transmission of the earth's atmosphere is essentially complete. Not until the action of the earth's ionosphere becomes important, due primarily to the F_2 layer in the decameter wavelength range, does the transmission of radio waves again terminate. The dotted line at the extreme right of Fig. 1 suggests the limit of propagation at extremely low frequencies which will be imposed by the electron density in the interplanetary medium. This limit is given approximately by $f_c = 9\sqrt{n}$ kc/sec (where the electron density is given in number per cubic centimeter) and constitutes one of the basic objectives of the launch of low

TABLE II
EXPERIMENTAL OBJECTIVES OF CENTIMETER AND MILLIMETER SPACE RADIO TELESCOPES

Objective	Experimental technique
Extension of solar observations	Multichannel millimeter radiometric observations of the solar radio noise between 5 and 1 mm, this wavelength interval pertaining to the deepest layers in the solar radio envelope.
Lunar thermal studies	Multichannel millimeter radiometric observations of the lunar surface as a function of lunar phase and surface characteristics. Small millimeter telescopes operating in a satellite system orbiting the moon obtain each revolution information requiring 1 month's observation from the earth. Extension of the spectral interval under observation for information pertinent to the physical characteristics of the lunar surface material. Provide radio resolution of small regions on the surface of the moon impossible to observe individually from terrestrial locations.
Planetary thermal observations	Close proximity observations of the millimeter wave spectra of planetary surfaces and atmospheres. The variability of the thermal planetary spectrum from limb to limb, as could be observed by a fly-by probe or a satellite orbiting about the planet, provides information pertinent to the surface temperature of the planet, the composition and physics of its atmosphere; a thermal map of its surface provides information related to the planetary rotation rate and orientation of the rotation axis (e.g., Venus) and permits the resolution of surface features impossible to resolve from the earth.
Galactic continuum and radio star observations	Spectral distribution of the thermal component of cosmic radio noise in the galactic plane. Selected discrete sources, both thermal and nonthermal, with sufficient resolution and radiometric sensitivity may ultimately be observed between 1 and 10 mm.
Microwave spectroscopy of planetary atmospheres	Millimeter wave frequency scanning radiometers observing the spectral self emission of resonant transitions of molecules in planetary atmospheres. Frequency scanning observations of the microwave "Fraunhofer" spectrum by observing the planetary molecular transitions in absorption against the solar millimeter spectrum.

TABLE III
Intercomparison of Millimeter and Decameter Space Radio Telescopes

	Millimeter	Decameter
Resolution:	High resolution obtainable with small parabolas (1 to 5 ft in diameter)	Resolution very difficult to achieve. Dipoles offer limited resolution; true directivity must await more complicated antenna systems, such as log periodic types, which can be erected in space.
Antenna:	Horns and parabolas	Loaded whips and dipoles
Multichannel radiometers:	Superheterodyne and crystal video Dicke type radiometers	Tuned radio frequency, Dicke type TRF, superheterodyne, Dicke superheterodyne, and Ryle-Vonberg radiometers
Scanning radiometers:	Scanning superheterodyne, Dicke type radiometers employing swept frequency local oscillators (local oscillators for millimeter scanning systems constitute a major development problem)	Electronic and mechanically tuneable superheterodyne Dicke radiometers
Calibration:	Thermal resistive loads and gas discharge tubes	Resistive loads and noise diodes

frequency radio telescopes into space. Within the defined region of transmission is that portion of the electromagnetic spectrum where terrestrial radio telescopes around the world conduct their research programs.

The regions marked A and B in Fig. 1 constitute portions of the spectrum where important measurements will be made by space radio telescopes. Since the regions A and B are those where observations from the earth are completely impossible, these are the regions where the early experimental programs have developed. Both the short and long wavelength extremities of the radio astronomical spectrum are characterized by a number of important measurement objectives. Since each of these objectives constitute a topic involving considerable interest, we shall restrict ourselves to brief tables which describe some of the experimental objectives in the two spectral regions of interest.*

We shall examine two particular problems in the millimeter portion of the radio spectrum as examples of future radio experiments for space radio telescopes. The first of these will be a brief review of some recent

* Tables I and II provide brief descriptions of the scientific objectives for decameter and millimeter space radio telescopes. Table III compares the instrumental characteristics of the millimeter and decameter space radio telescopes.

work concerning the spectrum of terrestrial oxygen at a wavelength of 5 mm, which is chosen as an example of the microwave spectroscopy of a planetary atmosphere. The second example chosen is that of the recent revision of our concept of the physical conditions on the planet Venus. The new concept of the environment of Venus has led to a millimeter radio telescope experiment for a NASA Mariner fly-by space probe mission to the planet Venus.

Microwave Spectroscopy of Atmospheric Oxygen

Turning first to the spectrum of oxygen in the terrestrial atmosphere, we have an example where the physics of a planetary atmosphere may be investigated by microwave spectroscopic techniques. At wavelengths near 5 mm, the oxygen molecule is characterized by approximately 25 resonant transitions. An isolated single line occurs at a wavelength near 2.5 mm. The 5-mm series of lines, when examined over paths through the earth's atmosphere near sea level, are completely blended together by virtue of pressure broadening and a study of the individual lines is impossible.

The 5-mm series of lines is produced by transitions between the fine structure levels of the rotational states of the molecules. Oxygen has a permanent magnetic moment and therefore can absorb microwaves. The

TABLE IV
RESONANT TRANSITION OF O_2 NEAR $\lambda = 5$ MM

N	$N = J \rightarrow N = J + 1$ (kMc)	$N = J \rightarrow N + J - 1$ (kMc)
1	56.2647	118.7507 (~2.57 mm)
3	58.4469	62.4867
5	59.5915	60.3061
7	60.4355	59.1640
9	61.1513	58.3236
11	61.8009	57.6121
13	62.4119	56.9678
15	62.9885	56.3631
17	63.5687	55.7836
19	64.1276	55.2215
21	64.6782	54.6716
23	65.2227	54.1309
25	65.7626 (~4.55 mm)	53.5973 (~5.58 mm)

basic interaction is that of the magnetic moment with the "end over end" rotation of the molecule. The molecular state in question is $^3\Sigma$; states with odd rotational quantum number $N = 1, 3, 5$, etc., are permitted. Two transition types are distinguished: $J = N \rightarrow J = N + 1$, and $J =$

$N \rightarrow J = N - 1$. Table IV gives the frequencies of the 25 lines of interest as computed by Tinkham and Strandberg (1955) based on measurements by Mizushima and Hill (1954).

To compute the microwave emission or absorption spectrum of the terrestrial atmosphere requires a solution of the transfer equation throughout the path length of interest, which further requires a model of the temperature and pressure distributions throughout the atmosphere. In the higher levels of the terrestrial atmosphere, the 25 oxygen lines are reduced in their respective line widths, and the individual lines become observable. Early calculations by the radio astronomy group at Harvard demonstrated that the "Fraunhofer" spectrum of O_2 could be seen in absorption against the sun from high-flying aircraft or balloons. The equation describing the Fraunhofer spectrum of O_2 as seen from high altitudes is given as follows:

$$\Delta T(\nu) = T_s e^{-\tau(\nu)} + T_0[1 - e^{-\tau(\nu)}] \cong T_s e^{-\tau(\nu)},$$

where T_s is the brightness temperature of the sun near $\lambda = 5$ mm, $\tau(\nu)$ is the opacity of the terrestrial oxygen, and T_0 is the state temperature of the oxygen. Since $T_s \gg T_0$, the self-emission term may be ignored without appreciable error.

Meeks has shown that the Fraunhofer spectrum may be observed at modest altitudes. Assuming a radio brightness temperature for the solar disk of 5500°K, the Van Vleck-Weisskopf theory, and the terrestrial atmosphere, the Fraunhofer spectrum shown in Fig. 2 results. Several of the individual lines which form the oxygen complex can be clearly resolved in the Fraunhofer absorption spectrum as shown in Fig. 2. Two Fraunhofer spectra are shown, one for a zenith angle of 0° (the sun directly overhead) and one for a zenith angle of 60°. It is clear from Fig. 2 that Fraunhofer microwave spectroscopy of the terrestrial atmosphere can be undertaken at altitudes achieved by piston-driven aircraft. For high performance aircraft, and high altitude research balloons, the Fraunhofer spectra will become sharper as the line widths narrow due to decreasing pressure. This constitutes a new tool for atmospheric research; both the microwave spectroscopic radiometers and the aircraft and balloons are available.

The microwave spectroscopic observations of the Fraunhofer type are possible not only from aircraft and balloons, but also from satellites orbiting about a planet. For satellite Fraunhofer observations, the millimeter microwave radiometric device would be directed toward the sun and the ray path extending through the higher regions of the planetary atmosphere.

Within the core of the individual oxygen lines, in the terrestrial atmos-

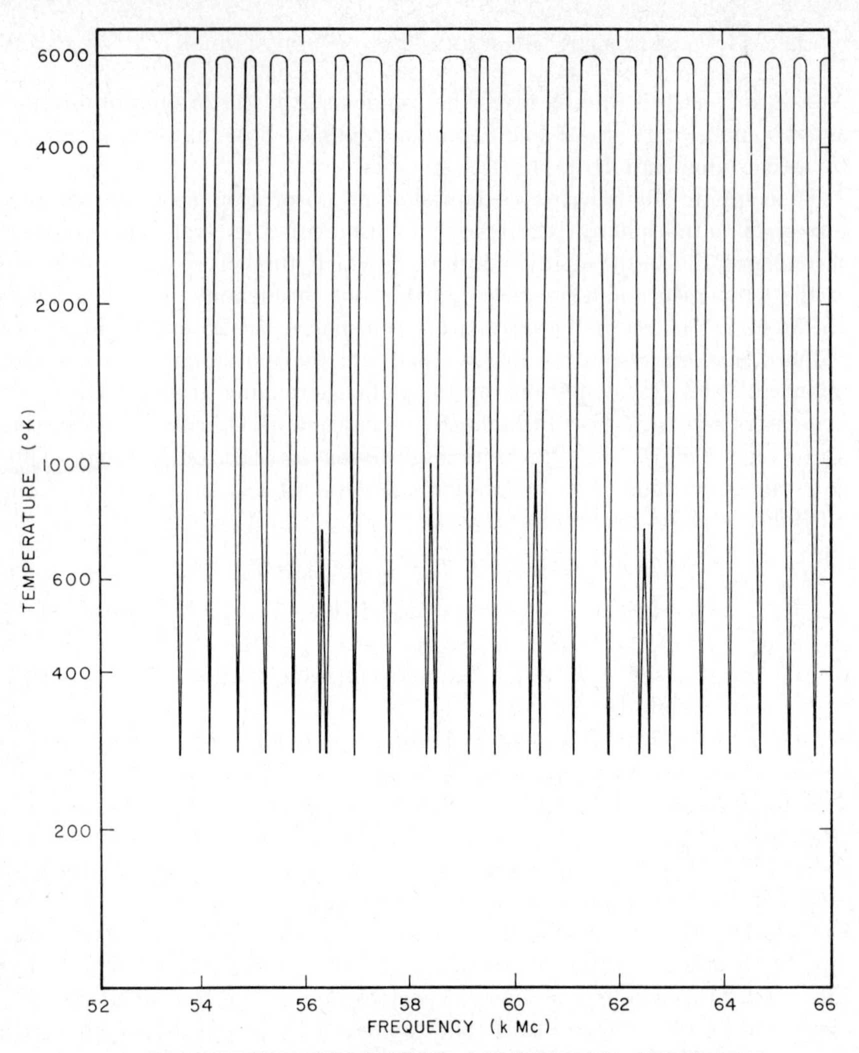

APPROXIMATE MICROWAVE FRAUNHOFER SPECTRUM OF ATMOSPHERIC O_2

FIG. 2. At intermediate altitudes and above, the 5 mm blend of oxygen lines may be seen in absorption against the radio sun. By analogy with optical spectra, this may be called the microwave Fraunhofer spectrum of terrestrial oxygen. Meeks has calculated the Fraunhofer spectrum using the ARDC model atmosphere and a brightness temperature for the solar disk of 5500° K. The Fraunhofer spectrum is shown in Fig. 2 for two zenith angles, 0° and 60°. It will be noted that the absorption line depths reach values of the order of 10^3 °K and provide very large signal-to-noise ratios for microwave spectroscopic equipment. An observational program of the Fraunhofer type would yield a spectrum which could be compared against the assumed model atmosphere and the Van Vleck-Weisskopf theory and thus provide a new technique for the study of the terrestrial atmosphere. In addition, we may look forward to similar techniques in the study of planetary atmospheres such as Venus and Mars.

phere, the line is essentially opaque even at extremely high altitudes. Observations carried out within the core of any of the individual oxygen transitions permit the determination of atmospheric temperature as a function of altitude. The opacity in the core of the line does decrease slowly with altitude, but this does not impose serious difficulty for the measurement of atmospheric temperatures with height. One may interpret the measurement of atmospheric temperature as a function of height in the core of an oxygen line as representative of a *hohlraum,* whose radius increases with altitude.

In addition to temperature, frequency scanning radiometers permit the determination of pressure with height since, for any elevation above the horizontal, the maximum line width is determined by the "local" pressure at the point of measurement.

When the vertical temperature distribution in a planetary atmosphere has a substantial reversal, such as that which exists between the stratosphere and stratopause and the terrestrial atmosphere, then the self emission of the atmosphere can produce spectral lines which can be observed by scanning radiometers operating from satellites orbiting the planet. This point has been investigated by Meeks (1961) who has calculated the emission spectrum of the terrestrial atmosphere in the 5-mm region. Using the ARDC model atmosphere, the Van Vleck-Weisskopf theory of the line structure, and solving the equation of transfer for an observer outside the terrestrial atmosphere looking toward the surface of the earth, Meeks has shown that the oxygen lines will appear in emission. Three of the transitions in question are shown in Fig. 3; it will be noted that near the line centers the temperature reaches a value of about 280°K, whereas in the line wings the temperature falls to about 220°K. The thermal reversal responsible for these lines may be seen in Fig. 4, which shows the temperature reversal between the stratosphere and the stratopause. The line width of the individual resonant transitions may also be seen in Fig. 4. We may interpret the resultant spectrum as a high-temperature low-pressure emission line viewed against a lower temperature high-pressure region of the terrestrial atmosphere. The details of the emission line temperature maxima, as would be revealed by satellite microwave observations, offer a new opportunity for the study of the physics of the earth's atmosphere, in particular the interesting region around 50-km altitude where ultraviolet ozone absorption is important.

A 5-mm scanning radiometer, viewing the earth from an orbiting satellite, would be able to observe the details of the high altitude oxygen distribution over the surface of the earth. Ideally one would employ a 5-mm oxygen radiometer in a satellite operating in a polar orbit, which would ultimately bring the entire atmosphere of the earth under investigation for the oxygen spectrum. Furthermore, a long lifetime system would not only provide full coverage of the earth, but would permit seasonal studies as well as time-dependent changes which may be the product of solar activity.

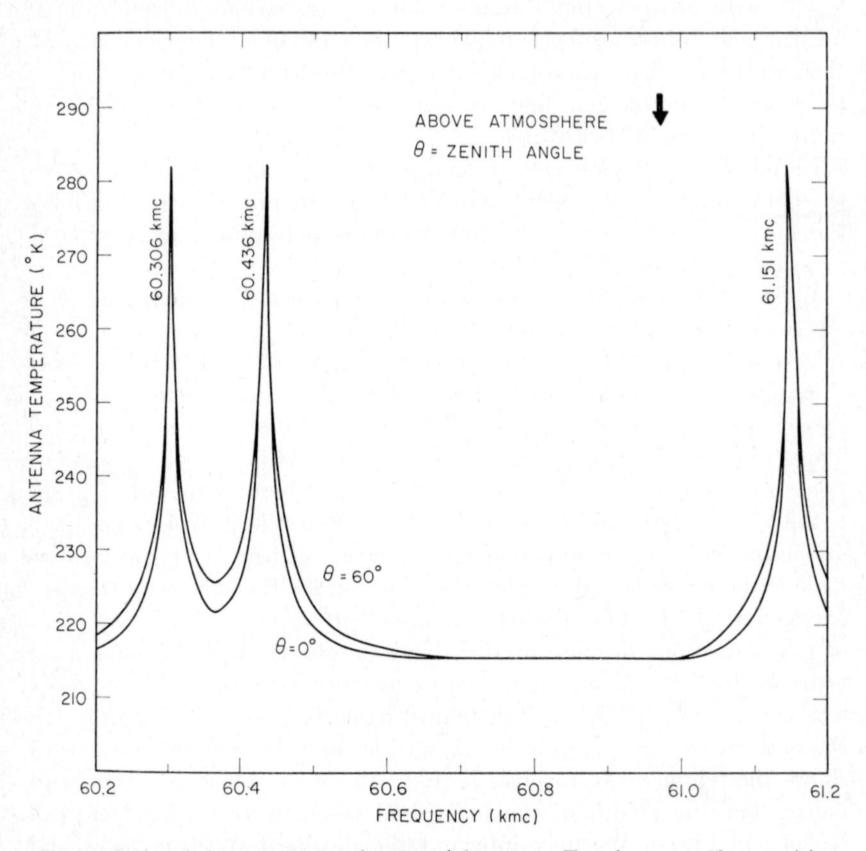

FIG. 3. Self-emission spectrum of terrestrial oxygen. For three specific transitions, the theory predicts emission lines of terrestrial O_2 as viewed from outside the earth's atmosphere. Based on the computations of Meeks, and the use of the ARDC model atmosphere, the emission line spectra of O_2 would be evident in the earth's atmosphere if viewed by a microwave spectral radiometer operating from a spacecraft orbiting the earth.

The case of oxygen is an example of the microwave spectroscopy of planetary atmospheres, and should provide an opportunity for adding new knowledge of the terrestrial atmosphere. Similar techniques may ultimately be applied to other planets in the solar system because the millimeter portion of the spectrum is rich with lines of molecules which are important to the study of planetary atmospheres.

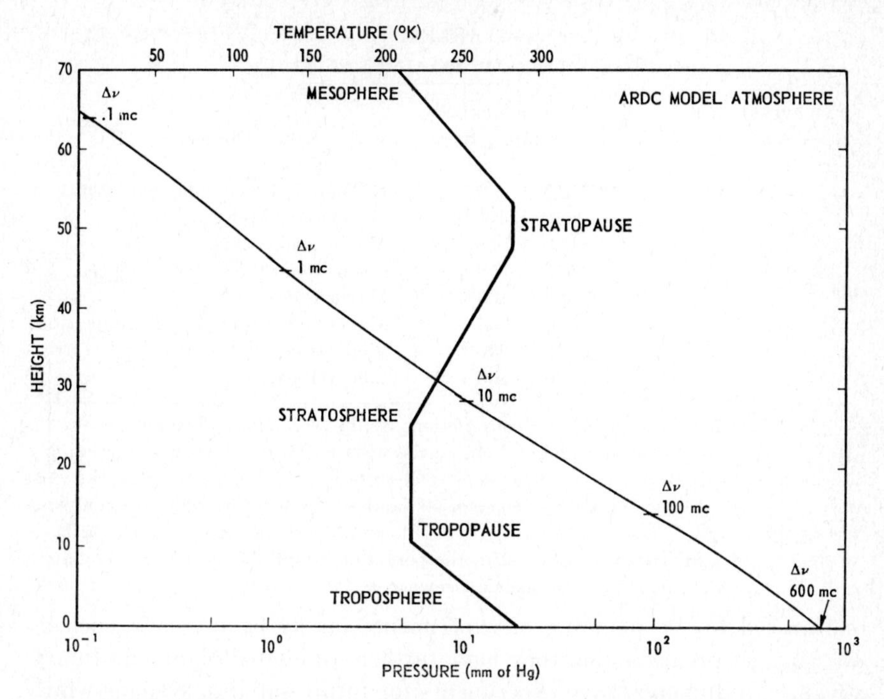

FIG. 4. Temperature and line-width distribution of terrestrial oxygen (ARDC Model Atmosphere). Temperature as a function of height adopted for the calculation of the self-emission spectrum of terrestrial oxygen as viewed from space is shown above. Along the temperature profile, the temperature reversal between the stratosphere and the stratopause is particularly important in the prediction of the terrestrial O_2 spectrum as seen from space. Along the pressure curve with height, a few values of the oxygen line width are shown. The quantity $\Delta\nu$ is the half-width of the individual lines at half-maximum.

The Radio Spectrum of the Planet Venus

Venus is constantly covered with optically opaque clouds which have prevented optical astronomers from direct photographic mapping of surface features, in contrast to the case of the planet Mars. Not only have the clouds prevented a visual determination of the surface features of Venus, but because the clouds are opaque to visible and infrared radiation, the optical attempts to measure the temperature of the surface have necessarily determined only the temperature in the upper layers of the gaseous envelope of Venus.

Radio observations of the planet Venus, made with ground-based radio telescopes, have completely revised concepts of the physical properties of the environment on that planet. These observations, which are summarized in Table V and Fig. 5, have stimulated new discussions which

TABLE V
RADIOMETRIC OBSERVATIONS OF VENUS

Wavelength (cm)	Equivalent blackbody disk temp. (°K)	Observer
0.80[a]	315 ± 70	Kuzmin and Salomonovich (1960)
0.86	410 ± 160	Gibson and McEwan (1959)
3.15	620 ± 55	Mayer *et al.* (1958)
3.37	575 ± 58	Alsop *et al.* (1958, 1959)
9.4	580 ± 160	Mayer *et al.* (1958)
10.3	600 ± 65	Mayer *et al.* (private communication)
12.5	600 ± 200	Victor *et al.* (1961)
21[b]	630 ± 200	Lilley (1961)

[a] Value for 17 days after inferior conjunction; results were phase dependent.

[b] The observations of the planet Venus at a wavelength of 21 cm are exceedingly difficult because of the λ^{-2} flux dependence. Observations of Venus made at Harvard during March 1961 yielded values between 600 and 800°K for the brightness temperature of the planet Venus at a wavelength of 21 cm. The value quoted in the table is the average of 7 drift curves obtained in the period of March 23–28, 1961. A complete analysis at $\lambda = 21$ cm is to be published elsewhere.

in turn led to the planning of experiments for fly-by missions, such as the Mariner program, and they have further stimulated planning of more advanced millimeter wave experiments for future satellite systems which will orbit about the planet Venus.

The unusual characteristic of the microwave spectrum of Venus is that the temperature measured in the radio domain (~600°K) is approximately twice the value measured optically (~285°K). The constancy of the temperatures observed at 3 and 10 cm by Mayer *et al.* (1958) was first interpreted as evidence for a thermal emission mechanism. If one assumes that the gaseous envelope surrounding Venus is transparent to 3 and 10 cm radio waves, then one plausible interpretation of the radio data is that the observed microwave radiation originates at the "surface" of Venus. There is some uncertainty in the radio data, as evidenced by the values quoted in Table V, and therefore it is of considerable importance to extend the radio observations to the longest wavelength observable. Unfortunately the radio detection of Venus becomes rapidly

FIG. 5. Infrared and radio spectrum of Venus. The approximate spectrum of the planet Venus is shown ranging from the infrared to a long wavelength limit near 21 cm. Two measurements in the infrared at 0.8 and 8.13 μ are shown followed by a lower limit observation of less than 350°K at 4 mm. The remainder of the radio observations range from 8 mm to 21 cm and define the variation of temperature with wavelength that constitutes the ground-based radio telescopic determination of the Venus spectrum. The dashed line is a free curve through the observational points. The flatness of the spectrum from 3 to 21 cm is regarded as evidence for a thermal radiation mechanism.

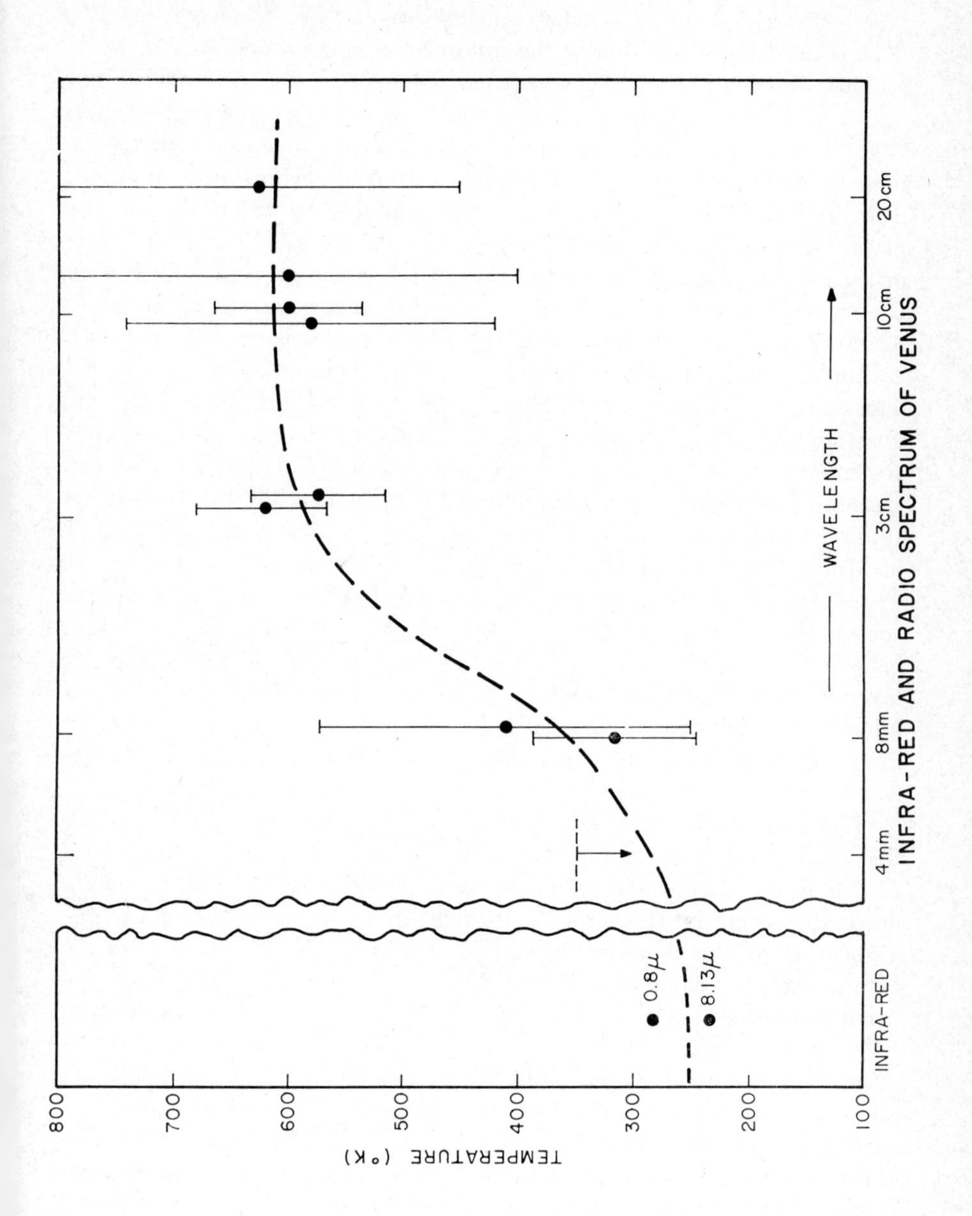
TEMPERATURE (°K)
800
700
600
500
400
300
200
100
INFRA-RED
0.8μ
8.13μ
4mm
8mm
3cm
10cm
20cm
WAVELENGTH
INFRA-RED AND RADIO SPECTRUM OF VENUS

more difficult with increasing wavelength because of the decreasing gain of antennas. However, during the inferior conjunction of Venus in April of 1961, observations of Venus were carried out at a wavelength of 21 cm, and have been reported by Lilley (1961). In this case the lack of gain at the longer wavelength was compensated for by a three-level solid state maser, which permitted a successful detection of the planet's radiation. The results of the 21-cm measurements, included in Table V, approximately doubled the previous long-wavelength limit, offering new evidence for the probable thermal nature of the radiation source on Venus. Observations carried out in the future at longer wavelengths should again show a temperature near 600°K if the source is actually thermal.

Can the planet Venus actually have a surface temperature of 600°K? This is a temperature hotter than a broiling oven, and to answer this question one must obviously look for help to the greenhouse effect. Recently there have been two independent theoretical studies of the greenhouse effect on Venus, and, interestingly enough, the two theoretical studies result in essentially opposite conclusions. The first work is that of Mintz (1961) who has concluded that a 600° surface temperature on Venus is difficult to explain. "It is clear that we cannot accept the centimeter radiation as being of thermal origin and at the same time believe that the clouds are water clouds. For this would imply a cloud layer that is incredibly thick. . . . And a cloud layer hundreds of kilometers thick would not permit downward penetration of sunlight necessary to maintain the high surface temperature and the convection necessary to maintain the clouds."

"If the clouds are not water clouds, the limiting lapse rate could be the adiabatic rate for a dry gas, and to reach the surface temperature of 600°K the cloud layer would not need to be more than 30 to 40 km deep. But even in this case it is difficult to see how the shortwave absorption by the cloud would remain small enough for enough sunlight to penetrate the cloud to maintain the high surface temperature and the convection necessary to keep the cloud particles suspended. A greenhouse will not work, after all, if it is made of very dirty glass."

On the other hand, Sagan (1960) has also studied the greenhouse effect on Venus, and concludes that with an appropriate atmospheric mixture a surface temperature of 600° can actually be maintained by a greenhouse effect at Venus. "It is evident that a surface temperature of 600°K demands a very efficient greenhouse effect. Extrapolation to long paths of CO_2 and H_2O emissivities at elevated temperatures shows that . . . of the order of 1 gm/cm^2 (water vapor) is required for a synchronously rotating Venus in order that the required greenhouse effect be achieved."

It is interesting to note that in Sagan's calculations, he considered both a synchronously and a nonsynchronously rotating Venus. Evidence for a slow rotation rate has been obtained by a radar experiment conducted at the Jet Propulsion Laboratory (Victor *et al.*, 1961).

An alternate hypothesis for the microwave radiation source on Venus has been proposed by Jones (1960) of the Jet Propulsion Laboratory. Jones suggests that a very dense ionosphere at Venus with an electron temperature of approximately 600°K is responsible for the observed microwave spectrum. The equation governing the ionospheric radiation source is given by

$$T(\nu) = T_s e^{-\tau_e(\nu)} + T_e[1 - e^{-\tau_e(\nu)}],$$

where T_s is the surface temperature of Venus, T_e is the electron temperature of the Venus ionosphere, and $\tau(\nu)$ is the opacity of the ionospheric medium. The result of the calculations based on this equation produces a remarkable agreement between the theoretical model and the observed microwave radiation.*

Advanced planning for reconnaissance vehicles to explore the planets is well under way. Possibly no two planets compete for such favorable attention as the earth's "twin," Venus, and Mars. The first efforts of the United States at planetary reconnaissance will be made with the "Mariner" vehicles. Microwave observations are planned for the Mariner program. The basic objective of the spacecraft microwave observations will be to determine the physical basis of the unusual radio spectrum of the planet Venus.

Calculations show that the greenhouse model will exhibit limb darkening, or a gradual temperature decrease seen near the edge of the planetary disk as viewed from a "fly-by," or orbiting spacecraft at Venus. On the other hand, the ionospheric model predicts a limb brightening effect, or a "halo" of higher temperature at the periphery of the planet as seen from the spacecraft. Not only should it be possible to distinguish between the physical mechanisms producing the unusual microwave spectrum of Venus, but once the distinction is made, it should be further possible to examine the physical structure of the atmosphere or ionosphere by means of the detailed behavior of the several wavelengths observed in the experiment. In a proposed radio experiment for Venus, four wavelengths have been selected to cover the critical portion of the microwave spectrum where the structure, or change of temperature with wavelength, is most significant. A 4-mm channel is close to the microwave minimum,

* The ionospheric model spectrum can be made to agree with the observed radio spectrum if the surface temperature $T_s \sim 260°K$, the electron temperature $T_e \sim 600°K$, and $\int n^2 dz \sim 4 \times 10^{25}/cm^5$, requiring the ionosphere of Venus to be much richer than that of the earth.

where the radio temperature agrees more closely with the infrared values, whereas the longest wavelength, near 20 mm, coincides with a temperature of approximately 600°K. In addition to an intermediate value at 8 mm, which lies between the two extremities in temperature, the fourth channel, at 13.5 mm, coincides with a resonant transition due to water vapor, and offers a further opportunity for the detection and confirmation of the existence of water vapor in the Venus atmosphere.

A further problem in connection with the Venus radio spectrum is the report of a substantial phase variation by Kuzmin and Salomonovich (1960). The Soviet radio observations at 8 mm indicate that the observed temperature depends upon the phase of the planet as seen from the earth. Basically they find that the temperature of the planet at 8 mm increases as the illuminated crescent of the planet increases as seen from the earth. This is shown in Fig. 6 where the brightness temperature of the planet, T_b, which is calculated by*

$$F = (2kT_b/\lambda^2)\Omega_p$$

is plotted against the constant k, which is the area of the illuminated portion of the planet divided by the total area of the planetary surface as seen from the earth.

An independent study by Lilley of data provided by Mayer at 3 and 10 cm indicates a phase variation at the longer wavelengths. The phase variation points up a further need for spacecraft millimeter radio telescopic observations. The temperature dependence on phase suggests that the sunlit portion of the planet Venus has a different temperature than the dark side, and that temperatures characteristic of the illuminated portion of the planetary atmosphere are substantially higher than those on the dark side. This clearly suggests different radio spectra for the sunlit and the dark sides of the planet.

The phase variation requires detailed confirmation. We would like to obtain radio spectra from the subsolar point, around the planetary atmosphere, across the terminator, and to the midnight point. Observations of this type are hopelessly out of the question for ground-based radio telescopes and can only be conducted by radiometric devices transported to the immediate vicinity of the planet.

Very modest spacecraft antenna sizes produce respectable resolutions. A 2° beam may be easily achieved for parabolas of the order of 1 ft in diameter. Such small radio telescopes, transported to the immediate vicinity of the planet Venus, can resolve features on the planetary surface of the order of 100 miles in diameter. As seen from terrestrial dis-

* F is the observed radio flux, T_b is the equivalent brightness temperature of the planet at a time when its solid angle is Ω_p.

tances, this corresponds to resolutions better than one square second of arc.

If it were possible to construct a radio telescope giving a resolution of one square second of arc, and if material strengths were capable of supporting physical structures to the required precision, it is unlikely that properties of the earth's atmosphere would permit meaningful

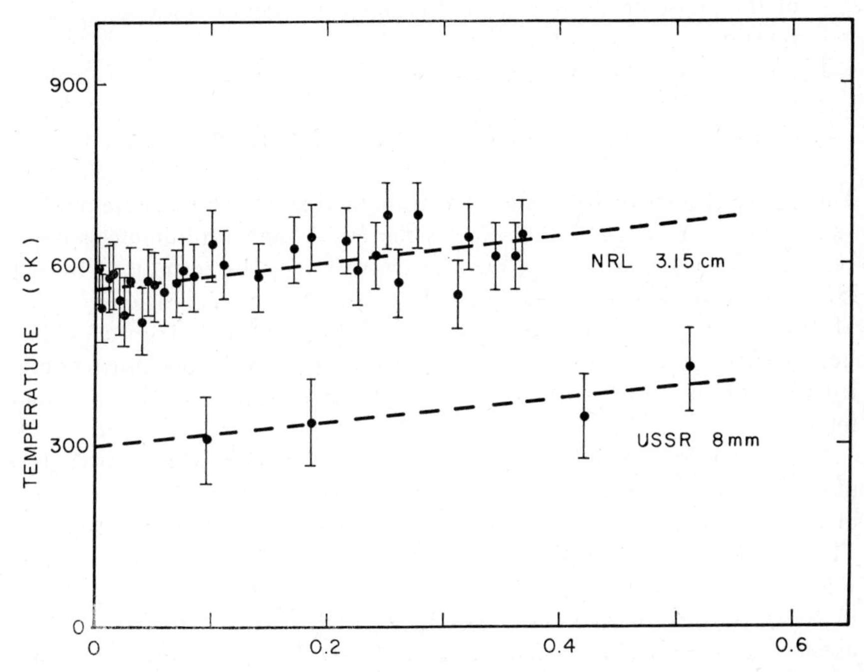

FIG. 6. Venus radio data phase variation. Observational points at 3.15 cm and 8 mm were obtained, respectively, in the United States and the Soviet Union. The brightness temperature of the planet is plotted against the phase constant k (normalized fractional area of the illuminated disk). The dashed lines are least squares solutions through the observational points. The suggested increase of brightness temperature with k would imply a higher average temperature on the sun-lit side than on the dark side of the planet Venus.

observations. Granted the availability of spacecraft for the transportation of radiometric devices to the immediate vicinity of a planet like Venus, a small amount of microwave equipment can conduct important measurements. The same experimental objectives, if attempted from ground-based radio telescopes, would be prohibitively expensive and have little guarantee of success.

To summarize the objectives of the planned Mariner millimeter space radio telescope experiment, the four-channel radio telescope will provide data to:

1. establish the physical basis of the Venus radiation mechanism; *e.g.*, discriminate between the greenhouse and ionospheric models.
2. obtain precision spectra in the microwave region for detailed studies of the physics of the Venus environment;
3. obtain precision measurements of the microwave spectrum of Venus on the sunlit and dark side, for the further investigation of the phase effect and its bearing upon the environment and the rotation rate of the planet;
4. provide preliminary thermal mapping of the planet with high resolution;
5. conduct a search for water vapor in the Venus atmosphere.

These objectives can be achieved with a modest amount of equipment, as may be seen in Fig. 7. This shows the four-channel millimeter spacecraft radio telescope. Its use on a spacecraft may be visualized by an examination of Fig. 8, which presents one of the configurations of the Mariner spacecraft under study by the Jet Propulsion Laboratory. The four-channel radio telescope may be seen attached to the boom extending from the spacecraft, and is indicative of the future of space radio telescopes.

More advanced vehicles will follow the early fly-by experiments with attempts to land packages of scientific instrumentation on the surface of the planet Venus and conduct a number of important investigations. These explorations will form part of the inevitable exploration of the solar system during this decade. The unusual importance of the radio investigations can perhaps be best emphasized by examining the requirements imposed upon the scientific apparatus to be placed upon the surface of Venus. If the Sagan "greenhouse" model is correct, that is, that the surface temperature can actually be 600°K, then the scientific instrumentation must be designed in a manner which will permit effective operation in an environment totally unlike any considered so far. New systems development programs will be required to make available instrumentation which will operate "normally" at 600°K. In this manner, we may look forward to successful conduct of experiments on the surface of the planet in an incredibly hot environment.

On the other hand, suppose that the ionospheric explanation of the Venus radio spectrum is correct. In this case we may anticipate landing the scientific instrumentation on a surface which has a "comfortable" temperature, not too unlike that of the earth, and the scientific instrumentation itself will require no unusual protection from the meteorological environment at the surface of Venus. However, the basic objective of any payload landed on the surface of Venus is to conduct measure-

FIG. 7. Four-channel millimeter-wave radio telescope for a Venus space probe. The space-probe radiometric payload is composed of four millimeter channels operating at 4, 8, 13.5, and 20 mm. There are three antennae, with the two longer wavelength channels operating from a common antenna. The comparison horns for the four wavelengths can be seen at the left side of the photograph. The radiometers are of the crystal video type. The location of this radiometric system can be seen in Fig. 8 located near the end of a boom. (Courtesy the Ewen Knight Corporation and the Jet Propulsion Laboratory, NASA.)

ments of scientific interest and to convey the information ultimately to man on the earth. Unfortunately, if the ionospheric model is correct, none of the standard telemetry frequencies employed or planned would be able to propagate through the dense ionosphere around Venus. To communicate successfully with the packages on the surface, we shall be forced to go to exceedingly high frequencies of the order of 30 kMc and higher. Again, new telemetry systems development will be required for transmission capability in a frequency range not considered at present.

Although the Mariner space radio telescope is an instrument designed to provide basic knowledge about the planet Venus, it can be seen from the discussion above that results of the space radio telescope observa-

FIG. 8. Space-probe multi-channel millimeter radio telescope. One of the possible radio telescope configurations for a Mariner spacecraft mission to the planet Venus is shown above. Of interest here is the position of the four radiometric telescopes which may be seen in the illustration extending from the end of the boom. Stabilization of the spacecraft enables an articulation motion of the boom, which permits a scanning of the planetary disk at the four wavelengths of interest. The wavelengths of operation are 4 mm, 8 mm, 13.5 mm (water vapor line), and 20 mm. By referring to Fig. 5, it can be seen that these four wavelengths cover the critical portion of the Venus spectrum where the maximum change of radio intensity with wavelength is evident. (Courtesy the Jet Propulsion Laboratory, NASA.)

tions will be of immediate practical use in the design and development of future instrumentation for the exploration of the planet.

References

Alsop, L. E., Giordmaine, J. A., Mayer, C. H., and Townes, C. H. (1958), Observations using a maser radiometer at 3-cm wave length, *Astrophys. J.* **63,** 301; (1959), Proc. IAU Symp. No. 9–URSI Symp. No. 1 (R. N. Bracewell, ed.); pp. 69–74. Stanford Univ. Press, Stanford, California.

Gibson, J. E., and McEwan, R. J. (1959), Proc. IAU Symp. No. 9–URSI Symp. No. 1 (R. N. Bracewell, ed.), pp. 50–52. Stanford Univ. Press, Stanford, California.

Jones, D. (1960), A microwave radiometer experiment for the planet Venus, *Proc. Natl. Electronics Conf.* **16,** 489–493.

Kuzmin, A. D., and Salomonovich, A. E. (1960), Radio emissions from Venus in the 8-mm bandwith. *Astron. J.* (*U.S.S.R.*) **37,** 297–300.

Lilley, A. E. (1961), The temperature of Venus, *Astrophys. J.* **66,** 290.

Mayer, C. H., McCullough, T. P., and Sloanaker, R. M. (1958), Observations of Venus at 3.15 cm wave length, *Ap. J.*, **127,** 1–10; (1958), Measurements of planetary radiation at centimeter wavelengths, *Proc. I.R.E.* **46,** 260.

Meeks, M. L. (1961), Atmospheric emission and opacity at millimeter wavelengths due to oxygen, *J. Geophys. Research* **66,** 3749.

Mintz, Y. (1961), Temperature and circulation of the Venus atmosphere. *Planetary and Space Sci.* **5,** 141–152.

Mizushima, M., and Hill, R. M. (1954), Microwave spectrum of O_2, *Phys. Rev.* **93,** 745–748.

Muhleman, D. O., Holdridge, D. B., and Block, N. (1962), The Astronomical Unit Determined by Radar Reflections from Venus, *Astrophys. J.* **67,** 191.

Pettengill, G. H., and others (1962), A Radar Investigation of Venus, *Astrophys. J.* **67,** 181.

Sagan, C. (1960). The radiation balance of Venus, Jet Propulsion Lab. Rept. 32–34.

Tinkham, M., and Strandberg, M. W. P. (1955), Theory of the fine structure of the molecular oxygen ground state, *Phys. Rev.* **97,** 937–951.

Victor, W. K., Stephens, R., and Golomb, S. W. (1961), Radio exploration of Venus, Jet Propulsion Lab. Tech. Rept. 32–132.

13.2 *Radio Astronomy Below 10 Mc/sec*

FRED HADDOCK

UNIVERSITY OF MICHIGAN OBSERVATORY,
Ann Arbor, Michigan

Jansky's detection of radio waves from our galaxy at 20 Mc, in 1932, was a wholly unexpected discovery and still is one of the most intriguing problems in all astronomy. This discovery had to await the development of low-noise receivers to get above the critical frequency of the ionosphere which varies from about 1 to 15 Mc. This limit shifts back and forth, and it is this region that restricts our observations of the galaxy, the sun, and the planets. Three years ago, when we first started thinking of instrumenting satellites and rockets in this frequency band for looking at solar bursts, measurements had only been made down to about 20 Mc. Since that time measurements have been made of Jupiter and the sun in bursts down to 5 Mc, although under these conditions the ionosphere is usually badly perturbed and the records are suspect, at least as far as the intensity distribution is concerned.

Jansky's original data showed an intense region toward the galactic center and some elongation along the galactic plane. The general level of apparent radio brightness of about 100,000° at high latitudes was impossible to account for by any process known at that time.

Figure 1 shows the critical frequency for the altitude region where the index of refraction approaches zero. The densities in the planetary ionospheres and exospheres range from 100 electrons up to a million per cubic centimeter. One might refer to the corresponding frequencies as the planetary frequencies because the critical plasma frequencies in this range seem to match in the envelopes of several planets.

On the planet Jupiter, the fact that circular-polarized radiation is observed around 20 to 27 Mc, seems to indicate quite strongly that the field in the region where the bursts originate is of the order of about 5 gauss.

A cosmic background brightness temperature spectrum is depicted in Fig. 2. In the low-frequency region the interstellar thermal electrons are sufficiently absorbing and at a temperature of about 10^{4}° the medium will become opaque, so that an extremely fundamental measurement could be made at 100 kc.

Such experiments would give us some fundamental information about what is called the emission measure of interstellar gas; it would be the most sensitive determination of electron density. One interesting but complicating fact is that the ionized gas lies principally in the galactic plane and toward the lower frequencies this gas becomes opaque, blocking out the bright ridge along the galactic equator, so that at about 1 Mc the appearance of the galaxy is quite reversed. Thus there appears to be

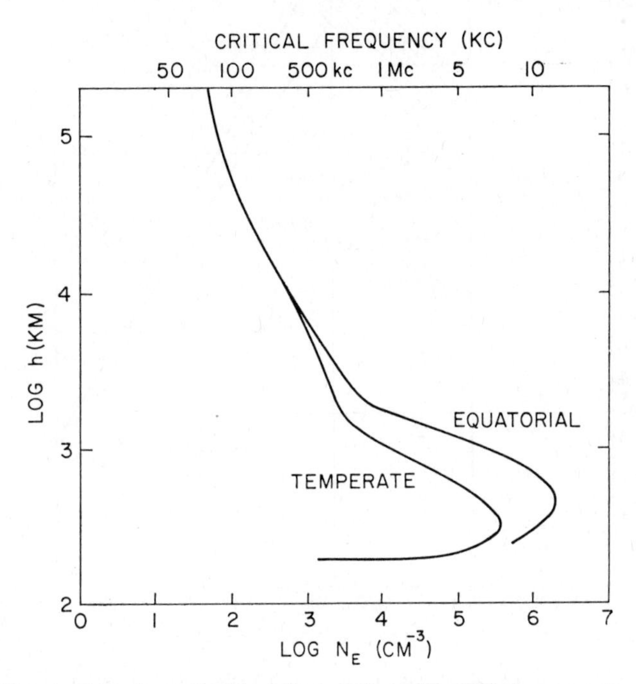

FIG. 1. Variation of critical frequencies with altitude on earth.

a cold belt through the galactic plane, and the galactic poles will be the last to disappear. The radio galaxy at these low frequencies might appear as two bright spots with a very cold region at the lower galactic latitudes. A determination of its temperature may be one of the most precise measurements of the temperatures of the interstellar electrons. This is the cosmic noise. The average brightness of static atmospheric noise from lightning discharges go all the way from 10^4 to 10^{16}°K at 10 Mc.

One can trade off one noise for another. Above the ionosphere, most noises from city and urban areas are eliminated. The limit is usually of the order of 5 to 7 Mc, so that above the ionosphere there is a sudden cutoff in man-made signals and an increase in galactic background noise. This has been observed by some of the early rocket experiments

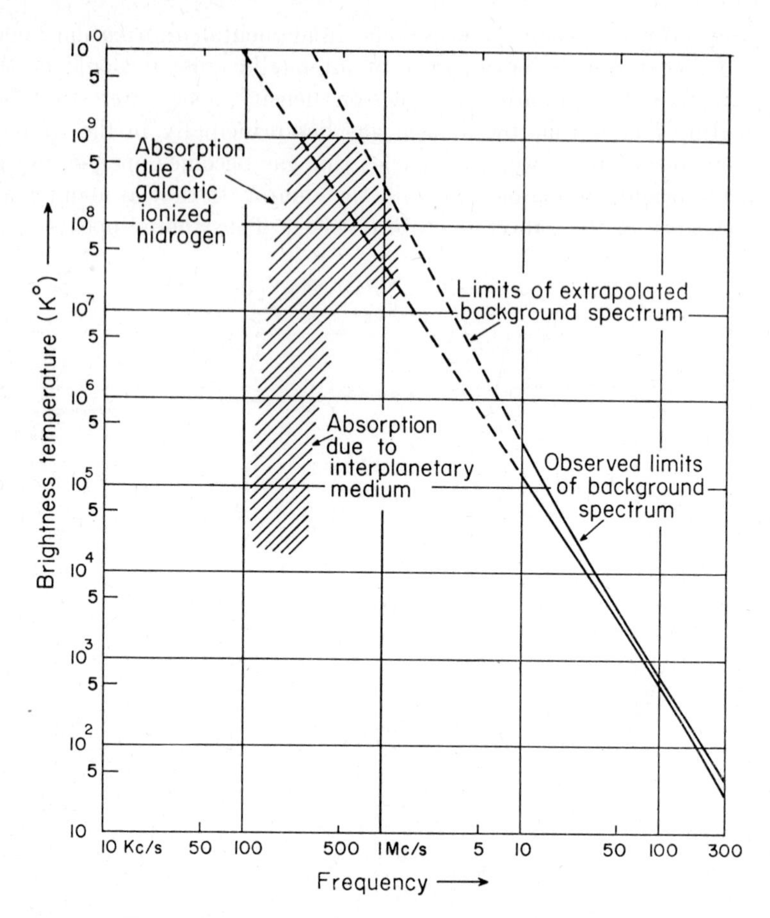

FIG. 2. Cosmic radio background brightness spectrum.

and satellite experiments and by the recent Topside sounding measurements by our National Bureau of Standards.

Discussion

DR. H. C. VAN DE HULST: Have you taken into account in your calculation the possibility that, even with the very strong cutoff by the interstellar thermal gas which exists near 100 kc/sec, there may still be a region close to the sun in which enough nonthermal radiation is generated to outshine the thermal component? Even one parsec might be sufficient.

DR. F. I. HADDOCK: Yes. That is certainly a lower bound, and as you move down, instead of a smooth blackout, it is likely to be quite patchy; in between the patches it is going to be exceptionally bright. It will be exceedingly interesting to map these bright and dark patches. By extrapolating from the measurements made on the ground at higher frequencies downward from the absorbing regions and even going up as high as the centimeter wave lengths, to find out where there is thermal emission along the galactic plane as measured by Dr. Westerhout and others, a first approximation to this problem may perhaps be made. We have not yet done that. We are trying to put the model of the galaxy and the nonthermal component on a computer, and in different models of the thermal patchiness and different layers of stratification of the thermal electrons, and study many models of the sky at different frequencies. We are now in the process of programming a computer for this purpose.

DR. J. L. GREENSTEIN: I should point out that this question of the low-frequency cutoff is a very serious one in determining the total energy emitted by the synchrotron process. Unfortunately, the integral of the emitted power, which varies as $\nu^{-0.5}$, will give a divergence. The shape at low frequencies tells us by how much one will have to multiply the total observed radio energy, and it also tells us about the electron density in the emitting source.

DR. G. MÜNCH: My picture of the appearance of the sky at 1 Mc looks quite different from what Dr. Haddock visualizes. At 1 Mc I would expect radiation from H II regions in large excess of the thermal value. There is evidence in the optical region that the mass motions present in H II regions dissipate very fast. The most effective way of damping the mass motions is by longitudinal plasma oscillations. The plasma frequency is identical to the critical frequency for transmission, but the density fluctuations (and possibly also fluctuations in the magnetic field) provide the coupling between the longitudinal oscillations with the transverse ones or electromagnetic waves. The maximum emission would be expected around the plasma frequency, which in the Orion nebula for example, ($N_e = 10^4 \text{cm}^{-3}$), would be 1 Mc/sec.

CHAPTER 14

Future Large Vehicles of Long Life

14.1 The Role of Chemically Fueled Launch Vehicles for Astronomical Research

DAVID H. GARBER

GENERAL DYNAMICS/ASTRONAUTICS, A Division of General Dynamics Corporation, San Diego, California

Existing United States launch vehicles all depend on chemical release of energy for propulsion. The well-known Thor, Atlas, and Titan I missiles are examples of major stages of launch vehicles which are fueled by liquid oxygen and RP-1 propellants.

The present discussion of launch vehicles surveys some concepts and trends which will probably be representative of future growth of large chemical rockets. Detailed study of such rockets inevitably leads to the requirement for high-energy upper-stage vehicles, and eventually to the requirement for performance characteristics that are beyond the capabilities of chemical rockets.

A primary requirement for a high-energy upper stage is to utilize a propulsion system with high specific impulse. This term (I_{sp}) is defined as the ratio of propulsive thrust to propellant mass flow rate. Specific impulse has the dimension of time and is usually expressed in seconds.

Physically, specific impulse is a measure of propellant exhaust velocity v (in ft/sec) according to the relations $I_{sp} = F/(dM/dt) = v/g$, where F is the propulsive thrust in pounds, dM/dt the mass flow rate in lb/sec, and g the gravitational acceleration at earth sea level in ft/sec^2. Thus a propulsion system with high specific impulse can produce a given momentum change with less expenditure of propellant mass than a system with low specific impulse. The penalty paid for this advantage is a reduction in achievable thrust. For some extremely high specific impulse systems, take-off is not possible from a ground launch site in a terrestrial gravitational field. In such a case the high specific impulse system can only be used for upper stages of a launch vehicle.

Table I lists specific impulses between 250 and 420 sec for a few combinations of chemical fuel and oxidizer. The numerical values are nominal, because specific impulse varies substantially in each case with engine design and with method of operation, such as the ratio of oxidizer to fuel or the ambient atmospheric pressure. Only combinations of liquid propellants are listed; most solid propellants operate with specific impulse somewhat less than 250 sec, although there is promise that 280 sec may be attained after several years of development.

TABLE I
CHEMICAL PROPULSION

Oxidizer	Fuel	Specific impulse (sec)
Liquid oxygen	RP-1	250
Inhibited red fuming nitric acid	Unsymmetrical dimethyl hydrazine	280
Liquid oxygen	Liquid hydrogen	420

It is not possible to go much higher in specific impulse for practical chemical propellants than is shown in Table I. A practical limit arises in the attempt to store more chemical energy per pound of stable propellant. Another limitation is that imposed by the temperature characteristics of materials from which the rocket engine combustion chamber is made, since higher exhaust velocity means higher combustion temperature.

It is possible to increase specific impulse significantly over that achievable with chemical rockets by utilizing a nuclear reactor heat source. A propellant material is ejected at high exhaust velocity after receiving heat energy from the reactor. No combustion occurs.

A nuclear propulsion system using hydrogen as propellant can provide specific impulse estimated at some 800 sec. However, such a system still is limited in practical exhaust velocity by the high-temperature characteristics of materials in contact with the exhaust gas. Another limitation is imposed by the requirement for a radiator with large area in order to reject heat from the reactor heat exchanger.

Much hope exists for increasing specific impulse by another one or more orders of magnitude through the use of electrical acceleration of ions or plasma in conjunction with a nuclear reactor heat source and an electrical convertor. For example, a cesium ion propulsion system may provide a specific impulse of many thousands of seconds, the range depending on the practicability of increasing acceleration and field shaping voltages in the ion accelerator. Since such voltages correspond to effective exhaust energies of many millions of degrees Kelvin, it is clear that thermal achievement of such energy is out of the question with conventional chemical combustion.

To return to chemical rockets, Fig. 1 shows some existing, planned, future, and potential launch vehicles, their propellants, and their take-off thrusts. Any presentation such as this of future launch vehicles is obsolete almost as soon as it is set down, but Fig. 1 is representative of an

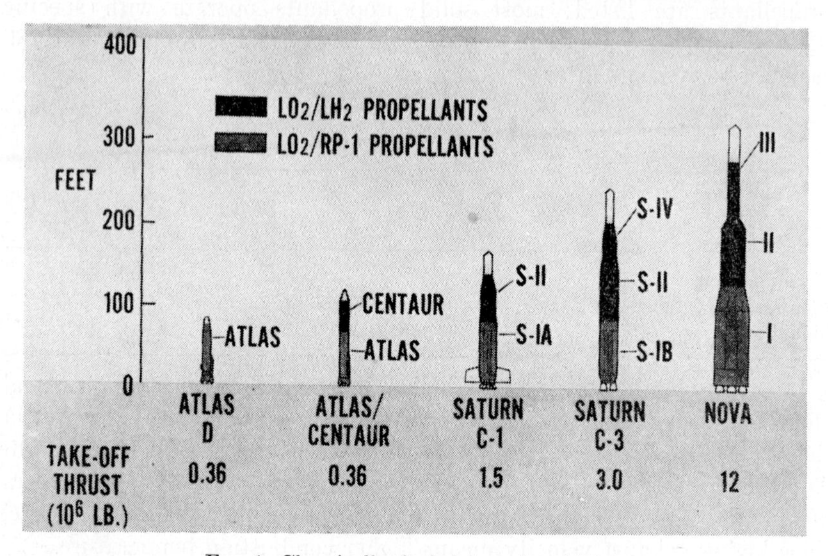

FIG. 1. Chemically fueled launch vehicles.

evolutionary trend in launch vehicles as they appear today in the U. S.

The Atlas/Centaur combination is an example of a launch vehicle which is soon to go into flight test. It is shown in Fig. 2 during recent tests at the Atlantic Missile Range, Florida. Centaur will be the first United States high-energy upper stage. It is scheduled to launch the National Aeronautics and Space Administration (NASA) Surveyor spacecraft towards the moon for a soft landing of instruments in 1963. It will launch the NASA Mariner spacecraft for a Venus flyby in 1962. It will launch various satellites into the synchronous or "24-hr" orbit at 19,323 N. miles altitude. It will launch later Mariners for a Mars flyby and possibly for instrumented planetary capture or landing. Centaur should truly become a workhorse for exploration of the inner solar system.

The first stage is the United States Air Force Atlas D booster. Atlas is powered by three rocket engines with total take-off thrust of over 360,000 lb.

FIG. 2. Atlas/Centaur at Atlantic Missile Range.

The NASA Centaur upper stage is 10 ft in diameter, the same as Atlas. The over-all Atlas/Centaur is some 107 ft high, the exact height varying with size of payload.

Centaur is powered by two rocket engines using liquid oxygen and liquid hydrogen as propellants. Because of the extremely low storage

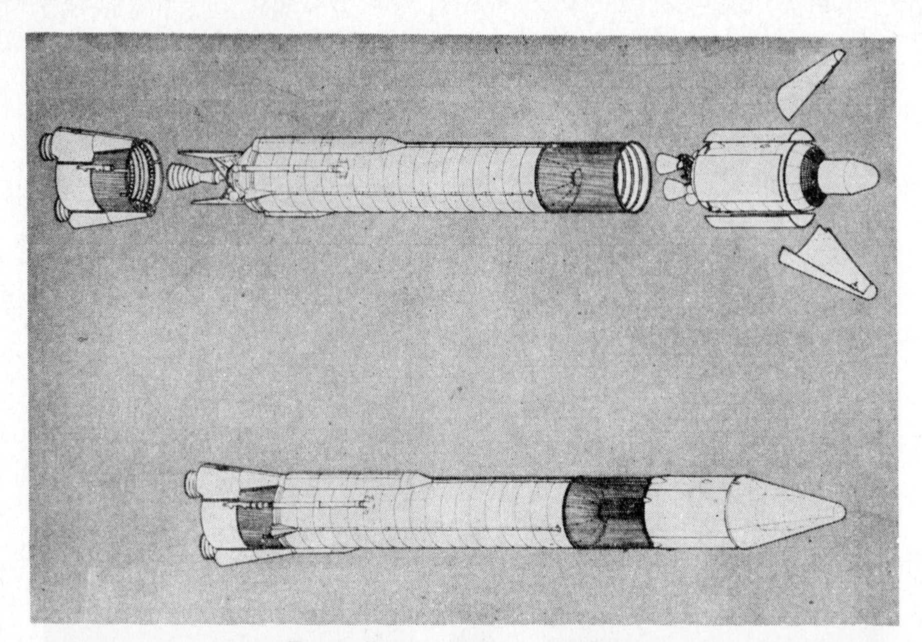

FIG. 3. Centaur in-flight separation.

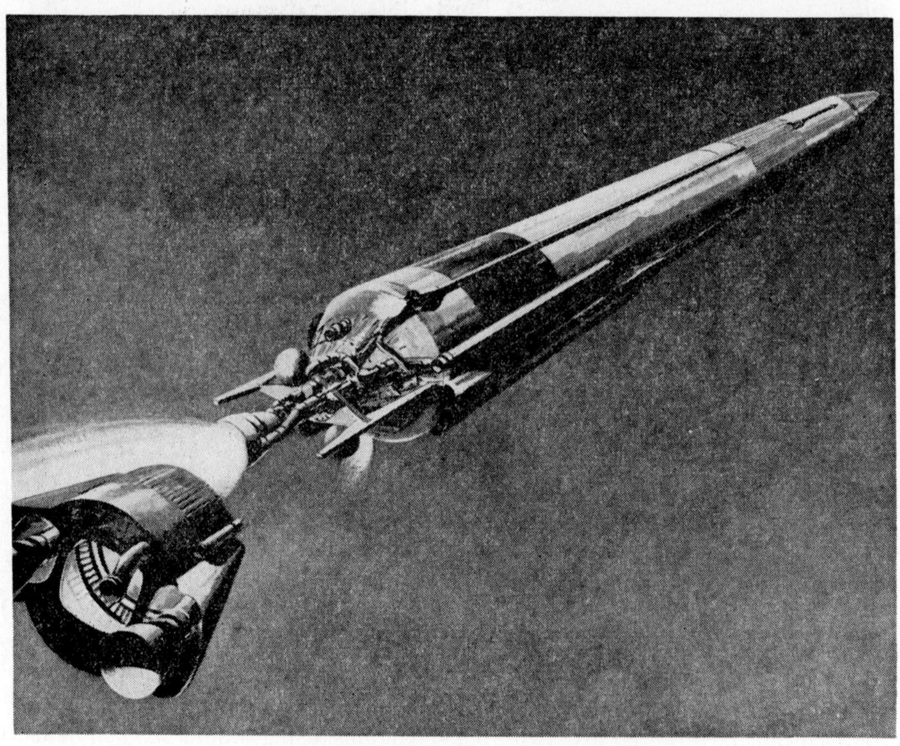

FIG. 4. Atlas/Centaur booster separation.

temperatures of liquid hydrogen (—423°F or 20°K) and liquid oxygen (—297°F or 90°K), insulation panels surround the propellant tanks. For aerodynamic protection during launch the payload is surrounded by a nose fairing.

Figure 3 shows the assembled Atlas/Centaur and its separated sections. In flight Atlas first releases two booster engines and a protective housing, and continues with a single sustainer engine. The sequence of separation is illustrated in Figs. 4–6. Figure 4 shows separation of the Atlas booster section which occurs after approximately 2 min of flight with about 80%

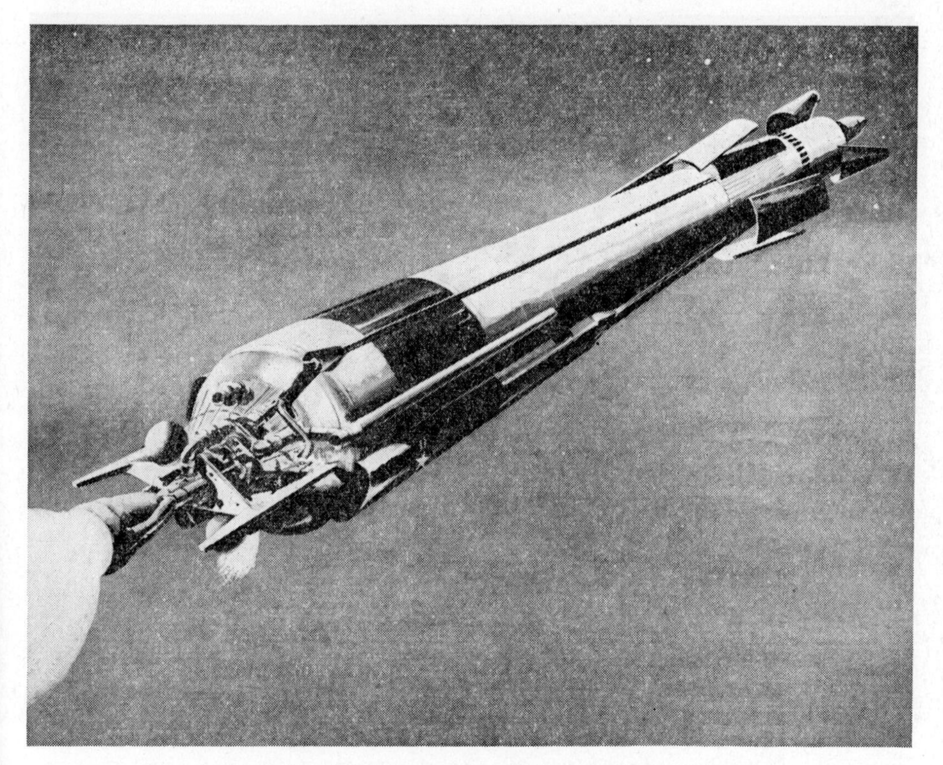

FIG. 5. Separation of Centaur nose fairing and insulation panels.

of the fuel exhausted. Figure 5 shows release of the Centaur insulation panels and nose fairing which occurs as soon as practicable in order to lighten the upper stage. After sustainer operation has ceased, Atlas and Centaur separate and the Centaur engines ignite, as shown in Fig. 6.

The exact sequence and timing of these events depends of course on the mission. As an example, to launch a satellite into a geostationary or synchronous equatorial orbit, the sequence shown in Fig. 7 is used.

Thrust from the Atlas first stage and from the first Centaur firing places Centaur in a circular parking orbit, shown here at 110 N. miles, although this value may be different for other missions.

After a suitable period, shown here as a little over one-half revolution, the Centaur engines fire again to put the vehicle into a transfer ellipse with the desired apogee. In the case illustrated, after about 6 hr from launch another firing puts Centaur into its circular equatorial orbit, with a 24-hr period at 19,323 N. miles, so that it remains stationary above the desired point on the earth's equator.

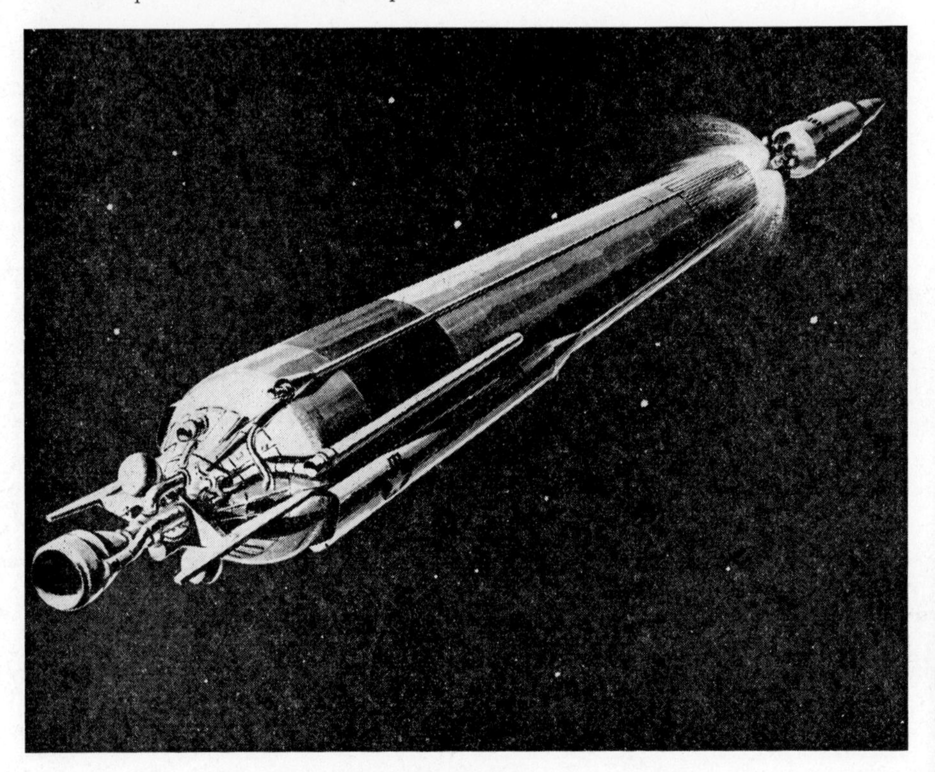

Fig. 6. Separation and ignition of Centaur stage.

Centaur is designed to put some 9000 lb into a 300 N. mile orbit, or about 1000 lb into a 19,323 N. mile orbit. Centaur will deliver about 750 lb to the moon for a soft landing, or about twice that for a close circumlunar satellite orbit. It will launch 1000 to 1200 lb for a Venus or Mars flyby.

The successful development of Centaur is providing necessary experience with liquid hydrogen and liquid oxygen propellants that is basic to the evolution of the NASA Saturn family of launch vehicles.

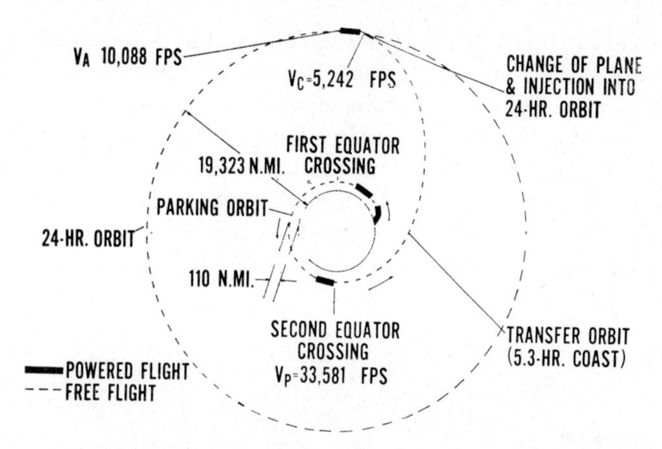

FIG. 7. Centaur 24-hr orbit sequence. Ascent into 24-hr orbit in equator plane from AMR, positioning satellite at longitude 105 W.

Saturn has existed in the planning stages in many configurations. The name of Nova has also been used in connection with advanced designs of very large launch vehicles. The configurations for these vehicles are still changing, but some versions are shown in Fig. 1. Saturn C configurations are also shown in Figs. 8 and 9. Configurations A and B are obsolete.

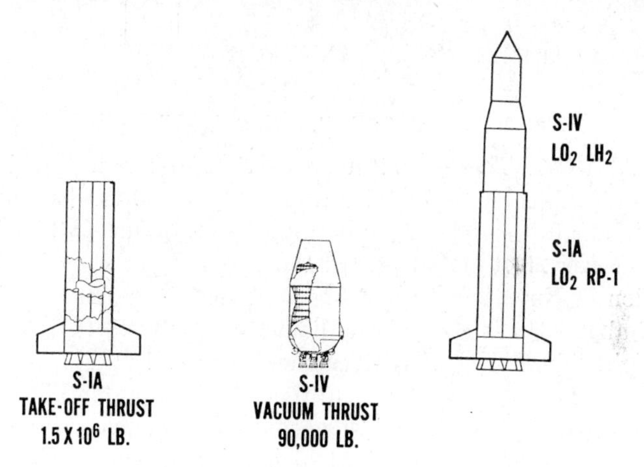

FIG. 8. Saturn C-1: S-I and S-IV stages.

Saturn C-1 is shown in Fig. 8, with two stages. On the left is the first stage S-I, a cluster of nine propellant tanks. Eight engines provide total take-off thrust of 1.5 million pounds. The propellants are liquid oxygen and RP-1. The second stage S-IV, shown in the center of Fig. 8, utilizes liquid oxygen and liquid hydrogen propellants. There are six engines, similar to the Centaur engines, with total thrust of 90,000 lb. As in the case of Centaur, the liquid oxygen tank is at the bottom and is smaller than the liquid hydrogen tank, partly because of the much higher density of liquid oxygen (1.14 gm/cm^3) compared with liquid hydrogen (0.070 gm/cm^3) at their respective boiling points. Saturn C-1 is about 170 ft high and over 21 ft in diameter at the base (excluding fins).

Saturn C-3 is shown in Fig. 9 with three stages. (C-2 has been abandoned.) A modified first stage S-IB is shown at the left, with two engines totalling 3.0 million pounds in thrust. The propellants are liquid

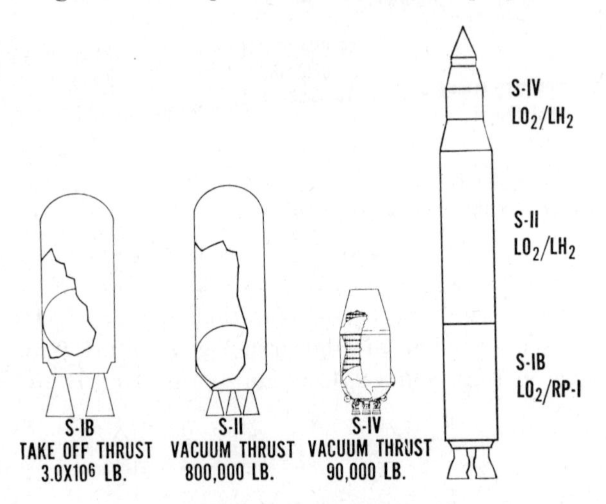

Fig. 9. Saturn C-3: S-IB, S-II, and S-IV stages.

oxygen and RP-1. The second stage S-II utilizes four liquid oxygen-liquid hydrogen engines with total thrust of 800,000 lb. The third stage S-IV is similar to the S-IV stage of Saturn C-1. Saturn C-3 is about 250 ft high and over 26 ft in diameter at the base.

A version of Nova is shown in Fig. 1. It has three stages with a total height of about 340 ft and a base diameter of over 43 ft. Its first stage utilizes eight liquid oxygen-RP-1 engines with total take-off thrust of 12 million pounds. The upper stages utilize liquid oxygen and liquid hydrogen as propellants. The second stage has eight engines which produce 1.6 million pounds thrust. The third stage has two engines which produce 400,000 lb thrust.

It is interesting to note that recurring costs for successive launches of an operational multistage chemically powered vehicle are already nearly as low as they are likely to get. Atlas/Centaur launch into a 300 N. mile orbit will cost of the order of $1000 per pound of payload, excluding cost of the payload. It is doubtful whether reduction to less than $300 per pound can be expected even for the much larger Saturn. However

Saturn C-1 can put about 20,000 pounds into a 300 N. mile orbit, and Saturn C-3 upwards of 150,000 pounds. Further reduction in delivery cost per pound of payload requires taking the next step with nuclear propulsion and nuclear-electric propulsion upper-stage vehicles.

For astronomical applications, orbiting telescopes, spectroscopes, and other instruments will provide much new information for many years. With fairly modest weight payloads, using remotely controlled equipment, the astronomer will be able to make observations above the interference of the earth's atmosphere. Such a step permits significant improvement in resolution because of removal of atmospheric perturbations to the optical path, and it also provides expansion of the available portion of the electromagnetic spectrum. Current NASA planning is for a 36-in. orbiting telescope, and instruments of larger diameter are being studied.

The capabilities of chemical rockets are appropriate for lunar and planetary probes, first for instrumented flyby spacecraft, followed by impact vehicles, captive lunar and planetary satellites, and soft-landing spacecraft. To augment astronomical observations from a distance, manned landings will permit scientists to study lunar and planetary environments at first hand. Following manned space flight it will be possible to establish manned observatories on the moon or even on an asteroid. Chemically powered rockets are appropriate for instrumented solar probes. Performance will also permit launching a probe directly through the head of a comet in the inner solar system, provided the comet is not too far from the plane of the earth's orbit.

For more remote targets, the chemical rocket is not competitive with the electrical propulsion rocket. In the case of a Jupiter flyby the comparison may be close, but beyond Jupiter the chemical rocket is inadequate.

Atlas/Centaur can be fitted with an ion-propulsion third stage, including a SNAP-8 60-kw reactor as a power supply. For example, such a configuration can carry more payload to a 1000 N. mile capture orbit about Mars than can an all-chemical Saturn C-1, if it is required that C-1 also carry the same reactor. The point is that the reactor is needed for space communication anyway, and it must be taken along for the ion rocket as an energy source during the propulsion phase of the trip.

For exploration of the outer solar system or for extra-ecliptical exploration, Saturn plus an ion rocket is required. The chemical rocket will be required for terrestrial and planetary take-off, as a lower stage, and probably for upper stages as well. For remote exploration of the outer solar system, nuclear-electrical propulsion is required.

14.2 The Electric Engine as a Propulsion System for the Exploration of Space

GERHARD B. HELLER

RESEARCH PROJECTS DIVISION, MARSHALL SPACE FLIGHT CENTER, NASA, Huntsville, Alabama

Spacecraft of the future will be propelled by electric engines in the exploration of space. Electric propulsion devices are suitable exclusively for the propulsion of spacecraft and not for boosting of heavy vehicles. Their operation begins after the spacecraft has been placed into orbit.

The development of electric engines has proceeded along three different basic lines (Fig. 1): (1) electrostatic or ion engines; (2) electrothermal or arc engines; (3) electromagnetic or MFD engines. These electric engines require an electric power supply as the prime energy source. They are low thrust devices and operate over long periods of time.

The ion engine operates in a range of 5000 to 50,000 sec specific impulse. Specific impulse is the ratio of the exhaust velocity to the standard acceleration due to gravity at the surface of the earth. The ion rocket is the electric engine which has received more attention than any other space propulsion system. The earliest known record on the principle of electric propulsion goes back to Goddard, the American rocket pioneer, who investigated this possibility in 1906 (*1*). The theory has been described in Oberth's book, "Roads to Space Travel" (*2*). Stuhlinger has discussed the design principles and the mission applications for both ion and arc engines in numerous publications since 1947. The cesium ion engine and a mission of an electrically propelled spaceship were described by Stuhlinger in 1954 (*3*). Theory and design aspects of arc and ion engines are treated in Stuhlinger's contribution to the "Handbook of Astronautical Engineering" (*4*).

Ion and arc engines have progressed about equally, to the point of active engine development. Figure 1 shows the main components of an ion engine: the tank with cesium propellant, and the flow control. The cesium atoms are ionized at the surface of hot tungsten in the ion source; the cesium ions are accelerated by an electrostatic field. The current of the ion jet is space charge limited. Unless neutralization by electrons is achieved, the ion engine could not produce sufficient thrust. The power supply and instrumentation are essential components of all electric engines.

The arc engine, also shown in Fig. 1, consists of many of the same elements. The propulsion is achieved by heating the propellant with an arc and producing a nearly adiabatic-isentropic expansion of the hot gas

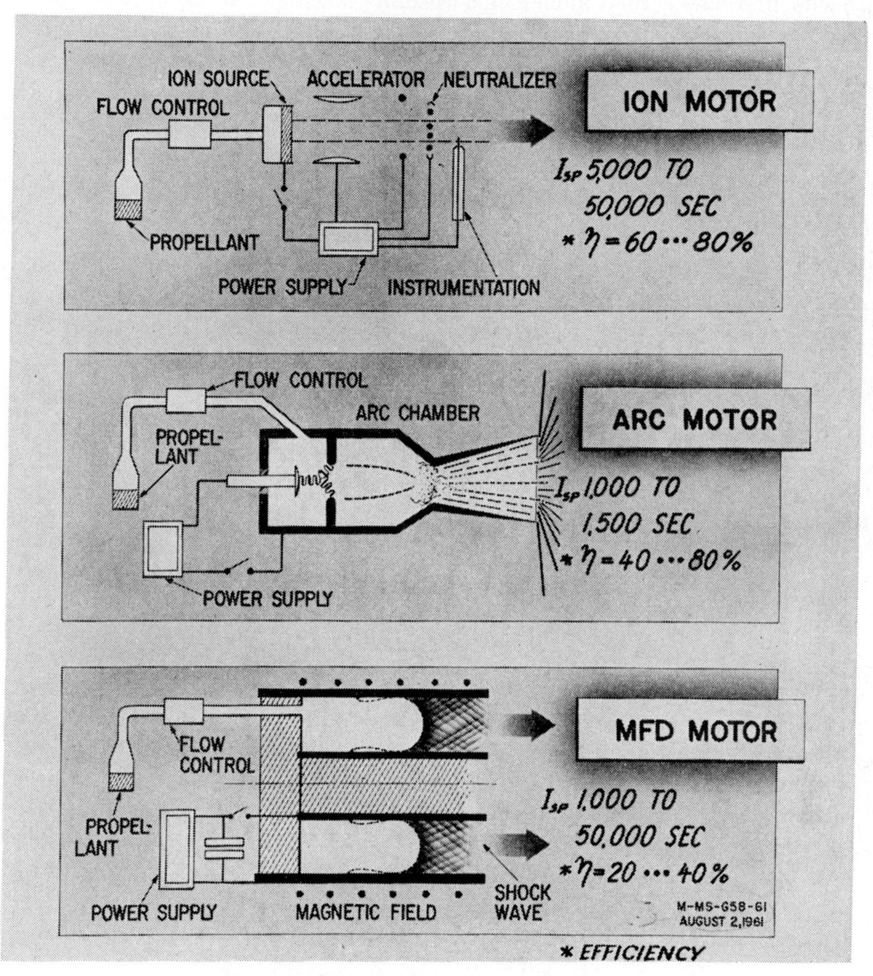

FIG. 1. Three types of electric engines.

or plasma in a convergent-divergent duct. The exhaust jet of an arc engine expands freely in vacuum and fills nearly an expansion hemisphere or plume similar to that of conventional rockets in the vacuum of space.

Magnetofluiddynamic engines are characterized by the use of strong magnetic fields which interact with a plasma to produce acceleration.

There are many different types and configurations. The MFD engines are not considered to be as advanced as either ion or arc engines. In this discussion, emphasis will be placed on the ion and arc engines.

History and Status

The first laboratory model of a cesium-tungsten ion motor was operated by Stavisskii in the U.S.S.R. in early 1958. In America, the first cesium-tungsten engine was run by Forrester at Rocketdyne in the fall of 1958. Other engines followed, such as the one by Electro-Optical Systems, the bombardment-type engine by Lewis Research Center of NASA, and many others.

Presently, major engine developments for 30-kw ion engines are carried out by Lewis Research Center, by Hughes Aircraft under NASA sponsorship (Fig. 2), and by Electro-Optical Systems under AF sponsorship.

FIG. 2. Hughes ion engine.

Figure 3 shows the Electro-Optical ion engine in operation.

The first laboratory model of an arc with gas feed and a supersonic nozzle was run by Peters in Germany in 1954. Using the basic principle of this device, arc jets have been developed in this country for the simulation of re-entry conditions. This work started at several places in

FIG. 3. Electro-Optical ion engine in operation.

1956. An arc jet can be used for simulation of parabolic re-entry of space vehicles into the earth's atmosphere. Arc engines for propulsion have been developed since 1958 by AVCO and Plasmadyne. The National Aeronautics and Space Administration has contracts for the development of arc engines with AVCO and GE for 30-kwe* engines, and with Plasmadyne for a 1-kwe engine; and the AF has a contract for a 30-kwe engine with Plasmadyne.

The 30-kwe arc engine operates from the SNAP-8 nuclear electric power supply that is presently under development. The 1-kwe arc engine is developed for the attitude and position control of advanced spacecraft. Its power supply can be either the SNAP-8, or a smaller power supply.

Table I shows the thrust that can be achieved with electric engines. The specific impulse and efficiency values are within the present state of the art. Up to 1.2 lb thrust can be achieved with a 30-kwe engine and 0.18 lb with an ion engine of the same power level, at impulse values shown. It is a well-known fact that for a given power source and the same conversion efficiency, thrust and specific impulse are inversely proportional to each other. The arc engine has the highest thrust-to-

* kwe denotes kilowatt electrical energy.

TABLE I
THRUST OF ELECTRIC ENGINES

	Power (kwe)	Specific impulse (sec)	Energy conversion efficiency (%)	Thrust (lb)
Arc engines	1	1000	40	0.02
		1500	30	0.01
	30	1000	80	1.2
		1500	40	0.4
	300	1000	80	12
		1500	40	4
Ion engines	30	5000	60	0.18
		10,000	80	0.12
	300	5000	60	1.8
		10,000	80	1.2

power ratio in the family of electric propulsion engines and, therefore plays a vital role.

Development Problems

The ion development program is connected with a number of research problems which are summarized in Table II. Some of these problems have not been solved, but are being pursued by a number of investigators. Complete new approaches or breakthroughs are not required, but some of the problems require an advancement of the state of the art, as in porous tungsten technology, ion optics, charge exchange and lifetime

TABLE II
TECHNICAL PROBLEMS IN ION PROPULSION

1. Configuration of porous tungsten ion source
2. Fabrication and bonding of ion source
3. Wire bundles as ion source
4. Sputtering and secondary emission
5. Ion source efficiency
6. Charge exchange of neutrals and ions
7. Corrosion by cesium
8. Electrical breakdown
9. Design of ion optics (accelerator)
10. Propellant flow control
11. Measuring techniques for jet diagnostics
12. RF communication with ion engine on
13. Neutralization of ions
14. Interaction of a space ship with a running ion engine and the space environment

effects due to sputtering. The problem of beam neutralization has received considerable attention in the past year. Although the problem is much better understood than in the early phase of ion development, a definite solution cannot be found until flight tests are carried out.

Table III lists the technical problems connected with the arc engine development.

TABLE III

TECHNICAL PROBLEMS IN ARC PROPULSION

1. Throat and nozzle design and interaction of arc with nozzle used as an anode
2. Design of electrodes, length of arc column
3. Heat transfer
4. AC or DC arc engines
5. Cryogenic or noncryogenic propellant
6. Regenerative and radiative cooling
7. Electrical breakdown
8. Propellant flow control
9. Measuring techniques for investigation of the jet or exhaust plume of an arc engine
10. RF communication with arc engine on
11. Interaction of a space ship with a running arc engine in the space environment
12. Optimum voltage of arc
13. Recombination during the expansion

Presently, arc engines have arrived at two design concepts. One type is shown in Fig. 4, which is a DC engine mockup (*5*). The rear electrode or cathode is made of tungsten; the throat and nozzle is the anode. The arc strikes either shortly upstream of the throat, or passes through the elongated throat and attaches to the divergent part of the nozzle. The attachment point is dependent upon aerodynamic and electromagnetic forces and is, therefore, also dependent on the flow rate and specific impulse. This basic type is applicable to either AC or DC. The second type, by Ghai and Martinek (*6*), uses an arc striking between several electrodes (Fig. 5). This type is especially attractive for 3-phase alternating current. More attention has been given up to now to the type shown in Fig. 4 for space propulsion. The optimization of the electrodes and the interactions of the arc with the nozzle are some of the main problems encountered by arc engine technology in the search for high efficiencies combined with long lifetimes. Figure 6 shows a 30-kwe arc engine by Spongberg (*7*) in operation.

Early arc investigations had the requirement to simulate the re-entry conditions of the IRBM. The required enthalpy for an arc jet was 2500 cal/gm. This requirement goes up to 7500 cal/gm for the simulation of satellite re-entry conditions; for return from the moon, the air in front of the capsule is turned into a plasma with about 15,000 cal/gm enthalpy.

Fig. 4. DC arc engine.

Fig. 5. AC arc engine.

Simulation of such conditions by arc jets has been achieved by Plasmadyne (1960). The demands upon arc engines for space propulsion considerably exceed those for re-entry simulation. They are in the range of 20,000 to 100,000 cal/gm, and higher. Ducati (*8*) has recently achieved a value of 220,000 cal/gm. The temperature in the chamber of an arc engine operating at 1000-sec impulse, using ammonia as propellant, is 10,000° to 13,000°K depending on engine efficiency. Arc engines have been successfully operated under such conditions. Problems are in the areas of heat transfer, regenerative and radiative cooling, and high temperature materials for electrodes and insulators.

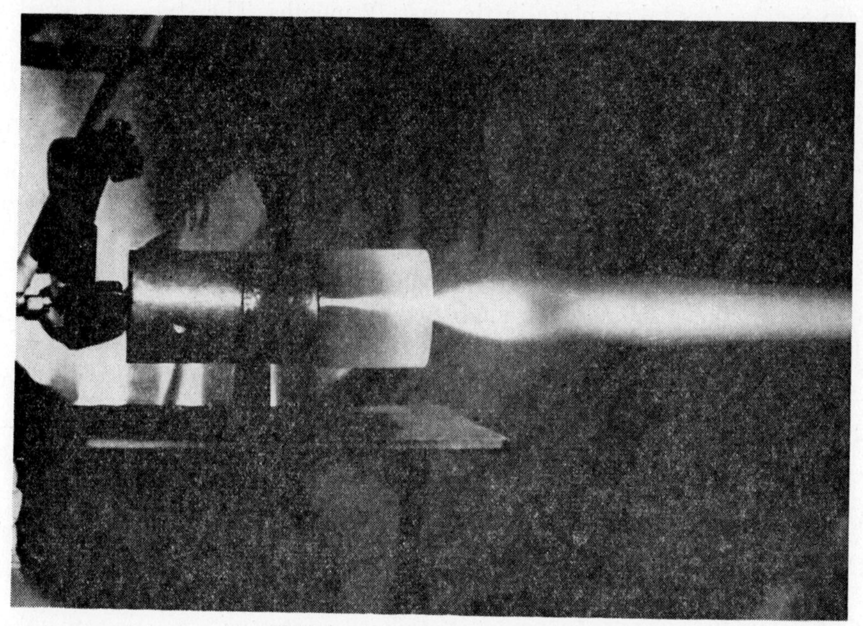

FIG. 6. Arc engine in operation.

Studies carried out by AVCO under sponsorship of the National Aeronautics and Space Administration, in connection with the arc propulsion program, have analyzed some of the problems connected with the use of cryogenic propellants such as hydrogen and ammonia. These two propellants turned out to be the top contenders for space applications. Another possibility under consideration is lithium.

Problems exist in the areas of: (1) propellant density, (2) insulation and storability in space for hydrogen, (3) high temperature electrode geometry, and (4) high temperatures for ammonia. The voltage applied across the electrodes affects the starting characteristics and the engine lifetime. Electrode life can be extended by lowering the current density.

Voltages should be in the range of about 110 volts for 1-kwe arc engines and 110 to 500 volts for 30-kwe engines. The efficiency of arc engines depends strongly on the recombination of atoms and atoms to molecules, and on the recombination of ions and electrons to atoms or molecules.

Related problems are those which concern electrical breakdown, the propellant feed system, measuring techniques, RF communications with running engine, and the interaction of an electrically propelled space ship with an unknown space environment. None of the solutions to these problems are beyond present technology, but many require an advancement of the state of the art. Much of the progress made toward flyable arc engines has taken place in the past 12 months. The status achieved is impressive considering that the active development of arc engines had a late start.

Flight Testing

Electric engines are used for the propulsion of spacecraft. It is, therefore, imperative that the engines be proven under space conditions. The flight testing phase is emphasized in the development of these engines. Each flight is preceded by a thorough ground test and a check-out procedure under simulated ground conditions. Figure 7 shows a mock-up of the test capsule to be developed by RCA under a NASA contract. The test capsule will be flown on a Scout vehicle as a vertical flight with an altitude of about 4000 miles and a flight time above 200 miles of about 1 hr 10 min. The two electric engines located at the end of movable arms are powered by silver-zinc batteries. The batteries are located at the periphery of the capsule to obtain a disk-type mass distribution. This will allow the maintenance of a stable spin around the axis of the major moment of inertia. The two engines will be operated in sequence, each for about half an hour. The capsule can accommodate both ion and arc engines. Flights are scheduled for the fall of 1962. The first two flights will carry one arc engine by Plasmadyne and three different ion engines by the NASA Lewis Research Center, Hughes Aircraft and Electro-Optics. More advanced arc and ion engines will be flight tested in 1963 and the years following. The flight testing program has the following objectives:

(1) A scientific evaluation of engine performance leading to an improved design.

(2) A demonstration showing the capability of the entire system to produce thrust under the conditions in a space environment. The preparation and successful evaluation of flight instrumentation is part of this requirement.

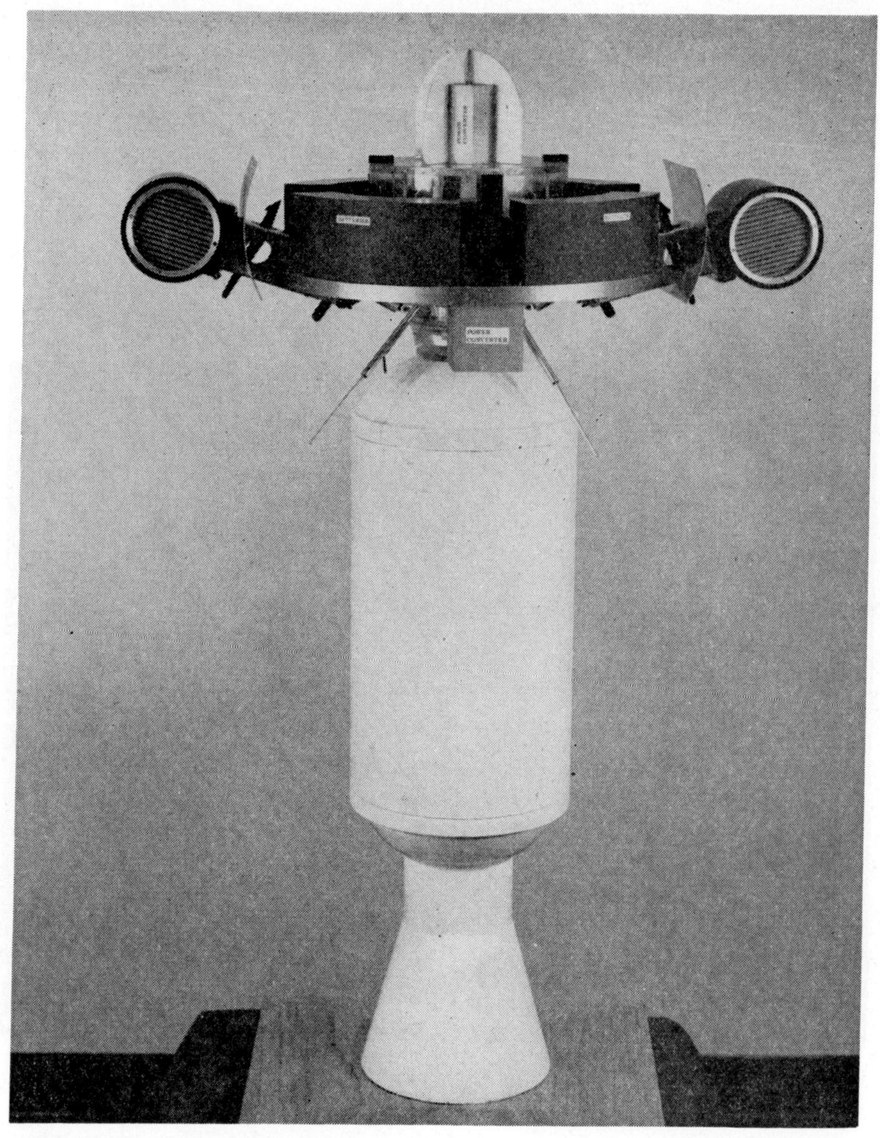

FIG. 7. RCA test capsule for arc and ion engines.

(3) The implementation of a flight test, to convert a laboratory model into a piece of flyable hardware, is an essential phase of the development program. The flight test will invariably uncover a great number of problems. Once uncovered through flight testing, these can be easily solved by thorough ground testing.

(4) The investigation of phenomena due to the unknown and variable space environment in which the engines have to operate for a long time, and especially the interaction with its environment of the spacecraft and its running electric engine.

The culmination of the first development phase will be the long-duration flight of both arc and ion engines on an Atlas-Centaur vehicle, which will be possible in 1965, and consecutive flights in 1966 and 1967. The engines will be powered by a 30-kwe SNAP-8 nuclear electric power source. Figure 8 is an artist's conception of this test craft in flight. It shows the general structure, nuclear reactor, power conversion system,

FIG. 8. Test craft for arc and ion engines.

propellant tanks, and the radiators that serve as a heat sink for the power source and for cooling of electronic equipment. The ion engine is shown in operation. The jet will be actually invisible; however, the glowing ionizer surface will attest that the engine is running. Figure 9 shows a graph of the payload capability of this test craft, assuming that the test flight is carried out between an initial 300-mile orbit and a lunar orbit, or the equivalent in total velocity increment. It can be noted that the payload capability is a function of the ratio of arc and ion propul-

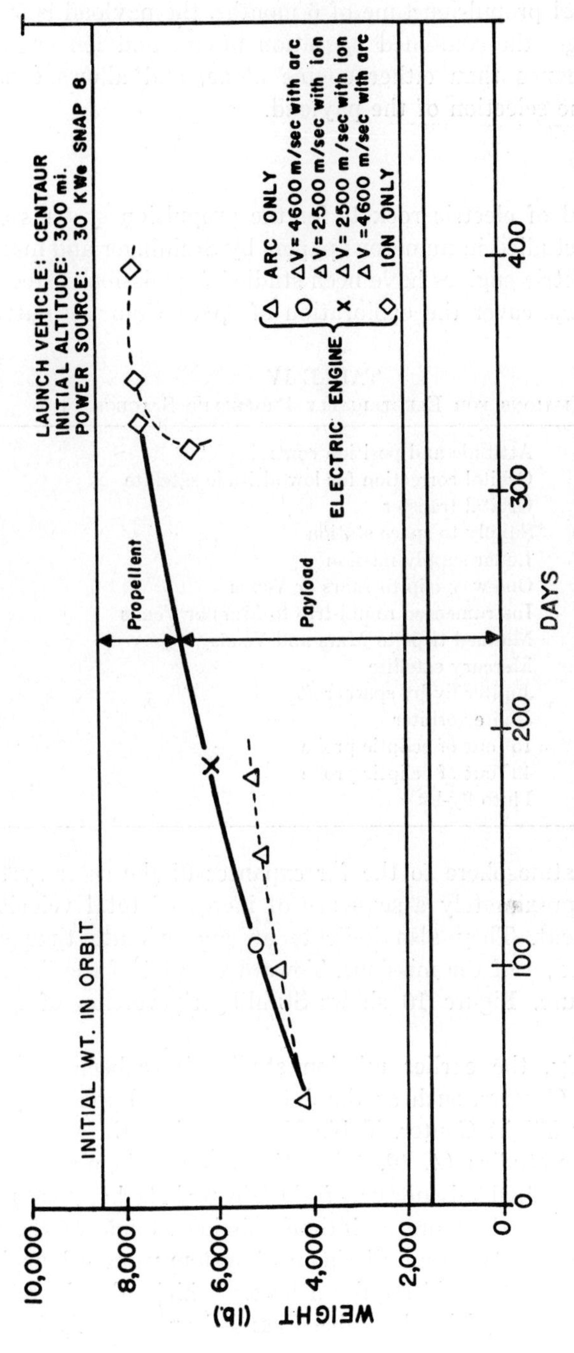

FIG. 9. Payload capability of an electrically propelled test craft going into a lunar orbit. Launch vehicle: Centaur; initial altitude: 300 miles; power source: 30-kwe Snap-8.

sion. For a total propulsion time of 6 months, the payload is 5900 lb. In the whole range, the combined operation of arc and ion engines gives higher performance than either engine alone, and allows considerable flexibility in the selection of the payload.

Missions

The potential of electric rockets for the propulsion systems of spacecraft has been studied in numerous papers by Stuhlinger and many others since 1947. Electric engines have been studied for missions listed in Table IV. The missions cover the exploration of space from the outer fringes

TABLE IV
MISSIONS FOR ELECTRICALLY PROPELLED SPACECRAFT

Attitude and position control
Orbital correction for low altitude satellite
Orbital transfer
Supply to space station
Lunar supply mission
One-way trip to Mars or Venus
Instrumented round-trip to Mars or Venus
Manned trips to Mars and Venus
Mercury satellite
Jupiter fly-by spacecraft
Jupiter orbiter
15° out of ecliptic probe
40° out of ecliptic probe
Pluto fly-by

of the earth's atmosphere to the far expanses of the solar system, and they follow approximately a sequence of increased total velocity increment requirement. They also indicate an approximate time scale for possible realization of the missions. Toward the end of the list are those far in the future. Figure 10 shows Stuhlinger's version of a manned Mars ship (*9*).

Quite recently, the earlier mission studies have been amplified by various NASA Centers, such as the Jet Propulsion Laboratory and the Goddard Space Flight Center. Table V summarizes the results of some of these mission studies (*4, 10, 11*) and compares chemically propelled vehicles. The payload advantage of electric rockets becomes more and more attractive for the more ambitious missions. Some of the missions cannot be done at all with an all-chemical system using a launch vehicle like the Centaur, but would require a larger vehicle like the Saturn.

Studies for arc propulsion have been carried out recently by Goddard

Fig. 10. Manned Mars ship.

Space Flight Center and by a number of NASA contractors such as AVCO, United Aircraft, and GE (*12, 13*).

Figure 11, taken from a study by Dangle of Goddard Space Flight Center (*14*) shows the payload capability of a 24-hr satellite mission using an Atlas-Centaur vehicle that delivers 8500 lb into an initial orbit

TABLE V

Payload and Flight Times of Spacecraft Based on Atlas-Centaur[a]

Mission	Chemical		Electric rocket using 60 kw Snap-8	
	Payload (lb)	Time (days)	Payload (lb)	Time (days)
Venus fly-by	1300	110		
Venus capture (ellipt. orbit)			1850	240
			4200	380
Mars capture (ellipt. orbit)	660	230	1500	300
			3200	400
Mars orbiter (circ. orbit)	320	260	800	320
			2250	400
Jupiter fly-by	0		900	630
			1800	850
Saturn fly-by	0[b]		~300	~700

[a] Ghai and Martinek (*6*).
[b] Inferred

of 300 miles. From here the space craft spirals out to 22,400 miles. By using an arc engine as electric propulsion, together with a SNAP-8 power supply, the thrust vector is changed at every crossing over the equator. In so doing, the inclination angle to the equator can be reduced to zero during the orbital transfer. The payload capability is a function of time.

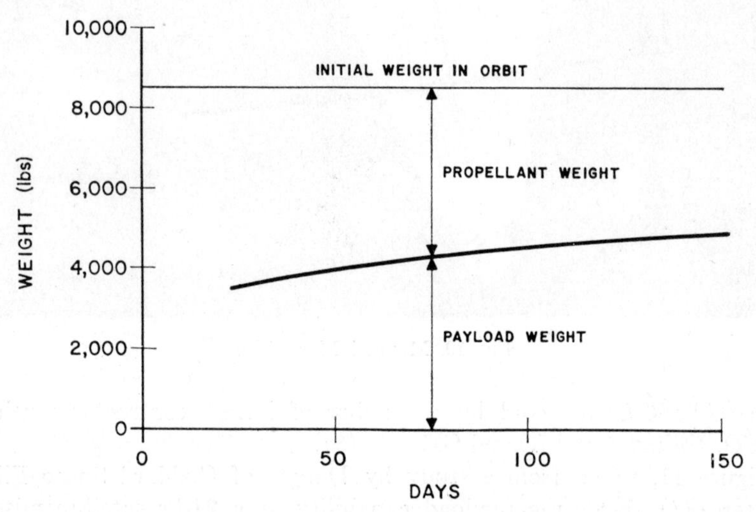

Fig. 11. 24-hr communication satellite; payload vs. time of propulsion. Vehicle: Atlas-Centaur; space propulsion: arc engine; power source: Snap-8.

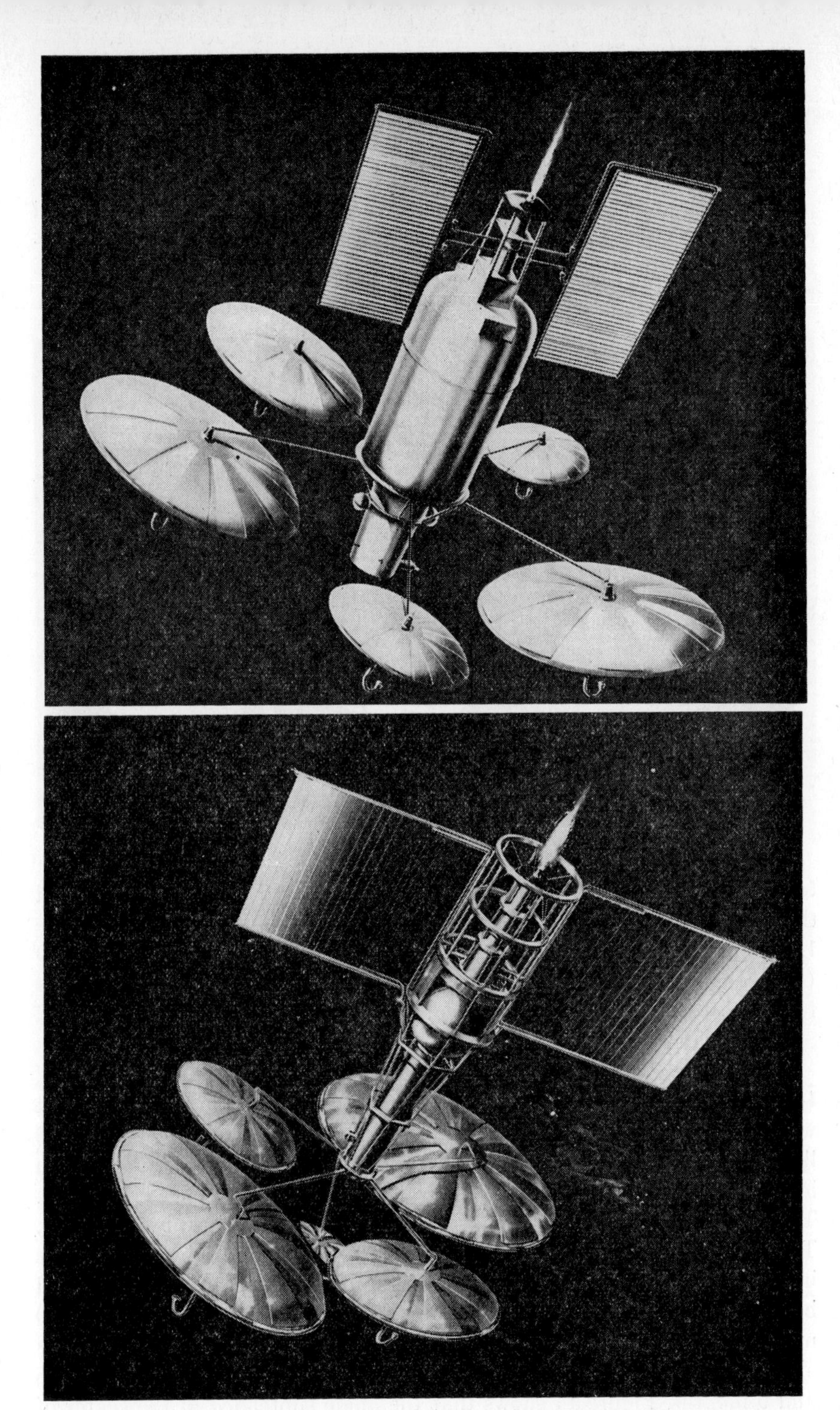

FIG. 12. (a) above: Twenty-four hour communication satellite with arc engine and nuclear power supply, propellant: hydrogen. (b) below: Twenty-four communication satellite with arc engine and nuclear power supply, propellant: ammonia.

If 100 days transfer time is considered reasonable for this mission, the payload in the final orbit is 4500 lb, which corresponds to the payload capability of the Saturn C-1. The payload includes power supply, structure, control equipment, communications equipment, and instrumentation. This compares to the Centaur capability of 1200 lb, if the mission is

FIG. 13. Precision control of communication satellite.

to be accomplished with an all-chemical system. It has to be considered that 2000 lb of the 4500-lb payload constitutes the power source. Figure 12 is an artist's conception of such a satellite based on studies by AVCO (*13*); Fig. 13 shows a communication satellite using electric engines for precise control, based on an earlier study by members of Marshall Space Flight Center in 1959 (*9*).

Not all the various mission studies performed are discussed here. Fig. 14 shows a heliocentric trajectory of the Pluto probe plotted. The boost vehicle is again an Atlas-Centaur which places an initial weight of 8500 lb into a 300-mile orbit. From here the space craft is propelled by an ion rocket. The power supply is an advanced nuclear electric source. The power level is 520 kwe and the weight-to-power ratio is 5.8 lb/kw. The ion engine operates at 80% over-all conversion efficiency at a specific impulse of 20,000 sec and 0.95 lb thrust. The high impulse is indicated because the mission requires the high velocity increment of 144,000 meters/sec. The spiral out of the gravitational field of the earth takes about 2½ months, and the propelled interplanetary trajectory 2 years and 9 months. Figure 14 shows that the angle subtended at the center of

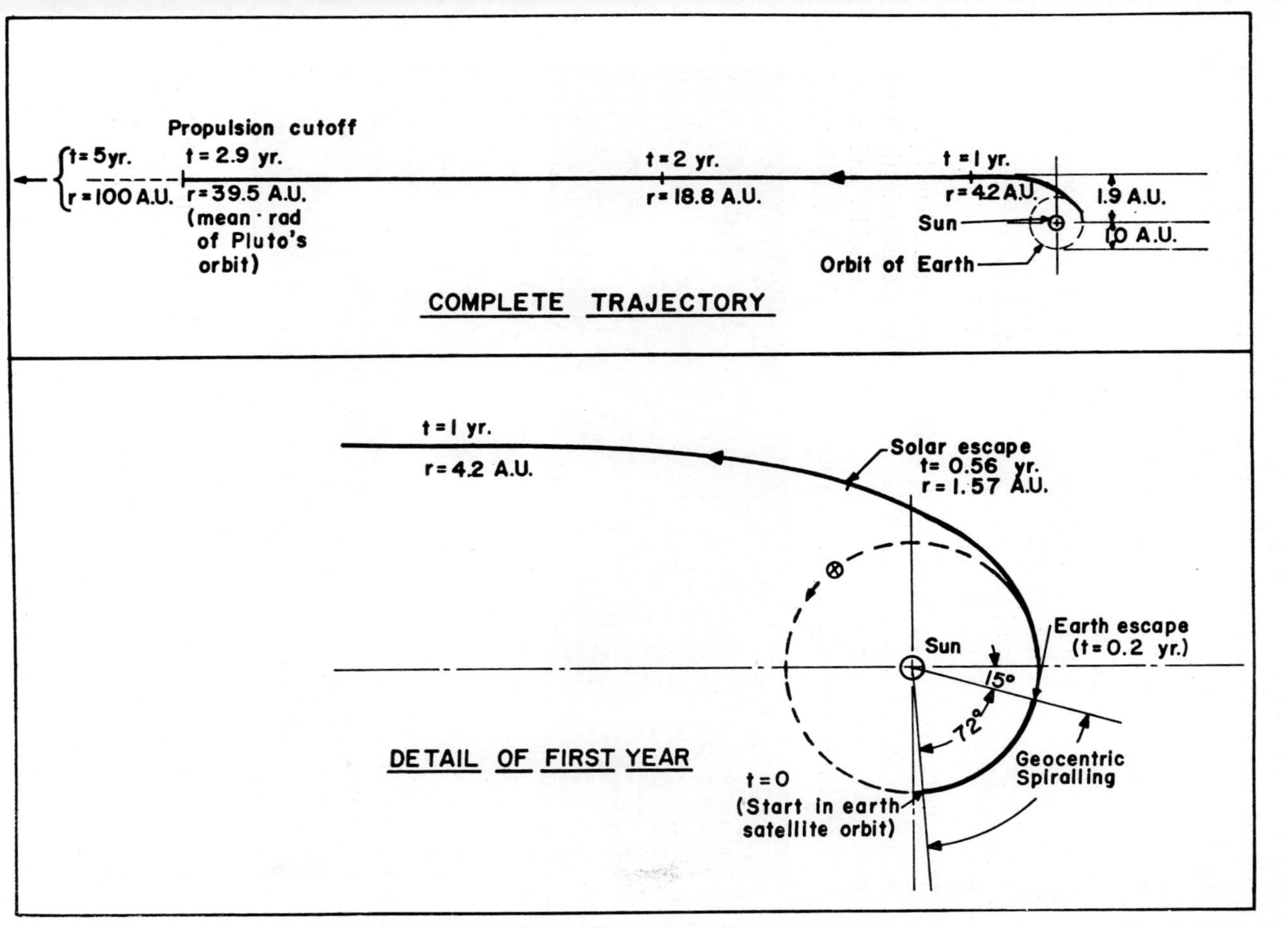

Fig. 14. Trajectory of Pluto probe satellite.

the sun is about 270°. The space craft will be propelled throughout the whole trajectory until it reaches Pluto. Since it has at this point obtained a hyperbolic velocity, it will pass by Pluto and leave the solar system. The weight breakdown is as follows:

Power source	3000 lb
Ion rocket, control	300 lb
Tank weight	220 lb
Propellant	4420 lb
Payload	530 lb

The 530-lb payload includes scientific instruments and telemetry.

Possible instrumentation for this spacecraft might include the measurement of cosmic radiation, electric and magnetic fields, and micrometeorites. Figure 15 is an artist's conception of such a deep space probe

FIG. 15. Deep space probe.

[taken from (*9*)]. A space craft that carries a telescope out to 100 a. u. distance, as proposed by Dyson (*15*) can be carried into orbit by a Saturn C-1 vehicle, and propelled by an electric rocket. It will arrive at 100 a.u. distance in 5 years.

An important requirement is the development of an advanced power source and the development of electric propulsion. An ambitious mission like this will require not only the development of an electric rocket, but also an advanced nuclear electric power source and, as pointed out during the symposium by Rechtin, an advanced communications system.

References

1. R. H. Goddard, An autobiography based on R. H. Goddard notebook dated September 6, 1906, *Astronautics* **4,** 24 (1959).
2. H. Oberth, "Wege zur Raumschiffahrt." R. Oldenbourg, München-Berlin, 1929.
3. E. Stuhlinger, Possibilities of electric spaceship propulsion, IAF Congress, Innsbruck, Austria, August 1954.
4. E. Stuhlinger, *in* Handbook of Astronautical Engineering (H. H. Koelle, ed.), chapter on Electric Propulsion. McGraw-Hill, New York, October, 1961.
5. R. R. John *et al.,* Arc engine—Performance and theory II, Paper 61-101-1795, given at Joint IAS-ARS Meeting, Los Angeles, California, June 13–16, 1961.
6. M. Ghai and F. Martinek, Private communication (see also F. Martinek *et al.,* Dynamics of arc jet system, Paper 61-98-1792 given at Joint IAS-ARS Meeting, Los Angeles, California, June, 1961).
7. R. Spongberg, Performance characteristics of the 3000-cycle electrothermal rocket, Joint IAS-ARS Meeting, Los Angeles, California, June, 1961.
8. A. Ducati, Private communications. For more details and further references, see G. B. Heller and B. P. Jones, A survey on arc propulsion, paper presented at the ARS Nuclear-Space Conference in Gatlinburg, Tennessee, May 1961.
9. E. Stuhlinger, Space missions for ion propulsion systems, AAS paper, January, 1960.
10. R. W. Koerner and J. J. Paulson, Nuclear electric power for space missions, JPL Tech. Release No. 34-230 (January, 1961).
11. J. W. Stearns, Jr., Applications for electric propulsion systems, JPL Tech. Memo No. 33-47 (April 10, 1961).
12. T. N. Edelbaum, Mission comparison of 30 kw and 60 kw SNAP-8 electric propulsion systems, United Aircraft Corporation.
13. M. I. Yarymovych, Thermal arc jet engine mission study, First Quarterly Progress Report, AVCO (RAD-SR-61-100).
14. E. E. Dangle, Private communication from Dangle, Goddard Space Flight Center.
15. F. J. Dyson, Proposal for high velocity space probe carrying parallax telescope, Institute of Advanced Studies, Princeton, New Jersey.

Discussion

DR. A. B. MARTIN: Mr. Heller mentioned development programs for electric propulsion systems up to 30 kw. Are there any programs for the development of an electric propulsion system larger than this?

MR. G. HELLER: Yes; use of the 60-kw version of the SNAP-8 nuclear electric power source is definitely being considered. In the case of arc propulsion, two 30-kw engines could be used on a spacecraft. The ion engines are clusters of elements, so a 60-kw engine would have twice as many elements. Incidentally, the test craft version of the SNAP-8 that is illustrated in Fig. 8 was based on design studies made by Jet Propulsion Laboratory.

14.3 *Capabilities of Advanced Vehicles for Astronomical Research*

M. W. HUNTER† and D. S. MERRILEES

DOUGLAS AIRCRAFT COMPANY, Santa Monica, California

Continued growth of interest and activity in space exploration indicates that very high performance space vehicles are likely to become available in the foreseeable future. Such vehicles would normally not be developed simply as scientific research tools, since rather large development expenditures would be required. A high-speed, low operating cost space vehicle might well be developed to facilitate lunar or interplanetary transport for manned exploration, for military purposes, or for commercial exploitation. We shall not attempt here to justify the development of such vehicles. Rather, under the assumption that there are a number of reasons for developing economical and convenient space transportation systems, we shall speculate upon their possible characteristics, and then consider what scientific astronomical missions may be accomplished by these high-performance spacecraft.

A good transportation system is characterized by both convenience and low cost of operation. Convenience of operation means, among other things, that travel times will be sufficiently short, and also that operations can be performed at any time desired. For example, if one can go to the moon at all, the operation becomes relatively convenient since travel times are only a few days, and suitable launch times occur on the order of once each day. For transportation to the nearer planets, however, travel times with low-energy rockets are of the order of 9 months, and it would sometimes be necessary to wait 2 years for favorable launch dates.

Figure 1 gives an indication of the velocity required in order to make earth-Mars travel time "reasonable." This shows travel time versus launch time for different values of total velocity,* with due consideration

* The term "total velocity" denotes the integral of the scalar value of the thrust acceleration with respect to time throughout the entire mission and is an approximate measure of the propulsion system energy necessary for execution of the mission.

† Now National Aeronautics and Space Council, Washington, D. C.

of the braking maneuver required upon arrival at Mars. It can be seen that total velocities of the order of several hundred thousand feet per second are required to reduce the travel time to a few months and render year-round operation possible. Thus, to be convenient, interplanetary transport will be required to operate at these high velocities.

It seems, intuitively, that the economical achievement of such velocities would be problematical. However, theoretically, nuclear rockets should be capable of achieving such velocities economically. The key to a relatively low operating cost lies in having so high an exhaust velocity that not only the fuel consumption for the entire mission is reasonably low, but also that single-stage vehicles are acceptably small, with the

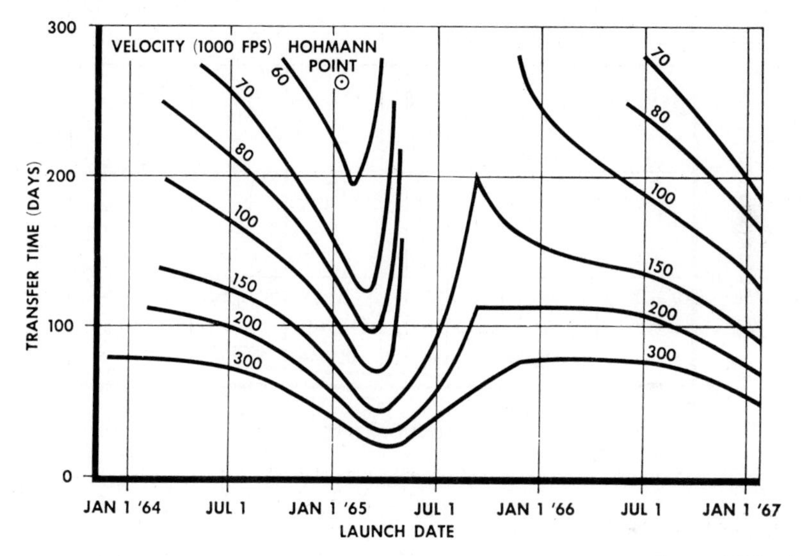

FIG. 1. Impulsive velocity requirement for earth to mars transfer and Martian landing.

corollary that they can be made recoverable and reusable, and thus amortize their intial cost over many missions. Once the vehicle cost is reduced by such reuse, just as it is done for normal air transports, or, for that matter, for almost any sort of transportation, the operating costs would not be startlingly high.

Figure 2 shows two examples of such cost estimates in terms of dollars per pound of useful load as a function of total velocity capability of the ship. The curve for early fission rockets indicates the possibilities of solid core Rover-type nuclear rockets which may well be available in the next decade. The curve labeled "ultimate fission rockets" assumes that there are no technical impossibilities involved in the construction and operation of nuclear rockets—a daring assumption perhaps—and that it will be possible to utilize any temperature necessary in the propulsion system with perfect containment of the hot gases or plasmas. Although no one now has a very good idea of how to advance very far on this curve, it is interesting to note the vast capabilities of nuclear rockets if the technical problems can be solved. In the case of both curves, single stage, completely reusable vehicles were assumed with relatively conservative hypotheses with regard to construction costs

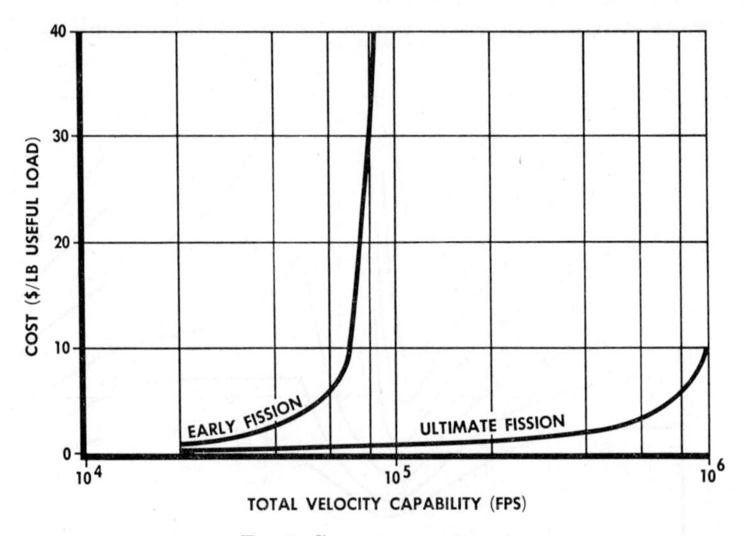

FIG. 2. Cargo transport cost.

and number of repeated uses before scrapping. It should be noted that these curves extend up to velocities of the order of 1,000,000 ft/sec, higher than indicated necessary by the interplanetary transit-time curves of Fig. 1. This is done simply to indicate that if this class of device is developed for the reasons previously explained, then we might as well consider the scientific mission possibilities of these extremely high velocities. High velocities might be achieved simply by carrying only very light loads in a large transport rocket originally designed for other missions. A picture of a single stage reusable nuclear powered spaceship is shown in Fig. 3. This is an artist's conception of an early fission rocket utilizing hydrogen as the working fluid. It is capable of re-entering the earth's atmosphere from escape speeds with only 2 g's deceleration load being applied to ship or cargo; it can be a very light structure. Such vehicles of roughly 1,000,000 lb gross weight would be able to place

150,000 lb of payload in earth orbit. It is to be expected that any practical space transportation system will include rendezvous capabilities, since not only refueling but maintenance and emergency rescue capabilities are highly desirable. The problems of orbital rendezvous do not seem severe in the light of the capabilities of current guidance equip-

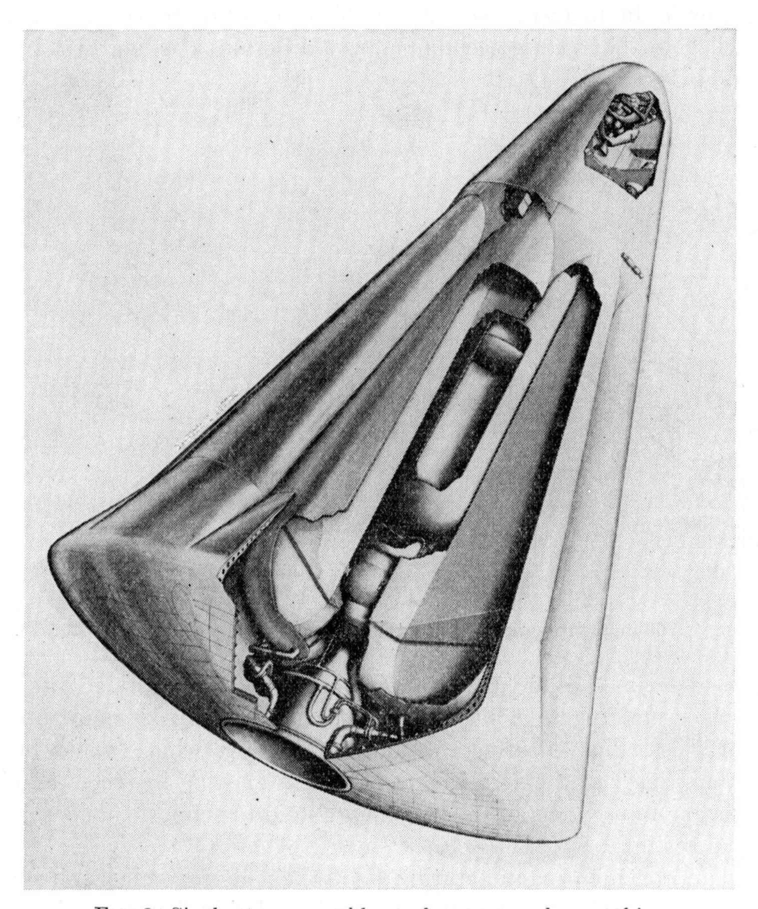

FIG. 3. Single-stage reusable nuclear powered spaceship.

ment, especially with a propulsion system which has reserve power capabilities. This capability should be an integral part of any practical transport system. It could, of course, be used either for the assembly of large observatories in orbit, or for the carrying of personnel to and from large equipment items in space.

Two examples of massive pieces of astronomical equipment which may be ferried into space are shown on the next two figures. Figure 4 is a

200-in. diameter optical telescope. The mirror can be carried up to orbit intact with necessary precautions being taken to prevent excessive loads and temperatures on the mirror. The entire telescope and camera assembly is contained in one spacecraft and has a total weight of approximately 4000 lb. This low weight might be achieved by making the telescope mirror in meniscus shape with a 1 in. uniform thickness. It is assumed here that future techniques would permit grinding of a precise

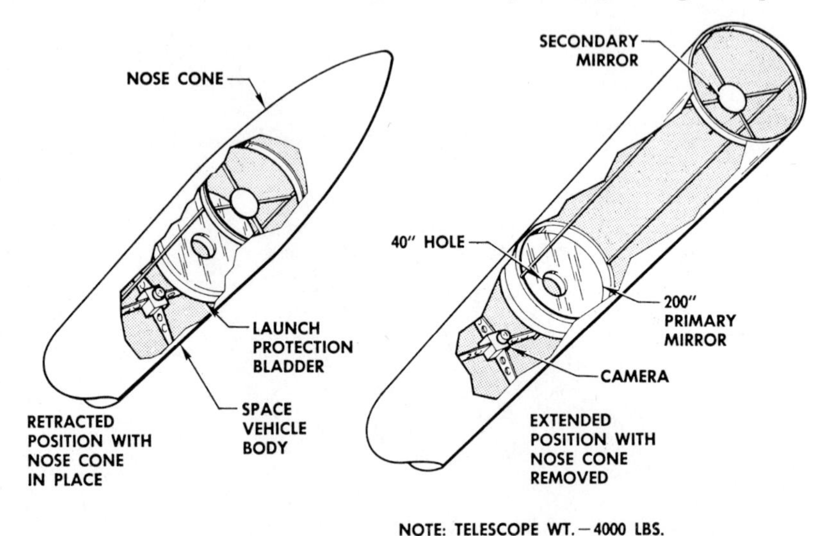

FIG. 4. 200-in. astronomical space telescope. Telescope weight is 4000 lb.

surface with a contoured support and subsequent testing while the meniscus is floating in a fluid whose specific gravity is approximately that of glass, thus ensuring the uniform support which would be the closest approach to the zero weight condition existing in space. It might be desirable to use a gelatin rather than a fluid to support the lens during the final testing.

This approach to manufacturing lightweight astronomical mirrors for use under zero gravity conditions could probably be verified experimentally with smaller diameter models. The transportation costs to orbit for a telescope of this type might actually be less than the cost of the Hale telescope.

Similar consideration of a radio telescope with a 1000 ft antenna is shown in Fig. 5. The telescope shown consists of an inflated balloon with one-half of the internal surface aluminized and a horn placed at the focus. A parabolic contour of the surface is generated by inflating an annular ring at the edge of the structure. A 50-ft diameter antenna of this type has already been fabricated by one of the electronic companies and the weights shown in Fig. 5 are from an extrapolation of this design.

We will not attempt to discuss here all of the possible uses of such equipment. We simply wish to point out that basic space transportation requirements may well lead to vehicles which could perform massive trucking operations far cheaper than many people consider even remotely possible. Therefore, a certain amount of speculation as to the

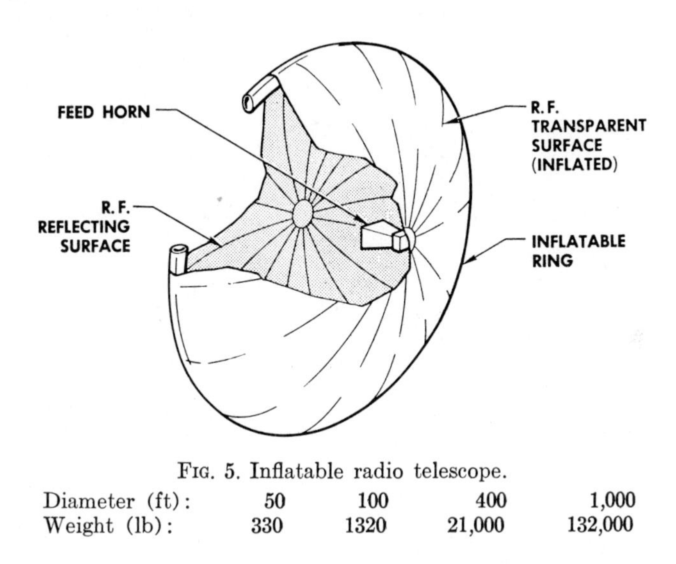

FIG. 5. Inflatable radio telescope.

Diameter (ft):	50	100	400	1,000
Weight (lb):	330	1320	21,000	132,000

future desirability of such things is perhaps appropriate. The orbital load carrying capability of nuclear rockets may well be equalled or even exceeded by massive chemical rockets, although probably at much higher operating cost. The real advantages of nuclear rockets become evident as velocity requirements increase. The very high-velocity capabilities of nuclear propelled transports then lead to the question of other types of astronomical research missions which these velocities might make feasible.

One such possibility involves the obtaining of direct experimental data on meteoric matter. It is conceivable that a vehicle could go into space, pick up meteoric material, perhaps from the asteroid belt, and then inject this material into the earth's atmosphere at a known velocity and time such that instrumentation for observing its re-entry could be set up. The characteristics of the original meteoric material before re-entry could be accurately determined in the ship. Using such equipment to test small size samples may, perhaps, be likened to shooting a fly with an elephant gun. The job may actually be done much easier with small probes. Only if it were deemed scientifically interesting enough to be performed with the massive meteors of tons of initial weight, need nuclear rockets be considered.

A typical mission profile is shown in Fig. 6, where it is assumed that the vehicle goes out to the asteriod belt, and, depending upon the class of experiment desired, returns to earth's orbit either in direct or retrograde motion in order to provide either a low- or high-meteoric material

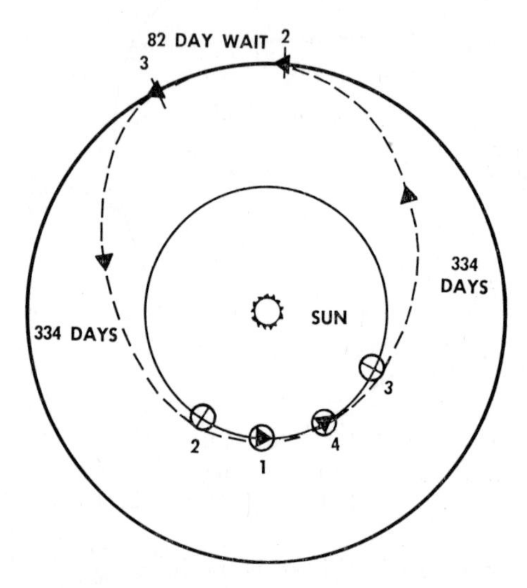

FIG. 6. Meteoric experiment (minimum velocity experiment). 1, departure from earth; 2, arrival at asteroid belt; 3, departure from asteroid belt; 4, arrival at earth.

entry speed as may be desired. The end game of this operation is illustrated in Fig. 7. The ship must aim itself at earth, accelerate to the desired speed, place the meteoroid on course, deflect itself so as to avoid the earth, and then kill all of its excess speed so it can land on earth.

Table I is a tabulation of total velocities required for both a minimum velocity and a maximum velocity experiment of this type. The maximum velocity experiment requires a total velocity of approximately 450,000 ft/sec, which is the magnitude desirable for a good interplanetary transport, and which may someday be feasible with nuclear rockets. Figure 2 shows that it should be possible to deliver meteoroids in the maximum velocity experiment, with an ultimate fission rocket at a direct

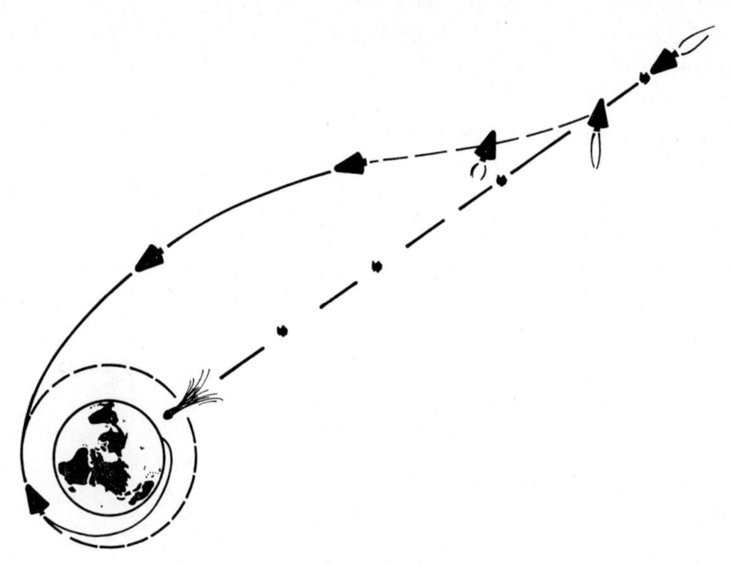

FIG. 7. Meteoric experiment (end game).

TABLE I
METEOR EXPERIMENT VELOCITY REQUIREMENTS

	Minimum (fps)	Maximum (fps)
Meteor velocity at re-entry of earth's atmosphere	41,000	240,000
Earth launch	40,000	40,000
Asteroid braking	13,000	13,000
Asteroid launch	13,000	123,000
Earth acceleration	25,000	25,000
Evasive maneuver	35,000	230,000
Establish circular orbit	10,000	10,000
De-orbit and land	2,000	2,000
Total mission velocity	138,000	443,000

operating cost* of $2 per lb. Should the ship fail to make its deflection maneuver on approaching earth, then one of the most spectacular meteor trails ever seen would be well recorded by the observing stations.

Another use for a very high velocity spacecraft mission involves the close range examination of comets. Again, the experiment itself will not

* Direct operating cost comprises the cost of fuel and propellant expended and a prorated share of vehicle structure and engine costs.

be considered, but only the techniques of intercept and the velocity requirements for a successful cometary escort. These differ widely, depending upon the orbital elements of the comet and the position of the earth relative to it. To keep discussion within bound, we shall assume that the comet moves in the plane of the ecliptic.

A schematic diagram of the model being considered is shown in Fig. 8 for a direct comet orbit with the perihelion at the mean distance of the orbit of the planet Mercury. If the perihelion were in the most advantageous position from the point of view of velocity requirements, it would

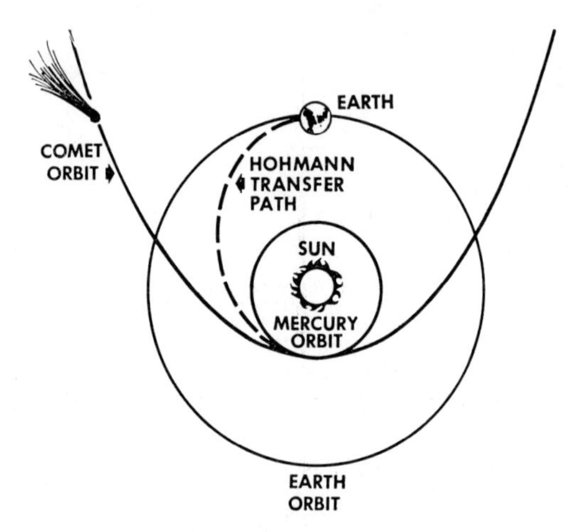

FIG. 8. Comet probe mission.

be such that the ship would leave the earth on a Hohmann transfer path and when it arrives at a position opposite the sun from its launch point, the comet would be there. At this point, if the ship were to land on an inner planet, it would have to brake some of its excess speed to match planetary velocity. In the case of the comet mission it would maneuver to match the velocity of the comet, escort it for a while and then maneuver to initiate a return to the earth. For direct orbits, the minimum velocity requirement is found to be a Hohmann transfer rendezvous with the comet at the comet perihelion on the opposite side of the sun from the launch point. On the other hand, the highest velocity requirements occur for rendezvous with comets traveling in retrograde orbits. In this latter case much higher velocities are required to fly formation with the comet since a retrograde transfer orbit is required to intercept the comet near perihelion.

An appreciation of the magnitude of these numbers may be obtained by looking at Fig. 9; this gives the time from Earth launch to comet

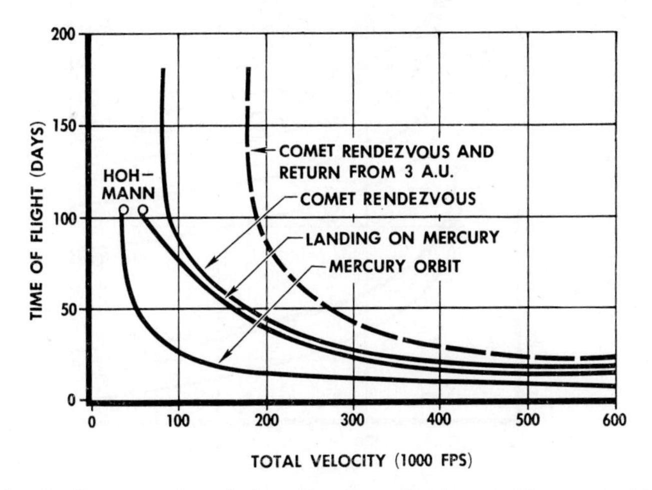

FIG. 9. Comet probe mission. Comet perihelion at Mercury orbit.

rendezvous, calculated for the minimum velocity requirements to fly formation with a direct motion comet with perihelion at the mean distance of the planet Mercury. The difference in velocity requirements is shown for just arriving at the orbit of Mercury, for landing on the planet Mercury, for matching velocities with the comet and for returning to earth from about 3 a.u. on the comet orbit. The time plotted is that from launch to intercept. In Fig. 10, these warning times are translated

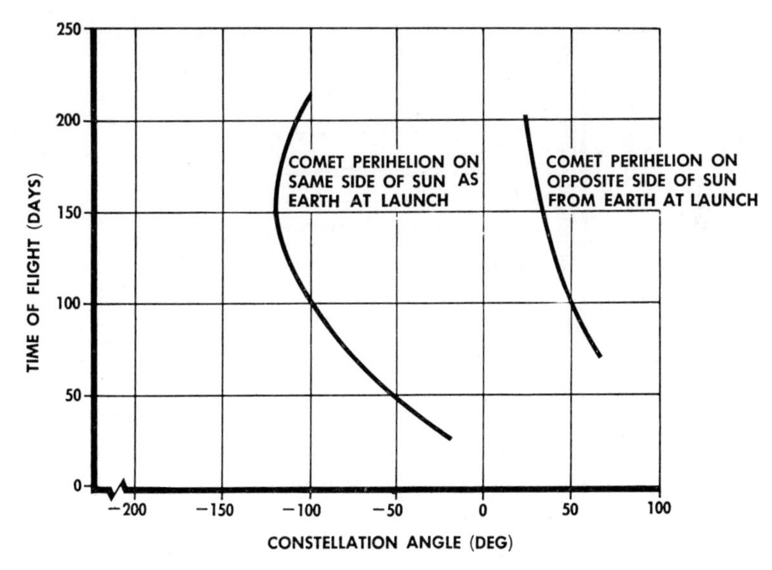

FIG. 10. Comet probe initial configuration; minimum velocity requirements.

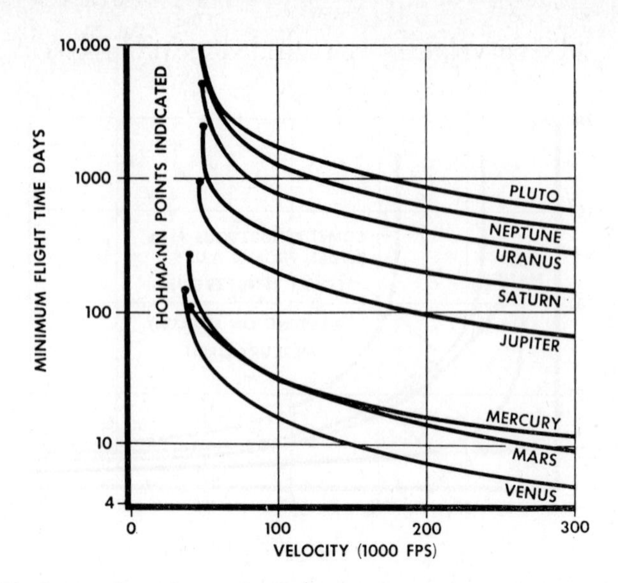

FIG. 11. Earth to other planets ballistic transfer minimum flight times for inter-orbital transfer.

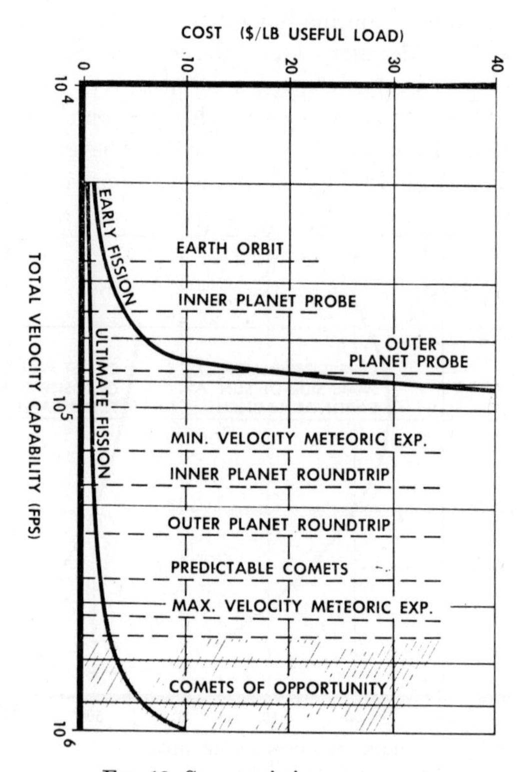

FIG. 12. Space mission cargo cost.

into the constellation angles* at launch for the minimum velocity mission. A wider range of constellation angles is noted for comet orbits with perihelion on the same side of the sun as the earth at launch. The general conclusion is that, surprisingly enough, only a few hundred thousand feet per second is required to make comet intercept for comets with direct motion about the sun, and this represents only a modest increase in velocity above what is required for landing on Mercury.

To be able to fly formation with a comet which happens to be in retrograde orbit or in a disadvantageous location, or which has only been newly discovered, requires velocity capabilities on the order of 500,000 to 1,000,000 ft/sec. With these, warning times of only one to two months are required. Thus, the interception of comets of opportunity presents the highest velocity demands yet considered for astronomical missions.

Very high velocity capability will also be demanded of scientific exploration of the solar system to its outer reaches. The time required for such exploration can be substantially reduced by attaining high velocities, as indicated in Fig. 11. Launch at the optimum time in the synodic period was assumed in constructing this figure, since purely scientific exploratory missions can be so scheduled. Not even the requirements for reaching Pluto on this basis are as extreme as one might at first think; a 300,000 ft/sec vehicle can reach the orbit of Pluto in one year.

These scientific missions can presumably be accomplished by such high-performance space vehicles which will probably be developed for other reasons. Estimated operating cost for these various missions is indicated in Fig. 12. It appears that all missions can be performed economically at some time in the future if the theoretically great nuclear rocket performance does materialize.

Discussion

DR. D. H. GARBER: I would like to ask a question of Mr. Hunter. I refer to the techniques for injecting an extremely large telescope mirror into orbit. If its structure is very light, as is obviously desirable, you expose it to the hazards of acceleration and vibrations on take-off. Have you examined the possibility of taking it in pieces into orbit and assembling them there? Would this be practical from the astronomer's viewpoint?

MR. M. W. HUNTER: We examined each of these possibilities to determine how large a telescope could be orbited in case this should be shown to be desirable. The results of our study indicated that the type of vehicles which we considered were capable of boosting a large mirror into orbit. A substantial margin can be allowed for weight increases which might be incurred in protecting against these

* Constellation angle is defined to be the angle between a line from the sun to the earth and a line from the sun to the comet.

hazards. The second possibility of segmenting the mirror presented the problem of how accurately it could be assembled in space. A discussion of whether it could be assembled to the required precision would be welcome.

CHAIRMAN A. L. KLEIN: I might ask Dr. Greenstein if he would care to make a remark on segmented telescope mirrors.

DR. J. L. GREENSTEIN: In general, if one is thinking of a very large thin mirror, even in the absence of gravity, it is very hard to believe that its figure will in fact be stable. The tolerance is of the order of a quarter of a wavelength of light—less than 10^{-5} in. How do we assemble it in place against any reference frame? This reference frame must have the same kind of accuracy. Where would you put collimation or assembly markers to define a plane rear surface? What about the inertial forces? These are just first thoughts, and some of the orbiting-telescope people might have definite ideas. Nobody has mentioned here the control systems or how much they weigh.

MR. R. A. NIDEY: Our fond hope at the Kitt Peak National Observatory is that we might be able to devise a suitable 50-in. primary mirror for the orbiting telescope on a weight budget of the order of a 1000 lb. Assuming that the weight of the primary would vary as the cube of the diameter, to ask for a 200 in. primary weighing as little as 4000 lb, exclusive of structure, strikes me as being overly optimistic.

CHAIRMAN A. L. KLEIN: Those of us who have been in the aircraft business know we cannot build a lightweight structure without proper regard to handling problems. We have many cases where parts have to be designed and made to withstand the handling loads. I would think that the hardest problem with a lightweight telescope is to get it into the launcher. The loads on the structure originate only from its own inertia forces. Theoretically you can design the structure of any weight if you can avoid having things like flies walk on it.

The Palomar 200-in. telescope came out weighing a million pounds because the designers assumed it to weigh a million pounds when they started. I always thought that if they had assumed it was going to weigh 500,000 lb, it would come out weighing 500,000, because the parasitic weights—namely, one astronomer, one photographic plate, and the mirror—are the only parts which are fixed. All the rest is just holding itself up.

MR. M. W. HUNTER: I like your numbers better. If I scale yours up by the cube, I get 64,000 lb.

MR. R. A. NIDEY: In the case of the large aperture, diffraction limited primary, the principal handling problem occurs in the figuring. How is the mirror to be supported during the action of the grinding tool on the surface? This requirement may well set the minimum thickness of the plate. Dr. Meinel mentioned that ¼ in. provided encouraging results on our 28-in. prototype.

To interject a somewhat facetious note, when we later undertake a 5000 in. telescope—and I have quoted this figure as approaching the ultimate—then a weight of even 64,000 lb is going to look rather modest.

MR. M. W. HUNTER: I would like to know if you can do that one with a segmented mirror?

UNIDENTIFIED SPEAKER: I would like to ask the question whether it has been considered to figure such a large mirror in space? The main difficulty seems to be that the mirror and structure have to withstand a much higher load during launch acceleration than they would on the ground. So once we got through the acceleration phase and have the structure in space at zero gravity, then we could make our adjustment there.

MR. R. A. NIDEY: Suggestions have indeed been made for figuring large aperture mirrors in space; two in particular have been at least half-seriously considered. One, by de Vaucouleurs, is that the mirror might be shaped as required by putting an array of electric heaters on the rear face, dissipating thermal energy at the appropriate points. A second, by Pierce, suggests the use of an electron gun to mill the surface. Both of these suggestions beg the question as to how to measure the figure in space. It is a difficult task to determine quantitatively what is wrong with the figure before undertaking any corrective action. The cumulative testing of the 120 in. telescope at Mount Hamilton involved months of tedious analysis. The total number of bits of information that were processed in this analysis was fabulous. To duplicate the mensuration alone by remote control in space would be a formidable task.

CHAIRMAN A. L. KLEIN: We would be faced with the other problem of not knowing what would stick and what would not stick or weld, before we started grinding. We now know too little about the surface chemistry or physics of bodies in a very hard vacuum. Those of us who have had to face up to some devices in this field feel pretty lost. If we want to run two spur gears against each other, we do not even know such a simple thing as what to make them out of.

MR. M. W. HUNTER: We ought to be able to solve that on something less than a 5000-in. lens.

CHAIRMAN A. L. KLEIN: I think so, we just do not know the answer at this date to this question.

MR. A. D. GOEDEKE: Are the aiming requirements of 0.01 sec of arc, as quoted by Mr. Nidey, a necessity for lunar telescopes? Might not the utilization of the moon as a base open up possibilities for some worthwhile astronomical experiments? Would there not be tasks for optical experiments in space, for which a substantial platform such as the moon would be desirable?

MR. R. A. NIDEY: I would answer the question with two points: First of all, the bearing noise in the explicit gimbals required in a lunar-based telescope will inherently limit the accuracy much more severely than in free fall. I believe that we should not expect to control a lunar-based telescope to an accuracy better than the order of 1 sec of arc, whereas in space we can realistically expect at least one, if not two, orders of magnitude greater precision.

Secondly, the gravitationally induced distortion of the primary mirror and of the collimation structure even in the $\frac{1}{6}\,g$ field on the moon will preclude the use of the lunar base for the high performance telescope. Certainly a telescope of the order of a 24 in. could be logically placed on the moon to advantage, but not one 10 times larger.

DR. J. L. GREENSTEIN: I must somewhat object to this statement because our one-g telescope at Palomar operates with much better accuracy. Our roughness of guiding is probably of the order of a hundredth of a second of arc or less, although this is hard to test in the presence of seeing conditions which seldom get much better than 0.2 or 0.3 sec. There is certainly no such roughness in our 500-ton monster.

MR. R. A. NIDEY: This is, of course, true with conventional lubricants, at atmospheric pressure. However we can hardly hope to have equally satisfactory bearing lubricants exposed to the extremely hard vacuum on the moon.

DR. J. L. GREENSTEIN: Is this a straw man? Is it literally impossible to shield bearings even in a hard vacuum? Powders pack down and become hard, but is this really decisive?

MR. R. A. NIDEY: Decisive, no. I state this merely as a personal conviction.

DR. H. C. VAN DE HULST: I was puzzled by your estimates of cost per weight. Did you quote figures in the order of a dollar per pound? That is about what I had to pay coming here from Europe.

MR. M. W. HUNTER: That is correct. This was one of the surprising things we discovered in investigating the effect on space transportation costs of employing single-stage, re-usable, nuclear powered vehicles. These direct operating cost estimates include only the cost of fuel and propellant expended and a prorated share of vehicle structure and engine costs. Theoretically this cost per pound number is obtainable for large payloads provided we can achieve the technical advancements required. Tremendous changes occur in transportation costs when re-usable vehicles can be employed. They are between two and three orders of magnitude cheaper than large throw-away chemical products.

MR. R. A. NIDEY: The possibility has been suggested of using signals derived from the image to correct its position. This technique has been applied, at least experimentally, by DeWitt at Dyer Observatory. It has a great deal of promise, especially because of the potentially high-frequency response. A band pass of sufficient width to correct for the noise in the explicit bearings could be obtained, by means of suitable electronic gear.

My own feeling is that such a system is not justified in orbit. If we are to have a manned lunar station and want to provide a telescope as a part of the station complex, then we could improve the performance of the lunar telescope by using the technique you have cited as an alternative to sealing the bearings. It is certainly an approach that has a great deal of merit on earth, and even more on the moon.

MR. W. H. SCOTT: In this discussion as to whether you should put the telescope in orbit or on the moon, I would like to turn the question around and ask, are there any real advantages to putting it on the moon? We have all the difficulty of landing there and then of directing the telescope. On the other hand, in orbit we do have a beautiful gimbaling system. I can't see what the reason would be for putting it on the surface of the moon; maybe some astronomers have definite reasons.

CHAIRMAN A. L. KLEIN: The question has already been adequately answered. I am inclined to agree with the last speaker. The human body unfortunately does not have a precisely fixed center of gravity and it generates physical noise. Therefore if you want to get the utmost precision from the instrument, the man must be removed from the immediate proximity of the vehicle. You may be able to accompany the vehicle and control by some sort of walkie-talkie, but this does not look very attractive.

MR. G. HELLER: From the propulsion viewpoint—this is what the panel was discussing here—I don't think that it would be advantageous to put the telescope on the moon. The requirements definitely would be more difficult to meet to put the observatory on the moon than in orbit.

14.4 Auxiliary Power Units for Space Applications

A. B. MARTIN

COMPACT SYSTEMS, ATOMICS INTERNATIONAL, Division of North American Aviation, Inc., Canoga Park, California

In order to provide for optimum utilization of larger booster systems and advanced spacecraft that are planned for the future, auxiliary power units for these systems are being developed under programs sponsored by the Atomic Energy Commission, the National Aeronautics and Space Administration and the Department of Defense.

Table I shows the power range and operating life required of such auxiliary power units for a number of space missions that have been announced. With the exception of payloads consisting of only scientific

TABLE I
SPACE POWER REQUIREMENTS

	Function	Power range	Operating life (years)
Auxiliary power	1. Scientific instruments	1 watt to 5 kw	0.001 to 0.5
	2. Communications satellites	100 watt to 300 kw	0.5 to 5
	3. Navigation satellites	100 watt to 30 kw	1 to 5
	4. Weather (cloud cover survey)	100 watt to 30 kw	1 to 5
	5. Space stations	3 kw to 3 Mw	2 to 3
	6. Lunar & planetary stations	0.5 Mw to 20 Mw	2 to 5
Propulsion	1. Electric propulsion		
	(a) 0.01 to 1 lb thrust	3 kw to 300 kw	1 to 2
	(b) 10 lb thrust	3 Mw	1 to 2

instruments, the power requirements are generally greater than 100 watts, extending to several kilowatts for many missions and to the megawatt range for very advanced payloads and for electric propulsion. The required operating life is of the order of 1 year or longer.

Figures 1 and 2 show the general consensus of experts in the field regarding the suitability of auxiliary power systems of different types for space applications. Power systems which can meet the 1-year operating life requirement include radioisotope power sources, solar cells, solar mirrors, and nuclear reactor power plants. For power requirements up to about 100 watts or so, solar cells and radioisotope power sources appear to be most suitable, primarily because of their ability to meet these small power requirements with relatively simple, lightweight systems.

Above a few hundred watts, solar cells become impractical because of the large collector areas required and radioisotope power sources start to become expensive and to have problems associated with radioactivity hazards in the event of missions which may abort, either on the launch pad or before a suitable orbit is achieved.

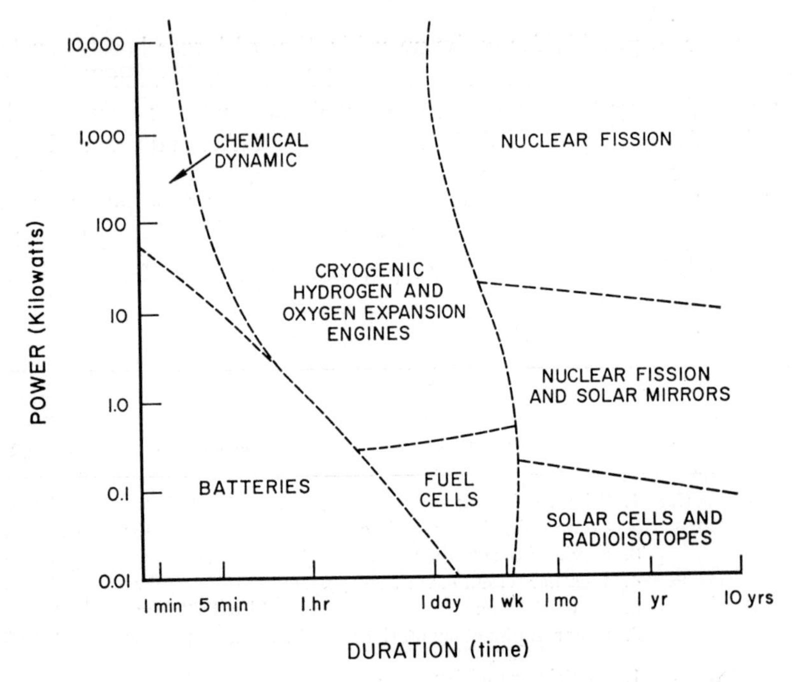

FIG. 1. Space auxiliary power systems.

For power levels between a few hundred watts and about 10 or 20 kw nuclear reactors and solar mirrors appear to be most suitable. As the power requirements exceed a few tens of kilowatts, problems associated with large solar mirror surfaces, precise alignment of large mechanical structures and damage due to meteorite bombardment make the use of solar mirrors impractical.

The nuclear reactor then appears to be the most suitable power source for the higher power requirements, and even for the lower power requirements may have important advantages over solar cells with regard to compactness, ruggedness and ability to withstand meteorite damage, and

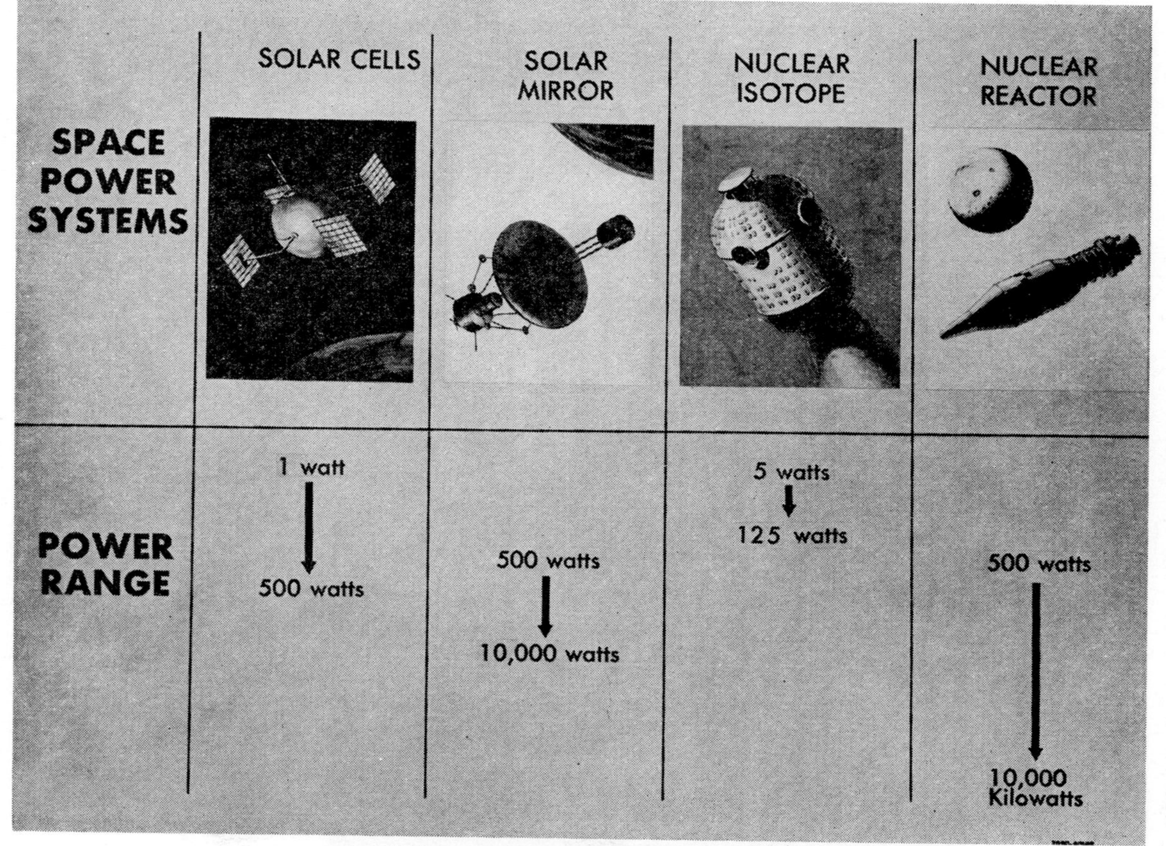

FIG. 2. Space power systems and power ranges.

advantages over the isotope power sources with regard to radiological safety.

The three reactor power units that are presently under development at Atomics International are the SNAP-10, which is a 500-watt thermoelectric system, the SNAP-2, a 3 kw turboelectric system and the SNAP-8, a 30–60 kw turboelectric system. Other space power systems which are

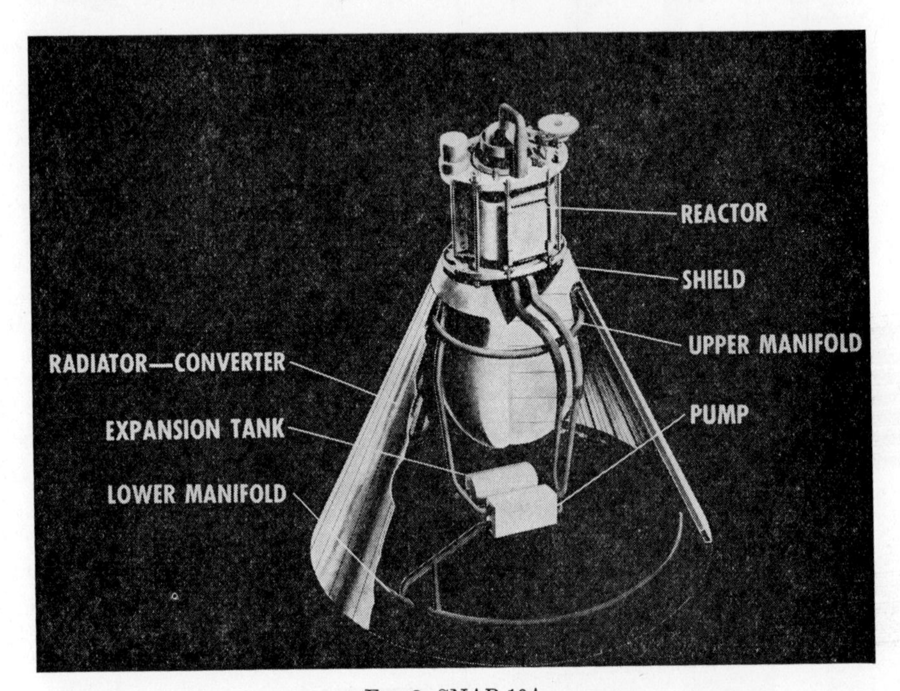

FIG. 3. SNAP-10A.

under active development are the SNAP-3, which is a 5-watt radioisotope thermoelectric system under development by the Martin Company for the USAEC, and the Sunflower system, which is a 3-kw solar mirror, turboelectric system under development by Thompson Ramo Wooldridge for NASA.

There are presently no active programs for the development of auxiliary power units above the 60-kw level of SNAP-8. There is a preliminary feasibility study of a 300-kw auxiliary power unit of an advanced type being conducted by Aerojet and Airesearch for the Air Force. This is called the SPUR program.

A SNAP power unit consists of a nuclear reactor and a power conversion unit to change the heat of the nuclear reactor into electricity. In order to meet the high temperature heat transfer conditions associated with radiating the excess heat to outer space, a liquid metal coolant is used to transfer the heat from the reactor core to the power conversion system.

The 500-watt SNAP-10 power unit (Fig. 3) utilizes a thermoelectric power conversion system. The liquid metal coolant transfers heat from the reactor core to the hot junctions of thermoelectric elements located in the skin of the vehicle. The cold junctions of these elements are integral

FIG. 4. SNAP-2 APU.

with the outer skin of the vehicle which radiates the excess heat to outer space. With a coolant temperature of above 900°F the over-all efficiency of this system is about 2%. The weight of the entire system, except for the radiation shield, is about 600 lb. The size, shape, and weight of the radiation shield will depend on the particular payload in the vehicle and the susceptibility of this payload to radiation effects during the mission.

The 3000-watt SNAP-2 unit (Fig. 4) employs a turboelectric power conversion system which operates on the mercury Rankine cycle. In this unit the liquid metal reactor coolant is pumped to a mercury boiler where mercury is vaporized and heated to 1150°F. The coolant then returns to the reactor through a rotating electromagnetic pump. The mercury vapor flows through a two-stage axial flow turbine, then to a radiator condenser unit integral with the skin of the vehicle. The liquid mercury is returned to the boiler by a centrifugal pump. The mercury is also used as a lubricant for the bearings of the rotating shaft.

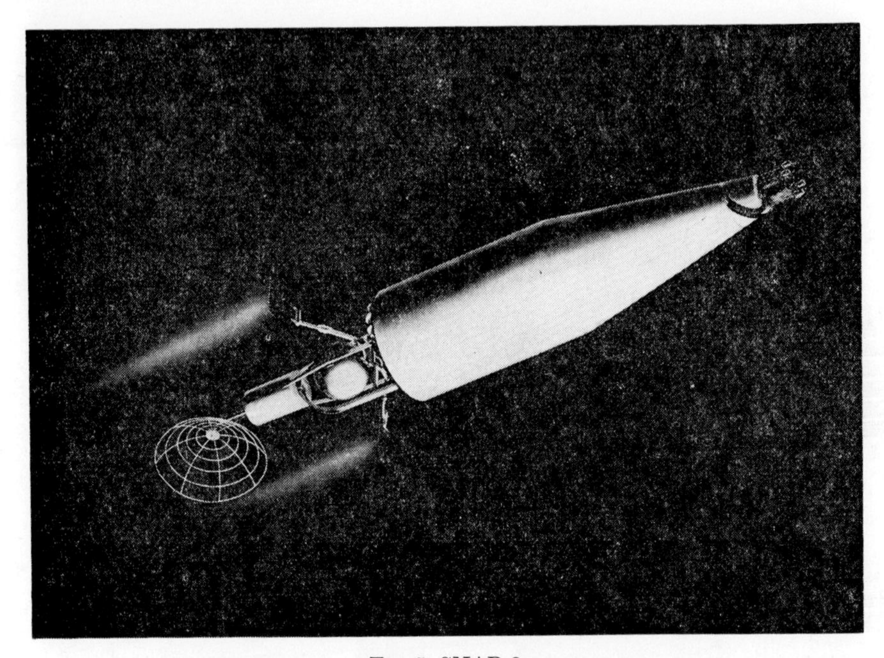

FIG. 5. SNAP 8.

The 30-kw SNAP-8 power unit is essentially a scaled up version of the SNAP-2 system. It also uses a turboelectric power conversion system operating on a mercury Rankine cycle and the reactor is designed to produce enough heat to operate two 30-kw turbines, providing a total power output of 60 kw. Figure 5 is an artist's conception of a SNAP-8 unit being used as a source of power for an ion propulsion engine.

Table II indicates the system requirements for the SNAP-10A, SNAP-2, and SNAP-8 power units. These units are considered to be completely feasible from an engineering standpoint based on the state of the art today. They require only further engineering development and prototype testing to achieve the required reliability of operation over an extended lifetime and a maximum possible reduction in weight.

The figure of merit for a space power system is the specific weight, in

TABLE II
System Requirements

	SNAP-10A	SNAP-2	SNAP-8
Electrical power (kw):	0.5	3	30
Total weight shielded for typical unmanned vehicle (lb):	775	1050	1800
Endurance (years):	1	1	>1
Radiator area (ft^2):	70	110	400
Startup		In orbit	
Availability	1963	1964	1965

pounds per kilowatt of power capability (Fig. 6). The thermoelectric power conversion systems, using reactor heat sources, result in specific weights of the order of 1000 lb/kw for power outputs up to about 1 kw. Substantial improvements in specific weight can be made for larger power units of this type, until a size of several kilowatts is reached. At this point, the higher efficiency of the turbo-generator systems using the mercury vapor cycle can achieve lower specific weights, due primarily to the smaller portions of waste heat to be rejected and therefore smaller radiators required, up to about 100-kw output, where a specific weight of about 30 lb/kw might be achieved.

Beyond this point, it is necessary to go to higher temperature power conversion systems, such as a rubidium or potassium direct-cycle boiling system, which might achieve a specific weight of about 10 lb/kw. In order to approach the ultimate goal of about 5 lb/kw, it will probably be

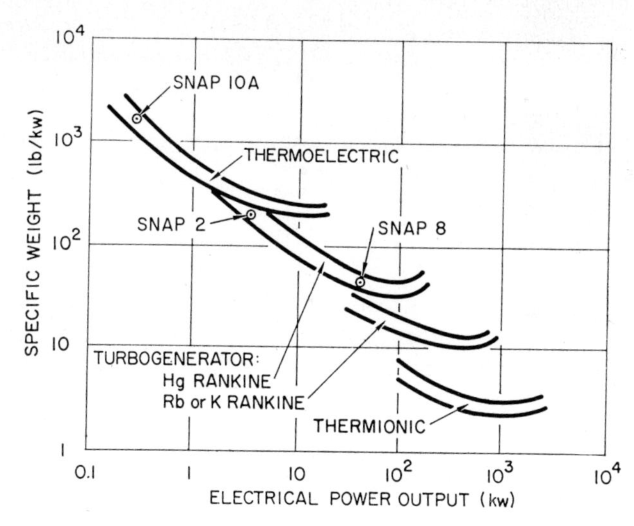

Fig. 6. Specific weight vs. power output for nuclear power systems.

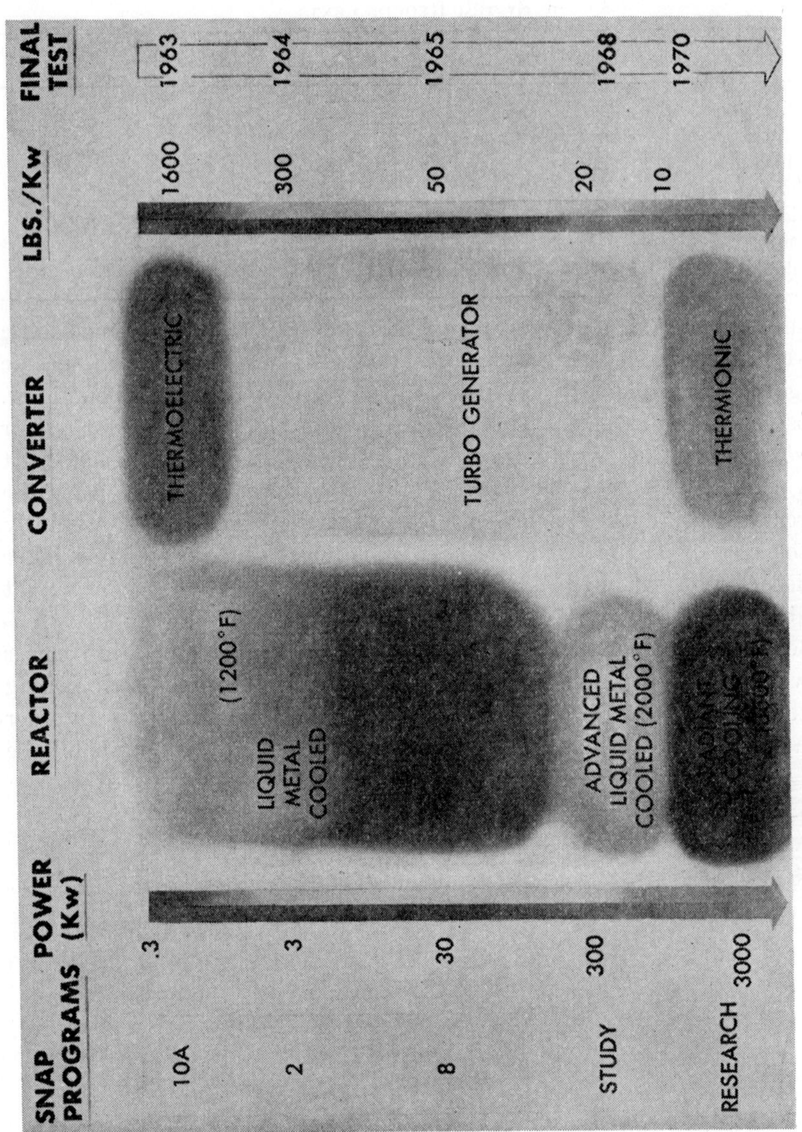

Fig. 7. Probable courses of future development.

necessary to develop thermionic power conversion systems and very high temperature radiant-type reactor fuel elements.

Figure 7 indicates the probable course of future developments in this field. The reactor power units which I have described, based on presently available reactor technology, are adequate for power outputs up to about 150 kw and, using turbo-generator power conversion systems, can attain specific weights of about 30 lb/kw. Such units can be available for use in the 1965–1966 time period. To obtain higher power outputs and lower specific weights, more advanced systems must be developed. Studies are now being conducted based on fast reactor technology using direct cycle boiling liquid metal power conversion systems, operating at temperatures up to 2000°F. The thermionic nuclear power systems, based on very high temperature reactor operation (3500°F) are still in the research stage and probably will not be available for use in space programs until 1970 or later.

Discussion

CHAIRMAN A. L. KLEIN: I would like to ask about protection of the condensers and coolers from meteor penetration. What work is going on in that direction?

DR. A. B. MARTIN: This is indeed a problem; namely to provide protection of the radiator condenser tubes from meteorite damage. One is after minimum weight in these systems, and so the tendency is to make the tubes as thin-walled as possible. On the other hand, the approach to protection against meteor damage is to thicken the tubes on the side that is exposed to meteor impact. One could think of tubes with an offset hole, so that the outer part of the tubes is thick enough to withstand the calculated micrometeorite bombardment.

CHAIRMAN A. L. KLEIN: It has been intimated that the condensers may be the major weight in the systems.

DR. A. B. MARTIN: This is probably true in the lower efficiency systems such as the thermoelectric systems, where a large amount of heat must be rejected, and where the temperature of rejection is limited by the properties of the thermoelectric materials themselves. I mentioned a figure of 900°F as the maximum temperature for the thermoelectric system. The heat rejection temperature varies from that figure to about 600°F, which is the minimum temperature of the fluid coming out of the condenser.

In the case of the turboelectric systems, however, where one does not have the same temperature limitations, the maximum heat rejection temperature is higher; for example, for SNAP-2 it is 1200°F; for SNAP-8 it will be 1300°F. So for the turboelectric systems the radiator condensers can be made smaller.

Another instance of the condensers not necessarily being the largest weight components in the system could occur on missions where rather large and heavy radiation shields might be required.

SECTION III

Celestial Mechanics Problems in the Solar System, Planetary Exploration, and Related Engineering Problems

CHAPTER 15

Celestial Mechanics Problems

15.1 Scale and Mass in the Solar System

SAMUEL HERRICK

UNIVERSITY OF CALIFORNIA, Los Angeles, California

1. The Astronomical Unit and the Kilometer

The astronomical unit and the kilometer, a.u. and km, are the foci of an interesting controversy over the preferred unit of distance for heliocentric orbits. The controversy is substantially between the celestial mechanic on the one hand and the engineer or physicist or, specifically, the electronics guidance specialist on the other. A related and perhaps more important controversy is concerned with the need for accurate determinations of the ratio of the two units. In exploring and commenting on these controversies, we note first the following:

(1) Orbit and ephemeris calculations will have to discard the cgs G, which is known to only three significant figures, in favor of the Gaussian k_s, which is known to eight or nine significant figures because of a selection of appropriate units of length, mass, and time, whether or not the units of k_s are changed.

(2) One should properly use the term "ratio of the astronomical unit to the kilometer" instead of saying "the value of the astronomical unit in kilometers," or at least imply the former concept by a consciously loose usage of the latter phrase or of something equivalent (see Section 2). Literally, "the value" implies erroneously that the astronomical unit is less precise than the kilometer, whereas the converse is probably true; and in any event the ratio has been less precise than either. The astronomical unit is the basis of measurement in the solar system. In this unit, mutual distances are known to an accuracy that approaches, in the best instances, the eight or nine significant-figure accuracy of k_s. The

comparable mutual distances of a first-order survey on the surface of the earth are accurate to about five significant figures. Whether the greater accuracy of the current standard of the kilometer can be extended to gross measures, rather than differential ones, of more than five significant figures, is one of the interesting questions of the present time. Whatever the circumstance, one should degrade neither system by unjustifiably associating it with an inaccurate ratio.

(3) With the kilometer we associate not only other terrestrial units such as feet or miles, but also the "light second," or the distance light and radio waves travel in a second, in terms of which the radio engineer is actually making his measures of distance. It may well be that it is the ratio of the astronomical unit to the light second, perhaps qualified to the interplanetary medium, that will prove to be the significant ratio of the future.

(4) The "solar parallax," in its literal sense, is a concept outmoded by recent determinations of the "ratio" and would only complicate the discussions of the present section. It will be reserved, along with a discussion of actual determinations of both "parallax" and "ratio," to Section 2.

It is often said that the Gaussian k^2, or k_s^2 as we shall call it to distinguish it from the geocentric value, k_e^2, is equal to, or has the dimensions of, $Gm_\odot$, where G is the cgs value of the gravitational constant, and $m_\odot$ is the mass of the sun in grams. Such a change of dimensions leads to conceptual difficulties when we use k_s in equations that involve forces as well as in equations that involve accelerations. It is preferable to regard k_s^2 and G as dimensionally the same, with differences only in the units involved, and perhaps only in the unit of mass, G is tied up inextricably with the gram, but k_s^2 has $m_\odot$ as the unit of mass.

Accordingly, we may regard Gauss's original value, $k_s = 0.017{,}202{,}098{,}95$, as the a.u.-$m_\odot$-day value of k_s, and from it derive a centimeter-$m_\odot$-second value. The former is to be employed when the a.u. is being used as unit of distance; the latter, when the cm or km is being used. The former we may regard as having no appreciable error, not because of the astronomical practice of holding it fixed and forcing the error elsewhere, but rather because the error would be in the eighth or ninth significant figure in any event. The latter will then have an error arising primarily in the conversion from a.u. to km.

The centimeter-$m_\odot$-second value of k_s is derived as follows:

$$\begin{aligned} k_s &= 0.017{,}202{,}098{,}95\ (\text{a.u.})^{3/2}\, m_\odot^{-1/2}\ \text{day}^{-1}, \\ 1\ \text{a.u.} &= 1.496\,(1 + R') \times 10^{13}\ \text{cm}, \\ 1\ \text{day} &= 86{,}400\ \text{sec.} \end{aligned} \tag{1}$$

From these values we obtain

$$\begin{aligned} k_s &= 1.152{,}034\ (1 + \tfrac{3}{2}R') \times 10^{13}\ \mathrm{cm}^{3/2}\ m_\odot^{-1/2}\ \mathrm{sec}^{-1}, \\ k_s^2 &= 1.327{,}182\ (1 + 3R') \times 10^{26}\ \mathrm{cm}^3\ m_\odot^{-1}\ \mathrm{sec}^{-2}. \end{aligned} \tag{2}$$

The quantity R' serves both for the correction of k_s and k_s^2 and for the estimation of their uncertainties, on the basis of a correction to, or estimate of the uncertainty of, the above adopted ratio of the astronomical unit to the kilometer or centimeter. For example, an uncertainty of ± 5000 km (or $R' = \pm \frac{1}{3} \times 10^{-4}$) in the metric measurement of the astronomical unit corresponds to a relative uncertainty in k_s of 5×10^{-5}; i.e., the cm-$m_\odot$-sec value of k_s would have exactly four significant figures. Similarly, ± 500 km corresponds to five significant figures in k_s.

The practical significance of the four or five figure accuracies of the "ratio" and of the corresponding cm-$m_\odot$-sec value of k_s, as contrasted with the eight or nine figure accuracy of the Gaussian or a.u.-$m_\odot$-day value of k_s, should be measured not merely by the contrast in significant figures, but more realistically by effects on orbit determination and rendezvous. A study of the latter area should consider both accuracy and convenience, and both "ballistic" (uncorrected) trajectories and the effects of observation and differential correction ("midcourse guidance").

It may be inferred, or demonstrated in several ways, that the choice of a unit of distance does not affect the accuracy of an orbit calculation, i.e., that the error of the "ratio" will affect all such calculations equally. It must be clearly understood, however, that to obtain the same results with the kilometer as with the astronomical unit, one must (1) discard G in favor of k_s obtained above from the Gaussian value and (2) use one and the same value of the "ratio," or of R', in k_s as obtained from Eq. 2, in the coordinates and velocities of any other planet that enters into the calculation. One cannot use planetary tables converted to kilometers at different times with different ratios, nor can one change horses (ratios) in midstream (as better information on the ratio becomes available). With these restrictions the kilometer becomes rather a fraction and adjunct of the astronomical unit than an independent or terrestrial unit, and the whole of a trajectory calculation is merely adjusted by a factor of proportionality.

For purely ballistic trajectories, then the choice between astronomical unit and kilometer is one of convenience rather than accuracy. The convenience of the former as contrasted with the latter is very great indeed. It is far simpler to convert the three components of initial geocentric velocity from the original kilometers to astronomical units than to convert complete planetary tables to kilometers, as one would have to do for observations and for perturbation calculations. It is far simpler not to convert planetary tables at all than it is to reconvert them every time a new "ratio" becomes available. If a new ratio becomes available during the course of a calculation, it is easier to correct differentially for changes in the initial components of velocity than to correct for changes in the planetary tables and in k_s.

With midcourse guidance, by observation and differential correction, new and interesting factors enter into the problem. Our study may be focused on the following equation and its derivatives:

$$\rho \boldsymbol{L} = \boldsymbol{r} + \boldsymbol{R} \tag{3}$$

Here $\boldsymbol{R}$ is the position vector of the dynamical center referred to the "point of observation," which may be the position, terrestrial, or other, of either the observer of the vehicle or of the point observed from the vehicle. We shall suppose $\boldsymbol{R}$ to be known exactly in astronomical units. The vector $\boldsymbol{r}$, which is directed from the dynamical center to the vehicle, depends upon the orbital elements that are to be brought into conformity with the observations and with the assumed value of the "ratio." The scalar ρ is the distance (or "range") from the point of observation to the vehicle; if it is observed at all, we may suppose that ρ is obtained in kilometers. Finally $\boldsymbol{L}$ is a unit vector directed from the point of observation toward the vehicle; it depends upon the observed angular coordinates (e.g., α and δ), which are quite independent of the unit of distance. The velocities α, δ, and ρ ("range rate") are brought in by the first time-derivatives of Eq. (3). Accelerometer readings may bring in the second time derivatives of Eq. (3) and other components of $\boldsymbol{\rho} = \rho \boldsymbol{L}$.

Considering first the classical astronomical observations of the angular coordinates (α and δ) alone, from which orbits may be determined by the elimination of ρ, we see simply that the uncertainty R' will not enter if $\boldsymbol{R}$ is expressed in astronomical units, but that it will if $\boldsymbol{R}$ is converted to kilometers. Accordingly, the astronomical unit has been the preferred unit of distance for the orbits of astronomical objects so observed. A determination of the "ratio" has been quite unnecessary to orbit work of this kind. Lack of appreciation of this point among nonastronomers led them first to a mistaken insistence upon the need for an accurate value of the "ratio" to "improve" astronomical data. An interesting and equally mistaken contrary opinion now prevails among astronomers and nonastronomers alike, to the effect that the "ratio" does not need to be known accurately for any practical purpose. Apparently this opinion stems in part from a growing appreciation of the classical astronomer's independence of it, and in part from ill-considered beliefs that radar range and range-rate observations can solve the whole problem without the use of direction observations, and that they are equally free of R'.

Radar observations of distance and radial velocity (range rate) have indeed a very great impact upon these problems and questions, but a re-study of them leads us unequivocably to conclude that the astronomical unit cannot be discarded, and that its ratio to the kilometer (or light second) is of prime importance. First considering three-dimensional "fixes," or "complete" position observations (of ρ together with α and δ or other components of $\boldsymbol{L}$), we see that the uncertainty R' enters through ρ alone if ρ is converted from kilometers to astronomical units, but through all three components of $\boldsymbol{R}$ if they are converted from astronomical units to kilometers. With either procedure the ratio becomes less critical as the vehicle approaches its target, in an interception problem, if the target itself is the "point of observation." In general, however, a statistical handling of the problem will be the stronger if the systematic error R' enters into only one equation out of every three (i.e., in ρ but not in α or δ). In practical terms, these considerations mean that a careful early analysis of observational residuals, together with an accurate value of the "ratio," will make possible an early correction that will greatly diminish the fuel cost of terminal guidance.

Considering finally the circumstances in which range alone is observed —we may easily extend the study to range rate—we note first that range observations on six dates (rather than three-component fixes on two dates) can be fitted to an orbit in spite of an error in the "ratio." Accordingly, it will take observations on more dates to determine an orbit, by differential correction of the "ratio" as well as the elements, that does not do violence to subsequent observations. Choice between the astronomical unit and the kilometer is primarily a matter of convenience, as discussed above, but the need for an accurate "ratio" is greater than in any other circumstances.

The notion that radar observations can solve an interplanetary rendezvous problem without benefit of existing astronomical tables may be dismissed as naive. It is an extension of terminal guidance concepts far beyond their capacity, not only in distance (e.g., in early differential correction) but also in the replacement of relative distance observations (e.g., of the target from the interceptor) by differences of distance observations (i.e., from the earth) that may provide no accurate information on relative distance or relative velocity.

It should be noted, on the other hand, that the aim of the various national almanac offices is to produce planetary theories and ephemerides that are consistent over long periods of time with adopted values of basic constants, both physical constants and constants of integration. It is only through such consistency that observation residuals can be used to improve theories. Neither the physical constants nor the ephemeris positions, however, are necessarily the best that can be obtained from contemporary data, and it is these best that are required for observation and rendezvous of particular space vehicles at particular times. Exactly the same best data are necessary in such observational problems as the determination of the "ratio." The celestial mechanic should reach a compromise with the enthusiastic radar guidance specialist. Neither radar observations nor astronomical tables should be used alone. The celestial mechanic should supply the forms for empirical terms that may serve to correct planetary tables, so that current observations of all kinds may be used to improve instantaneous positions, without doing violence to the long term effects, especially in the mean motion, that cannot be improved without the use of a very great span of observations.

2. The Solar Parallax

The solar parallax is the quantity in which the ratio of the astronomical unit to the kilometer traditionally has been embodied. Since the term, the quantity, and the reasons for using them are a bit puzzling to nonastronomers, some discussion is in order.

First we shall define the "solar parallax" as the equatorial horizontal geocentric parallax of the sun when it is at a distance of 1 a.u. from the earth. (It is equally possible to define it in terms of the earth's mean distance from the sun, but more complex to do so. The distinction has not heretofore been significant.)

A parallactic displacement, p', of an object S is the angle subtended at S by the line between two observers O_1 and O_2 (Fig. 1), and it is likewise the angular displacement of S against a stellar background. Geocentric parallax, p, is the angle subtended at S by the radius of the earth, OE, at the observer's position O. Equatorial horizontal geocentric parallax, Π, is the maximum value of p for distance d, when the object S is on the horizon of O, and when the observer O is on the equator, so that OE is the equatorial radius a_e (Fig. 1). Thus the solar parallax, $\Pi_\odot$, is the value of Π when d is 1 a.u.

The "ratio," R, and $\Pi_\odot$ are accordingly related to one another by

$$R = \frac{d(\text{km})}{d(\text{a.u.})} = \frac{a_e(\text{km})}{1 \text{ a.u. } \sin \Pi_\odot} = \frac{206{,}264''8 \; a_e(\text{km})}{1 \text{ a.u.}(\Pi_\odot'')}, \tag{4}$$

where $\Pi_\odot''$ is $\Pi_\odot$ expressed in seconds of arc.

In geometrical determinations of the solar parallax from observations of the parallactic displacement of a planet such as Eros (Hinks, 1904; Spencer Jones, 1941) it is possible to proceed to $\Pi_\odot''$ without committing oneself to a particular value of a_e, such as would be required for a subse-

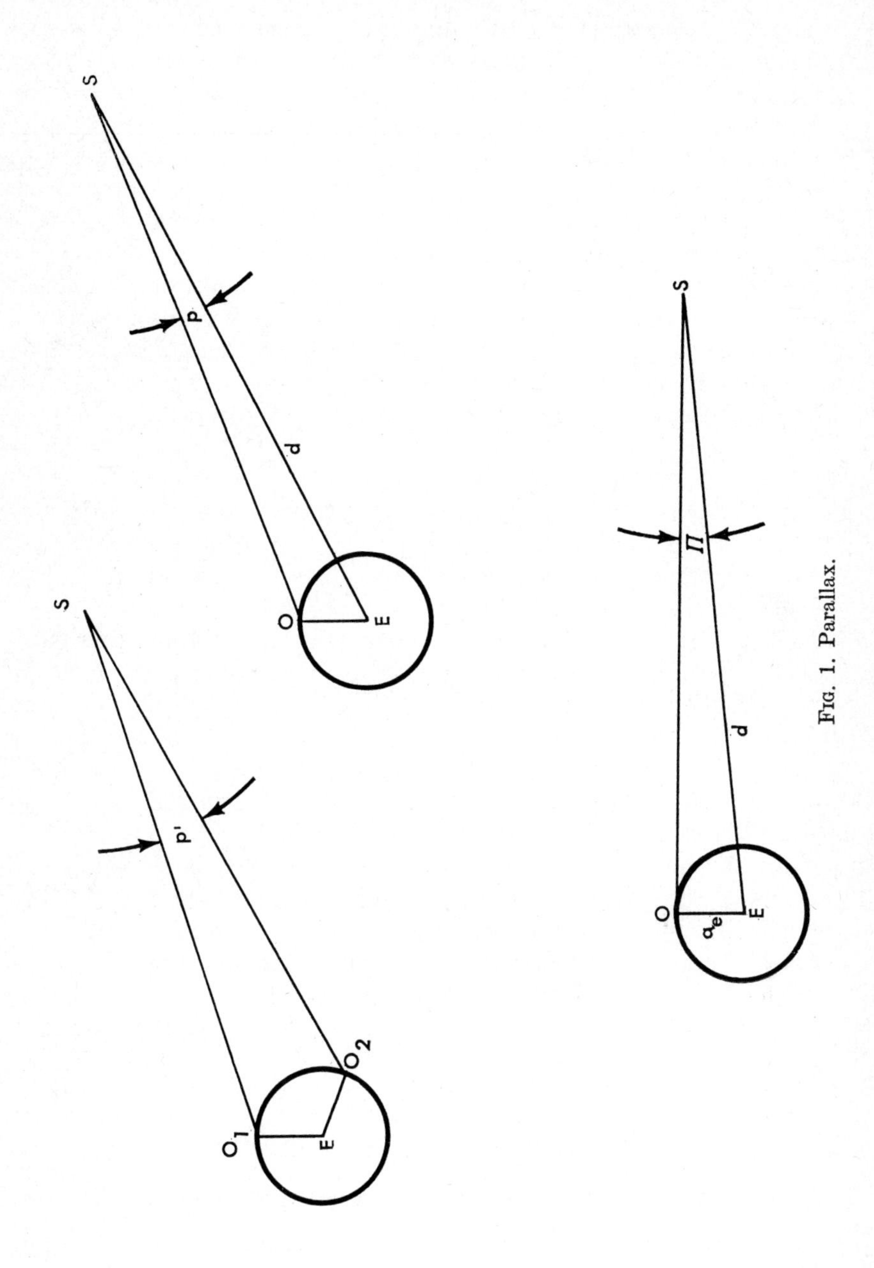

FIG. 1. Parallax.

TABLE I

SELECTED DETERMINATIONS OF THE "SOLAR PARALLAX"[a]

Investigator	$\Pi_{\odot}$	$R \times 10^{-6}$	
Hinks (1904), Eros (triang.)	8.806 ±4	149.40 ±7	
Adams (1941), radial velocities	8.805 ±7	149.42 ±12	
Spencer Jones (1928), radial velocities	8.803 ±4	149.45 ±7	
Witt (1935), Eros (dynam.)	8.799 ±1	149.52 ±2	
Rabe (1950), Eros (dynam.)	8.79835 ±39	149.5322 ±66	
Makemson *et al.* (1960), compilation	8.798 ±2	149.54 ±3	
de Vaucouleurs (1961), compilation	8.7979 ±2	149.536 ±3	*b*
McGuire *et al.* (1961), Pioneer V radar	8.7974 ±8	149.548 ±14	
Weinberg (1904), compilation	8.7958 ±14	149.576 ±23	
Maron *et al.* (1961), Venus radar	8.79460 ±?	149.5960 ±?	*c*
Pettengill (1961), Venus radar	8.794491 ±24	149.59785 ±40	*d*
Victor *et al.* (1961), Venus radar	8.79445 ±3	149.5985 ±5	*e*
Kotelnikov (1961), Venus radar	8.79439 ±5	149.5995 ±8	*f*
Thomson *et al.* (1961), Venus radar	8.7943 ±3	149.601 ±5	*g*
Brouwer (1950), parallactic inequality	8.7925 ±30	149.63 ±5	
Spencer Jones (1941), Eros (triang.)	8.790 ±1	149.67 ±2	*h*

[a] Note: For consistency the International Ellipsoid value of a_e, 6378.388 km (Hayford, 1910), is used in deriving $\Pi_{\odot}''$ or R, the one from the other, except where noted (cf. footnote *b*).

[b] Uses $a_e = 6378.200$, a too-much rounded value from Cook (1959), instead of the International Ellipsoid value or improved values such as in Chovitz and Fischer (1956), Fischer (1959), or Kaula (1961).

[c] The RCA BMEWS (Moorestown, New Jersey) determination of the uncertainties stated in the reference (±0.″00001 and ±0.0002) are not included in the present tabulation because they do not appear to be comparable to the others; they seem to be least readings for a coincidence of four of the eight observations.

[d] Revision of the Millstone (1961) values, 8.79450 and 149.5977, which replaced the discarded 1958 values of Pettengill and Price (1961), 8.8022 and 149.4673 (cf. also Herrick *et al.*, 1959). Pettengill reports that new studies of the 1959 observations, which

quent determination of R from Eq. (4). It is this fact that led astronomers originally to regard $\Pi_{\odot}''$ rather than R as the fundamental quantity to be determined. Except for the lunar parallactic inequality method, however, all other methods for determining $\Pi_{\odot}''$ determine R first; for these it is $\Pi_{\odot}''$ rather than R that requires an assumption as to a_e. Examples are the aberrational method, the stellar-radial-velocity or spectroscopic method (Spencer Jones, 1928; Adams, 1941), and especially the powerful Eros dynamical method (Witt, 1935; Rabe, 1950). The recent radar observations of Venus (cf. Table I) actually give the ratio of the astronomical unit to the "light second" as it is conditioned by the interplanetary medium (cf. Section 1), one step further away from $\Pi_{\odot}''$ than R itself.

The most important practical use of these quantities at the present time is in the utilization of radar observations of distance in conjunction with astronomical tables. Accordingly it is clear that the two "ratios" (a.u. to km and a.u. to light second) are now more important than $\Pi_{\odot}''$ and should be emphasized in the future. The term "solar parallax," however, has been used loosely to cover the first of the two "ratios" as well as $\Pi_{\odot}''$; and it seems advisable to recognize and continue this loose usage, and to extend it to the ratio of the a.u. to the light second. "Solar parallax" is more distinctive and succinct than "value of the astronomical unit," whose loose usage was discussed in Section 1.

The present status of the numerical values of $\Pi_{\odot}''$ and R is confused (cf. Table I), and an astronomical world that has been "stung" several times on the solar parallax (cf. Table I, footnotes *c*, *f*, and *g*) will be slow to accept a new value. The striking agreement of the 1961 Venus radar values is offset by their disagreement with the Eros-dynamical values of Witt (1935) and Rabe (1950), recently regarded as the strongest determinations. The presence of systematic errors in one or both of the determinations is strongly indicated. Confirmation of the Venus radar values, by a set of Venus values for another time, or a set of Mars values, is greatly to be desired (cf. Table I, footnote *c*).

---

failed to confirm the 1958 values, are beginning to show confirmation of the 1961 values.

[e] The Jet Propulsion Laboratory determination.

[f] The original Russian press reports gave $R \times 10^{-6} = 149.477$. According to Rechtin, they possibly ignored through misunderstanding the additional term "$\pm 0.130\, p$," with p "a positive integer" subsequently stated to be 1, so that $R \times 10^{-6} = 149.577$. It would have been more clearly stated as "$+0.130\, p$, with p a positive or negative integer." The change from 149.577 to 149.5995 resulted from a refinement of the reductions, according to Kotelnikov.

[g] The Jodrell Bank values. The 1958 values confirming the Millstone 1958 values are now likewise discarded.

[h] Generally thought to have indeterminable systematic errors.

Pending resolution of the systematic discordance between the Eros-dynamical values and the Venus determinations, or the unequivocal confirmation of the latter, it seems best to adopt the rounded but correctable value of Eqs. (1), or

$$R = 1.496\,(1 + R') \times 10^{13}\ \text{cm}$$
$$= 149{,}600{,}000\,(1 + R')\ \text{km}.$$

To this value corresponds, if we use the reference $a_e = 6378.388$ km,

$$\Pi_\odot'' = 8''.7944\,(1 - R').$$

3. The Geocentric Constants

The geocentric constants that correspond to k_s and R are k_e and a_e, the "geocentric gravitational constant" and the earth's equatorial radius.

The advantage to be gained from using the "radius" as unit of distance for geocentric orbits, as compared with the centimeter, kilometer, or megameter (10^6 meters), is conspicuously less than that afforded by the astronomical unit in heliocentric orbits, except for the possibility of fixing k_e as k_s has been fixed (Herrick *et al.*, 1958). The radius is nevertheless a key link in the determination of k_e from the acceleration of gravity, which is still the best source, as it was in 1958 and before.

Both k_e and a_e are affected by improvements in the earth's flattening, f, or the related coefficient of the second harmonic in the earth's gravitational field, as well as by the higher harmonics.* Accordingly the value of a_e from the "Hough ellipsoid," 6378.270 km for $f = 1/297$, adopted as best in 1958, is automatically reduced to 6378.145 km for $f = 1/298.3$, currently accepted as a "best value." The recent work of Fischer (1959) and Kaula (1961) suggests that the latter figure should be increased by about 0.020 km. Both changes affect k_e (or the earth's mass, according to the conceptual preferences of those interested).

A new study of the basic relationships among these constants and others, inclusive of the third and higher harmonics in the earth's gravitational field, is strongly indicated. Conferences are necessary to adopt both current "best values" and formulae for automatically improving those constants affected by a new determination of any one of them.

References

Adams, W. S. (1941), Some results with the Coudé spectrograph of Mt. Wilson, *Astrophys. J.* **93,** 11–23.

Brouwer, D. (1950), A new determination of the solar parallax from the parallactic inequality in the moon's longitude . . . , *Bull. astron.* **15,** 165–180.

* For a discussion of the higher harmonics reference is made to the chapters by I. G. Izsak (Chapter 6.2) and P. J. Message (Chapter 15.4).

Chovitz, B., and Fischer, I. (1956), A new determination of the figure of the earth from arcs, *Trans. Am. Geophys. Union* **37,** 534–545, October.

Cook, A. H. (1959), Developments in dynamical geodesy, *Geophys. J.* **2,** 222–240.

de Vaucouleurs, G. (1961), The astronomical unit of distance, solar parallax, and related constants, Geoph. Corp. of America, Boston, Spec. Publ. (iv + 49 pp.) (January).

Fischer, I. (1959), A tentative world datum from geoidal heights based on the Hough ellipsoid and the Columbus geoid, *J. Geophys. Research* **64,** 73–84.

Hayford, J. F. (1910), "Supplementary Investigation of the Figure of the Earth and Isostasy. Washington, 1910 (includes the "Hayford spheroid of 1909").

Herrick, S., Baker, R. M. L., Jr., and Hilton, C. G. (1958), Gravitational and related constants for accurate space navigation. *Proc. VIII Intern. Astronaut. Congr., (Barcelona 1957)*, pp. 197–235; U.C.L A. Astron. Paper **1,** No. 24, 297–338.

Herrick, S., Westrom, G. B., and Makemson, M. W. (1959), "The astronomical unit" and the solar parallax, *U.C.L.A. Astrodyn. Rept.,* No. 5 (25 pp.).

Hinks, A. R. (1904), Reduction of 295 photographs of Eros . . . with a determination of the solar parallax. *Monthly Notices Roy. Astron. Soc.* **64,** 701–727; See also (1909), *ibid.* **69,** 544–567; (1910), *ibid.* **70,** 588–603.

Kaula, W. M. (1961), A geoid and world geodetic system based on a combination of gravimetric, astrogeodetic, and satellite data. *J. Geophys. Research* **66,** 1799–1811.

Kotelnikov, V. A. (1961), Radar contact with Venus. Presented at the XIIth Intern. Astronaut. Congr. Washington, D. C., October 4, 1961.

Makemson, M. W., Baker, R. M. L., Jr., and Westrom, G. B. (1960), Analysis and standardization of astrodynamic constants. *U.C.L.A. Astrodyn. Rept.,* No. 12 (37 pp); (1961), *J. Astronaut. Sci.* **8,** 1–13.

Maron, I., Luchak, G., and Blitzstein, W. (1961), Radar observations of Venus, *Science* **134,** 1419–1420.

McGuire, J. B., Spangler, E. R., and Wong, L. (1961), The size of the solar system, *Sci. American* **204**(4), 64–72.

Millstone (Staff of the Radar Observatory) (1961), The scale of the solar system, *Nature* **190,** 592.

Pettengill, G. H. (1961), Venus radar. Presented at the XIIth Intern. Astronaut. Congr., Washington, D. C., October 4.

Pettengill, G. H., and Price, R. (1961), Radar echoes from Venus and a new determination of the solar parallax, *Planetary and Space Sci.* **5,** 70–78.

Rabe, E. (1950), Derivation of fundamental astronomical constants from the observations of Eros during 1926–1945, *Astron. J.* **55,** 112–126.

Spencer Jones, H. (1928), Solar parallax from radial velocities of stars, *Ann. Cape Obs.* **10,** Pt. 8.

Spencer Jones, H. (1941), The solar parallax and the mass of the moon from observations of Eros at the opposition of 1931, *Mem. Roy. Astron. Soc.* **66,** Pt. 2 (56 pp.).

Thomson, J. H., Taylor, G. N., Ponsonby, J. E. B., and Roger, R. S. (1961), A new determination of the solar parallax by means of radar echoes from Venus at Jodrell Bank, *Nature* **190,** 519–520.

Victor, W. K., Stevens, R., and Golomb, S. W. (1961), Radar exploration of Venus, *Jet Propulsion Lab. Tech. Rept. No. 32–132* August 1.

Weinberg, B. (1904), Endgültige Ausgleichung der wahrscheinlichsten Werte der Sonnenparallaxe . . . , *Astr. Nach.* **165,** 133–142.

Witt, G. (1935), Solar parallax and mass of earth from the orbit of Eros between 1835 and 1931, *Astron. Abhand. Ergänzungsh. Astr. Nach.* **9,** 1.

Discussion

CHAIRMAN CLEMENCE: Professor Herrick has furnished us with an appreciable amount of material for discussion, as I hoped he would. But inasmuch as there seems to be some doubt about what is the latest value of the Russian determination of the solar parallax, I would like to ask Dr. Massevitch if she can enlighten us on that.

DR. A. G. MASSEVITCH: The correct value is 8.795 sec. This value appeared in the original scientific publication by Professor Kotelnikov and his collaborators and should be accepted. Unfortunately, a different value did once appear, but only in the newspapers.

The following abstract of a pertinent report,* on the recent radio location of Venus in the U.S.S.R., was communicated by Professor Vladimir Kotelnikov, Director of the Institute of Radio and Electronics of the U.S.S.R. Academy of Sciences in Moscow. It was from this experiment that the above value of the solar parallax was derived by his team.

"Radio location of the planet Venus was carried out in the USSR in April, 1961. The frequency of the signals sent was 700 Mc/s and consisted of impulses of a duration of 128 or 64 milliseconds. The intervals between the impulses were of the same duration. The reduction of the data received showed that the signals reflected from Venus had a wide spectrum, of the order of 400 c/s. In the middle part of it there was a narrow spectral line, of a width of several c/s. The spectral energy density in the narrow line was about two orders higher than that in the wide spectrum. The spectrum of the reflected signals was variable. The wide spectrum could be caused by the scattered reflection from the rough parts of the surface, and it corresponds to a period of rotation of Venus of not more than 11 terrestrial days. The narrow spectrum could be caused by the reflection from the smooth parts of the planet's surface. The value of the astronomical unit was found according to the shift of the narrow spectral line and the delay of the signal."

* This report was to be published in the Proceedings of the 1961 British Institution of Radio Engineers Convention in Oxford, England. Additional information on the details of the experiment was presented by Professor Kotelnikov at the XII International Astronautical Congress in Washington, D. C., October 1–7, 1961.

15.2 Progress and Problems in Analytical Celestial Mechanics

DIRK BROUWER

YALE UNIVERSITY OBSERVATORY, New Haven, Connecticut

Artificial Satellite Motion

Solid progress in celestial mechanics in relation to space age astronomy has been achieved primarily in the field of artificial satellite motion. In a sense the problem is an old one that also occurred among the natural satellites of the solar system. However, in applications to the motion of natural satellites it was never necessary to obtain as general and as detailed a solution as is required in applications to artificial satellites.

The basic or "main" problem is that of the drag-free motion of a small satellite about a planet with rotational symmetry. Once this problem has been solved, we can introduce the complications of atmospheric drag, tesseral harmonics, solar and lunar perturbations, solar radiation, and other conceivable circumstances that may affect the actual motion.

In the basic problem the rotational symmetry causes the longitude of the ascending node of the orbit to be an ignorable coordinate. Hence the problem can be reduced to one of two degrees of freedom.

The degree of complexity—or simplicity—of the problem may be judged by considering the Hamiltonian of the system if the Delaunay variables are used as canonical variables. This Hamiltonian may be expressed by

$$F = F_0(x) + \Sigma F_k(x, \rho, y, \omega),$$

in which F_k is of $O(J^k)$ in the oblateness parameter J.

The variables, y, ω are angular variables; the former is a fast-moving variable with mean motion

$$n \sim \frac{\partial F_0(x)}{\partial x},$$

while ω is a slow-moving angular variable with a mean motion of the order J. According to the principle of Delaunay's method, the integration is effected by performing a series of canonical transformations that in the end transform the Hamiltonian to the form

$$F^* = F_0{}^*(\bar{x}) + \Sigma F_k{}^*(\bar{x}, \bar{\rho}),$$

the angular variables y and ω having been removed. The solution of the final system is then

$$\bar{x} = \text{const}, \qquad \bar{y} = nt + \text{const},$$
$$\bar{\rho} = \text{const}, \qquad \bar{\omega} = \nu t + \text{const},$$

in which n and ν are known functions of x and ρ, while the transformation formulae yield

$$x = \bar{x} + \text{cosine series in } \bar{y}, \bar{\omega}$$
$$\rho = \bar{\rho} + \text{cosine series in } \bar{y}, \bar{\omega}$$
$$y = \bar{y} + \text{sine series in } \bar{y}, \bar{\omega}$$
$$\omega = \bar{\omega} + \text{sine series in } \bar{y}, \bar{\omega}.$$

The technique of obtaining the solution has been greatly simplified by von Zeipel's improvement of the Delaunay procedure. The solution depends on obtaining by successive approximations in powers of J a generating function S. The first approximation is found by

$$F_{0x}S_{1y} + F_1 - F_1^* = 0, \tag{1}$$

in which F_1^* is the part of F_1 that is independent of y. Equations of identical form subsequently yield S_2, S_3, ... Thus the short-period argument may be eliminated, and the problem is effectively reduced to one degree of freedom.

When next the attempt is made to eliminate the long-period argument ω, the interesting feature arises that in the new system the equation for S_1^* is

$$F_{1\rho}^*S_{1\omega}^* + F_2^* - F_2^{**} = 0.$$

Note that the factor of $S_{1\omega}^*$ is of $O(J)$, which is counterbalanced by the fact that the absolute part of the equation is of the second order. But it requires carrying out the developments to $O(J^2)$ in order to obtain the long-period terms to $O(J)$.

The function $F_{1\rho}^*$ has $(1\text{–}5 \cos^2 I)$ as a factor. Consequently, this function appears as a divisor in S_1^*, and causes the solution to become highly unsatisfactory or even illusory when I is close to the critical inclination, $\tan I_c = 2$; $I_c = 63°26'$. Actually, for I only a degree away from I_c, the general solution is not seriously impaired by the small divisor. For orbits less than 1° from the critical inclination, a different form of solution is desirable. Several authors (G. Hori, B. Garfinkel, and others) have obtained solutions expanded in power of $J^{1/2}$, by a well-known procedure in celestial mechanics that is effective for dealing with motions in resonance regions.

The term "critical inclination" is, I believe, appropriate. Near the critical inclination the motion of the argument ω becomes vanishingly small, and this argument becomes a critical argument in the sense in which this term has been used in celestial mechanics for many years. It is perhaps unfortunate that the word resonance has been used to characterize the motion in the vicinity of the critical inclination, merely because the equations resemble those of the motion in resonance regions in more complicated problems of celestial mechanics. There is no true resonance in the system, nor does the system have a true singularity at the critical inclination. The problem in this region may be compared with that of the mathematical pendulum that presents a point of indeterminateness and associated asymptotic solutions. Yet, with the aid of elliptic integrals or elliptic functions the solution can be expressed in terms of a single set of formulae for any set of critical data.

We shall now compare the satellite problem with that of the main problem of the lunar theory. For this problem the Hamiltonian may be put in the form

$$F = F_0\,(x_1,x_2) + \Sigma F_k\,(x_1,\rho_1,\rho_2,y_1,y_2,\omega_1,\omega_2),$$

a system of four degrees of freedom. By ignoring the inclination of the moon's orbit and the eccentricity of the sun's orbit, the problem can be reduced to two degrees of freedom with

$$F = F_0\,(x_1,x_2) + \Sigma F_k\,(x_2,y_1,y_2).$$

The equation for obtaining S_1 is

$$F_{0x_1}S_{1y_1} + F_{0x_2}S_{1y_2} + F_0 - F_1^* = 0. \tag{2}$$

This is a partial differential equation, while in Eq. (1) the partial differential equation has degenerated into an ordinary differential equation. As a consequence, in the artificial satellite problem the solution of S can be obtained in closed form—i.e., without requiring infinite series in the eccentricity. In the lunar theory the introduction of infinite series is unavoidable, simply because Eq. (2) is a partial differential equation. To sum up, in the solution of the main problem of artificial satellite theory infinite series in both the inclination and the eccentricity are unnecessary. Moreover, only a single small divisor appears.

The method of canonical variables is used to discuss the essential features of the problem. This particular method leads to the solution perhaps as quickly and as directly as any, but other methods may be used, just as for the lunar theory a variety of methods has been employed.

In general, the method of canonical variables is available for the solution of problems in celestial mechanics if the convergence in terms of the essential parameters of the problem is sufficient. If this is not so, other approaches may be more effective, but the general character of the solution can still be discussed by the method indicated.

Vinti's Potential

A special case of considerable interest is that of Vinti's potential, for which a solution of the satellite problem in closed form is available in terms of elliptic integrals. This problem has turned out to be analytically identical with the problem of the two fixed centers, known since Euler to be one of the integrable problems of dynamics. For this special potential no small divisors appear in the solution and the critical inclination does not exist. The coefficient of the fourth harmonic in the earth's potential appears to be about 40 or 50% greater than that required by Vinti's special potential. Yet it may be useful to employ Vinti's solution as an intermediary orbit, but the necessary detailed developments for such an application have not yet been published.

Atmospheric Drag

Introduction of atmospheric drag complicates the problem tremendously. Dr. Hori and the author made an effort to use canonical variables in the solution, treating the problem rigorously as a modification of the drag-free problem. Unfortunately, slowly convergent series appear. A device to overcome this lack of convergence is of limited effectiveness only. We succeeded, however, in establishing certain coupling effects between oblateness perturbations and drag. These coupling effects are not accessible by methods that treat the oblateness perturbations and the drag effect independently. These efforts by ourselves and others (I refer especially to Kinge-Hele and his associates) constitute a promising start. Further efforts are clearly necessary in order to achieve fully satisfactory analytical solutions.

The basic reasons for the relatively easy success within the short period of three years are, I think, twofold:

(a) The essential simplicity of the main problem of artificial satellite motion, which has been correctly called the simplest problem of celestial mechanics beyond the problem of two bodies.

(b) The fact that perturbation methods sufficed. Much of celestial mechanics of the past has consisted of the application of perturbation methods; and these methods, perfected over the past two centuries, were available for an effective attack on this problem.

Trajectories

When we deal with the problem of finding trajectories (say, from the earth to Venus or Mars, or from the earth to the moon) we find ourselves in an area in which the perturbation methods of celestial mechanics are of little or no help. The common feature of these problems is that the vehicle passes close to two singularities of the problem, while passage close to one singularity is enough to destroy the effectiveness of any typical perturbation method. As a consequence, it has been necessary to deal with these problems by the method of numerical integrations.

It is well known that for qualitative discussions of the problem of three bodies, and especially of the restricted problem, singularities have been removed by a transformation procedure known as regularization. So far, this procedure has never been used in quantitative problems dealing with trajectories. Regularized equations have a habit of looking frightfully complicated. Nevertheless, efforts in this direction may yield significant results.

Dr. Hori's recent solution of the hyperbolic case of artificial satellite motion is a step of a totally different character toward the solution of trajectory problems. He will discuss this in Chapter 15.3.

Numerical Integration

Let no one get the impression that the author looks down upon the method of numerical integration as an unavoidable evil. Far from it! Modern high-speed computers are so well adapted to numerical integration that it would be foolish not to take advantage of their possibilities to the fullest extent. Nevertheless, the method has its limitations and pitfalls. Its greatest drawback is the accumulation of error; this should always be kept in the mind of the programmer, and be allowed for in the interpretation of the results of a numerical integration.

Kovalevsky's Problem

From general considerations it is clear that a finite stretch of numerical integration of a set of ordinary differential equations must contain in latent form the information needed to construct a general solution, in the form of trigonometric series, of the mechanical problem that the equations represent.

Dr. Jean Kovalevsky made the first serious study of this problem and was successful in obtaining a general solution for the motion of Jupiter's eighth satellite that far exceeds the quality of previous efforts to construct such a theory by methods of perturbation theory. The limitation of his solution is that the motion of the perijove is so slow that it was necessary to ignore it. A stretch of 100 years of numerical integration data was simply inadequate to deal with a motion of the perijove that may be of the order of 15,000 years or more.

Kovalevsky's work is of interest not only because of its novelty, but also because it may well hold further promise toward the solution of difficult problems that are beyond our present ability to transform them to manageable forms.

15.3 The Hyperbolic Case of Artificial Satellite Motion

GEN-ICHIRO HORI

YALE UNIVERSITY OBSERVATORY, New Haven, Connecticut

I. Delaunay Variables in Hyperbolic Motion

The Delaunay variables in hyperbolic motion are

$$\begin{aligned} L &= -\sqrt{\mu a} & l &= nt + \text{const} \\ G &= \sqrt{\mu a(e^2 - 1)} & g &= \text{argument of perigee} \\ H &= \sqrt{\mu a(e^2 - 1)} \cos I & h &= \text{longitude of node.} \end{aligned} \tag{1}$$

Here a stands for the distance of the perigee from the center of the hyperbola; ae is the distance between the focus and the center; n is defined by $\mu = n^2a^3$; and I is the inclination of the orbit, the equatorial plane of the earth being the reference plane.

II. Equations of Motion

The equations of motion are

$$\begin{aligned} dL/dt &= \partial F/\partial l & dl/dt &= -\partial F/\partial L \\ dG/dt &= \partial F/\partial g & dg/dt &= -\partial F/\partial G \\ dH/dt &= \partial F/\partial h & dh/dt &= -\partial F/\partial H, \end{aligned} \tag{2}$$

with the Hamiltonian

$$F = F_0 + F_1,$$

where

$$F_0 = -\frac{\mu^2}{2L^2}$$

$$F_1 = \frac{\mu^4 k_2}{L^6}\left[\left(-\frac{1}{2} + \frac{3}{2}\frac{H^2}{G^2}\right)\frac{a^3}{r^3} + \left(\frac{3}{2} - \frac{3}{2}\frac{H^2}{G^2}\right)\frac{a^3}{r^3}\cos(2g + 2f)\right], \tag{3}$$

and where k_2 is a small parameter of the order of the second harmonic of the earth's potential. In Eq. (3), a^3/r^3 and $(a^3/r^3)\cos(2g + 2f)$ are understood as functions of the Delaunay variables by the following implicit relations:

$$\frac{a}{r} = \frac{1}{e \cosh u - 1}, \qquad \cos f = \frac{e - \cosh u}{e \cosh u - 1} \tag{4}$$
$$l = e \sinh u - u.$$

III. Canonical Transformation

Consider a canonical transformation $(L,G,H,l,g,h) \rightarrow (L',G',H',l',g',h')$, with the use of a generating function

$$S = L'l + G'g + H'h + S_1\,(L',G',H',l,g,-),$$

where a dash in S_1 indicates that the variable h is absent. A canonical transformation is then given by

$$\begin{aligned} L &= L' + (\partial S_1/\partial l) & l' &= l + (\partial S_1/\partial L') \\ G &= G' + (\partial S_1/\partial g) & g' &= g + (\partial S_1/\partial G') \\ H &= H' & h' &= h + (\partial S_1/\partial H'). \end{aligned} \tag{5}$$

The advantage of the use of a generating function is clear: with an arbitrary function S, Eqs. (5) give a canonical transformation, and we can concentrate our attention on determining the functional form of S in such a way that the new equations of motion, in the transformed variables, are easily handled.

In the case of elliptic motion, S is so determined that the new variables are mean values of the corresponding old variables. In hyperbolic motion, this procedure does not work simply because the variables have no mean values. An alternative procedure is available which is valid in the situation where, as t goes to infinity, r goes to infinity and therefore F_1 goes to zero. We can determine S in such a way that Eqs. (5) give a transformation

$$(L,G,H,l,g,h)_{t=t} \rightarrow (L,G,H,l,g,h)_{t=\pm\infty} = (L',G',H',l',g',h').$$

The new equations of motion are

$$\begin{aligned} dL'/dt &= \partial F^*/\partial l' & dl'/dt &= -\partial F^*/\partial L' \\ dG'/dt &= \partial F^*/\partial g' & dg'/dt &= -\partial F^*/\partial G' \\ dH'/dt &= \partial F^*/\partial h' & dh'/dt &= -\partial F^*/\partial H', \end{aligned} \tag{6}$$

with the new Hamiltonian, $F^* = -\mu^2/2L'^2$. Equations (6) can be immediately integrated to give

$$\begin{aligned} L' &= \text{const} & l' &= (-\mu^2/L'^3)t + l_0' \qquad (l_0' = \text{const}) \\ G' &= \text{const} & g' &= \text{const.} \\ H' &= \text{const} & h' &= \text{const.} \end{aligned} \tag{7}$$

IV. Determination of S_1

The energy integral

$$F_0(L) + F_1(L,G,H,l,g,-) = F^*(L') \tag{8}$$

will lead to the determination of S_1. Substitution of Eqs. (5) in Eq. (8) yields, after expansion in a Taylor's series,

$$F^* = F_0(L') = -\mu^2/2L'^2,$$
$$\frac{\partial F_0}{\partial L'}\frac{\partial S_1}{\partial l} + F_1(L',G',H',l,g,-) = 0,$$

or

$$\frac{\partial S_1}{\partial l} = -\frac{\mu^2 k_2}{L'^3}\left[\left(-\frac{1}{2}+\frac{3}{2}\frac{H'^2}{G'^2}\right)\frac{a^3}{r^3} + \left(\frac{3}{2}-\frac{3}{2}\frac{H'^2}{G'^2}\right)\frac{a^3}{r^3}\cos(2g+2f)\right].$$

Integration leads to

$$S_1 = \frac{\mu^2 k_2}{G'^3}\left\{\left(-\frac{1}{2}+\frac{3}{2}\frac{H'^2}{G'^2}\right)(f + e\sin f)\right.$$
$$\left. + \left(\frac{3}{2}-\frac{3}{2}\frac{H'^2}{G'^2}\right)\left[\frac{1}{2}\sin(2g+2f) + \frac{e}{2}\sin(2g+f) + \frac{e}{6}\sin(2g+3f)\right]\right\}$$
$$+ Z(L',G',H',g), \tag{9}$$

where the relation

$$dl = -\frac{L}{G}\frac{r^2}{a^2}\,df$$

was used in the integration.

The arbitrary function Z is determined by the relation

$$G_{t=\pm\infty} = G'. \tag{10}$$

In fact, Eq. (9) leads to

$$G = G' + \frac{\partial S_1}{\partial g}$$
$$= G' + \frac{\mu^2 k_2}{G'^3}\left(\frac{3}{2}-\frac{3}{2}\frac{H'^2}{G'^2}\right)\left[\cos(2g+2f) + e\cos(2g+f)\right.$$
$$\left. + \frac{e}{3}\cos(2g+3f)\right] + \frac{\partial Z}{\partial g}.$$

Condition (10) gives, if we prefer $t \to -\infty$ in order to fix the idea,

$$\frac{\partial Z}{\partial g} = -\frac{\mu^2 k_2}{G'^3}\left(\frac{3}{2}-\frac{3}{2}\frac{H'^2}{G'^2}\right)\left[\frac{\frac{2}{3}-e^2}{e^2}\cos 2g + \frac{\frac{2}{3}(e^2-1)^{3/2}}{e^2}\sin 2g\right]$$

or, by integration,

$$Z = \frac{\mu^2 k_2}{G'^3}\left(\frac{3}{2} - \frac{3}{2}\frac{H'^2}{G'^2}\right)\left[\frac{\frac{1}{3} - \frac{1}{2}e^2}{e^2}\sin 2g - \frac{\frac{1}{3}(e^2-1)^{3/2}}{e^2}\cos 2g\right] + Z_1(L'G'H'),$$

where Z_1 is another arbitrary function. By an analogous procedure, with the conditions

$$l_{t=-\infty} = l', \qquad g_{t=-\infty} = g',$$

we can determine Z_1 and then S_1 uniquely. The final result is

$$S_1 = \frac{\mu^2 k_2}{G'^3}\left\{\left(-\frac{1}{2} + \frac{3}{2}\frac{H'^2}{G'^2}\right)\left[f + e\sin f + (e^2-1)^{1/2}\right.\right.$$
$$\left. + \tan^{-1}\frac{1}{(e^2-1)^{1/2}} - \tfrac{3}{2}\pi\right]$$
$$+ \left(\frac{3}{2} - \frac{3}{2}\frac{H'^2}{G'^2}\right)\left[\frac{1}{2}\sin(2g+2f) + \frac{e}{2}\sin(2g+f) + \frac{e}{6}\sin(2g+3f)\right.$$
$$\left.\left. + \left(\frac{1}{2} - \frac{1}{3e^2}\right)\sin 2g + \frac{1}{3e^2}(e^2-1)^{3/2}\cos 2g\right]\right\}.$$

As far as the first-order perturbations are concerned, the solution is given by

$$L = L' + \left(\frac{\partial S_1}{\partial l}\right)_{\substack{l\to l'\\ g\to g'}} \qquad l = l' - \left(\frac{\partial S_1}{\partial L'}\right)_{\substack{l\to l'\\ g\to g'}}$$

$$G = G' + \left(\frac{\partial S_1}{\partial g}\right)_{\substack{l\to l'\\ g\to g'}} \qquad g = g' - \left(\frac{\partial S_1}{\partial G'}\right)_{\substack{l\to l'\\ g\to g'}}$$

$$H = H' \qquad h = h' - \left(\frac{\partial S_1}{\partial G'}\right)_{\substack{l\to l'\\ g\to g'}},$$

with L', G', H', l'_0, g', h' as six constants of integration.

V. Concluding Remarks

The hyperbolic case of artificial satellite motion is an example of an application of von Zeipel's method of canonical variables. It is remarkable that this single method is applicable for such a variety of problems as oblateness perturbations, drag problems, lunar and solar perturbations of artificial satellite motion, and also for lunar and planetary problems in the solar system.

15.4 *Dynamical Astronomy and Artificial Members of the Solar System*

P. J. MESSAGE

GONVILLE AND CAIUS COLLEGE, Cambridge, England

In the past, dynamical astronomy, like other branches of astronomy, has been an observational rather than an experimental science, in the sense that the bodies whose motions have been studied have been out of the control of dynamical astronomers. Those particular orbits which are taken up by the natural members of the solar system have been in the focus of interest. Their study has received the attentions of the great mathematicians of the past who have made contributions to this subject, to the almost complete exclusion of other possible motions, and with the result that our knowledge of possible motions under the Newtonian law is concentrated on a few cases.

With the launching of artificial satellites, however, this limitation of interest has been breached. The study of the motions of these bodies has focused interest on new problems in celestial mechanics. As one result, the development of new methods has been stimulated; and as another, there have been brought to light hitherto unknown and unsuspected features of motion under the Newtonian law of gravitation, for example, the special behavior of the solutions near the critical inclination, about which Dr. Brouwer has just told us.

Now, the perturbation of the orbits of these bodies from the elliptic form is governed almost entirely by the departure of the earth's external gravitational potential from that of a spherically symmetrical body, and by the resisting effect of the atmosphere—the so-called "air drag." The first of these kinds of perturbations, that due to the oblateness of the central body, does appear in the motions of the satellites of Jupiter and Saturn, and in that of our own moon; but it is of very small relative importance in these cases, except for the fifth satellite of Jupiter. Even in this case, however, the oblateness perturbations are small enough for their computations to be a relatively simple matter. The eccentricity of the orbit is so small as not to be capable of being measured with any precision, so that the only important secular effect of the oblateness is in the regression of the node. In the case of the artificial earth satellites, however, the oblateness perturbation is very large, and it dominates the secular motions of the node and perigee. Its study has given rise to a large number of investigations using many varied lines of approach, many of them quite novel, and leading to several conclusions of interest. Of investigations making use of coordinates of the satellite as dependent variables, we may note that of King-Hele (1958), who uses spherical polar coordinates and takes as independent variable the longitude of the satellite measured in a mean orbit plane from the line of nodes. The resulting expressions have the merit of direct applicability to observations, without the use of intermediate quantities. But since the long period effects are essentially represented by the first term or two of their power series expansions, truncation errors increase as time elapses, and new values of the coefficients must be supplied from time to time. The derivation of the expressions to the first and second orders in J is quite simple, but for higher orders it becomes increasingly complicated as compared to other methods. The use of the radius vector r as one of the variables will be appropriate in the study of more distant satellites (for example, the proposed 24-hr satellite), for which this quantity may not be determined to so great a relative accuracy as are the angular coordinates. Therefore, fewer terms need be computed in the theory.

The use of rectangular cartesian coordinates (Brouwer, 1958) also has the merit of direct applicability to observations, and also the demerit of comparative difficulty of derivation of higher order perturbations.

On the other hand, use may be made of the elements of the osculating elliptic orbit as intermediate quantities, making use of Lagrange's equations for the time rates of change of these elements as in most of the classical investigations of planetary and satellite motion. This approach has been used by many authors. The essence of the method is described by Sterne in Chapter 5 of his "Introduction to Celestial Mechanics." It has been used in the construction of general theories by Merson (1961), by Zhongolovitch (1960), and Kozai (1959) *inter alia*, and in the discussion of special cases by, e.g., Izsak (1961a) and Kozai (1961). This method requires that the disturbing function be developed as d'Alembert series in terms of these elements and it uses intermediate quantities. But, on the other hand, the expressions are valid for longer periods of time than those more easily derived directly in the coordinates; and the long-period, short-period, and secular parts (those linearly increasing with time) may be much more easily discriminated. It is easier, also, to derive general results for the first order perturbations due to higher order harmonics in the earth's potential.

Many new developments in the use of the canonical equations of dynamics have arisen from the study of artificial satellite motions. The application of von Zeipel's method, which enables the short-period, long-period, and secular problems to be treated separately as far as terms of the first and second order are concerned, provides a solution valid for a relatively long time range. This was done by Brouwer (1959) for values of the inclination not close to the critical one, making use of Delaunay's canonical variables, and afterwards by Hori (1960) for inclinations in this vicinity. Garfinkel (1959) and Vinti (1959) have obtained a first approximation to the motion by solving the Hamilton-Jacobi equation with part of the potential due to the oblateness included. The method of variation of parameters is then applied. Garfinkel found a solution closely analogous to the solution of the Kepler problem, in which elliptic functions appear in place of the circular functions arising in the solution of the familiar Kepler problem. Vinti discovered that if a particular relation holds between the coefficients of different harmonics in the earth's potential, then the difficulties associated with the critical inclination do not appear.

The "air drag" perturbations are responsible for a secular diminution of the major semiaxis and the eccentricity. They have not proved so fruitful of elegant methods of solutions as those due to the figure, largely because the problem they pose is not capable of such simple mathematical formulation. Indeed, the observations have provided us with much information about the distribution of matter in the atmosphere. They have shown that it varies quite considerably with time, and they have verified its exponential decay with height, as predicted from the assumption of adiabatic equilibrium. The computation of these perturbations in practical cases is largely an empirical matter, although Brouwer and Hori (1961) have designed a theory, making use of Delaunay's canonical variables, on the supposition that the density is not time-dependent.

As more artificial bodies are launched into new kinds of orbit, the new problems which will arise will almost certainly lead to the discovery of new properties of solutions of the many-body problem. The motion of lunar and planetary probes both present the problem of orbits with large eccentricities which are subject to large perturbations, for example.

Now, one of the main tasks of celestial mechanics is the estimation of various parameters which determine the motion of the bodies of the solar system—for example, the masses of the planets and satellites, as well as the elements of their orbits, and the quantities specifying the figure of every body whose oblateness is dynamically important. The actual orbits in which the natural members of the solar system happen to move has hitherto placed an upper limit to the precision with which these parameters could be determined. With the launching of bodies into new types of orbit, however, new precision is placed within our reach. This is exemplified by the determinations of the coefficients of the leading spherical harmonics in the earth's external potential; these have been derived from observations of artificial satellites, to more than six times the accuracy formerly attained. It had previously been known that a close satellite was capable of providing important information about the figure of the parent planet, this being instanced by the case of the fifth satellite of Jupiter, already mentioned. Its mean distance from the center of the planet is rather less than three times the radius of the planet ($a \sim 112{,}000$ miles, equatorial radius = 44,350 miles, polar radius = 41,400 miles). The oblateness of Jupiter causes the line of nodes to regress by about 2°5101 per day, which is close to 1/288 of the mean motion n of the satellite. In the case of the earth, however, the best determination of the oblateness was previously that derived from surface gravity measures. From a discussion of these by Jeffreys (1943) the value of the coefficient (J_2) of the second spherical harmonic in the earth's external gravitational potential was determined to be $(1091 \pm 1) \times 10^{-6}$. ($J_n$ is the coefficient of $(GM/R)(R/r)^{n+1}P_n$ in the potential, where R is the earth's equatorial radius.) The best determination from astronomical sources was that derived from certain periodic terms in the moon's motion; it has an uncertainty about five times that from the gravity measures. The values given by King-Hele (1961), from a discussion of many satellite observations, are

$$
\begin{aligned}
J_2 &= (1082.79 \pm 0.15) \times 10^{-6} \\
J_3 &= (-2.4 \pm 0.3) \times 10^{-6} \\
J_4 &= (-1.4 \pm 0.2) \times 10^{-6} \\
J_5 &= (-0.1 \pm 0.1) \times 10^{-6} \\
J_6 &= (0.9 \pm 0.8) \times 10^{-6}.
\end{aligned}
$$

Thus, the third and fourth harmonics also have significant coefficients. The existence of the third harmonic makes it clear that the distribution of matter within the earth is not consistent with the hypothesis of hydrostatic equilibrium. Recently Izsak (1961b) has made a first determination of the coefficient of the leading longitude-dependent term; $J_{22} = (-19.26 \pm 1.74) \times 10^{-5}$.

In addition to making use of the new orbits taken up by artificial bodies launched for other purposes, it is also within our power now to design experiments with celestial mechanical objectives in view. Thus, with regard to the question of determining the coefficients of the longitude-dependent terms in the earth's potential, if we could have a satellite whose orbital period is commensurable with the earth's rotation, then the longitude-dependent terms in the earth's potential would give rise to perturbations of augmented amplitude. Thus, a body moving in an orbit with period of very nearly 24 hr would possibly be able to provide us with much more information about such harmonics.

A body revolving about the moon, in its close vicinity, would also be of interest. Its period of revolution would give a direct determination of the mass of the moon, and the secular rates of motion of its node and pericentre would give two pieces of data on the figure of the moon, which would be of interest in the study of its internal constitution. (The present values of the constants of the figure are in conflict with the hydrostatic hypothesis.) Eventually, perhaps the same information could be obtained for the planets Venus and Mercury, by putting artificial satellites about them. Certainly a space probe passing near to any planet would provide a means of determining the mass of that planet. The requirement in all these cases is that the position of the artificial body be determinable with a fair precision relative to the natural body under study.

Finally, it may be remarked that an artificial planet with a large eccentricity and small major semiaxis, such as one projected from the earth in the opposite direction to the earth's with a speed close to the earth's orbital speed, could provide a further test of the general theory of relativity.

References

Brouwer, D. (1958), *Astron. J.* **63,** 433.
Brouwer, D. (1959), *Astron. J.* **64,** 378.
Brouwer, D., and Hori, G.-I. (1961), *Astron. J.* **66,** 193.
Garfinkel, B. (1959), *Astron. J.* **64,** 353.
Hori, G.-I. (1960), *Astron. J.* **65,** 291.
Izsak, I. M. (1961a), *Astron. J.* **66,** 129.
Izsak, I. M. (1961b), *Astron. J.* **66,** 226.
Jeffreys, H. (1943), *Monthly Notices Roy. Astron. Soc. Geophys. Suppl.* **5,** 55.
King-Hele, D. G. (1958), *Proc. Roy. Soc.* **A247,** 49.
King-Hele, D. G. (1961), *Geophys. J.* **4,** 1.
Kozai, Y. (1959), *Astron. J.* **64,** 367.
Kozai, Y. (1961), *Astron. J.* **66,** 132.
Merson, R. H. (1961), *Geophys. J.* **4,** 17.
Vinti, J. P. (1959), *J. Research Natl. Bur. Standards* **63B,** 105.
Zhongolovitch, J. D. (1960), *Bull. Inst. Theoret. Astron.* **7,** 521.

15.5 Determination of Ephemeris Time with an Artificial Satellite

JEAN KOVALEVSKY

BUREAU DES LONGITUDES, Paris, France

In order to define a gravitational time unit and scale, one has to provide both of the following:

(1) a body moving in a gravitational field, and

(2) a theory of the motion of this body, as a function of a certain independent variable, called "time," and as derived from the usual differential equations of celestial mechanics. The observations of the body, and the comparison of these observations with the theory, provide the time.

In the case of ephemeris time, which is the best approximation to gravitational time that astronomers can *define* (but maybe not *observe*), the body is the sun, and the theory of its motion is due to Newcomb. This provides a time scale and a unit, defined at a certain instant. However, the theory also provides a relation between this defined unit and any other measured time interval.

Since the apparent motion of the sun is slow, such a clock is bound to be observationally imprecise. But if one can take another, faster, clock, and relate it to the basic one, the problem is solved. Since the apparent mean motion of the moon is 12.5 times larger, it is clear that the observations of the moon might provide us with a more precise time, *provided that the lunar theory can be exactly related to the definition of ephemeris time*. So, such a secondary clock will consist of:

(1) a body: the moon;

(2) a theory: Brown's "improved lunar theory"; and

(3) a formula relating the argument of this theory with the argument of the solar theory by Newcomb. In the case of the moon, such a relation has been derived by Spencer Jones. But the time so obtained is the ephemeris time only within the errors of the theory of the moon and of this relation.*

* In the Berkeley meetings of the I.A.U. this particular time, measured with the moon, and which is a first approximation to ephemeris time, has been named E.T.O.

Such a relatively fast moving object as the moon provides us with (UT) — (ET) within a few hundredths of a second, but it gives only the mean difference for a whole year. All short period variations are smoothed down in these results. Other observational techniques, based upon comparison with atomic time, have shown that this is a coarse smoothing, and that it would be highly desirable to improve the frequency and precision of such determinations.

Even if, in some years, atomic time is to replace ephemeris time as our standard, celestial mechanics and space travel will still use the former, and therefore its determination will always be needed. Furthermore, comparison between ephemeris time (or, actually, any gravitational time) and atomic time might provide interesting cosmological data. It is therefore of a great importance that a better clock than the moon be set up in the future.

An artificial earth satellite, with precise specifications, is the only solution. This will provide us with a suitable body, for which a theory of the motion and its relation with the solar and lunar motion could be derived after a sufficient number of years of observation. Then, this will be a new, precise clock giving a new, better approximation to ephemeris time.

The characteristics of such a satellite should be such that the following requirements are fulfilled.

(1) The satellite should be easily observed from everywhere on the earth.

(2) As few as possible corrections for systematic nongravitational effects should have to be made.

(3) No irregular or unpredictable variations of its motion should exist of the order of magnitude of the required precision for at least 100 years.

(4) The mean motion should be larger than the moon's mean motion, but not too large, in order to make possible very precise observational techniques.

(5) For the same observational reasons, it should be bright and, hence, large.

Most of the first four requirements would be met with a spherical satellite revolving outside the outer Van Allen belt. A 24-hr satellite should, however, be avoided, since it will not be observable from every station, and its theory will depend too much upon our knowledge of the ellipticity of the earth's equator.

A 22- or 28-hr satellite with a small inclination and small (nonvanishing) eccentricity seems optimum. The third and fifth requirements are, however, somewhat contradictory. If one supposes that the satellite has the surface brightness of Echo I, a diameter of 60 meters is needed to produce a 6th magnitude satellite. For 8th magnitude, which is the faintest admissible, the diameter would still have to be 25 meters.

But such a large body will be very sensitive to nongravitational effects, unless it has a large mass. The most important of such effects is due to random meteoric impacts. Unless a very careful study be made on the probable mass (or energy) change due to such impacts, one should give the satellite such a mass that *no measurable* change in its mean motion occurs in at least 100 years. The launching of 2 or 3 of such satellites might eliminate possible effects of the improbable meteors of large mass.

The difference between atomic and gravitational time might be of the order of 10^{-11}. Therefore, the energy integral should be defined with the same accuracy over the same one hundred years. If there is a yearly asymmetry of meteoric impacts equivalent to a drag by 0.01 mg flowing at a speed of 30 km/sec, such a requirement would necessitate a mass of 10,000 tons for a 60-meter satellite, or 1500 tons for one of 25 meters.

These large figures, beyond our technical possibilities, are based on a very rough estimate from a figure of 4 $gm/km^2/year$ of meteoric dust with an average speed of 30 km/sec. However, precise preliminary measurements of the meteoric flow in magnitude, direction, and energy might give us an estimate of this equivalent mass within 10%. In this case, the preceding masses of the satellites could be divided by a factor of 10. If we adopt the figure of 300 tons for a 25-meter satellite, provided that the preceding figures are confirmed with the quoted precision, one arrives at a more satisfactory figure. However, it is still very important to keep in mind this order of magnitude of the mass if such an artificial satellite is to be launched for this purpose. Three hundred tons would actually represent a 6-cm thick aluminum shell, or a 2.5-cm thick iron shell.*

It seems that other statistical effects (solar radiation pressure, etc.) should cancel out on the whole, but they should be carefully studied before deciding upon a minimum mass of the satellite.

In conclusion, even if there might be some theoretical difficulties in quickly linking this clock to ephemeris time, a set of two or three such satellites will provide the best possible check for gravitational theory, for the comparison of atomic and gravitational times, and also for studying relativity effects.

* In discussions during this symposium, with Dr. Siry and others, it appeared that the methods proposed to solve this mass problem with appropriate instrumentation on the satellite are not adequate, due to the unreliability of such techniques over a century. A metallic sphere seems to be, in my mind, the only adequate approach to the long-range problems in connection with time (that is, actually, to all such problems).

15.6 *Informal Remarks on the Venus Radar Experiment*

EBERHARDT RECHTIN

JET PROPULSION LABORATORY, Pasadena, California

Dr. Herrick has pointed out the determination of the ratio of the astronomical unit to the kilometer has varied considerably in past years. Our organization, the Jet Propulsion Laboratory, has a particular interest in an accurate determination of the distance to Venus in order that we might guide our space probes to that target. More precisely, we were interested in determining the ratio of the astronomical unit to a more measurable metric, the radar light microsecond (rather than to a kilometer). We make this distinction because our guidance techniques use radio range and Doppler velocity of the space probe, not meter bars, to perform navigation. A set of range and velocity coordinates of our target in the same metric would therefore permit us to solve our guidance equations in a consistent set of units. For simplification in this discussion, however, we will convert from the radar light microsecond to kilometers by assuming that we know the velocity of the radar wave in the medium to somewhat greater accuracy (1:300,000) than the value of the astronomical unit expressed in kilometers (1:100,000).

Although astronomers some years ago had presumably determined the ephemerides of both Venus and the earth in angular coordinates to a high degree of precision, the measurements of distance (i.e., the ratio of the astronomical unit to the kilometer) were controversial. Some astronomers maintain that distances were known to a part in 10^5, other astronomers maintain to a part in 10^4, and still others maintain to a part in 10^3. What was worse, each group of astronomers apparently based their conclusions on much the same data.

If the angular motions of the planets were very well known, then any accurate velocity or range measurement in the solar system should complete the information we need to guide a space probe from the earth to Venus. (As it turned out, the angular motions were imprecise, too.) We decided to use the NASA/JPL Goldstone Space Communications Station, consisting of two 85-ft diameter antennas separated by seven miles of rugged terrain, as a bistatic CW radar to try to make the appropriate range or velocity measurements. The easiest radar target, other than the moon, was the planet Venus. Although we often used the moon as a checkout target for our radar equipment, its motions were so complex and its size was so large compared to its distance from us, that it did not make a suitable target for determining an accurate distance within the solar system.

Because we were interested in Doppler effect as well as range, we went to a great deal of trouble to make an extremely stable transmitter. It had to be extremely stable in frequency so that no drifts would occur in the transmitter while the signal was travelling to and from Venus, and it also had to be extremely stable in phase. Phase instability would have put jitter on the signal which could then confuse us badly on any measurement of a Doppler spread which we might expect due to rotation of a reasonably rough-surfaced planet. Because of the uncertainties in earlier radar attempts to see the planet Venus, we decided to construct our electronics so that we would obtain essentially real time indications that we were truly observing the planet. We put a television camera on our radio telescope and watched Venus in the center of our screen throughout the observation whenever weather conditions permitted. During the early phases of our experiment, we even pointed our transmitting antenna toward and then away from the planet a few degrees, waited an appropriate time interval, and then observed the appearance and disappearance of the received signal.

A difficulty in choosing Venus as an appropriate radar target was that the radar characteristics of the planet were not known. The rotational period of the planet was not known. Its surface roughnes, reflectivity, and depolarization characteristics were not known. Our first idea had been that the planet might be radar absorbing, rough, and rotating; and that consequently there would be quite some Doppler spread in a weak return signal. If the planet rotates as rapidly as the earth, we would have expected the Doppler spread of at least 10 kc/sec at our operating frequency of 2388 Mc/sec. Consequently, we had wide band (200 cps) filters quite comparable to those of the Russians (60 cps). The reflection coefficient was not known, and therefore we had a variety of detection schemes from multi-minute integrators to comparatively high speed phase-locked radio receivers. We planned to measure range by a variety of techniques including gating the transmitter and receiver off and on in various ways and at various switching rates. We also incorporated a pseudo-random switching code to remove ambiguities in the range measurement.

The first date that the radar was turned on and aimed at the planet Venus was March 10, 1961. That was the first time we thought that the planet was close enough to make observations worthwhile. The closest approach to the planet would be on April 10, one month later. We obtained a usable signal return almost immediately, although its unexpected characteristics caused us to take several hours to determine exactly what was happening. The first unexpected characteristic was that the returning Doppler shift did not agree with what it should have been using the Rabe astronomical unit. The measured frequency was consistently higher, indicating a larger value of the astronomical unit. Using this Doppler determination as a scaling factor, we scaled up the distances in the solar system so that Venus would be at least 10,000 km farther away than MIT and Jodrell Bank had stated it to be from earlier radar attempts in 1958.

The second unexpected characteristic was that of the Doppler spread, which we had anticipated as being many kc/sec was considerably less than 200 cps, so that much of the filter equipment which we had built had to be discarded. We therefore built spectral analysis equipment which was sensitive to frequency changes on the order of a few cycles per second, and, very rapidly, by a combination of filter banks, synchronous phase-lock receivers, and spectral density equipments—a variety of different techniques—we showed that the Doppler spread was less than 10 cps. Occasionally it was 12 cps, and often it was only 5 cps. This extremely narrow Doppler spread had two immediate consequences. The first consequence was that the returning signal was concentrated in a very narrow bandwidth and thus was much easier to detect against a background of noise than if it had been spread out across the spectrum by the differential Doppler shifts of a rough and rotating planet. The strong signal meant that we could obtain the value of the astronomical unit in light microseconds to a higher precision than we had anticipated originally. The extremely narrow bandwidth of the return signal also meant that we could lock our phase-lock radio receivers without difficulty and obtain continuous Doppler records for hours at a time. Using both regularly sampled Doppler and the so-called "integrated Doppler" (the Doppler measurement using a continuous counter so that roundoff error is not incurred), it was possible to measure the Doppler shift to a precision of about one part in 10^5. Using this kind of precision, and making periodic checks on our transmitter stability, we convinced ourselves that the scale factor of the solar system could not be the value given by Rabe. We then began ranging experiments. By this time, of course, we did not believe in anyone's astronomical unit, even our own. So, instead of just switching our transmitter on and off eight times a second in good faith, which was what Kotelnikov did in Russia, we experimented by switching very slowly, increasing our switching rate, and then using our pseudo-random code. We again found out that the range to the planet Venus was greater than had been predicted. Once again we had a consistent first order effect. The signal-to-noise ratio was quite high, at 10 db, throughout the system so that, in contrast to earlier radar experiments, ours required no elaborate statistical detection techniques.

At about this time, the MIT Lincoln Laboratory radar was also beginning to obtain reflections. The MIT system was about 10 db less sensitive than the Goldstone radar, but nonetheless they immediately confirmed that the astronomical unit had to be greater than previously indicated. They also noted that the depth of reflection from Venus was somewhat less than 100 km.

Our efforts at refining the value of the astronomical unit in light microseconds, however, now began to run into difficulties. There was very little question in our mind about the quality of the measurements themselves. But, when we attempted to put these measurements into a computer which was using the published ephemerides of the earth and Venus, we found that the corresponding calculation of the value of the astronomical unit was not the same from day to day. Not being experts in this branch of astronomy ourselves, we enlisted the help of some of the best experts in this field, Dr. Clemence of the Naval Observatory, and Professor Brouwer of the Yale Observatory. In inspecting the results of the computer calculation in detail, we found that the point to point coordinates of the ephemerides were very rough in comparison to the precision with which we could make Doppler and radar measurements. Furthermore, the apparent value of the astronomical unit from day to day seemed to be following a consistent curve. As it turned out, this *should* have been the case with the ephemerides which we were using. The Naval Observatory then supplied us with better ephemerides, incorporating Duncombe's corrections, which considerably reduced the apparent day by day change in the astronomical unit. Duncombe's corrections, incidentally, are concerned with angular differences of only a few tenths of a second of arc. The results of our calculations to date are given in Table I.

The apparent radar cross section of Venus was determined to be 11% plus or minus 2% of the geometric cross section. Its small scale (12 cm) roughness is similar to that of the moon. Our experimental results strongly, but not yet positively, indicate a rotational period of 200 to 400 earth days, suggesting a rotational period of 225 days or one Venus year. Of all of the measurements, the rotational period of Venus is the least certain.

In comparing our results with others, we find that both MIT and Jodrell Bank in measurements made in 1961 concur within measurement errors with our determination of the astronomical unit. They also agree on the reflectivity. We disagree sharply with the preliminary Russian value of the astronomical unit, even when it is corrected for ambiguities; however, the measurement errors of the Russian experiment have not yet been published, and consequently it is possible that the final report on the Russian experiment will show closer correspondence to the measurement by JPL, MIT, and Jodrell Bank. We did not observe any of the phenomena reported by the Russians which would indicate a rotational period as rapid as 9 to 11 days. Indeed, with the roughness factor

TABLE I
THE ASTRONOMICAL UNIT

Type of data	From Newcomb ephemerides (km)	From Duncombe corrections (km)
Closed-loop range[a,b]	149,598,862 ± 488	149,598,567 ± 470
Open-loop range	149,598,823 ± 41	149,598,701 ± 200
Doppler velocity[b] (before conjunction)	149,597,300 ± 200	149,598,700 ± 200
Doppler velocity (after conjunction)	149,599,500 ± 500	149,598,000 ± 500
Integrated Doppler (after conjunction)	149,599,700 ± 600	149,598,400 ± 600
JPL best estimate (July 1961)	149,598,500 ± 500	

[a] Radius of Venus: 6100 km.
[b] Speed of light: 299,792.5 km/sec.

(determined by depolarization measurements) apparently comparable to that of the moon at 12 cm, and with a rotational period of 9 to 11 days, it is highly unlikely that our phase-locked synchronous receivers would have worked at all. However, as remarked before, the rotational period is less certain than the other results. With increased radar sensitivity in the future, it should be possible to do a spectral analysis of the depolarized signal (a signal more sensitive to reflections from the limbs of the planet than to the center face), and consequently to resolve this dilemma as well.

GENERAL REFERENCES

1. Radar exploration of Venus, Tech. Rept. No. 32-132, Jet Propulsion Laboratory (August 1, 1961) (available on request).
2. Academician Kotelnikov, Russian Venus radar experiment, Presented at the 1961 British Institution of Radio Engineers Convention, Oxford, England.

CHAPTER 16

Comets

16.1 Objectives of Space Investigations of Comets

P. SWINGS

INSTITUT D'ASTROPHYSIQUE, Liège, Belgium

Comets are interesting objects from various points of view. The interpretation of their spectroscopic and photometric behavior requires considerations on low-temperature physics, fluorescence, photochemistry, and sublimation. Many observed phenomena have not yet received a convincing explanation. Yet the comets may eventually furnish essential data on the formation and evolution of the solar system.

What are the known essential characteristics of comets? The atoms, molecules and solid particles of the head and tail originate in a nucleus consisting of ices of various compounds, such as H_2O, NH_3, CO_2, etc., with an admixture of "meteoritic" material (metals, silicates, etc.). The gaseous molecules in the head and tail are radicals (neutral in the head: CN, CH, OH, NH, C_2, C_3, NH_2; ionized in the tail: CO^+, N_2^+, CO_2^+) which result from the photodissociation of stable parent molecules (H_2O, NH_3, CO_2) or from chemical reactions near the surface of the nucleus, or which were imbedded in the cold matrix. They emit the observed characteristic electronic spectra by a fluorescence mechanism excited by the electromagnetic radiation of the sun. They have a limited life, and eventually become photodissociated or photoionized. The atomic lines (essentially the D-doublet of Na) are emitted only at small heliocentric distances. The solid particles in the head and tail scatter the solar radiation and give rise to the continuous cometary spectrum; their nature and sizes are still unknown. The gaseous densities in the head and tail are so low that no thermodynamic equilibrium prevails; the intensity distribution within the observed bands lead to vibrational and rotational "temperatures" which have widely differing values for different molecules (from 50° to 4000°K!) and which are thus purely artificial.

How can we progress in our knowledge of the comets? To be sure, we have not yet fully exploited the observational possibilities from the surface of the earth. We still need spectroscopic observations with higher resolution; photometric and polarization measurements of greater accuracy, covering specific wavelength ranges; and better direct photographs in well defined spectral regions. Renewed efforts in the radio-range are desirable. However, the solution of various essential problems requires information which only space probes and satellites can provide.

We shall not envisage here the improvements in resolution of the photographs which may be obtained from outside the terrestrial atmosphere, especially from high-altitude balloons; although pictures with higher resolution would help in interpreting various phenomena occurring in the head and tail of comets, particularly in the close neighborhood of the nucleus.

We shall rather consider the following four space experiments, and find out what kind of information they would provide:

(a) the extension of the accessible spectral region;
(b) experiments with rockets releasing gases such as NH_3, CO_2;
(c) experiments with an orbiting artificial comet nucleus;
(d) comet probes.

From the considerations which follow it will be obvious that these space experiments will be fully efficient only if laboratory investigations are conducted simultaneously.

(a) Extension of the Covered Spectral Region toward the Vacuum Ultraviolet and the Infrared

It is reasonable to assume that the cometary emissions which will be found in the far ultraviolet are excited by the same fluorescence mechanism, as are the usual cometary bands of the ordinary region.* The ultraviolet region offers a possibility to discover cometary molecules and atoms which have their resonance transitions below λ 3000 Å. This is the case for H_2, N_2, O_2, N, O, C. On account of the weakness of the available solar energy† the far ultraviolet cometary spectrum will certainly be faint compared to the visual region.

Important differences arise in the excited emissions. In the region

* Absorption of far ultraviolet radiation leading to ionization (such as has been observed for N_2 in the laboratory) probably does not give rise to far ultraviolet cometary emissions.

† The ultraviolet region $\lambda < 3000$ Å contains only 1% of the total amount of solar energy.

3000 > λ > 1700 Å the exciting solar radiation is mainly the continuum; of course the profiles of the corresponding excited bands will be distorted by the solar absorption and emission lines. This distortion may be more pronounced than in the usual range, on account of the greater number of absorption lines, and also because of the presence of emissions, such as Si II. But shortward of λ 1500 Å the exciting solar radiation is mainly in the form of discrete lines, plus the Lyman-, He I-, and He II-continua. If cometary emissions are excited by radiations λ < 1500 Å they will thus not be real bands, but discrete resonance series, at least if secondary effects are not involved. There is a narrow spectral region in which the solar continuum and the solar discrete emissions may play an equal role. It is clear also that excitation by discrete solar emissions will be very sensitive to the radial velocity of the sun relative to the comet; in particular the ultraviolet pre- and postperihelion spectra of a comet may be entirely different.

At the 1960 Liège symposium we considered the neutral or ionized molecules or radicals which may be found in the ultraviolet, and described what the structure of their spectra should be. For example, we know that the N_2 molecules of the telluric atmosphere absorb the Ly-γ-emission of the sun. If we assume that the comets contain a sufficient number of N_2-molecules in the proper rotational level, these will also absorb solar Ly-γ and give rise to a discrete triplet-resonance series, consisting of the $P(6)$, $Q(5)$, and $R(4)$ transitions in the $(2 - v'')$ $(v'' = 0,1,2, \ldots)$ bands of the $b^1\Pi_u$–$X^1\Sigma_g^+$ system. Dr. Nicholls has kindly computed the relative intensities within this series; the intensity decrease with increasing v'' is very slow, so that the available energy will be distributed among many triplets which will presumably all be very weak. Other similar discrete resonance series may be excited in other molecules. It is likely that unexpected results will be found, as it is impossible to predict certain phenomena, as in the case of H_2. Refer to the Proceedings of the Liège symposium for details, and also to Appendix II of this chapter.

What should we expect to find in the near infrared region of cometary spectra? Essentially this region is characterized by vibration-rotation transitions of molecules. We may hope to find the fundamental (1-0) transitions of the radicals which are observed in the usual region; of other diatomic molecules such as CO; of certain probable parent molecules such as NH_3, CO_2, H_2O, . . .; and of intermediate radicals, such as CH_2 or CH_3. However we do not know the excitation mechanisms which prevail. If the vibration-rotation bands are excited by fluorescence only, they will be extremely weak, since the integrated solar energy for λ >

$2.5\ \mu$ represents only 2% of the total solar energy, and since the transition probabilities of the vibration-rotation bands are low compared to the usual electronic transitions. However, other mechanisms may play a major role for these emissions of low energy. For example, after the emission of the (0-1) band of the $^2\Sigma \rightarrow {}^2\Sigma$ electronic system of CN, the CN-radicals will be left on the $v'' = 1$ level of the ground electronic state, from which they will emit the fundamental (1-0) vibration band if they are not de-excited by another electronic absorption. Moreover, the vibration bands may also be excited by other mechanisms which release small amounts of energy, such as "flames."

Part of these infrared observations could be made from high-altitude balloons or aircraft. Predicted wavelengths are compiled in Appendix I of this chapter.

(b) Experiments with Rockets Releasing Gases which are Expected to Be Stable Parent Molecules in Comets

This release should be performed at altitudes such that the gases would be exposed to pure solar effects, without undue interference from the atmospheric constituents or from the Van Allen belts.

Among the most interesting gases we should mention NH_3, CO_2, H_2O, C_2H_2. It would probably be possible to obtain, from the ground, spectroscopic and photometric observations which would provide valuable information on the photodissociation and excitation of these gases by the solar radiation. Eventually such experiments may be of interest in fields other than the comets: for example, in photochemistry, or even in the investigation of the interplanetary space.

In the preparation of this experiment a valuable guide may be found in the numerous experiments performed with sodium- and other clouds.

(c) Experiments with an Orbiting Artificial Comet Nucleus

The theoretical mass loss rates from spheres of ices of H_2O, NH_3, CO_2, etc., by sublimation in vacuum, agree within a factor of approximately 10 at a heliocentric distance $r = 1$ a.u. These loss rates are sufficiently small so that an artificial icy conglomerate comet nucleus of about 1 ton could probably live for several days. A first artificial nucleus should probably be made of a single kind of ice, such as CO_2 or NH_3. Eventually an artificial "Whipple nucleus" should be made of a mixture of ices of the probable parent molecules (H_2O, NH_3, CO_2) with an addition of meteoritic material. The density should be low, of the order of 0.1 to 0.5. While it is fairly easy to estimate the mass loss rate for a sphere of pure H_2O ice, only a rough approximation can be estimated for a porous conglomerate of heterogeneous snows, with an addition of meteoritic particles and possibly solid hydrates.

This project has been discussed on various occasions with European colleagues in the course of the last year, and suggested to the European space research committee a few months ago. I understand that it has also been envisaged in the U.S., especially by Dr. B. Donn at the Goddard Space Flight Center of NASA. A 1-ton orbiting artificial nucleus would probably release enough gaseous molecules to give rise to an observable artificial cometary head which could be studied spectroscopically and photometrically. Fairly long periods of observation are desirable, in order that spectrograms may be obtained: hence a 24 hr-orbit would be preferred. Comparison of the spectra of the artificial and actual cometary heads would enable us to draw valuable conclusions on the chemical composition of real comets and would provide clues for the preparation of subsequent experiments.

It would be useful to place various instruments orbiting together with the artificial nucleus, especially a mass spectrometer.

(d) Experiments with Comet Probes

Every investigator of comets has cherished the same dream as every investigator of the planets or the moon, i.e., of securing direct data from probes. Comets come occasionally fairly close to the earth. For example, comet Tuttle-Giacobini-Kresak will have a close approach to the earth in April 1962 (geocentric distance 0.2 a.u.). It would be interesting to launch a probe which could gather telescopic, mass-spectrometric, micrometeoritic, spectroscopic, and other information about comets. One may think of a probe going through the head or tail, or even sharing the orbit of the comet and sending information. One may apply to comets many experiments which are being envisaged for the moon, Venus, Mars, or the interplanetary space. It is obvious that data on the nature of the nucleus (image, polarization, etc.), on the exact gaseous composition and ionization of the head and tail at various cometocentric distances, on the nature and sizes of the solid particles of the head and tail, etc., would be extremely welcome. It is probable that such information will be obtainable only with space probes, and it is certain that they would be most interesting not only for cometary physics itself, but also for the discussions on the origin and evolution of the solar system.

Appendix I.* Prediction of the Infrared Cometary Emissions

The wavelengths in air are expressed in microns.

* Our thanks are due to Mrs. D. Bosman-Crespin who performed the required calculations.

	CO			CO^+	
J	$R(J)$	$P(J)$	K	R	P
0	4.6562	—	0	4.5696	—
1	4.6480	4.6729	1	4.5615	4.5860
2	4.6400	4.6814	2	4.5536	4.5944
3	4.6320	4.6899	3	4.5458	4.6029
4	4.6241	4.6987	4	4.5380	4.6115
5	4.6164	4.7075	5	4.5304	4.6202

CH

K	P_1	P_2	Q_1	Q_2	R_1	R_2
1	—	—	3.6501	3.6491	3.5804	3.5650
			3.6499	3.6489	3.5802	3.5648
2	3.7252	3.7406	3.6530	3.6527	3.5475	3.5448
	3.7254	3.7408	3.6524	3.6520	3.5473	3.5445
3	3.7688	3.7713	3.6575	3.6573	3.5173	3.5159
	3.7691	3.7716	3.6564	3.6561	3.5170	3.5155
4	3.8142	3.8154	3.6635	3.6634	3.4892	3.4883
	3.8146	3.8159	3.6617	3.6614	3.4889	3.4879
5	3.8618	3.8626	3.6711	3.6711	3.4631	3.4625
	3.8625	3.8632	3.6683	3.6683	3.4627	3.4620

CH^+

J	$R(J)$	$P(J)$
0	3.6136	—
1	3.5801	3.6865
2	3.5484	3.7276
3	3.5185	3.7681
4	3.4904	3.8124
5	3.4638	3.8591

OH

K	P_1	P_2	Q_1	Q_2	R_1	R_2
1	—	—	2.8015	2.8015	2.7397	2.7558
			2.8017	2.8010	2.7396	2.7557
2	2.8690	2.8501	2.8036	2.8033	2.7171	2.72876
	2.8690	2.8502	2.8041	2.8030	2.7170	2.72879
3	2.9001	2.8851	2.8070	2.8066	2.6957	2.70406
	2.9003	2.88511	2.8077	2.8062	2.6955	2.70404
4	2.9335	2.9215	2.8112	2.8110	2.6753	2.6814
	2.9339	2.9216	2.8124	2.8107	2.6750	2.6813
5	2.9691	2.9596	2.8165	2.81642	2.6561	2.6606
	2.9697	2.9597	2.8184	2.8164	2.6559	2.6605

OH^+

K	P_1	R_1	P_2	R_2	P_3	R_3
1	3.4207	3.3148	3.4231	3.3145	3.4181	3.3127
2	3.4615	3.2839	3.4618	3.2836	3.4637	3.2831
3	3.5048	3.2552	3.5050	3.2551	3.5056	3.2548
4	3.5508	3.2288	3.5510	3.2287	3.5514	3.2285
5	3.5997	3.2046	3.5999	3.2044	3.6002	3.2043

	CN			CN^+	
	$P_1 + P_2$	$R_1 + R_2$	J	$R(J)$	$P(J)$
0	—	4.917	0	4.9873	—
1	4.936	4.909	1	4.9782	5.0062
2	4.945	4.900	2	4.9692	5.0157
3	4.954	4.891	3	4.9602	5.0254
4	4.964	4.884	4	4.9514	5.0353
5	4.973	4.874	5	4.9427	5.0452
6	4.985	4.866	6	4.9342	5.0554
7	4.993	4.857	7	4.9257	5.0656
8	5.003	4.849	8	4.9174	5.0760
9	5.013	4.841	9	4.9092	5.0865
10	5.024	4.833	10	4.9011	5.0972
11	5.034	4.825	11	4.8931	5.1080
12	5.045	4.818	12	4.8853	5.1189
13	5.055	4.810			
14	5.066	4.803			
15	5.077	4.795			
16	5.088	4.788			
17	5.099	4.780			

NO

Branches to $J = 15\frac{1}{2}$

$\Omega = \frac{1}{2}$: P branch from 5.3432 to 5.4917
R branch from 5.3287 to 5.1898

$\Omega = \frac{3}{2}$: P branch from 5.3540 to 5.4968
R branch from 5.3294 to 5.1872

NH

K	P_1	R_1	P_2	R_2	P_3	R_3
1	—	3.1370	—	3.1368	—	3.1362
2	3.2680	3.1090	3.2681	3.1089	3.2688	3.1087
3	3.3059	3.0828	3.3060	3.0827	3.3062	3.0826
4	3.3460	3.0584	3.3461	3.0583	3.3462	3.0582

CO_2	
⊥ band ν_2:	R branch from 14.927 to 14.268 (to J = 40)
	P branch from 15.015 to 15.698
Parallel band ν_3:	R from 4.2525 to 4.2060 (to J = 40)
	P from 4.2569 to 4.3198

N_2O	
⊥ band ν_2:	R from 16.955 to 16.485 (to J = 20)
	P from 17.004 to 17.475
Parallel band ν_1:	R from 7.7752 to 7.6799 (to J = 20)
	P from 7.7854 to 7.8871
Parallel band ν_3:	R from 4.4940 to 4.4636 (to J = 20)
	P from 4.4974 to 4.5325

HCN	
⊥ band:	R from 13.982 to 12.915 (to J = 20)
	P from 14.154 to 15.373

H_2O	
Main regions:	ν_2 5.35 to 7
	ν_3 near 2.7

C_2H_2	
⊥ band:	R from 13.627 to 12.840 (to J = 20)
	P from 13.768 to 14.65
Parallel band:	R from 3.0474 to 3.0065 (to J = 20)
	P from 3.0515 to 3.0962

NH_3	
Main regions:	2.9961 − 2.8482
	10.5 to 8.5, and 10.97 to 14.06
	10.19 to 8.0, and 10.535 to 13.77
	6.15 to 6.88, and 6.02 to 5.62

CH_4	
Main regions:	3.30 to 3.18 (R); 3.31 (Q); 3.32 to 3.45 (P)
	7.62 to 7.36 (R); 7.69 to 7.93 (P)

Appendix II. Prediction of the Ultraviolet Cometary Emissions

The following predictions may be added to those already published (Swings *et al.*, 1961).

H_2

Depending on the radial velocity and on populations on the lower rotational state, doublet resonance series may possibly be excited in the Lyman system of H_2 by the following solar emission lines:

λ 1085.1 He II and λ 1085.7 N II: $P(6) - R(4)$ and $P(3) - R(1)$ of the $(2, v'')$ transitions;
λ 1037.61 O VI: $P(1)$ of $(5, v'')$, or $P(4) - R(2)$ of $(6, v'')$;
λ 1031.9 O VI: $P(6) - R(4)$ of $(6, v'')$;
λ 1025.7 Ly-β: $P(1)$, $P(3) - R(1)$ and $P(4) - R(2)$ of $(6, v'')$;
λ 977.03 C III: $P(5) - R(3)$ of $(11, v'')$;
λ 972.54 Ly-γ: $P(3) - R(1)$ and $P(1)$ of $(11, v'')$;
λ 949.74 Ly-δ: $P(2) - R(0)$ of $(14, v'')$ and $P(7) - R(5)$ of $(15, v'')$.

Possibilities of triplet resonance series excited in the Werner system of H_2 by the following solar lines:

λ 989.8 N III: $P(4) - Q(3) - R(2)$ of $(1, v'')$;
λ 977.03 C III: $P(5) - Q(4) - R(3)$ and $P(7) - Q(6) - R(5)$ of $(2, v'')$;
λ 949.74 Ly-δ: $P(6) - Q(5) - R(4)$ and $P(2) - Q(1) - R(0)$ of $(3, v'')$;
λ 937.80 Ly-ε: $P(4) - Q(3) - R(2)$ of $(4, v'')$;
λ 930.75 Ly-ζ: $P(2) - Q(1) - R(0)$ of $(4, v'')$

N_2

Doublet or triplet resonance series may be excited in various electronic systems of N_2 by the following discrete solar emissions:

λ 972.54 Ly-γ: $P(6) - Q(5) - R(4)$ of $(2, v'')$ in $b\,^1\Pi_u - X\,^1\Sigma_g^+$;
λ 949.74 Ly-δ: $P(7) - Q(6) - R(5)$ of $(0, v'')$ in $m\,^1\Pi_u - X\,^1\Sigma_g^+$;
λ 937.80 Ly-ε: $P(2) - R(0)$ of $(4, v'')$ in $b'\,^1\Sigma_u^+ - X\,^1\Sigma_g^+$;
λ 834.46 O II: $P(6) - R(4)$ of $(2, v'')$ in $C_3\,^1\Sigma_u^+ - X\,^1\Sigma_g^+$.

Bands of N_2 may also be excited by the solar Lyman continuum in various electronic transitions.

N_2^+

An (0-2) emission of N_2^+ at λ 1660.2–λ 1662.4 may be excited by the solar continuum.

CN^+

The (0-0) band extending from λ 2179 to λ 2183 (for $J \leqslant 10$) may be excited by the solar continuum; a complex profile would be caused by the Fraunhofer absorption lines.

NH^+

The (0-0) and (1-0) bands near λ 2890 and λ 2730 may be excited; they would have complex profiles.

Reference

Swings, P., Bosman-Crespin, D., and Arpigny, C. (1961). *Mém. Soc. Roy. Liège* [5] **4,** 583.

16.2 Remarks on a Comet Probe

H. C. CORBEN

SPACE TECHNOLOGY LABORATORIES, INC., Redondo Beach, California

A number of us at Space Technology Laboratories have been investigating the feasibility and value of launching a space probe to intercept a comet. This possibility was so intriguing to many scientists and engineers with whom we discussed it, that we decided to conduct a preliminary study to give first answers to the questions "which comet?", "how difficult is the shot?" and "what do we do when we get there?". While the wisdom of making such a shot depends on what useful experiments one could perform during the flight, the question remains whether any comets are going to come within range during the next few years, and if so which is the one on which scientific and engineering considerations lead us to concentrate.

Twenty-four perihelion passages inside the orbit of Mars will occur within the coming decade, involving 14 known comets. These are listed in Table I. In addition, statistically we may expect approximately the same number of "new" comets; i.e., comets heretofore of larger perihelion distance, which are perturbed into closer orbits by Jupiter. Of course, these comets are unpredictable. As Dr. Swings mentioned, a new one—Comet Wilson, showed up last week. Who knows whether we will be challenged one day by a very bright new comet, which is so bright that it cannot be ignored, and which gives us less than a year to get a probe to it. But right now let us look at the regular performers.

The last four have perihelion distances so far away that we should remove them from the list. On this basis, Encke stands out from all the others in the closeness of its perihelion passage, and in the corresponding visual brightness and time before perihelion available for recovery. On its last passage it was recovered 6 months before perihelion, and it has been recovered as much as ten months before perihelion. Of all comets, Encke is by far the most regular performer, having been observed on 46 passages.

The closest approach of comet Encke to the earth for the next four returns will occur about July 12, 1964, when the distance will be 24 million miles. The orbits are such that it can never be less than 20 million

TABLE I

Expected Perihelion Passages Inside the Orbit of Mars until 1971

Name	Orbital perihelion distance (a.u.)	Perihelion passages	Greatest visual brightness (1951–60)
Encke	0.34	May 1964, Sept. 1967, Jan. 1971	5.1
Honda-Mrkos	0.56	July 1964, Sept. 1969	8.9
Grigg-Skjellerup	0.85	Dec. 1961, Nov. 1966, Oct. 1971	12.4
Giacobini-Zinner	0.99	Jan. 1966	8.8
Tuttle	1.03	April 1967	12.1
Finlay	1.08	July 1967	10.2
Tuttle-Giacobini	1.12	April 1962, Oct. 1967	17.4
Gale	1.15	Nov. 1970	16.2
Schaumasse	1.19	June 1968	9.8
Pons-Winnecke	1.23	Feb. 1964, June 1970	12.7
D'Arrest	1.37	Oct. 1963, July 1970	15.2
Tempel 2	1.39	May 1962, Aug. 1967	13.7
Borrelly	1.45	June 1967	13.9
Daniel	1.46	Dec. 1963, Aug. 1970	15.1

miles. Much of this earth-to-comet distance is in the direction of the ecliptic south pole, and the earth-to-comet transfer orbit is thus of a different kind from those encountered in studies of the interplanetary missions to Venus and Mars.

To penetrate the comet in mid-July of 1964, probes may be launched from Cape Canaveral three or four months earlier. To hold the date of interception near mid-July while varying the date of launch, from late

TABLE II

Some Parameters of Shots to Hit Comet Encke in Mid-July 1964

Date of launch (1964)	Time of flight (days)	Date of inter-ception (1964)	Distance from earth to probe at penetration (millions of N. miles)	Burnout velocity at 22 million ft from earth (ft/sec)	Uncorrected miss at the target (thousands of N. miles)	Velocity of closing on the comet (ft/sec)
2–24	140	7–13	23.6	41,848	664	92,009
3–10	125	7–13	23.6	40,570	446	92,149
3–25	115	7–18	29.1	40,123	297	84,087
3–31	108	7–17	28.0	40,210	245	85,254
4–5	104	7–18	29.1	40,351	210	83,665
4–16	92	7–16	27.0	40,896	165	86,901
4–25	80	7–14	25.0	41,818	139	90,594
5–5	70	7–14	25.0	43,223	125	90,462

February into early May, is to test possibilities of the orbit. Table II has been prepared in this spirit directly from digital computer runs.

For most of these shots, the probe recedes from the earth at between 200 and 300 thousand miles per day; but there is a class of orbits, e.g., launch February 16 for a 137-day flight, in which the probe remains within 22 million miles of the earth throughout the interval from May 20 to August 22—a valuable property for purposes of communication. This flight needs 41,700 ft/sec burnout velocity and the miss could be corrected with 60 lb hydrazine in a 320-lb payload.

The comet Encke will be very far south, and the transfer trajectory should include a coast period in parking orbit to limit the problems of range safety while leading to maximum of the useful payload.

Summing up, a ballistic problem of a kind new to us discloses features which remain to be reconciled in a best solution. We find low-energy orbits requiring burnout velocities above 40,000 ft/sec and higher energy orbits requiring less than 42,000 ft/sec. Checking these velocities against our experience of the requirements for fly-by missions to the 1962 presentations of Mars and Venus, we find that payloads of a few hundred pounds can be delivered to Encke in 1964. The misses are comparable with those on Venus and smaller than those on Mars, whereas the nucleus of Encke is much smaller than either planet, and the coma much larger. The mid-course fuel penalties on these payloads range between 15 and 25%, so that the weight of structure, power supply, telemetering apparatus and scientific payload ranges from 150 lb upwards. There are a number of acceptable launch dates in a family of orbits associated with a mid-July interception. Late June interceptions characterize a dual family not yet investigated. As may be expected, the telemetry problem for a comet probe does not look difficult, apart from the special requirements of any fly-by probe, which must pick up information very rapidly while in the neighborhood of the planet or comet it is passing.

Scientific measurements that one might hope to perform with such a probe have been mentioned by Dr. Swings. In planning such a probe, attention should be given to the possible use of a magnetometer, a meteor detector, a mass spectrometer, a neutral particle detector, a camera, and equipment for gas chromatography and direct pressure measurements.

Details of the STL work on a comet probe are to be found in a report by J. C. Lair, The mission to a comet, STL Rept. No. 9844-0023-MU-000 (July 11, 1961).

Discussion*

* For discussion of theories of comet tails, see pp. 201–202.

CHAPTER 17

Planetary Observations

17.1 Planetary Observations from Space Probes and Orbiters

G. DE VAUCOULEURS

UNIVERSITY OF TEXAS, Austin, Texas

This report presents a brief survey of the main observations and experiments of astronomical or geophysical interest which could be attempted from:

(1) interplanetary probes on one-way flights during the period of closest approach (fly-by or near miss), when primarily passive physical and mechanical observations of the planet and its environment can be made for a brief period only;

(2) artificial satellites (orbiters) placed in controllable, closed orbit, prior to escape on earth-bound trajectory or to burn-up by atmospheric penetration, when both passive and active physical and mechanical observations and experiments can be made for significant periods of time;

(3) penetrating probes, carrying simple physical, chemical, and meteorological sampling apparatus through the atmosphere for a short period of time prior to a (generally destructive) crash-landing with loss of communication.

The report does not cover observations and experiments involving nondestructive crash landings (i.e., without loss of communication) or soft landings.

1. Observations from Probes in Space

1.1. Magnetic Field and Radiation Belts

Cosmic radiation counters, weak-field magnetometers and micrometeorite probes will generally be included in the equipment of most planetary probes, for a routine check of the interplanetary environment, and they need not be considered specifically in a planetary exploration program.

However, the same basic equipment will serve for the detection of planetary magnetic fields and belts of trapped radiation. One might expect Venus to have a general magnetic field at least as strong as that of the earth and to be surrounded by possibly stronger Van Allen belts. The inner belt, if due to the cosmic ray neutron albedo of the atmosphere, may not be stronger; but the outer belt, if due to trapped protons of solar origin, could very well be stronger, since the solar corpuscular flux density should decrease roughly as the inverse square of the distance to the sun. Details of the interaction between solar and planetary magnetic fields may, however, modify this picture.

Mars offers a different situation. From dynamical and geophysical considerations we suspect that Mars has no core, or at most a very small core, and consequently a rather weak intrinsic magnetic field. Further, the low gravity and consequent extension of the atmosphere to great heights (at least twice the terrestrial values for comparable densities) are probably not favorable to the formation of corpuscular radiation belts. In consequence, trapped solar radiation near Mars should be of much lower density and intensity than near earth.

The maximum perceptible extent of the trapped radiation belt around the earth is of the order of 100,000 km; radiation and magnetic sampling of the planetary environment should begin at least at this range.

In addition to field strength, the direction of the magnetic axis of Mars and, especially, Venus will be of interest to decide whether the present location of the terrestrial magnetic poles in the geographic polar regions is an accident or a phenomenon of basic planetary significance.*

1.2. Optical Search for Satellites

Next to field and radiation observations, simple optical observations of the planets and their surroundings at moderate distances will probably be among the earliest technical possibilities. Here several observations of astronomical interest should be noted. Venus has no known satellite, a fact which has precluded an accurate determination of its mass;

* The field of Mercury would be interesting to study if electronic and other components can be protected against the fierce heat at this short distance from the sun. The astronomical evidence that the mean density is about 6, the highest of all planets, suggests that most light elements evaporated during the formation of this planet, leaving essentially the naked iron-nickel core of what would otherwise have become an earth-like planet of larger size. There is little to go on to predict what the magnetic field and radiation belts might be.

actually satellites as small as those of Mars—say, 10 to 20 km in diameter—would not be observable by ordinary techniques from earth. An optical search for small satellites could be made from a space probe approaching the planet when it is approximately in quadrature with the sun and at a distance from the probe of the order of 1,000,000 km. At this distance a satellite would appear some 10^4 times = 10 magnitudes brighter than from earth under ordinary conditions, and even small bodies would shine as bright stars; for instance, a satellite of diameter 12 km and having as low an albedo as the moon (0.07) would appear of 4th or 5th magnitude when observed in quarter phase at 10^6 km. At this distance the normal field of view of a 50-mm lens associated with, say, a vidicon tube with a 1-in. cathode, would be 5×10^5 km or approximately the earth-moon distance. Venus should be off-set to the edge of the field and the optics carefully protected from direct or indirect sunlight.

The *a priori* probability that Venus has captured small asteroidal satellites is not high. The odds are better for Mars which is close to the main asteroidal belt and has already two known satellites which are presumably captured asteroids. Because of the small mass of Mars, the search for martian satellites should be preferably attempted at a shorter range, say 10^5 km, to cover a smaller field with better resolution. At this range, a 1-km satellite of low albedo would appear of 5th or 6th magnitude in quarter phase; its rapid motion around the planet would facilitate detection.

1.3. Search for Gaseous Tails

While the probe is approaching the planet but still at distances of the order of 10^5 to 10^6 km, from which a wide field of surrounding space can be recorded by small optical instruments, another observation that might be attempted is a search for fluorescent gaseous tails. The Russian astronomer Fessenkov has suggested that in the region of the exosphere molecules can be expelled by radiation pressure from the sun and has interpreted some observations of the zodiacal light and gegenschein as evidence for the existence of such an appendage to the earth. A direct check might be possible, especially for Venus, by photographing the region of the sky directly opposite to the sun beyond the planet; a long exposure (or integration time) would be needed to reach the detection threshold set by the brightness of the zodiacal light, and accurate photoelectric guiders would have to maintain the image of the planet fixed on the film (or cathode) during the exposure. Great precautions should be taken to exclude all solar light and also multiple reflections and stray light from the planet itself, by using coronagraph techniques.

1.4. High-Resolution Photography and Television of Surface

At closer range—say, between 10^4 and 10^5 km from the target—the most important and urgent observations will be high resolution photography (or television) of the planetary atmospheres and surfaces. This is especially important for Mars, whose surface can be seen clearly through its thin atmosphere at all wavelengths longer than 0.5 μ; in the case of Venus, only details of its clouds and atmosphere—probably of less immediate interest—could be seen at all optical and near infrared wavelengths.

Because the high-resolution study of the martian surface is one of the most important and promising projects for the early phases of planetary reconnaissance, we shall consider it in some detail.

A preliminary remark may be made here: while the highest possible resolution is certainly attractive, it may not be needed or desirable in the early reconnaissance phases. Once a certain resolution threshold has been crossed, further progress merely adds detail, but not necessarily new fundamental information. For example the moon seen with the naked eye shows merely a pattern of dark and bright regions which give little indication of the nature of its surface; our present situation with respect to Mars and Mercury is very much the same. As soon as a magnification of 30 times (as used by Galileo) could be applied, simple telescopic examination was sufficient to show immediately that there are mountains, craters, etc., and further optical progress has merely added details to this first discovery. Mars is at least 150 times farther away at its nearest approach, and corresponding resolution would require a power of 4500, which is not practicable from earth. Instead of the rather meaningless, but illustrative notion of magnification, we can compare resolution limits. Our present resolution limit in telescopic planetary studies is of the order of $0''.2$, or 60 km at the minimum distance of Mars (it is often much worse). The corresponding limit in observations of the moon is $0'.5$, which can be achieved with a telescope having an aperture of 5 mm (0.2 in.) and a magnification of about 6 times. Little of significance can be seen on the moon under such conditions. This comparison suggests that significant features, i.e., structures that can be "recognized," do not emerge until details of the order of 10 km or less (visible on the moon with a 1-in. telescope, magnifying 30 times) can be clearly resolved. Considerations of this type indicate that a 7-in. focus lens (as used for aerial reconnaissance during World War II), resolving 3 km at a distance of 10,000 km, will lead to significant results in the early optical reconnaissance of Mars.

The smallest structures that can be photographed through earthbound telescopes (on rare occasions of superlative "seeing") subtend about 0.″2. This corresponds to 1° areocentric, or 60 km at perihelic oppositions with Mars at a distance of 6×10^7 km; most of the time the resolution limit is not better than several hundred kilometers. For comparison, a standard aerial photography camera with a 7-in. focus lens working at $f/4$ (scale 1 mm = 19.′3) gives a photographic resolution better than 0.05 mm = 1.′0. In order to match the maximum resolution possible from earth with large telescopes, it would have to be operated at a distance $(0.'2/60) \times 6 \times 10^7 = 2 \times 10^5$ km from Mars; at smaller distances it would be at an increasing advantage compared with the best earth-bound telescopes. For example, at a distance of 10^4 km from Mars this simple system would resolve 3 km, and the number of surface details distinctly recorded would be between 2 and 3 orders of magnitude greater than on the best existing photographs. The field of good definition of this system, about 20° or 60 mm, is larger than the photocathode of current television tubes. A 1-in. cathode would accept a field of view some 1500 km across and, provided the line spacing is adequate (at least 20 and preferably 40 lines per mm), would record some 25×10^4 distinct picture elements in this field. This would cover slightly over 1% of the surface area of Mars.

The relative velocity of the probe is not a problem at this relatively large distance and low resolution. Ordinary fast photographic emulsions will record a well-exposed image of Mars at $f/4$ in less than 1/100 sec; a Vidicon system would probably need little more than 1/1000 sec, allowing for filter transmission. The observations should be made through a yellow or, preferably, orange filter transmitting wavelengths longer than 0.55 μ. The motion of the probe, of the order of 10 to 15 km/sec with respect to Mars, is negligible in either case.

Although a full-face photograph would be very desirable, a photograph of a region close to the terminator might be more informative; for a study of shadows under the low sun would permit a first reconnaissance of the martian relief (which is still completely unknown) and effectively increase the discrimination capability. The solar illumination might be reduced to, perhaps, one-tenth of the illumination in the face-on view, but the tangential component of the relative velocity would also be much less than in the previous case. The radial velocity of the probe with respect to Mars would not be a limiting factor either; at 10 km/sec the relative dilatation of the field would be $10/10^4 = 10^{-3}$ per sec, or less than 1 picture element in the 1-in. field.

A resolution limit much better than a few kilometers would require greater focal lengths. Since the aperture cannot be very large, this requirement will lead to smaller f-ratios and consequently to a drastic reduction in the image illumination, requiring longer exposure or integration times; the motion of the probe will then become a significant factor. For example, consider a 10-in., $f/20$ Cassegrain reflector of equivalent focal length $f = 5$ meters, giving a scale of 41 sec of arc/mm. The resolution limit of 0.05 mm (20 "lines" per mm) then corresponds to 2 sec of arc or 10^{-5} radian; at a distance of 10^4 km the corresponding linear resolution limit will be 0.1 km, and the typical 1-in. field of view will correspond to 50 km. However, at $f/20$ the exposure time will need to be at least 25 times longer than at $f/4$, i.e., of the order of several tenths of a second for direct photography, and 0.01 sec for television. The motion of the probe during this time will be of the order of 1 to 0.1 km, i.e., greater than the resolution limit. Some means of stabilizing the image on the photosensitive surface will have to be devised, as in ordinary aerial photography.

Another point of importance in favor of small optics when payloads are still severely limited is that resolving power increases only as the first power of the aperture (at constant f-ratio), while the weight and volume increase as the third power. Note also that, with the f-ratios required to keep exposure times sufficiently short, the resolution limit is set by the receiver (granularity of the emulsion or raster of the television system) and not by diffraction (which would require f-ratios of several hundreds).

As to the targets, priority should go to one bright and one dark area near the evening terminator (the morning terminator is frequently hazy), i.e., while the probe is approaching Mars; then to the same types of regions under a high sun at the time of closest approach (if the probe stays inside the orbit of Mars); and to the polar regions in spring or summer if the probe passes above or below the orbital plane at a suitable range. Priority should go to the south polar regions with Mars at heliocentric longitudes between 300 and 360°, when the regression rate of the polar cap is at its maximum and active phenomena occur in the subpolar regions. Observations of the back (night) side from a probe crossing beyond the orbit of Mars will be considered in subsequent sections.

In the case of Venus mere photographic observation at optical wavelengths is not expected to disclose strikingly new information. Ultraviolet photographs would reveal some of the fine structure of the high-level haze, while photographs of the terminator in the visible and near infrared would, perhaps, make it possible to determine cloud heights above the top of the opaque cloud layer or lower atmosphere; but the very low contrast would require special techniques to bring out significant details in other regions. All in all the writer does not feel that high-resolution television of Venus at close range in the optical region calls for early efforts; certainly first priority must go to Mars.

On the contrary, close ups of the surface of Mercury might disclose an unexpected surface structure, whose comparison with the surfaces of Mars and, especially, the moon might be of great geophysical and cosmogonical interest.

1.5. Planetary Masses and Diameters

The masses of Venus and Mercury are not known with the same accuracy as the masses of the other planets. Even the mass of Mars is not known to better than a few parts in a thousand, and the diameters of the three planets are uncertain by several parts in a thousand (as much as several per cent for Mercury). In addition, the optical oblateness of Mars appears to be 2 or 3 times greater than the limit set by celestial mechanics. These uncertainties frustrate all attempts to derive the internal constitution of the terrestrial planets, whose comparison with the earth is essential to geophysical and cosmogonical theories. In addition more accurate diameter determinations would be useful for the terminal guidance of second-generation probes and orbiters.

While much better techniques will be available to orbiters, some significant determinations might be made from fly-bys. If the orbit has been accurately established by tracking of the probe on the out-bound leg of the orbit, a comparison of the orbital elements before and after the period of closest approach to the target planet will help determine its mass, provided the minimum distance is known with sufficient accuracy. This may involve an auxiliary active radar measurement of this minimum distance, and it also requires that no terminal guidance be used while the probe is in the critical part of its orbit. It does not preclude mid-course corrections, as long as a sufficient arc of the orbit is left undisturbed. Since even early probes will probably pass well within 10^6 km from a planet, the perturbations will be large, and order-of-magnitude improvements in planetary masses might be achieved.

The determination of planetary diameters may be made by at least two different techniques. One merely requires that a geometrically standardized photograph or television picture be taken at a known range, which need not be known to better than 10^{-4}—say, to 10 km at 10^5 km. The geometric standardization, or scale of the picture, could be simply derived from the positions of bright stars simultaneously recorded in the field of view. For example, the apparent diameter of Venus at a distance of 10^5 km will be 7°, or about 21 mm in the focal plane of the 7-in. focus lens previously considered. If the diameter of the image can be measured to an accuracy matching the assumed resolution of 40 lines per mm, the relative error per image will be of the order of 10^{-3}. This is better by a full order of magnitude than corresponding single measurements with earth-bound instruments (our present knowledge of the diameters, to 10^{-2} or 10^{-3}, is the result of over a century of persistent work). A dozen determinations of this type, over a range of distances, would give values of the planetary diameters accurate to a few kilometers. Such measurements at several wavelengths, from the near ultraviolet to the near infrared, would also give information on the altitude of haze layers, especially in the atmosphere of Mars, and on the oblateness of the surface of Mars.

Another technique, which cannot very well be applied on earth because of diffraction, seeing and guiding difficulties, but which might be applicable in space, is photoelectric scanning. Suppose that the probe spins around a precisely known axis and at a precisely known (slow) angular rate (determined, presumably, by radio techniques or by auxiliary optical observations with, say, a sun sensor). A photocell placed behind a narrow slit in the focal plane of, for example, a compact 6-in., $f/15$ Cassegrainian reflector (a 10 μ slit will match the diffraction limit) will scan a zone of the sphere. By proper programming or by on-board automatic controls, this zone can be made to include the target planet (but not the sun!). By accurate timing of the instants of maximum rate of increase and decrease of the luminous flux reaching the slit, the angular diameter of the planet might be derived. For example, suppose that the planet subtends 6°, and that the rate of spin has been reduced to 1 rpm; assume further that the optical system scans a great circle of the sphere (the least favorable case) and that measurement of small time differences is accurate to 10^{-3} sec. The planetary diameter will be traversed in 1 sec, and its value will be determined to 10^{-3} per turn. Detailed allowance for time constant, limb darkening, atmospheric and other effects will be needed; this will be facilitated by the transmission of a few samples of the complete photometric scan profiles. If the planet is not in the equatorial plane of the spin axis but closer to the pole, the time of traverse will be increased, but corrections for curvature of the scan should then be made.

Application of this method is limited to a short period when the planet is exactly in opposition as seen from the probe; at other times only the diameter perpendicular to the line of maximum phase defect could be measured. Note, however, that it applies even at very short ranges when the apparent diameter of the planet exceeds the field of view of television tubes and cameras.

1.6. Photometry, Spectroscopy, and Polarimetry

Most of the observations by the classical techniques of astronomy, which can be made from earth-based or stratospheric telescopes, should certainly not be needlessly carried out from probes. Nevertheless these techniques often suffer from some basic limitations due to their being applied from an unsuitable position in space. In such cases the application of these same techniques from a space station would not be unnecessary duplication.

For instance, while most of the infrared spectrum becomes accessible at balloon-ceiling altitudes of 100,000 ft, this is still too low to overcome absorption by the ozone layer of the ultraviolet region where $\lambda < 0.3\,\mu$. Ultraviolet photometry and spectroscopy of the planets from space probes might detect the expected fluorescence of several ions and molecules of their upper atmospheres even on the bright side.

An important observation that should be made from a probe, even though with low resolution, would be the photography and photometry of Mars in ultraviolet and blue light when passing through opposition with the sun (i.e., zero phase angle) as seen from the probe. This would be to check whether the preferential occurrence of the so-called "blue clearing"—or increased atmospheric transparency at wavelengths $\lambda < 0.5\,\mu$—near opposition as observed from earth is a purely optical effect due, e.g., to some unusual phase effect in the blue haze (in which case it should be also observed from a probe); or whether it is somehow related to a screening effect upon solar radiation by the earth and its magnetic field, as some astronomers have suggested (in which case it would not be observed from a probe).

As seen from the earth, the phase angle of Mars never exceeds 48° and it is not possible to observe its complete photometric and polarimetric phase curves, i.e., $I(\alpha)/I(0) = \phi(\alpha)$ and $(I_\parallel - I_\perp)/(I_\parallel + I_\perp) = p(\alpha)$. A complete knowledge of these phase curves, at a series of wavelengths from the vacuum ultraviolet to the near infrared, is essential for a realistic theory of atmospheric scattering from which fundamental data on atmospheric gas densities, particle size and distribution, and surface reflectivity could be recovered. It would be relatively simple to carry in a probe a small photoelectric photometer and polarimeter, constantly aimed at Mars and taking, at preset intervals of phase angle, readings of the integrated flux and polarization at a number of wavelengths isolated by filters. Similar observations would be also of interest for Venus, especially in the ultraviolet range inaccessible from the surface of the earth. Absence of atmospheric absorption and the darker sky background would make such observations much more reliable than from earth. Occasional standardization by stellar observations and/or by observation of a weakened, reduced image of the sun would be needed to derive absolute albedo values.

Such observations of the earth itself would be most valuable to help determine more precisely its planetary albedo over a wide range of wavelengths. The effective albedo for solar radiation is, of course, the basic quantity which determines the thermal radiation balance of a planet and its atmosphere. It is still very poorly known for most planets including the earth, whose (visual) albedo can be only roughly estimated indirectly by observation of the earthshine on the moon.

Note that the determination of complete phase curves requires that the probe's orbit reaches beyond the planetary orbit, a condition which will require mid-course correction at least in the case of a Mars probe. Such orbits will permit a whole series of important new observations of the night side of a planet.

1.7. Sunset and Twilight Phenomena

While optical observations of the illuminated side of a planet will give some general information on lower atmosphere phenomena, little will be learned of the vitally important upper atmosphere. Just as studies of the twilight and night airglow yielded most of our early information on the upper atmosphere of the earth, optical observations from probes of luminous phenomena in the twilight zone and night side of the planets should lead to a wealth of information on their upper atmospheres. We discuss first the sunset and twilight phenomena.

Photographic, photometric, and spectroscopic observations of the setting sun at the limb of a planet is a powerful technique to study its atmospheric structure and composition. The appearance of the phenomenon will depend greatly on the distance of the probe to the planet.

(a) At very great distances, say 10^6 to 10^7 km, the phenomenon is a transit of the planet in front of the sun's disk. It offers perhaps the best opportunity to measure accurately the diameter of the solid globe (Mercury, Mars) or of its opaque cloud layer (Venus). In the case of Venus, Mars, and the earth, a detailed geometric and photometric study of the ingress and egress phases would give the value of the refraction in the stratospheric regions, by the same method applied to the transits of Venus as seen from earth; a precise measurement of the diameter of the ring of refracted light would be needed to determine the altitude of the region probed.

(b) At intermediate distances, 10^5 to 10^6 km, the phenomenon is an eclipse of the sun, during which photometry and spectroscopy of the refracted solar image would give detailed information on the atmospheric absorption, refraction and composition in the lower stratosphere and upper troposphere regions as a function of height (cf. the study of ozone distribution by the spectrophotometry of eclipses of the moon from the earth).

(c) At still shorter range, 10^4 to 10^5 km, the phenomenon tends toward a normal sunset. Detailed photometry and spectroscopy of the solar disk would permit fine studies of the lower tropospheric regions, including determinations of the altitudes of cloud and haze layers, measurements of atmospheric transmission, spectroscopic search for minor constituents, etc. In addition, high-dispersion studies of line profiles in absorption bands at various distances above the limb would lead to determinations of atmospheric temperatures, while absorption and refraction studies would lead to atmospheric scale heights, and hence to the mean molar mass if the temperature is known.

At very short ranges, 10^3 to 10^4 km, when the probe is in the shadow of the planet, a great variety of photometric and spectroscopic studies could be performed on upper-atmospheric scattering and twilight phenomena. To note only a few of the more obvious ones: (1) search for high altitude scattering layers (meteoritic dust?) by photometry of the twilight zone; (2) determination of the scattering phase function of upper air aerosols; (3) search for fluorescence effects of minor constituents in the ionosphere similar to the "twilight flash" of N_2^+ (3914 Å), Na, etc., on earth. Ultraviolet spectroscopy of the twilight zone would be important in this respect.

1.8. Dark Side Optical Observations

With a probe in the shadow of the planet, say at 10^4 km, a number of significant observations could be attempted, but the time available would be short. For a relative velocity of 10 to 15 km/sec and a probe crossing the shadow in the orbital plane of the planet the duration available for observations would be less than 20 min for Venus, less than 10 min for Mars.

Photography, photometry, and spectroscopy of the night side should be attempted to detect and measure the permanent airglow and any auroral activity. The main radiations to look for on Mars and Venus are probably the CO_2^+, CO^+, OH (1.044 μ), and N_2^+ (3914 Å) bands. The detection of an aurora would be of special interest for Venus, where the higher density of the solar corpuscular flux and possibly stronger magnetic field might lead to spectacular effects; as noted earlier, an auroral glow on the dark side of Venus is suspected. Observations of auroral arcs in the polar regions may help to locate the magnetic poles, but more continuous observations than are possible from a single fly-by would be needed.

In addition to auroral phenomena a search might be made for lightning or corona discharges (N_2, CO_2 bands) in the atmosphere of Venus. These phenomena are not expected to be significant on Mars.

1.9. Infrared Thermal Emission

With receivers sensitive in the 2 to 20 μ band a search should be made for the thermal radiation from the surface of Venus. If it is at a temperature of 600°K, the surface should perhaps be detectable, especially on the night side, by observations at wavelengths where windows exist between the main absorption bands of CO_2 and H_2O, e.g., at 2.2 and 4.1 μ (the maximum of the Planck curve is near 5 μ). In addition, this may require that clear breaks exist in the cloud cover.

In any case, an important observation will consist in exploratory infrared scans of the bright and dark sides at several wavelengths in the intermediate infrared, especially in the stronger absorption bands of H_2O at 6.3 μ and CO_2 at 15 μ, to help determine the abundance of these molecules above the effective radiating layers and the thermal structure of the atmosphere of Venus.

In the case of Mars the same CO_2 band will be effective, but it may be necessary to go beyond 20 μ to detect water-vapor absorption. Predictions are difficult here, and an exploration of the whole thermal spectrum is in order.

A most important observation in the case of Mars will be the detailed spectrophotometry of the disk at close range, say 10^4 to 10^5 km, with good angular resolution ($\sim$1/100 of the apparent diameter), especially of the polar caps and of the dark regions in the near infrared to search for characteristic spectral features such as the drop of reflectivity of H_2O at 1.5 μ and the Sinton bands of the C—H bond in organic molecules near 3.5 μ. In the case of Mars, spectral scans of the dark side in the 5 to 40 μ range will also be needed to help estimate the night-time temperatures (especially in the polar regions in winter), which cannot be effectively determined from earth because of the phase angle limitation; at the plausible temperature of 150° to 200°K the emission maximum will be in the 15 to 18 μ region.

An interesting but difficult observation would be the detection of thermal emission from the dark side of Mercury; this is lower than 100°K and may be as low as 10°K and possibly less. Again, because of the short time available for the observations, only broad-band or filter observations may be possible initially, leaving detailed studies to orbiters.

1.10. Microwave Thermal Emission

The thermal emission of both Mars and Venus at centimeter wavelengths, which has been detected from earth, offers an important field of research from a probe at close range. Because of antenna size limitations, only the integral flux from the planet can be detected from earth.

At short range a much smaller antenna would achieve sufficient angular resolution; for example, at a distance of 10^4 km from their surfaces, the apparent diameters of Mars and Venus are about 29° and 44°, respectively. At a wavelength of 1 cm a parabolic reflector of 1 meter aperture has a beam width of the order of 0°.5 (at half-power), providing ample angular resolution for detailed studies.

The initial observations should include scans of the bright and dark sides at a number of wavelengths from, say, 1 mm to 10 cm, to check the thermal nature of the emission and departures from black body radiation, in particular at wavelengths where atmospheric absorption is likely to be serious and informative, such as the H_2O resonance at 1.34 cm. A detailed mapping of microwave thermal emission and its spectrum over the face of a planet would lead to very complete data on its surface temperature distribution and on the composition and thermal structure of its atmosphere, especially when analyzed in conjunction with observations of the infrared thermal emission.

1.11. Nonthermal Radio Emission in the Meter Range

At wavelengths greater than 10 to 20 cm the thermal emission of the terrestrial planets is negligible, but nonthermal emission may become significant. Although undetected as yet from the earth, it may be detectable from probes. Here the greater wavelengths will prevent attaining significant angular resolution even at close range, as long as it is not practical to operate antennas of large aperture in space. A simple dipole (or array of dipoles), with little directivity, may be sufficient for early operations. With it a search should be made for nonthermal radiation originating by cyclotron or synchrotron emission in the trapped radiation belts, or in the ionosphere, or from electric discharges ("atmospherics") in the troposphere. If the radiation is detected, a determination of the power spectrum and ionospheric absorption cutoff could give preliminary information on the critical frequency, i.e., the maximum electron density of the ionosphere.

1.12. Ionospheric Sounding and Radar Probing

Active ionospheric probing would be possible during a fly-by at close range with a sweep-frequency transceiver used for "top side" sounding. It is difficult to predict the critical frequency, but by analogy with the earth the maximum electronic density might be in the range 10^6 to 10^7 electrons cm^{-3} ($f_0 \approx 10$ to 30 Mc/sec) for Venus, and 10^5 to 10^6 electrons cm^{-3} ($f_0 \approx 3$ to 10 Mc/sec) for Mars; the altitude of maximum ionization might be slightly higher on Venus than on earth, and about twice as high on Mars as on earth. If, then, waves in the meter range ($f > f_0$)

penetrate the zone of maximum ionization, they will most likely be reflected by the ground and the difference of echo times for $f > f_0$ and $f < f_0$ will give a direct measurement of the altitudes of the ionospheric layers of given electron density which lie higher than the layer of maximum density.

Another radar transmitter-receiver operating at still higher frequencies in, say, the 1 cm to 50 cm range (in particular 1.34 cm) may be able to receive echoes from lower atmospheric layers; e.g., from the top of the cloud layer on Venus, leading to the most important determination of the altitude of the opaque cloud layer (or layers).

2. Observations from Orbiters

The placing of a space probe in a permanent or temporary closed orbit around another planet will open the way for a great variety of critical observations.

2.1. Mass and Radius

If a heavy, dense satellite is placed in a high equatorial orbit (i.e., roughly in the orbital plane of the planet) well above the atmosphere, it can be used for an accurate measurement of the mass and radius of the planet. Atmospheric friction on earth satellites is insignificant at altitudes greater than 1000 km, where the atmospheric density is less than 10^{-17} gm cm^{-3}. The equivalent altitude might be of the order of 1500 km for Venus (and Mercury ?), and 2000 km for Mars (Fig. 1); the corresponding periods of revolution and velocities (in a circular orbit) are given in Table I.

TABLE I
Periods and Velocities of Stable Artificial Satellites

Planet	Mercury	Venus	Earth	Mars
Altitude (km)	1500 ?	1500	1000	2000
Orbital radius (km)	3900	7600	7378	5400
Period	2 hr 56 min	2 hr 03 min	1 hr 42 min	3 hr 22 min
Velocity (km/sec)	2.32	6.45	7.57	2.81
Doppler shift Δf (cps) at f = 1000 Mc/sec	±7750	±21,500	±25,200	±9400
$\theta_0 = \alpha$ [a]	38°	53°.5	60°	39°

[a] Maximum inclination for eclipses, and apparent semidiameter of planet from satellite.

The total amplitude $2\Delta f$ of the Doppler shift of the frequency of a radio transmitter monitored from a station in the plane of the orbit of the satellite is given for an assumed rest frequency $f = 1000$ Mc sec^{-1} ($\lambda = 0.3$ meter). If the frequency of the transmitter is stable to 10^{-9}, at least over periods of the order of 1 day; and if it can be monitored to, say, 1 cps, the orbital velocity could in principle be derived to 10^{-4} or better; and over a period of some days or weeks the amplitude of the Doppler shift could be determined to 10^{-5} or better.

The planet will behave as a "single-line" spectroscopic binary. The mass is given by

$$\mu = \frac{kP^2}{4\pi^2 a^3 \sin^3 i},$$

where k = Gauss' gravitation constant, P = period of revolution, a = radius (or semi-major axis) of orbit, i = complement of the inclination θ of orbital plane to line of sight. The observed Doppler shift gives directly the orbital velocity and radius a $= VP/2\pi$, hence

$$\mu = 2\pi k/PV^3 \sin^3 i$$

It is essential that the satellite be placed in an orbit of precisely known inclination i—for instance, in the orbital plane of the planet—for otherwise only the product ($a \sin i$) could be derived. For small angles, $\cos \theta \approx 1 - \theta^2/2$; in order that μ may be derived, say, to 10^{-4}, it is necessary that $\theta^2 < 2 \times 10^{-4}$, i.e., $\theta < 0\overset{\circ}{.}8$. P is known accurately from the periodicity of the Doppler shift, and from the eclipses of the transmitter by the planet if θ is smaller than θ_0. The limiting value for eclipses, θ_0, is given in Table I; it is also equal to the apparent semidiameter of the planet as seen from the satellite.

The orbital radius a is the sum of the planetary radius and the altitude z of the satellite. If the satellite carries a radar altimeter for measuring z, the radius of the planet may be derived, essentially to the same accuracy as a, about 10^{-4} or ≈ 1 km or better. In principle, the diameter of the planet could be derived from the duration of the eclipses, i.e., the period of silence of the transmitter; however, precise allowance for ionospheric refraction would be required, and the refraction may not be known with sufficient accuracy in the early experiments. Further, in an elliptic orbit, an independent determination of the orbit by radar would be a valuable check.

More stable transmitters, more accurate frequency measurements, and more precisely known orbital inclinations might eventually lead to the determination of planetary masses and radii of high precision. The effects of radiation pressure, residual atmospheric drag, orbital eccentricity, solar perturbations, etc., will have to be taken into account.

Note that the mass so determined will be in the system of astronomical units, i.e., expressed as a fraction of the sun's (hence the earth's) mass; the mass in grams is known only to the limited accuracy of the gravitational constant in cgs units.

The radial velocity of the planet relative to the earth, and consequently a determination of the solar parallax, will be among the by-products of the observations.

2.2. Dynamical and Physical Ellipticity

A similar experiment with a satellite in a near-polar orbit (i.e., roughly normal to the plane of the ecliptic) would lead, in addition to a check on the mass and radius values, to determinations of the dynamical and physical ellipticities (from orbital precession and radar altimeter data) and of the higher harmonics of the gravity field from orbital perturbations. The orbital plane of such a satellite will be seen exactly edgewise every half synodic revolution of the planet, and at other inclinations up to its maximum value at other times (cf. the variable aspect of Saturn's rings seen from earth). The inclination could, therefore, be derived from the variable amplitude of the Doppler shift, if it is followed for at least half a synodic revolution, whatever the initial injection angle in a polar orbit. In particular, the times of maximum amplitude will precisely define the times at which $\theta = 0°$, when the earth is in the orbital plane. This would be the preferred orbit for mass and radius determination, if it were not for the fact that initially it will be probably easier to achieve a satellite orbit close to the orbital plane of the probe prior to capture, rather than one involving a large angular deflection of the velocity vector.

2.3. Optical Mapping

For Mars and Mercury a polar satellite is the ideal vehicle for continuous, high-resolution strip-mapping of the surface. For example, at the typical altitude of 2000 km considered in Table I, the apparent diameter of Mars is 78°, which is well within the field of ordinary wide-angle lenses. The angular resolution of a 28-mm focus lens and a television system "resolving" 40 lines/mm would be 3.′0 or 1.8 km at the surface of the planet in the center of the field. The theoretical angular field of view on the planet is 102° planetocentric, and effectively about 50 to 55°, allowing for a 25° zone of excessive foreshortening near the limb; this matches the field covered by a 1-in. photocathode, about 54°.

With a period of revolution of 3 hr 22 min for the orbiter, and a period of rotation of 24 hr 37 min for the planet, successive passages will be shifted westward about 49°; a complete strip-mapping of the planet would be possible in less than 1 day (7.35 revolutions per Martian day vs. $360°/54° = 6.7$), with no point of the planet more than 25° from the central meridian at the time of the nearest passage.

Picture taking need not be continuous; 8 to 10 images per revolution (i.e., every 36° to 45°), or one every 20 to 25 min, would be enough for minimum overlap. The total number of pictures needed to cover completely the surface of the planet would be of the order of 60 to 70, and the number of picture elements to be transmitted about $(25)^2 \times (40)^2 = 10^6$ per image, a total of 6 or 7×10^7 bits for the whole planet.

Higher resolution surveys would presumably have to be limited to sampling of the centers of a smaller number of fields. For example the 7-in. focus lens considered in section 1.4 would resolve (40 lines/mm at 2000 km) about 0.3 km at the surface in a field limited only by the useful area of the image tube (280 km square for a 1-in.^{2} photocathode). The 10-in., $f/20$ Cassegrain system would resolve (also for 40 lines/mm) about 10 meters at the surface of the planet (the theoretical diffraction limit for unit-contrast grids would be about 5 meters in red light).

With such high resolution, compensation of the motion of the satellite may be needed. The motion of the image in the focal plane of a fixed camera will be $360°/P = 108$ sec per second of time, and a compensatory rotation of the optic axis (or equivalent device) by this amount will be required if the exposure times exceed 2 sec for the 28 mm lens, 0.3 sec for the 7-in. focus lens, and 0.01 sec for the 10-in. telescope. At the light levels available, only the third combination may require image motion compensation.

2.4. Photometric, Spectroscopic, Infrared, Microwave, Radar and Magnetic Surveys

Most of the observations described in Sections 1.6 to 1.12 should be repeated with higher spectral and angular resolution from artificial satellites in order to secure nearly continuous surveys of the optical, thermal and microwave emissions from the planetary surface and atmosphere. Here again, a polar orbit would be ideal, especially to search for auroral optical emission on the night side; to patrol the infrared and microwave thermal emission of the surface and atmosphere as a function of latitude and time of day and night; to map the magnetic field and locate the magnetic poles; for a continuous radar mapping of the surface relief and roughness; and, of course, for a finer exploration of the structure of the trapped radiation belts.

By staying at the altitudes listed on Table I, lifetimes of the order of several years or more would be achieved, giving ample time to obtain the observations even if transmissions are intermittent because of power limitations.

By placing a Doppler radar system in a high-level, polar orbit it should be possible to determine the rotation velocities and location of the polar axis of Venus by systematic scanning of the planet's disk at right angles to the orbit.

For Mercury a polar orbit will scan the planetary surface at a rate fixed by the sidereal period of revolution of the planet (88 days); but even after allowance for the libration in longitude, only two thirds of the total surface will be accessible to optical observations in sunlight.

2.5. Upper-Atmospheric Densities

By placing in a low orbit, i.e., at initial altitudes of the order of one-half the altitudes of Table I, a low-density (hollow shell) satellite, atmospheric drag and density could be derived throughout the ionosphere down to the level of ultimate burn-up and destruction. This altitude is near 100 km on earth; it may be of the order of 120 km on Venus, and 200 km on Mars. Such low-density satellites could carry

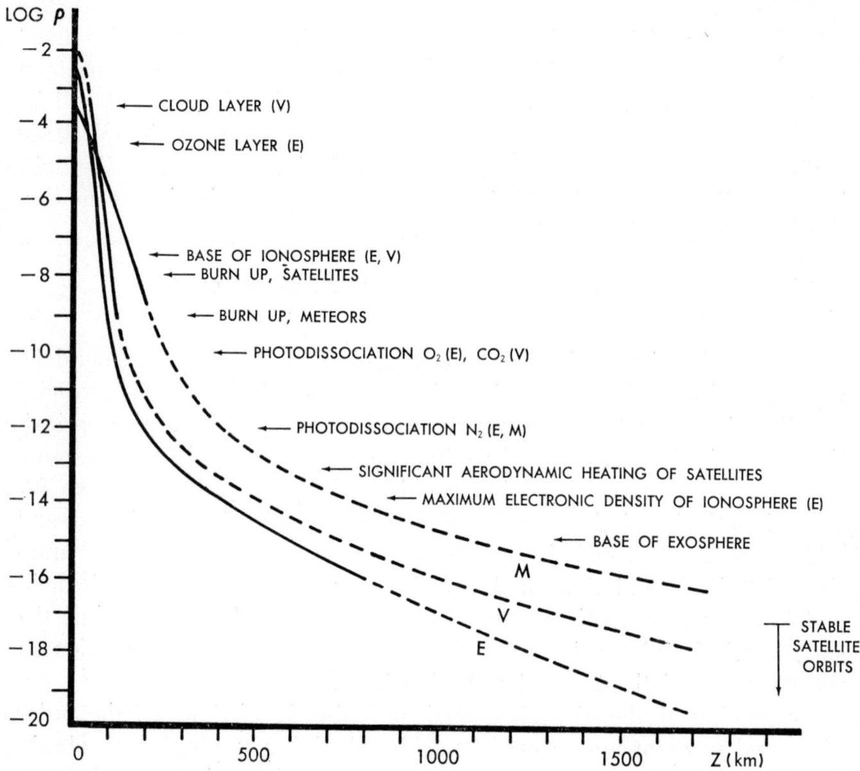

Fig. 1. Atmospheric densities (gm/cm^3) as function of altitude for Mars, Venus, and Earth.

only a low-power transmitter and should presumably be monitored from a heavy, relay satellite in a higher, stable orbit.

By monitoring a passive balloon satellite which has a large area/mass ratio, after release in a high orbit from a small, heavy satellite such as used for the observations of Sections 2.1 and 2.2, the exospheric densities up to the levels of Table I could be derived. A "guesstimate" of the range of densities covered is illustrated in Fig. 1.

2.6. Upper-Atmospheric Absorption

Low-level satellites carrying suitable radiation sensors could determine the penetration of X-ray and ultraviolet solar radiations in the atmosphere. Photon counters with Be, Al, or mylar windows transmit X-rays in the ranges $\lambda < 8$ Å, 8 to 20 and 44 to 60 Å, respectively; these penetrate the earth atmosphere down to the level of the E layer. Photoelectric scanning of the range 60 Å to 1000 Å with a grazing incidence grating monochromator can detect the important λ 304 Å line of He II, which penetrates in the earth atmosphere down to about 200 km, near the bottom of the F layer. Ionization chambers with appropriate gas fillers and windows can select small spectral ranges between 1000 and 1500 Å: nitric oxide with LiF window for λ 1050 to 1350 Å, including Lyman-α; nitric oxide with CaF window for λ 1225 to 1350 Å; xylene with sapphire window for λ 1425 to 1500 Å, including a region of strong O_2 absorption. The penetration of Lyman-α down to the base of the D layer on earth, near 70 km, where it is absorbed by O_2, may be duplicated on Venus. There it would be absorbed by CO_2, whose absorption coefficient about 30 times less than O_2 is compensated by an abundance about 40 times greater. The level corresponding to the dissociation and ionization of N_2, about 200 km on earth, may be around 400 km on Mars and 250 km on Venus. By high resolution studies of the profile of the solar Lyman-α line at different altitudes, the narrow absorption core due to neutral hydrogen in the upper atmosphere could lead to values of the density of neutral atomic hydrogen, which probably arises from photodissociation of OH.

2.7. Ionization Phenomena

The ionosphere could be sampled by placing instrumented satellites in low orbits, i.e., at initial altitudes of 200 to 500 km for Venus, and 400 to 1000 km for Mars.

(1) Multichannel or sweep frequency transceivers could be used to determine ionospheric critical frequencies from both above and below the maximum ionization level, at altitudes of the order of 350 km

(Venus) to 700 km (Mars). Electron densities may be of the order of 10^5 to 10^6 (Mars) and 10^6 to 10^7 cm^{-3} (Venus).

(2) Mass spectrometers, ionization gages, and Langmuir probes flown in the ionospheres could determine ion densities and masses, and kinetic temperatures as a function of altitude down to the destruction level.

(3) Photometry and spectral analysis of the night airglow (including L-α diffuse emission), above and below the satellite, would determine the altitude distribution of the luminescent layers. Analysis of line-width by means of Fabry-Perot etalons or interference spectroscopy could determine kinetic temperatures.

2.8. Upper-Atmospheric Winds and Turbulence

The release of sodium and other metallic vapors from a low level satellite, shortly before burn-up, would permit a study of winds, turbulence, diffusion rates and possibly of the kinetic temperature of the atmosphere at around 100 km on Venus, and 200 km on Mars. Lower altitudes could be reached by firing small rockets downwards from the satellite. The optical and radio observations could be made from a monitoring relay-satellite in a higher orbit. Optical observations involving fluorescence of Na require that solar ultraviolet radiation of $\lambda < 2400$ Å reach the vapor cloud; they should be made under twilight conditions, when the luminescent cloud could be seen against the background of the night side of the planet.

3. Penetrating Probes

Actual penetration of the stratosphere and lower atmosphere by means of instrumented re-entry vehicles released from a satellite and slowed down by retro-rockets, or by means of probes provided with automatic final guidance systems, drag parachutes, and/or winged gliders will permit detailed geophysical and meteorological observations.

3.1. Atmospheric Pressure, Density, and Temperature Profiles

Determinations of the pressure, density, temperature, dielectric constant (by RF resonant cavity), etc., should be made as functions of altitude as continuously measured by radar altimeter. Since only a low-power radio transmitter could be carried by the probes, observations should be monitored from the high-level satellite (or mother probe) prior to retransmission to earth. Continuous monitoring of the deceleration (by accelerometer or Doppler radar tracking) during atmospheric penetration prior to a hard landing of a capsule of well-known cross section and drag coefficient, e.g., a smooth sphere, could give additional information on the atmospheric density profile.

3.2. Atmospheric Transmission

On the day side a penetrating probe carrying batteries of photocells with narrow-band filters aimed at the sun could record atmospheric transmission as a function of altitude, especially in the near infrared bands of H_2O (ρ, ϕ, ψ, Ω bands), CO_2 (bands near 0.8 μ for Venus, near 1.6 μ and 2.0 μ for Mars), and O_2 (A band); and in the near ultraviolet for a study of the continuous absorption at $\lambda < 4500$ Å (Mars, Venus). Rapid changes in the absorption coefficient would signal the passage through cloud layers and determine their altitudes and thicknesses; the wavelength dependence of the absorption would give some indication of their nature (composition, particle size).

A knowledge of the intensity and spectral composition of solar radiation reaching the lower atmosphere and surface of a planet (especially Venus) is of fundamental importance for the planning of subsequent landings of equipment (in particular, television cameras and solar batteries), as well as for the theory of radiative exchange.

3.3. Atmospheric Scattering

At various levels in the lower atmospheric layers the brightness distribution in the solar aureole at several wavelengths (outside molecular absorption bands) could be measured by photoelectric scanning of the area of the sky surrounding the sun from an attitude stabilized instrument capsule. From such measurements of the atmospheric scattering and phase function, the particle size, density distribution and scale height of aerosols could be derived. A search should also be made for other meteorological optics effects which might occur, such as coronas, halos, etc. especially in the cloud layers of Venus.

3.4. Twilight Photometry

Additional information on atmospheric densities and high-level dust layers (meteoritic ?) could be obtained by filter photometry of the sky brightness near the zenith and at low elevation in the azimuth of sunset during twilight. Narrow-band filters should be used to search for O_2, N_2, Na, and other likely atomic and molecular fluorescence lines or bands, as in the earth atmosphere. Night sky photometry and spectrophotometry would probably be more easily performed from an orbiter during passages through the shadow than from a penetrating probe because of the time and coverage factors. However, probes would permit a finer study of the altitude distribution of the luminescence. A free-falling probe with zero initial velocity in the vertical direction would take about 5 min to fall from 500 to 100 km on Venus and 8 min to fall from 700 to 200 km on Mars, neglecting atmospheric drag. The terminal velocities would be about 2.5 km/sec at 100 km on Venus, and less than 2.0 km/sec at 200 km on Mars. This would give enough time for low resolution spectral scans of the twilight, auroral and possibly airglow emissions along horizontal paths at several altitudes; and for photoelectric scanning of Fabry-Perot etalon rings (to determine line widths and kinetic temperatures) of selected emission lines, once these have been located and identified.

3.5. Ballistic Landings

Just prior to hard landings without braking action the spectrum of the high temperature compression wave which may form ahead of the vehicle at high altitude (50 to 100 km on Venus, 100 to 200 km on Mars) might be observed from the vehicle itself or from a monitoring satellite and so give some indication of atmospheric density and composition. Also, radio observations of the ionized gas tail in the wake of the vehicle could be attempted (diffusion and recombination rates).

On Mercury and Mars it might be possible to observe from a monitoring satellite the spectrum of a (chemical) explosion set off at or near the impact point to help locate the landing site. Also, by releasing from the landing vehicle a few seconds prior to landing (i.e., at some 10 to 20 km altitude) a parachute instrumented with optical and sound recording equipment, it might be possible to observe both the flash and the acoustic wave of the explosion, and to derive the velocity of sound in the lower atmosphere (hence a relation between γ, p and ρ, or γ, T, and μ for a perfect gas). Plausible values for the lower atmospheres are shown in Table II.

TABLE II
Velocity of Sound in Lower Atmospheres

	Venus	Earth	Mars
T (°K)	500	273	200
μ	40	28.9	28.2
γ	1.30	1.40	1.41
$V = [\gamma(RT/\mu)]^{1/2}$ (meters/sec)	368	333	288

3.6. Penetrometer and Hardness Tests

The deceleration and destruction of a cone or penetration spike at impact can be used for preliminary hardness tests of the surface (cf. lunar impact experiments) where a layer of dust (Mercury, Mars ?) or liquid surface might be expected. This is not a very promising, nor very useful experiment for the terrestrial planets.

Discussion

MR. A. H. KATZ: My major observation concerns the emergence, in the last few years, of a new service: large trucks going out into space. There is, understandably, both an obvious fascination with this new tool and a desire to use the trucks for useful scientific missions and explorations. I am convinced that for many astronomers there is a different kind of fascination, which arises because one can go out to a launching pad and often see, going up in smoke, a sum of money equal to the annual cost of astronomy around the world. Space experiments are expensive, and will remain so for a long time. This implies that one must not only have a comprehensive catalog or shopping list of experiments, such as we have just heard, but that these experiments must be ordered by priority and importance, and must be carefully thought out.

When doing this, and planning an experiment, one is immediately impaled on the horns of a dilemma. In order to maximize the chances of success on a flight one should carry as few experiments as possible. But the constant realization that each flight is so expensive, that the phasing and scheduling of experiments may greatly postpone the next experiment—this makes one want to cram and pack the payload with "just one more little package." My own experience with multiple experiments on the ground, in the air, and in space has been uniformly unfavorable.* But others may have different views, experiences, and values.

Many of us here who are interested, not in the truck, or the trucking industry, but in performing an experiment in space, have some considerable impatience with the problems of the trucks, their balkiness, care, cost, complexity, and unreliability.

But we must remember that we are dealing with a new invention and a new industry. Most of the important roadblocks to progress—the problems which must be solved before major attention will be placed on the payload, and not on the trucks—are now connected with basic mechanisms, equipment and techniques. We need basic advances in guidance, stabilization, communication systems, power supplies, control, thrust, and above all in reliability. None of these problem areas are under control of, or sensitive to, the advice of astronomers. This is the trucking problem—not simply building a truck, but operating a fleet of trucks, controlling them, communicating with them, and scheduling their operations.

Superimposed on these problems is another problem to which insufficient attention has been paid. The scheduling of space shots is a complicated process, dependent on many factors and considerations in addition to the purpose of the experiment. It is therefore likely that experiments must be planned in detail before the results of earlier and related experiments are available. Completely logical phasing of activities and experiments is therefore not always possible. The schedule, and the activities related thereto, dominate—and perhaps not improperly.

One of my major interests is photography. From my point of view—which is to say, from my set of prejudices, tastes, and biases—there seems to be an insufficient interest in photography. This may well derive from the observation that whatever is familiar, understood, and easily explained cannot be very scientific.

* This and related matters are argued in more detail in A. H. Katz, On Style in Research and Development, The Rand Corporation Paper No. P-2030 (January 26, 1960), *Air Force Space Digest,* February 1962, 45–48.

But sense will prevail, and on that assumption we should begin to think of the physical return of data and photography. It is likely true that for many of the kinds of probes that have been discussed here physical return of the data or of photographs will have to wait; certainly physical return of data from deep space will be paced a few years behind the earlier securing of telemetered data.

These two kinds of return of data are not at all incompatible. They serve different purposes. One can easily conceive of systems wherein the principal goal is physical recovery of the data, but where, for insurance, data is also (and earlier) telemetered back on the same mission. Certainly in the case where one is interested in geometrical fidelity of photography, the rubbery renditions secured via television are probably of marginal utility. So one can, and should, think of a combination of these methods. Certainly if one is getting prepared to think of physical recovery of samples from the planets or comets, and of physical recovery of men from man-made satellites or from the moon, or even from planetary voyages, we can much more easily contemplate the physical return of photographs as well.

Dr. G. de Vaucouleurs: I concur with Mr. Katz's opinion that not enough consideration has been given to the use of photography in the planning of optical experiments from space probes.

17.2 *Problems of Instrumentation for a Mars Probe*

DONALD H. MENZEL

HARVARD COLLEGE OBSERVATORY, Cambridge, Massachusetts

Harvard University has just completed for the Jet Propulsion Laboratory a study of the optical system for a Mars probe.

Our study summarizes current knowledge of the photometric characteristics of Mars in various wavelengths. We have re-examined the question of the albedo of Mars and the brightness of the sunlit surface at various phase angles. Such data are essential for the calculation of the average illumination falling on the vidicon and will also help in the eventual determination of the number of shades of gray to be employed. The analysis indicates the urgent need for re-determinations of the luminosity and albedo of Mars, as well as of the moon and other planets, by a consistent, sensitive, and modern technique. With this objective, Harvard Observatory has just inaugurated a new photometric study in a large number of wavelengths. The investigation will employ photoelectric photometers of great stability and high sensitivity. The actual observations are not yet under way.

As part of our Mars probe study, Dr. James G. Baker carried out a study of the orbital characteristics of the probe in the vicinity of the planet. Hyperbolic orbits, with selected distances of periares, measured from the center of the planet, of 4000, 8000, 16,000, and 32,000 km, were adequate for the study.

As the primary objectives of the observational studies from the probe, we have recommended as most desirable what we termed the "pioneering approach." This would aim at achieving a significant improvement of resolution of the planetary detail over that attainable with terrestrial telescopes. Moreover, one would concentrate on the major portion of the illuminated face of Mars rather than upon a small area of the surface achieved with high resolution. We have no objection to the inclusion of some close-ups, but we feel that the major effort should be devoted to the pioneering studies.

It was interesting to note that an orbit with periares of 55,000 km gives a drift rate to the satellite that almost exactly matches the planet's rate of rotation. The satellite, as seen from a point on the planet, would appear to hover and remain in position for a considerable length of time.

For certain studies this would have an advantage, but it would clearly not be the best for a general mapping of the surface of the planet. A periares of the order of 100,000 km would, in many respects, be preferable to a nearer approach. The slightly smaller diameter of the planet could be offset with the use of a telescope with longer focal length, say of the order of 60 in.

Pioneering studies could be started when the probe is approximately 240,000 km from the planet, and considerable information could be obtained at that distance, provided the power requirements are not excessive. This would then make the most effective use of the available telescope time.

A study of selected optical systems comprises a large portion of the report. It is believed that the range of optical systems here presented will assist in the matching of the system to the problems of recording and telemetry, for which the Jet Propulsion Laboratory has the responsibility.

The systems range from the simplest, standard Cassegrain reflectors, to the most complicated Schmidts. Since speed may be important, one may use a standard Cassegrain of $f/5.0$, though one achieves appreciably improved resolution by going to ratios $f/6.3$ or even $f/8.0$. The Schmidt telescopes, on the other hand, may be as fast as $f/0.63$ if desired, though $f/1.5$ gives the better field and resolution.

The specifications are based on an assumed focal length of 20 in. They may be scaled, however, to any other desired value. In all of them except the Schmidt, Dr. Baker has provided for rear clearance for the mounting of the vidicon.

The designs for 13 different scopes provide for the following. First and simplest are two Cassegrains (Figs. 1 and 2), capable of further modi-

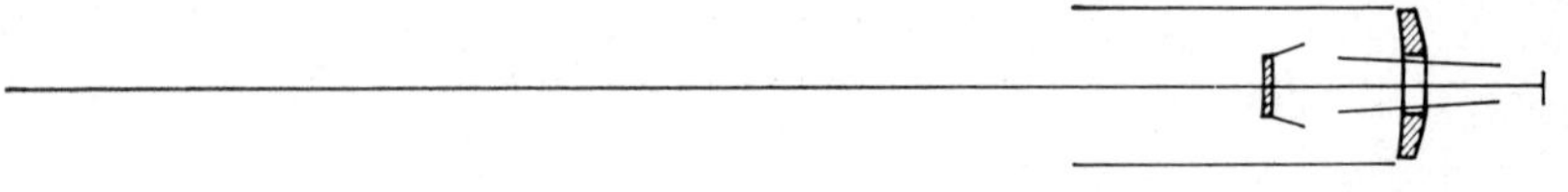

FIG. 1. Standard Cassegrain system at $f/5.0$ (relative height at secondary, 0.4).

FIG. 2. Standard Cassegrain system at $f/5.0$ (relative height at secondary, 0.5).

fication if desired, with the secondary coated on a zero-power glass shell. There are two Ritchey-Chrétien telescopes (Figs. 3 and 4), one Maksutov (Fig. 5), and four of the type commonly known as ADH (Figs. 6–9), a

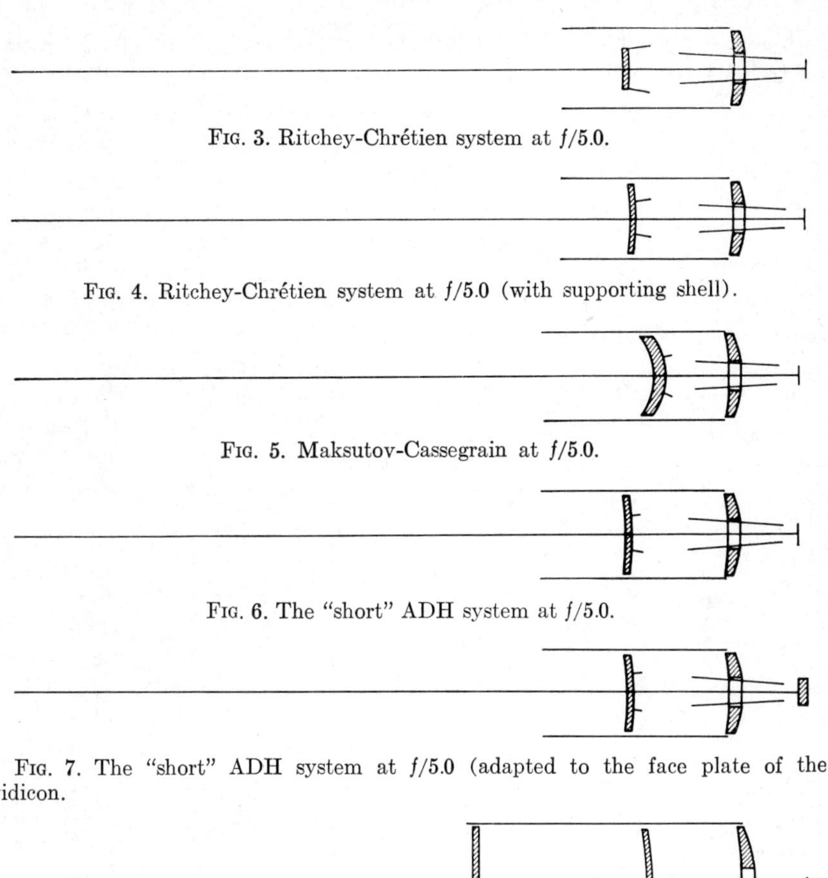

FIG. 3. Ritchey-Chrétien system at $f/5.0$.

FIG. 4. Ritchey-Chrétien system at $f/5.0$ (with supporting shell).

FIG. 5. Maksutov-Cassegrain at $f/5.0$.

FIG. 6. The "short" ADH system at $f/5.0$.

FIG. 7. The "short" ADH system at $f/5.0$ (adapted to the face plate of the vidicon.

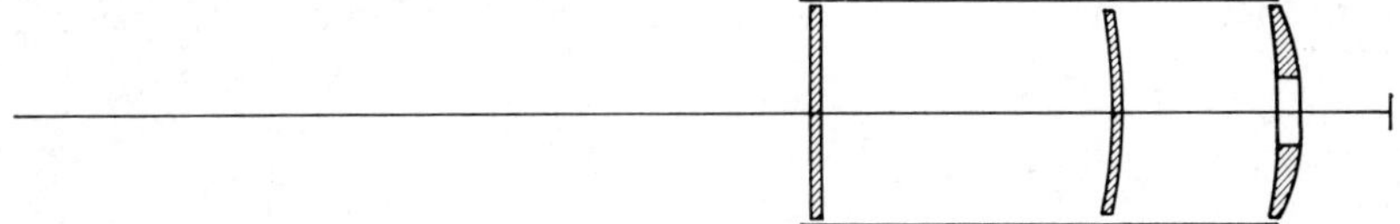

FIG. 8. The "medium" ADH system at $f/3.0$.

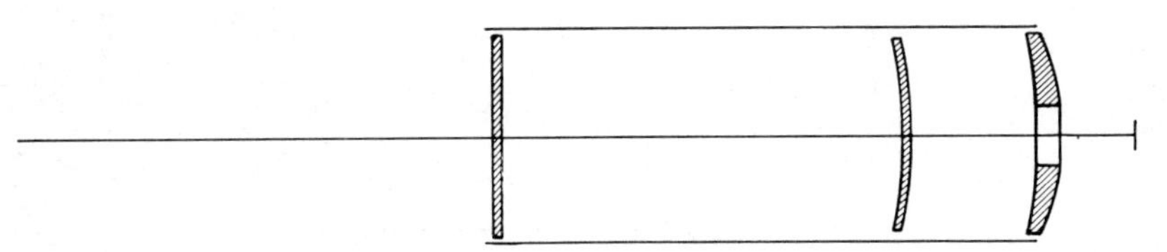

FIG. 9. The "long" ADH system at $f/2.5$.

Baker-Schmidt originally designed for the Armagh-Dunsink-Harvard telescope in the Boyden Observatory in South Africa. Such telescopes have excellent fields and, unlike the classical Schmidt, do not require a curved plateholder.

There is one additional variety of ADH telescope, which has been specially adapted to the face of the vidicon (Fig. 10). One curved field

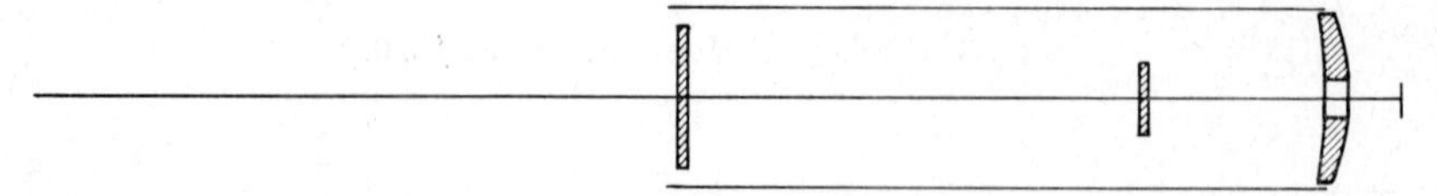

FIG. 10. A special ADH system.

apochromat and one flat field apochromat, working, respectively, at $f/2.5$ (Fig. 11) and $f/2.0$ (Fig. 12), are the recommended lens systems.

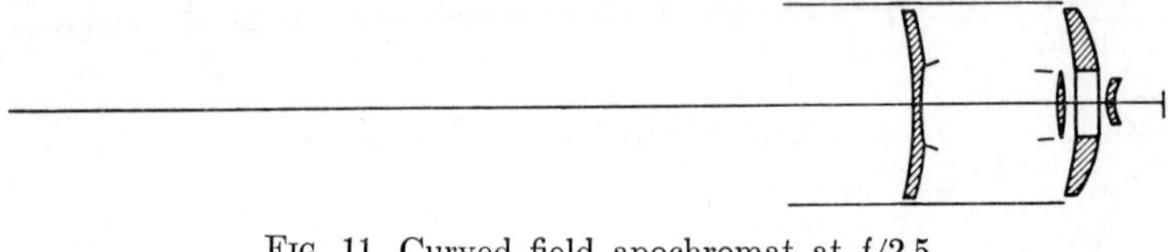

FIG. 11. Curved field apochromat at $f/2.5$.

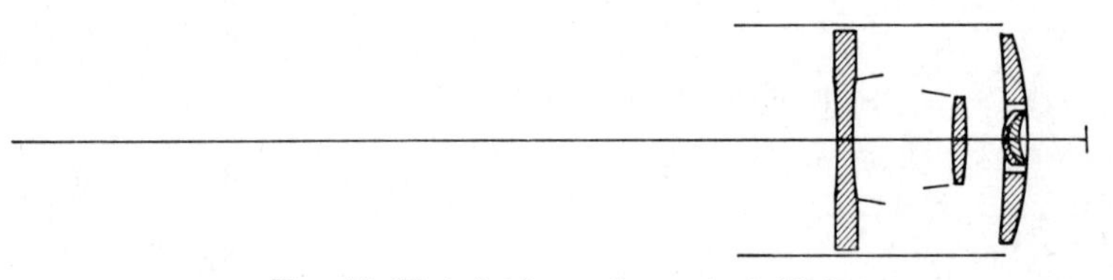

FIG. 12. Flat field apochromat at $f/2.0$.

Finally, we come to the classical Schmidt system, with a ratio of $f/1.5$ (Fig. 13). Maximum chromatic correction is achieved for wavelength 5461 Å.

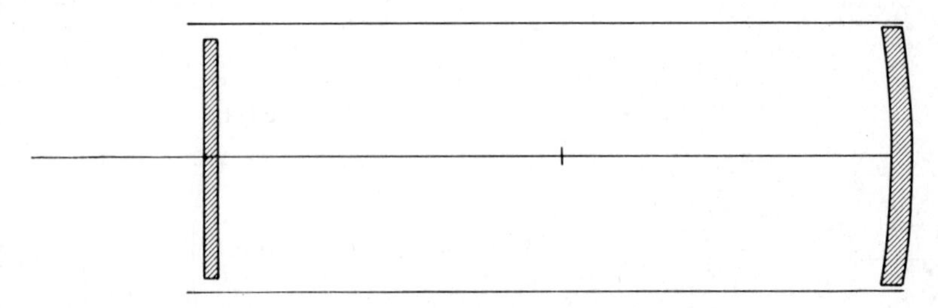

FIG. 13. Classical Schmidt system at $f/1.5$.

Twelve of the designs were made without reference to the vidicon, with requirements similar to those for recording on a flat photographic plate. In other words, the lenses do not allow for the aberrations introduced by the passage of light through the face plate of the vidicon. This is the primary reason for the special study of the vidicon-adapted ADH.

Dr. Baker also analyzes the problem of ground-based planetary telescopes. After discussing the conventional approach to the design of planetary telescopes, Dr. Baker points out many fallacies in the common reasoning, including the suggested limitation of diameter imposed by weight of the glass. He indicates that it would be quite feasible to make a lens with a diameter of 60 in. and recommends an air-spaced triplet as having the best characteristics for planetary observation.

This supplemental study emphasizes the importance that we place on ground-based astronomy. It is extremely vital that a program of planetary astronomy from space probes be extensively supported by observation from ground-based stations. This will greatly assist in the interpretation of planetary features detected by space probes.

I am indebted to Dr. de Vaucouleurs and Dr. Baker, whose studies comprised the major contribution.

17.3 Stereoscopy from Space Satellites

DONALD H. MENZEL

HARVARD COLLEGE OBSERVATORY, Cambridge, Massachusetts

and

GAIL MORETON

LOCKHEED SOLAR OBSERVATORY, Burbank, California

Stereoscopy, which has proved to be a practical tool for mapping the surface of the earth, can be expected to play a similar role for mapping the surface features of the sun, moon, and planets. The principle is elementary and well known. Two photographs, taken from different angles, when viewed through a stereoscope, display the three-dimensional appearance characteristic of stereoscopic vision. If changes in the object or its illumination are sufficiently slow, the pair of pictures need not be taken simultaneously. A single orbiting camera can, for example, provide a series of pictures which can be studied by stereoscopic means.

To ascertain what such studies can provide in the way of scientific information, we have examined selected photograph pairs of the solar surface taken from the Lockheed high-speed H_α patrol, the earth serving as the orbiting vehicle.

The synodic period of a point on the solar equator is about 27 days, corresponding to an angular rotation of about 0.55° per hour. The stereoscopic effect resulting from the binocular examination of two pictures spaced 1 hr apart is equivalent to that of a tennis ball viewed by a pair of eyes separated by 2½ in. and about 20 ft away from the ball. Two hours corresponds to the ball at 10 ft, 4 hr at 5 ft, and so on. The rotation is ample to give a marked stereoscopic effect, as long as changes in the solar surface are so slow that they do not give spurious stereoscopic patterns.

Suitably selected pairs of such pictures* show, as expected, a sun with pronounced sphericity, with the sunspots as somewhat irregular depressions. One pair of on-band pictures depicts a dark filament clearly elevated above the surface and taking the form of a wall. Since we know

* Several samples of such pictures were projected by the Polaroid Vectograph method for the benefit of the symposium audience.

that the material of the prominence is rapidly flowing downward to the surface, we conclude that the permanence of form is due to persistence of the structure of the supporting magnetic field rather than of the prominence matter.

These pictures demonstrate the value of stereoscopy for recognition of important details of the surface of the sun, moon, and planets. Since circumlunary or circumplanetary probes are likely to have a much more rapid angular rate, it appears feasible to secure pairs located far enough apart in space but near enough in time to minimize the deleterious effect of changing illumination caused by the rotation of the object.

17.4 *Sounding Rocket Techniques Extrapolated to Planets*

HERBERT FRIEDMAN

U. S. NAVAL RESEARCH LABORATORY, Washington 25, D. C.

Introduction

Many of the experiments conducted in sounding rockets to determine the characteristics of the terrestrial atmosphere are applicable in principle to the study of planetary atmospheres. Let us assume that the means are available to drop an experimental payload through the planetary atmosphere and to telemeter signals back to earth or to a space relay station. Pressure could be measured by the familiar gauge techniques. Mass spectrometers could determine neutral and ion composition. Radio propagation and probe methods could determine ionospheric electron density. Most of the experiments mentioned are too familiar to need any elaboration. In this chapter the discussion will be devoted to (1) the distribution of solar radiation versus depth within a planetary atmosphere, (2) the possibility of observing extended hydrogen atmospheres such as the geocorona, (3) measurements of albedo and airglow, and (4) the usefulness of direct spectroscopic analysis.

Determination of Atmospheric Structure from the Variation of Optical Thickness as a Function of Wavelength

If a volume of gas is traversed by a beam of monochromatic radiation, the number of molecules per square centimeter column can be computed from the observed attenuation, provided the absorption cross section is known (*1*). Using the sun as a light source and radiation detectors carried in a rocket, it appears possible to determine the height distribution of all the major and some minor constituents of the terrestrial atmosphere to its outermost reaches. As the rocket moves through the atmosphere, the change in the overhead mass of atmospheric gas can be computed from the variation of intensity received at the rocket.

In treating the absorption or emission of radiation in a gaseous atmosphere, it is convenient to use the concept of optical depth as a measure of the attenuation between a reference level and a point outside the atmosphere. The optical depth τ_h at a point h within the atmosphere is defined by

$$\tau_h = \int_h^\infty \mu dh$$

where μ is the linear absorption coefficient. At a given wavelength, the optical depth of an atmospheric constituent is simply the product of its absorption cross section and the number of molecules per square centimeter column above that altitude, if the cross section is independent of altitude. Unit optical thickness is reached at the level where the incident radiation is attenuated to $1/e$ (e = natural base of logarithms).

If a given solar wavelength is absorbed by only one constituent of the atmosphere, the concentration can be determined rather accurately for a range of $\pm$ one scale height of that constituent above and below the altitude where $\tau = 1$. Consider the situation in the terrestrial atmosphere. Above 1200 Å, nitrogen is essentially completely transparent. Because the ultraviolet spectrum from 2000 to 3000 Å is absorbed by ozone, the attenuation in this broad band has permitted the mapping of the ozone distribution up to 70 km. The attenuation of Lyman-α (1216 Å) is a gage of the molecular oxygen concentration in the D-region and may also be useful in determining the concentration of water vapor. The absorption cross section for O_2 at Lyman-α is about 2.8×10^{-20} cm^2 and for H_2O several thousand times as great.

At a wavelength of 1450 Å, the cross section of O_2 reaches 1.4×10^{-17} cm^2 and $\tau = 1$ at about 110 km. With more than three decades of range in absorption cross section, the concentration of O_2 can be accurately determined between 70 and 130 km when the sun is overhead. Close to sunrise or sunset, the slant air mass approaches 38 times the vertical air mass. Measurements near sunset have determined O_2 concentrations to levels as high as 170 km.

In the X-ray region absorption is almost independent of chemical composition, so that it is possible to determine the total density of the atmosphere. Using the wavelength interval 44–60 Å, atmospheric density has been measured from 100 to 160 km.

The cross sections involved in the above-mentioned examples fall in the range 10^{-20} to 10^{-17} cm^2, and are associated with processes of ionization and dissociation. In resonance absorption, however, the cross section may be greater than 10^{-13} cm^2 in the center of the absorption line. Resonance lines of atomic hydrogen, oxygen, and nitrogen appear in the solar ultraviolet spectrum. These lines are absorbed so strongly by the atomic constituents of the atmosphere that it is possible to observe the attenuation effects out to distances of thousands of miles from the surface of the earth.

To perform the radiation measurements from a rocket, it is feasible to work with spectrographic apparatus or to use various photodetectors designed to respond to restricted bands of wavelengths. In rocket experiments conducted over the past 10 years by the U. S. Naval Research Laboratory, a variety of narrow-band photodetectors were used, which responded primarily to solar radiations in wavelengths near 6, 8, 40, 304, 1216, 1300, 1450, and 2000 Å. Most spectrographic measurements have employed photographic registration, but all are adaptable to photoelectric recording. Hinteregger (*2*), at the U. S. Air Force Cambridge Research Center, has employed an electron multiplier in conjunction with a grazing incidence concave grating spectrograph to record the spectrum from Lyman-α to well below the resonance line of singly ionized helium at 304 Å. The instrument is well suited to telemetering the height variation of extreme ultraviolet wavelengths.

The variation of linear absorption coefficient versus wavelength for O_2, O_3, CO_2, and H_2O are shown in Figs. 1–3 from Watanabe *et al.* (*3*). CO_2

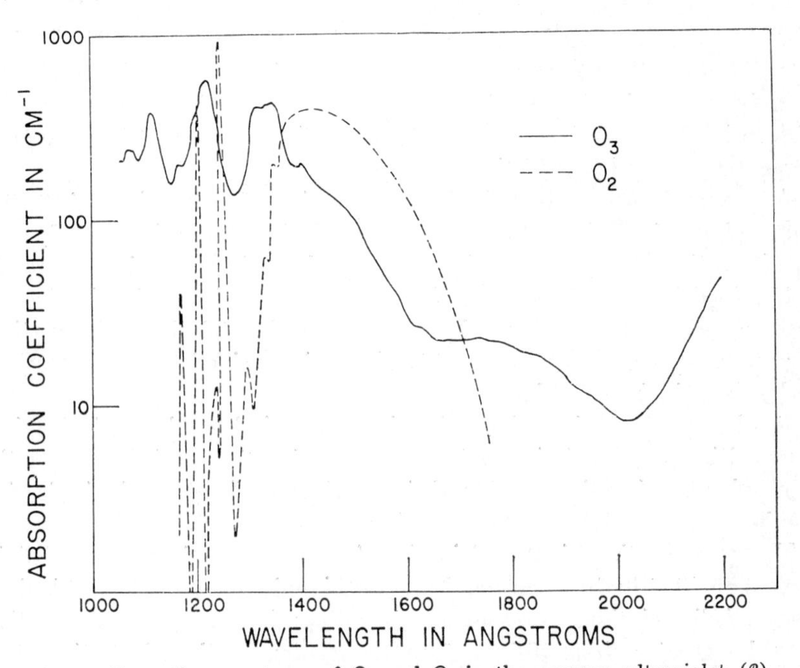

FIG. 1. Absorption spectrum of O_2 and O_3 in the vacuum ultraviolet (*3*).

exhibits a spectral behavior similar to O_2, but is a much weaker absorber. In the terrestrial atmosphere H_2O is dissociated primarily by radiation

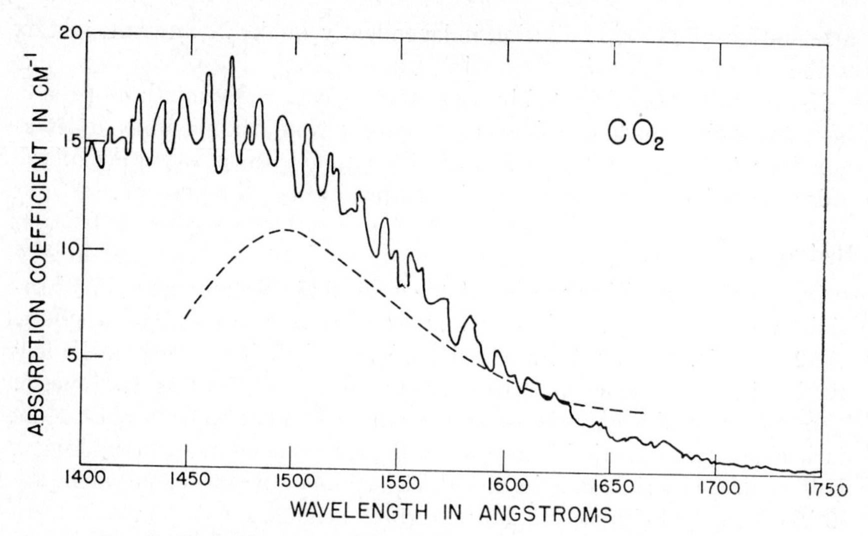

FIG. 2. Absorption spectrum of CO_2 in the vacuum ultraviolet (*3*).

in the range 1700–1850 Å at an altitude near 80 to 90 km, where the O_2 absorption is still comparatively weak. In a planetary atmosphere where CO_2 and N_2 are major constituents, radiation would penetrate to dissociate any H_2O that might be present down to comparatively low altitudes. In the absence of appreciable O_2, CO_2 could be gaged by the

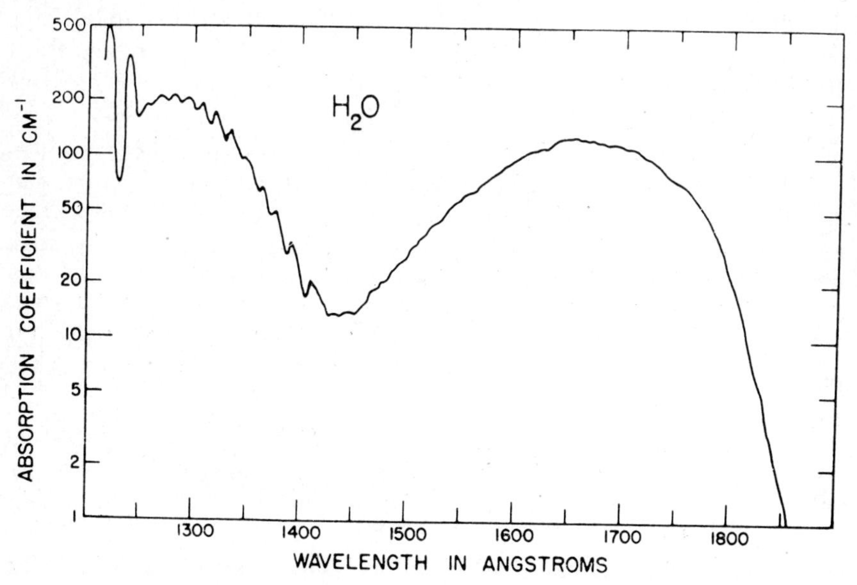

FIG. 3. Absorption spectrum of H_2O in the vacuum ultraviolet (*3*).

attenuation of 1450 Å radiation independently of the N_2 present, just as is the case for O_2 in the terrestrial atmosphere.

X-rays would be absorbed by CO_2, CO, or N_2, or any mixture of these, in very much the same fashion as by air. It would be possible to determine the total density from X-ray absorption with an accuracy of the order of 50% at any altitude without knowing the composition.

Hydrogen Coronas

One of the surprising results of the very first measurements of ultraviolet radiation in the night sky was the discovery of the Lyman-α glow at 1216 Å (*4*). As seen from a rocket above a height of 100 km, the sky overhead radiates about 3×10^{-3} erg cm^{-2} sec^{-1} ster^{-1} at this wavelength. The source of the glow is solar Lyman-α resonantly scattered to the dark side of the earth by an extended geocorona of neutral hydrogen. This hydrogen originates in the dissociation of water vapor near the 90-km level and diffuses rapidly to great heights. Several models have been proposed for the hydrogen cloud but the experimental measurements fix only the total content above 100 km and do not yet permit a definitive determination of the altitude distribution. A model developed by Johnson (*5*) places the hydrogen concentration approximately equal to that of atomic oxygen at the base of the exosphere and arrives at about 10 atoms per cc at a distance of 10 earth radii. Brandt (*6*) has considered the expansion of the geocorona by a mild solar breeze and finds a distribution with the center of gravity at about 10 earth radii. In the first two payloads developed for the U. S. Ranger series of experiments, a 10-in. telescope with a Lyman-α ionization chamber detector at its focus is included. As the rocket moves out into space, the telescope is programmed to scan the receding earth and map the extent of the geocorona.

A hydrogen corona may be expected to exist about any planet that contains water vapor in its atmosphere. Even if the water vapor content on Venus, for example, were very small, the absence of O_2 and the weak absorption at CO_2 will permit solar ultraviolet radiation to penetrate deeply and dissociate the water vapor at comparatively low levels. The brightness of a hydrogen corona such as the earth's would be detectable on Venus or Mars from a Ranger-type probe operating just beyond the earth's geocorona.

The atomic oxygen resonance line near 1300 Å should fluoresce under excitation by solar radiation in much the same manner that hydrogen does. Because atmospheric oxygen is concentrated largely below the exosphere and because the solar flux of the O I triplet near 1300 Å is so weak compared to Lyman-α, no glow has been detected in the night sky. On the daylight side, the atmospheric glow in the 1300 Å region has been measured from a height of 185 km and found to be only an order of magnitude weaker than the Lyman-α glow. From a probe outside the atmosphere, the fluorescence of oxygen should be readily detectable. The detection can be made quite specific by use of an ion chamber equipped with strontium fluoride window and filled with nitric oxide. Such a detector is sensitive to the narrow band, 1290–1350 Å.

Albedo

If one measures the albedo of a planet in the far ultraviolet, he may observe a spectral continuum of scattered sunlight below 3000 Å due to molecular scattering, dust scattering, or surface reflection. If oxygen exists in the planetary atmosphere, ozone will also be present and the albedo may be reduced to zero between 2000 and 3000 Å. Venus could have appreciable ozone, perhaps an amount comparable to the earth, and Mars may have virtually no ozone, in which case Venus would look black but Mars would reflect sunlight in the 2000–3000 Å range.

The measurement of the reflectivity of a planet in the 2000–3000 Å region can be accomplished with small rocket techniques (*7*). Such data were in fact obtained with an Aerobee rocket, launched from White Sands Missile Range in 1957. A photomultiplier was used in combination with an interference filter sensitive to a 300 Å wide band of wavelengths centered near 2700 Å. The photometer was mounted against an aperture in the skin of the rocket looking outward in a direction normal to the length of the rocket. The rocket was unstabilized and the scan of the sky was accomplished by the rolling and precessing motion. In the course of its sweeps of the sky, the photometer received signals from Mars and Jupiter. The respective fluxes at 2700 Å were 2×10^{-8} and 1.5×10^{-7} erg cm^{-2} sec^{-1} per 100 Å. The reflectivities computed from these fluxes were 24% for Mars and 26% for Jupiter, with an estimated accuracy of ±15% for the latter. The Mars signal was close to noise level and the accuracy therefore much poorer. Such a high reflectivity would seem definitely to rule out the existence of ozone in the Martian atmosphere. This type of experiment could be greatly improved and needs to be repeated.

Airglow and Aurora

Airglow measurements from rockets in the visible spectrum have been conducted by the U. S. Naval Research Laboratory for many years to determine the altitude distributions of the various emissions (*8*). Simple photometers using photomultiplier tube detectors and band-pass spectral isolation filters measure the intensity of airglow emission remaining overhead at some selected zenith angle, as they are carried up to and

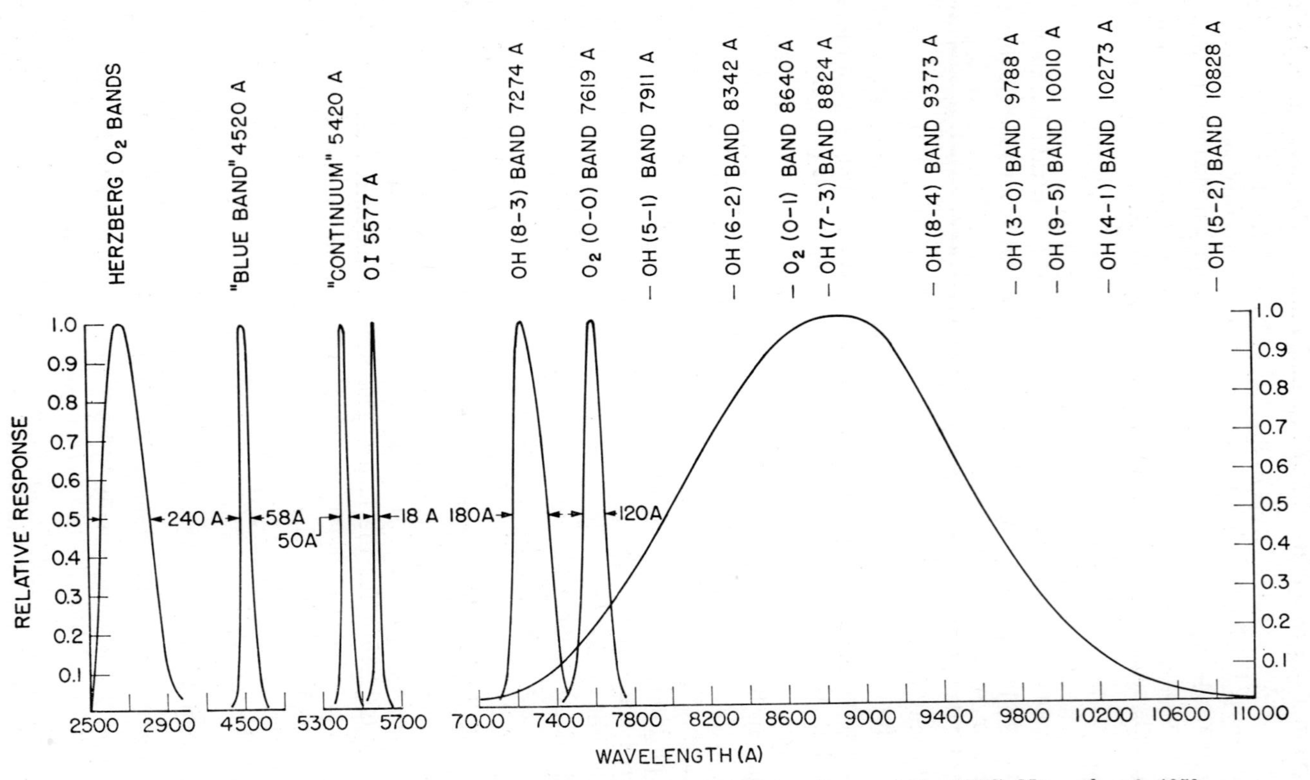

FIG. 4. Wavelength responses of photometers used in NRL Aerobee rocket, 2.78C, November 6, 1959.

through the emitting layers by the rocket vehicle. The radiations investigated and the spectral characteristics of typical isolation filters, employed by the NRL group, are shown in Fig. 4.

Most of the emissions exhibit altitude distributions with fairly sharp lower boundaries, widths at half-intensity of about 20 km, and a relatively slow decrease with altitude above the maximum concentration. The green line of O I at 5577 Å occurs consistently within a narrow layer with a concentration peaked near 95 to 97 km. Most of the measurements have been made with Aerobee rockets which do not achieve an altitude high enough to locate the maximum of the 6300 Å red line emission of O I. The observations show that it originates over a fairly broad range of altitudes above 100 km and most of it is still above the peak altitude for Aerobees, about 200 km.

The peak emission from molecular oxygen occurs at 90 to 93 km, as determined from observations of the Herzberg bands, 2500–2900 Å, and the atmospheric (0-0) band at 7620 Å. The emission from the (0-1) atmospheric band at 8640 Å also occurs in this same altitude region. Observation of the Na I emission at 5890–96 Å is hampered by the presence of OH bands very close to the sodium *D* lines. Nevertheless, altitudes of 85 and 90 km have been found for the sodium emission. Attempted measurements of OH layer heights have not yet clearly defined the altitude of its emission.

The night airglow emissions of Mars and Venus may resemble the terrestrial emissions in many ways and similar probings of the altitudes of emission could reveal important clues to the structures of their atmospheres.

As has already been mentioned, the spectrum of the day airglow is rich in the atomic resonance lines. Also to be expected are the fluorescence bands of molecules such as the Schumann-Runge bands of molecular oxygen above 1750 Å and the Lyman-Birge-Hopfield bands of molecular nitrogen above 1100 Å. Venus may also exhibit carbon monoxide bands between 1100 and 2800 Å.

All of the airglow emissions appear with great intensity in the aurora. Between 1100 and 2600 Å, the Lyman-Birge-Hopfield bands appear strongly and contain the major portion of all the energy radiated by an aurora. Other important features are the Vegard-Kaplan and Goldstein-Kaplan bands of nitrogen, the atomic oxygen line at 2972 Å, the (0-0) band of O_2, and the first negative band of nitrogen at 3914 Å as well as the oxygen green and red lines. All of these features may be studied with interference filter and narrow-band photoionization chamber techniques, but high-resolution spectrophotometry is also feasible. The Ebert-Fastie photoelectric spectrometer has been utilized successfully to measure the auroral ultraviolet spectrum from an Aerobee and can be adapted to the payload specifications of planetary probes.

Direct Spectroscopic Analysis

It has been suggested that direct spectroscopic analysis may be applied by means of instrumentation carried through a planetary atmosphere. The spectrum could be excited by a Tesla coil, using a power of 1 watt or less, and certain key lines or bands could be monitored by photoelectric cells. A qualitative estimate of the characteristics of the spectra that may be expected has been made by P. G. Wilkinson, as follows:

1. Discharge through CO_2: CO_2 is the only positively identified constituent of the atmosphere of Mars. A discharge through low pressure CO_2 produces mainly CO emission bands from 2000 to 6600 Å; possibly CO^+; CO_2^+ unlikely; possibly atomic oxygen, 2500–8500 Å.

2. Discharge through Martian atmosphere proposed by de Vaucouleurs:

Gas:	N_2	O_2	Ar	CO_2	H_2O
m-STP:	1650	<2	70?	40	Very small

In the emission from a discharge through a gas mixture such as given above, one might expect:

a. CO emission bands, 2000–6600 Å;
b. Ar lines, 2100–10,000 Å;
c. N_2 emission bands, 2800–6800 Å;
d. NO emission bands, 2000–5270 Å;
e. O_2 emission bands, 2000–5000 Å;
f. OH emission bands, 2400–3500 Å, 7000–8000 Å;
g. Atomic oxygen emission lines, 2500–8500 Å;
h. Atomic nitrogen emission lines, 2308–9000 Å;
i. Atomic carbon, perhaps a few lines, 2160–9000 Å.

3. Discharge through Martian atmosphere proposed by Kuiper (see the accompanying tabulation):

Gas	cm-STP	Gas	cm-Stp
CO_2	400	C_2H_6	<1
SO_2	<0.003	NH_3	<1
O_3	<0.05	H_2	—
N_2O	<200	N_2	—
CH_4	<10	O_2	—
C_2H_4	<2		

In the emission from a discharge through a gas mixture such as given above, one might expect, in addition to those bands and lines mentioned in paragraph 2 above:

a. Emission bands of SO_2, 2100–4300 Å;
b. Emission bands of SO, 2400–3900 Å;
c. Emission bands of H_2, 4000–8000 Å;
d. Emission bands of C_2, 4365–6677 Å, 2378–3283 Å;
e. Emission bands of CH, 3143–4890 Å;
f. Emission bands of C_3, 3600–4200 Å;
g. Emission bands of NH_2, 4465–6332 Å;
h. Possible emission bands of O_3;
i. Atomic emission lines of sulfur, 2000–8000 Å.

If a fairly high dispersion experiment were made between 2000 and 8000 Å, a *semiqualitative* analysis might indicate the following:

a. Presence or absence of molecules containing N, O, C, H, S.
b. Presence of Ar and possible estimate of abundance.

In addition, some guesses could be made of the presence of the molecules and atoms given in the accompanying tabulation.

(1) Molecules

Bands found	Possible molecular origin
CO	CO or CO_2
CO^+	CO or CO_2
N_2	N_2
NO	NO, N_2, O_2, oxides of nitrogen
O_2	O_2, O_3
OH	H_2O
SO_2	SO_2
SO	SO_2
C_2	hydrocarbons
C_3	hydrocarbons
CH	hydrocarbons
NH_2	NH_3
H_2	H_2, hydrocarbons

(2) Atoms

Atomic lines found	Possible origin
O	O_2, O_3, H_2O, oxides of N, CO, CO_2
N	N_2, NH_3, oxides of N
C	CO, CO_2, hydrocarbons
H	hydrocarbons, H_2O, NH_3
S	SO_2
Ar	Ar (definite)

If the experiment is based on having only a few photocells set at appropriate wavelength positions, and N_2, NH_2, SO_2, and OH bands (or any combination of these) were found, it could be stated fairly definitely that N_2, NH_3, SO_2 and H_2O are present in the Mars atmosphere. If argon lines were found, some estimate of its abundance could be made.

The certain identification of any of the species considered above by monitoring radiation with only a few photocells seems quite remote and quantitative measurement out of the question.

References

1. T. A. Chubb, E. T. Byram, H. Friedman, and J. E. Kupperian, Jr., *Ann. Geophys.* **14,** 109 (1958).
2. L. Heroux and H. E. Hinteregger, *Rev. Sci. Instr.* **31,** 280 (1960).
3. K. Watanabe, M. Zelikoff, and C. Y. Inn, AFCRC Tech. Rept. No. 53-23 (1953).
4. J. E. Kupperian, Jr., E. T. Byram, T. A. Chubb, and H. Friedman, *Ann. Geophys.* **14,** 329 (1958).
5. F. S. Johnson and R. A. Fish, *Astrophys. J.* **131,** 502 (1960).
6. J. Brandt, Private communication.
7. A. Boggess, III, and L. Dunkelman, *Astrophys. J.* **129,** 236 (1959).
8. D. M. Packer, Symposium on Aeronomy, Copenhagen, July 1960. *Ann. Geophys.* **17,** 67 (1961).

17.5 The Atmosphere of Mars

W. W. KELLOGG

THE RAND CORPORATION, Santa Monica, California

Many of the ideas presented in this chapter are the result of the discussions held by some 15 or 20 scientists who met at the invitation of the Space Science Board of the National Academy of Sciences to discuss the atmospheres of Mars and Venus. The meetings were held at CalTech, with the Jet Propulsion Laboratory helping in the local arrangements. For a total of about 6 days last winter we argued and speculated about our neighboring planets. We will not go into the composition of this Panel, since our report is expected to be published by the Space Science Board of the National Academy of Sciences in November 1961; it will be generally available. It is enough to say that the participants were chosen to represent a sort of cross section of the many different disciplines that need to be invoked when discussing the planets, and that we were given enough time to learn to understand each other's language.

The purpose of our meetings was primarily to decide what we did and did not know about Mars and Venus and to clarify the bounds of our uncertainty. Out of such an exercise it was hoped to see more clearly what needs to be done in order to resolve the many outstanding questions—and this we did also. We will attempt to review these conclusions.

Mars is, next to the earth, the best understood planet, because we can see its surface, though dimly. We can see the rotation and measure it quite accurately. We can watch the clouds that move across the face of Mars and change in a matter of hours. We can watch the changing polar caps. We can measure the temperature of the surface. We can say quite a bit about Mars, and yet it would be impertinent indeed to suggest that we really have a very clear picture of the Martian atmosphere. We do not, and the extent of our knowledge is given in Table I.

Surface temperature has been measured by thermocouples a number of times. The maximum temperature observed occurs at noon near the equator, and is about 300°K. We cannot measure the coldest place on Mars because that would be the polar cap on the winter side, and this is always turned away from the earth when Mars is close enough to make an observation. We can only say that it is less than 200°K. However, the temperature of Mars measured by bolometry is not necessarily the temperature of the *air* near the surface. In fact, there is no reason why it should be, although, for lack of anything better, a great many people have assumed that this was so. Professor Yale Mintz of UCLA, a member of the Panel, was inspired to really look into this matter. By extending the experience that we have from dry deserts on earth and extrapolating to a Martian desert, he concludes that the air temperature a few meters above the surface at noon can be as much as 50°C cooler than the temperature of the surface itself. Anybody who has walked on

TABLE I
MARS

Albedo (diffuse)	Composition
0.3 at 7000 Å	CO_2 identified {3100 cm-STP, 2–3%}
0.04 at 4500 Å	
	H_2O deduced (10^{-3}–10^{-2} gm cm^{-2})
Surface temperature	CO deduced
Max ~300°K	N_2 probably main constituent
Min <200°K	Ar as on Earth?
Temperature of near-surface air	
<250°K	Aerosols
	Blue haze ?
Surface Pressure	White clouds {H_2O, CO_2}
85 mb	
(within about a factor of 2)	Yellow clouds dust

a hot desert barefoot will vouch for the fact that the sand is a great deal hotter, by a good many degrees, than the air a meter above the sand. So, we say that the near-surface air temperature must be less than 250°, or at least 50°C less than the maximum temperature observed. This has quite an implication on any model of the Mars atmosphere that one might draw.

Many models of the Mars atmosphere, in terms of its vertical temperature distribution, have been suggested. They are all entirely speculative; or, as, for example, in the calculations that Goody has made, based on theoretical calculations without full knowledge of the boundary conditions that would apply.

If there were ozone in the Martian atmosphere (we have no evidence whether there is or not) it would, of course, have a tremendous effect on the upper atmosphere temperature of Mars. It has been suggested that this could not be less than 140°K, because at this temperature the carbon dioxide that we know exists on Mars would precipitate out. However, this is not a very conclusive argument, because we are not sure there are no ice crystals floating in the Martian atmosphere. We notice that our own stratosphere precipitates out water vapor, so why could not the Martian stratosphere precipitate out carbon dioxide?

The surface pressure has been measured by Dr. de Vaucouleurs, and is about 85 mb which corresponds to 230 gm/cm^2 of atmosphere. There is probably an uncertainty factor of about 2 in that estimate.

Turning to the composition of the Martian atmosphere, carbon dioxide has definitely been identified spectroscopically. Two or three per cent appears to be the carbon dioxide mixing ratio. This corresponds to about 3000 cm-STP of carbon dioxide in the vertical. We have no direct spectroscopic evidence for any other constituents. We guess that water vapor is there. There is no reason to doubt that. We think that the polar caps are made of ice crystals. One can, based on this assumption, deduce that the total amount of water vapor on Mars is between 10^{-3} and 10^{-2} gm cm^{-2}. Carbon monoxide is probably there, because carbon dioxide is there. Nitrogen is, by analogy with the earth, probably the dominant constituent, but there is no way that we can identify it spectroscopically (or otherwise) from the earth. Oxygen has not been identified, so it must be there only in trace amounts. Argon is probably there for the reason that it is heavy and would not escape, and it exists in the earth's atmosphere.

The aerosols in the Martian atmosphere are usually divided into three general types, viz., the *blue haze;* the *white clouds,* which are usually temporary; and the *yellow clouds,* which are also extremely variable. The blue haze is always present to some extent; as has been shown by Wilson and Richardson, Öpik, de Vaucouleurs, and others, it changes in a peculiar way—rather rapidly at certain times. We can guess that the white clouds are composed of ice or water, or possibly carbon dioxide crystals. We can guess that the yellow clouds are dust. But we are quite at a loss to explain the composition and behavior of the blue haze.

The albedo of Mars is 0.3 at 7000 Å, 0.04 in the ultraviolet. In other words, it is obvious that Mars is a red planet, because it reflects more in the red than in the blue. In calculating the heat budget of the planet, we must take this general or diffuse albedo into account.

Finally, we must discuss the general circulation of the Martian atmosphere. There are a few things we can say about it, because we can observe something about the patterns of the clouds that move across the Martian disk. We seem to see moving clouds more in the winter hemisphere than in the summer hemisphere; they also occur near the Martian equinox. These clouds may be related to cyclonic disturbances in the lower atmosphere. Quoting Professor Mintz, who has applied meteorological theory to this question, we would expect that the Martian atmosphere would display the same kind of instability that our own atmosphere displays in winter. That is, a rotating planet such as Mars or the earth, with a thin atmosphere on it, and gently heated at the equator, will have a stable and regular circulation, with rising air in the hot part and descending air in the cold part. However, as the heating at the equator (and cooling aloft) is increased, it reaches a point where it no longer remains in the stable circulation regime. Then it breaks down into an unstable type of circulation known as the Rossby wave circulation regime. This is the regime that exists on our own earth in winter and in summer. Mintz thinks that on Mars in the summer there is probably a regular circulation, and in early winter the transition takes place to the irregular wave circulation.

Our chief uncertainties about Mars' atmospheric temperatures and composition can be summarized as follows: We would particularly like to know about the quantity of water vapor and molecular oxygen. (Molecular oxygen may occur in trace amounts. If it is present in as much as even one part in 10^4, it could produce an appreciable ozone layer, enough to have greatly modified the temperature in the upper atmosphere.) The composition of the blue haze would be a third crucial question that we would like very much to have resolved. We would like, furthermore, to observe the general circulation (the winds and the weather) of Mars.

The experiments that are suggested by these questions are briefly as follows. Starting with an earth-bound experiment, we recognize that infrared spectroscopic observations of Mars from balloons would be extremely valuable in making observations about its atmosphere. Such observations would detect water vapor if there is as much as we think. Also, using balloons we could get high resolution pictures of Mars which would tell us much more about the cloud forms that we now see very imperfectly, and this would reveal much about the general circulation.

From fly-by vehicles it is quite clear that we could gain a great deal more. In the infrared, we could have very high spatial resolution as well as spectral resolution. We could determine the upper air temperature by carefully measuring the carbon dioxide emission at 15 μ, an experiment that has been suggested by Dr. Lewis Kaplan, a member of the Panel. The water vapor could be measured quantitatively; and, of course, the question of organic matter (life?) on the surface might be resolved by this experiment also. A second type of experiment from the fly-by vehicle that would tell us a great deal about Mars would be a mapping of the intensities and polarization of the scattered light in the visible and ultraviolet. This would tell us definitely whether there is ozone, and something about the distribution of ozone in the upper atmosphere. It would also tell us about the heights of the haze layers, which, of course, scatter light differently from the molecular components of the atmosphere.

The ultimate experiment on Mars would be a capsule that would enter the Martian atmosphere, drift down making measurements as it went, land and continue to observe and transmit like a remote weather station. It is fair to say that the Martian sky is the limit for such an instrument.

Discussion

DR. E. RECHTIN: I have a very short question for Dr. Kellogg. He intrigued us by saying that the air temperature close to the surface of Mars was not quite as high as the surface itself. Can a similar statement be made about Venus? In other words, what is the air temperature just off the surface of Venus?

DR. W. W. KELLOGG: Dr. Rechtin has raised a good point. I think the point here is that the large temperature difference between a hot noontime desert surface and the air immediately above is due to the fact that the air just does not have a chance to catch up to the surface. Now, Mars has, of course, a length of day about like the earth's. So there is no chance to establish a thermal balance between the surface and the air above it during the middle of the day. But in the case of Venus, which has a very low rotation rate, this argument does not apply at all.

17.6 The Physical Environment of Venus: Models and Prospects

CARL SAGAN

UNIVERSITY OF CALIFORNIA, Berkeley, California

1. Introduction

In the preceding chapter, Dr. Kellogg has mentioned the meetings of the Planetary Atmospheres Study Panel of the Space Science Board. I think it is fair to say that the most exciting discussions we had were about the physical environment of Venus. We reached fair agreement on the structure of the upper atmosphere of Venus, but we were able to come to no accord at all on the nature of the lower Cytherean* atmosphere and surface. We did manage to delineate three mutually exclusive models, each of which is to a certain extent self-consistent but has, I think, certain weak points which need further work. In the following we will try to outline both the models and the weak points; for the details and literature citations, the reader is referred to the full panel report and to the bibliography.

2. Observations of Venus at Various Wavelengths

There are a number of wavelengths at which Venus can be observed. In some cases Cytherean temperatures can be extracted from the observations. In the visible, Venus is an almost featureless disk; in the ultraviolet, cloud patterns can be discerned. Neither visible nor ultraviolet observations lend themselves to temperature determinations. In the near infrared lie a number of carbon dioxide absorption bands—CO_2 is the only molecule identified in large quantities on Venus to date. The amount of carbon dioxide on Venus is much greater than on earth. From radiative transfer theory a rotational temperature of about 285°K has been obtained for the 8000 Å CO_2 bands, on the assumption that the distribution of scattering particles follows the distribution of absorbing carbon dioxide molecules. On the other hand, if the scattering layer is assumed to have a sharp upper boundary, then the rotational temperature is greater.

* Cytherean = pertaining to Venus (= Venerian).

In the far infrared, measurements of the Cytherean temperature have been made by thermocouple bolometry in the 8 to 13 μ window in the terrestrial atmosphere. The temperatures so derived are about 234°K, and clearly do not arise from the same level as does the 8000 Å rotational temperature. The far infrared temperatures probably arise from higher altitudes than do the near infrared temperatures.

Measurements made in the 8 mm microwave region give brightness temperatures near inferior conjunction of around 350°K.

So far, none of these temperature determinations are entirely unexpected, and the difference among them is easily attributed to the fact that at different wavelengths we are looking at different atmospheric depths. 350°K is about the surface temperature on Venus that one expected several years ago.

Therefore, the discovery of a 600°K microwave brightness temperature between 3 and 21 cm wavelengths has been a considerable surprise, and this is the principal datum which the following models attempt to explain. The 8-mm radio emission from Venus appears to be a strong function of phase, increasing markedly as we see more and more of the illuminated hemisphere of Venus. There is also some evidence that the emission at centimeter wavelengths varies with phase.

3. The Greenhouse Model

Figures 1 and 2 show the thermal structure and the levels of radiation origin for the first model of the physical environment of Venus, the Greenhouse model. In this picture, some visible light from the sun penetrates the cloud layer, and strikes the surface. The surface heats up and radiates in the infrared. However, the infrared radiation has difficulty escaping from the lower atmosphere, because of molecular absorption in the atmosphere and light scattering in the cloud layer. The surface temperature therefore rises to an equilibrium value much higher than if there were no atmosphere.

The 3 to 21 cm radiation arises from the surface on the Greenhouse model, so the surface is at 600°K or possibly even hotter on the bright side of Venus. The 8000 Å and 8 mm radiation arise from the atmosphere. Radiation at these wavelengths is attenuated by the clouds and by dust in the lower atmosphere.

The opacity required to make the greenhouse effect work cannot possibly be provided by the carbon dioxide present on Venus. Too many atmospheric windows exist in the infrared. However, if we assume about 10 gm cm^{-2} of water vapor—just a few times the amount in the terrestrial atmosphere—the windows seem to be filled in, and the required atmospheric opacity appears to be achieved. Assuming a constant mixing ratio

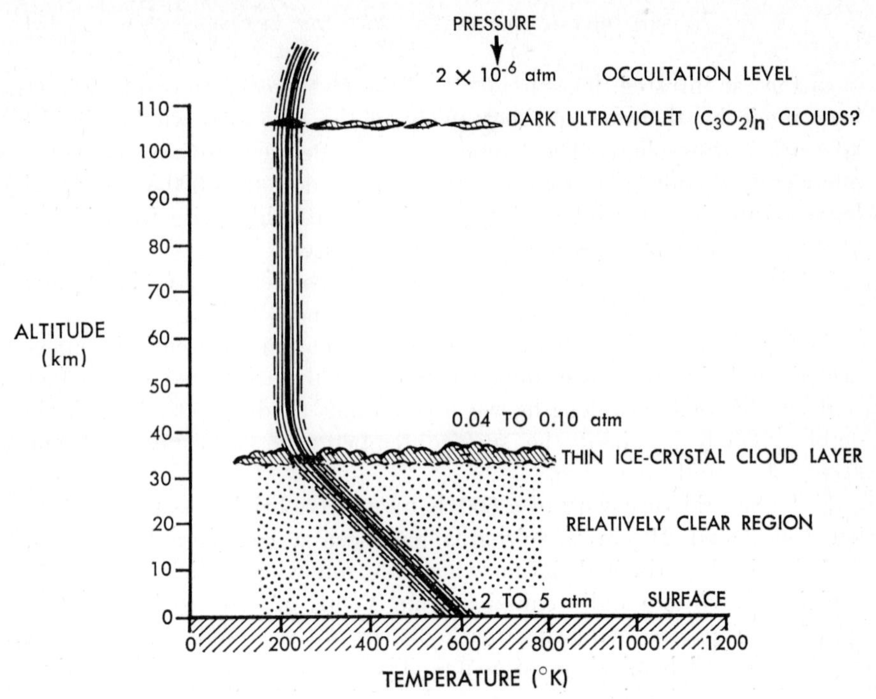

Fig. 1. Greenhouse model, thermal structure.

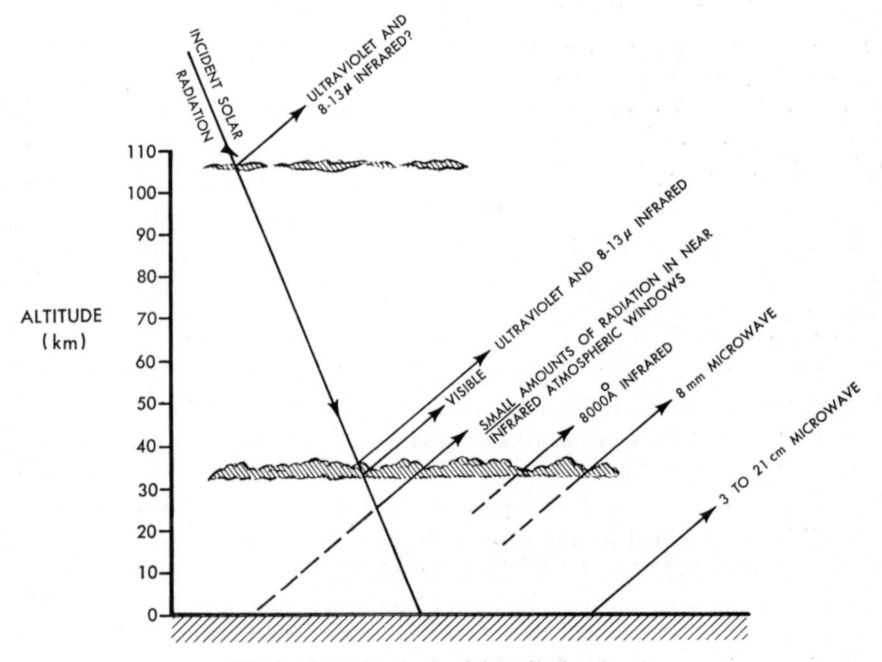

Fig. 2. Greenhouse model, radiation levels.

of H_2O and an adiabatic lapse rate, water saturates the atmosphere at about 36 km altitude. The temperature at this altitude is just the far infrared thermocouple temperature, so the Greenhouse model gives an ice crystal cloud layer at the observed temperature. Furthermore, recent near infrared spectrophotometry by Sinton has shown absorption features attributed to ice at the same temperature level from which the far infrared thermocouple radiation arises.

4. The Aeolosphere Model

Figures 3 and 4 show the thermal structure and levels of radiation origin of the Aeolosphere model of Venus. There is a thick dusty stirred region, the top of which is the visible cloud layer. The opacity in the visible is so great that essentially no visible radiation penetrates to the surface. The upper atmospheric circulation is thermally driven, thereby transferring momentum downwards, and stirring the dusty region below. The surface is heated by dust and gas friction in the lower atmosphere.

The surface temperature is 600°K in the Aeolosphere model, and the surface is the origin of the 3 to 21 cm radio emission. The thermal struc-

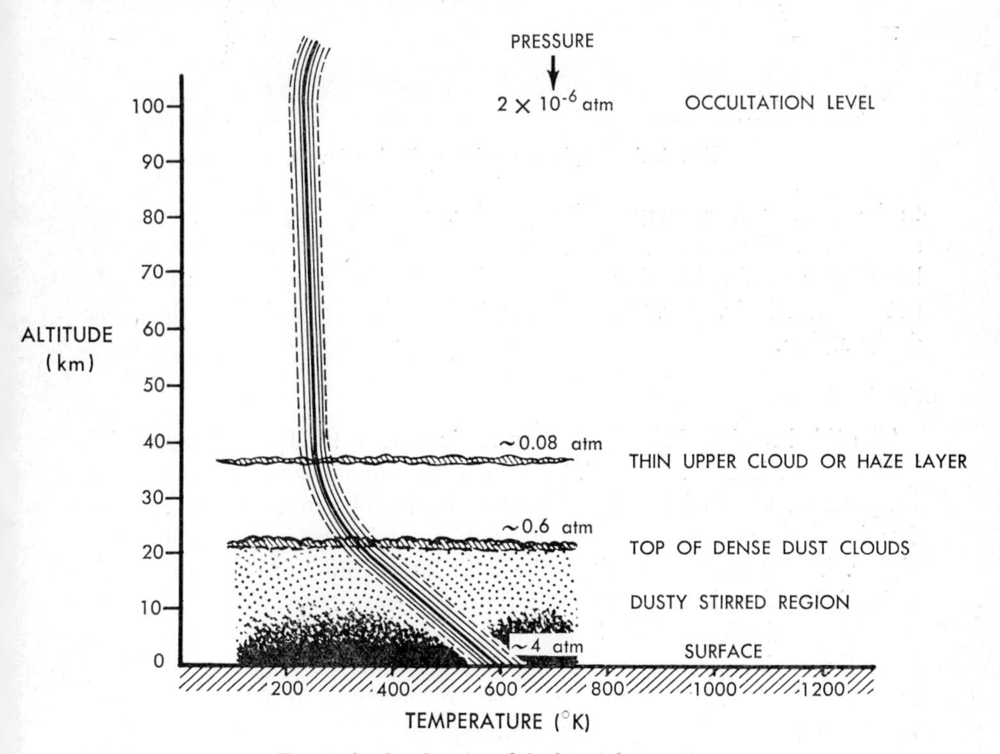

FIG. 3. Aeolosphere model, thermal structure.

ture of the upper atmosphere is not extremely different from that of the Greenhouse model, except that the temperature of the visible cloud layer is the 8000 Å rotational temperature (or even higher), rather than the far infrared thermocouple temperature. The cloud composition is thought

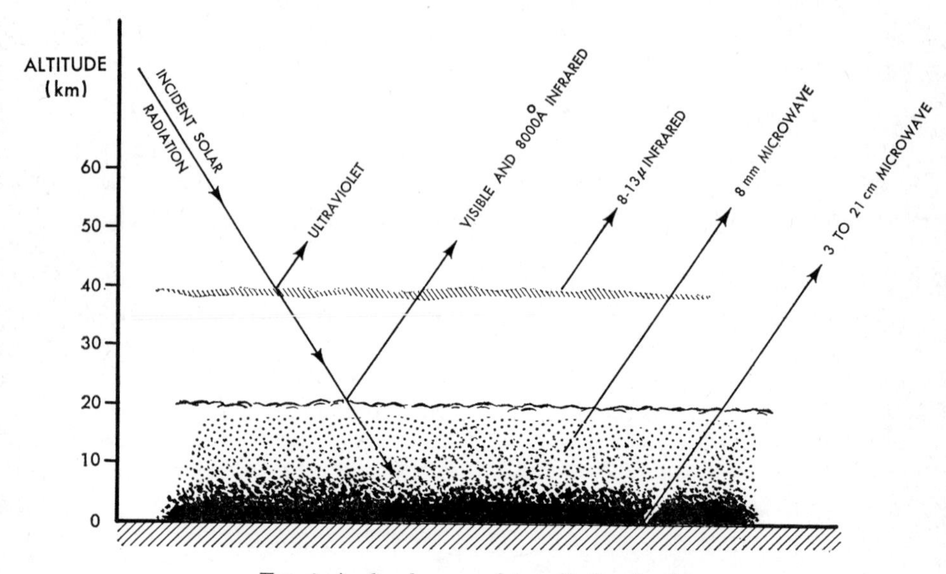

FIG. 4. Aeolosphere model, radiation levels.

to be a very fine, very white powder, possibly largely made up of carbonates. The far infrared and ultraviolet radiation both arise from a haze layer at about 36-km altitude of unspecified composition; but it is not composed of water. The 8-mm emission arises from deep in the lower dusty region.

5. The Ionospheric Model

The third model of the Cytherean environment, the Ionospheric model, is illustrated in Figs. 5 and 6. The night-time ionosphere has an electron temperature of 600°K and an electron density of about 10^9 cm^{-3}. In the day hemisphere the electron temperatures and densities are somewhat higher. Under these conditions the 3 to 21 cm microwave radiation is emitted by the electrons making free-free transitions. At about 1-cm wavelength the ionosphere is becoming transparent, and some radiation from the surface is escaping to space. At 8 mm, the emission is largely from the surface. This model very neatly accounts for both the microwave spectrum and the phase variation.

On the Ionospheric model the far infrared thermocouple temperatures arise from a cloud layer some 15 km above the surface of Venus. The 8000 Å bands arise from rather near the surface. Because the microwave emission comes primarily from the ionosphere in this model, there is no strong determination of cloud composition and structure of the lower atmosphere.

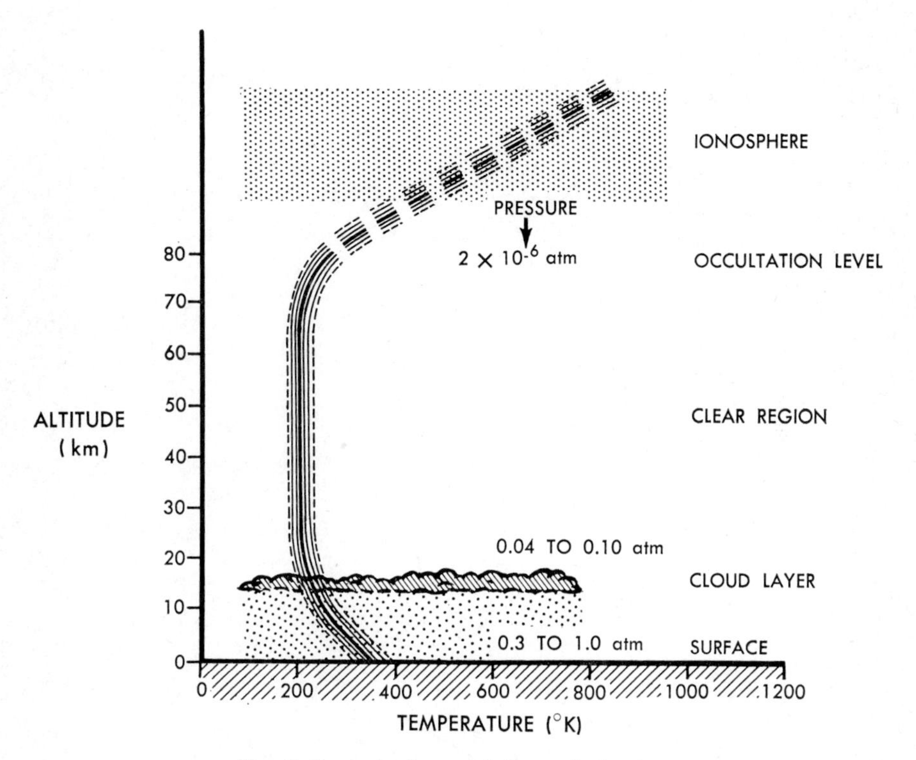

Fig. 5. Ionospheric model, thermal structure.

In order to match the observed microwave spectrum, the surface temperature of Venus must be below the boiling point of water on the Ionospheric model. This is the only model, therefore, which permits oceans on the surface of Venus. In the past several arguments have been presented which favor the presence of oceans on Venus. Very recently, Kuz'min and Salomonovich have reported a day-to-day variability in the radio emission of Venus at 9.6 cm. The variation is sometimes as great as several hundreds of degrees. If verified, such variations would provide strong support for the Ionospheric model; however, other workers at neighboring wavelengths have been unable to confirm this observation.

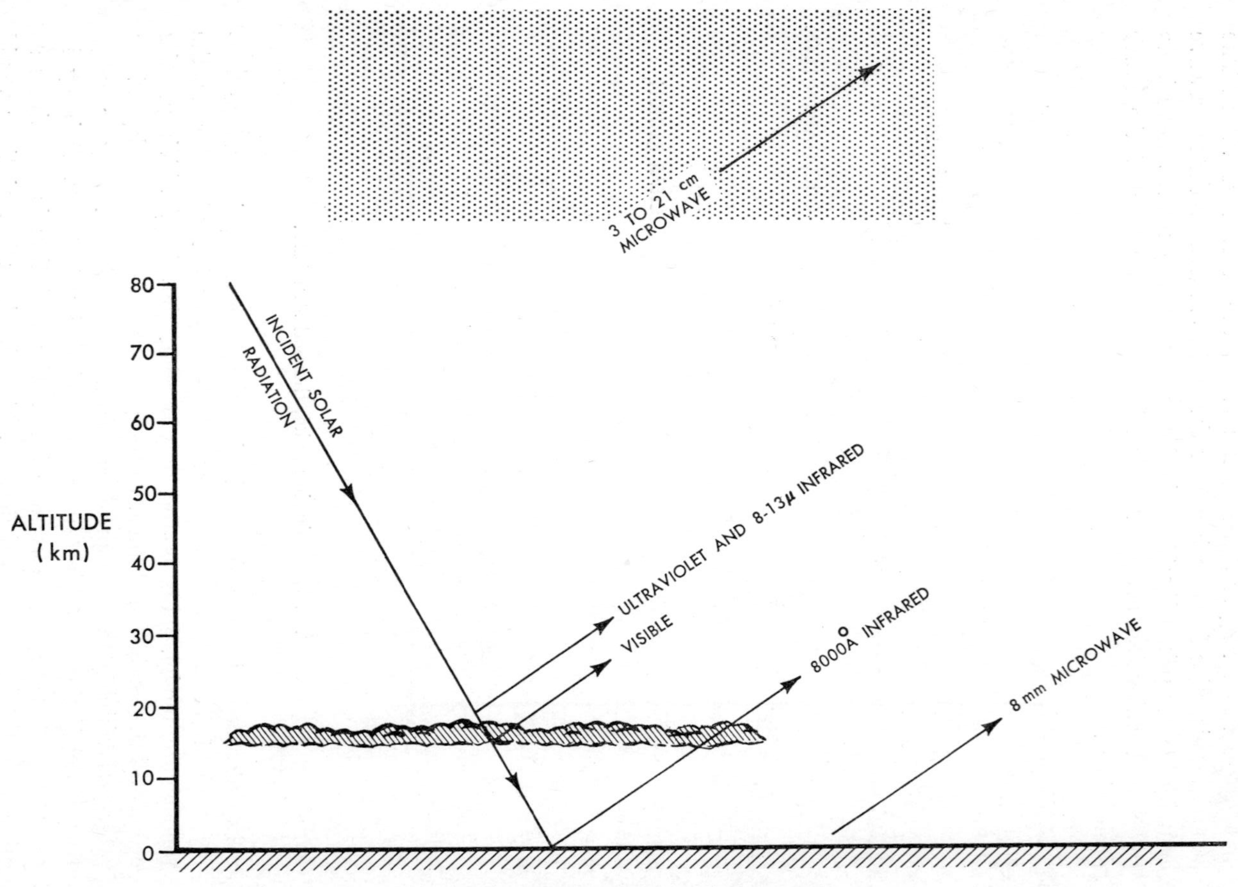

Fig. 6. Ionospheric model, radiation levels.

6. Difficulties with the Models

We now come to the weaknesses of these models. There may well be other weaknesses besides the ones which are mentioned, but let us try to state the major difficulties.

In the Greenhouse model, there is still the question whether the required infrared opacities will be achieved. Unfortunately, at the present time there are no direct spectroscopic data for the long paths, high temperatures, and moderately high pressures which the model requires. The opacity calculations have been based first on existing long path length absorptivities in the boiler and furnace technology literature; but, these data only give the opacities integrated over all wavelengths. Secondly, calculations have been made based on existing spectra for short paths, and scaled by a theoretical model of the curve of growth for molecular bands—for example, the error function law. Both methods indicate that the required opacities will be achieved, but both are based on extrapolations. They do not conclusively prove that the absorption is sufficiently great.

A second possible difficulty with the Greenhouse model concerns the question of whether the steep vertical temperature gradient can be maintained against convection. There should be a tendency for both vertical convection and horizontal advection to equalize temperatures, but it is not known to what extent such equalization will be successful. Calculations are in progress on this point.

The details of the circulation in the Aeolosphere model remain to be worked out. It is still to be demonstrated that the momentum transport necessary to heat the surface by friction does indeed exist. Secondly, Sinton's suggestion that the far infrared thermocouple temperatures arise from an ice crystal cloud layer is in apparent contradiction with the Aeolosphere model, where these temperatures arise from a cloud of dust. Finally, the model is inconsistent with marked phase effects in the microwave emission, especially if the brightness temperature of Venus is a minimum at inferior conjunction, as seems to be the case. With a massive dust layer blanketing the surface, one would expect surface temperature to adjust itself sluggishly if at all to a change in the insolation.

It is very difficult to explain the high electron densities required by the Ionospheric model. They are just barely possible if (1) Venus has a magnetic field strength less than 10^{-3} gauss, so solar protons can reach the atmosphere, (2) the highest published value of the solar wind proton flux is valid, and (3) dissociative recombination is excluded in the Cytherean ionosphere. Under more realistic assumptions, there seems to be no source for the required ionization.

Another problem with the Ionospheric model is that, if it is taken at face value, there should be no radar return from Venus at all. The opacity for free-free transitions increases as the square of the wavelength. The microwave emission spectrum requires unit optical depth near 1 cm. At radar frequencies, we should have very high opacities indeed, the radar pulse should be completely absorbed, and we should see no returned signal, contrary to observation. The only way out of this dilemma is to assume a hole in the night-time ionosphere of Venus. On a slowly rotating planet such a hole is not entirely out of the question, but it has the disadvantage of all *ad hoc* hypotheses.

7. Critical Space Probe Experiments

The situation is not entirely satisfactory. A series of experiments which could distinguish among these three models would be of considerable interest. Space vehicles are necessary to acquire the needed critical information. In the remainder of this discussion we will indicate what such a series of experiments might be like. The list will not be exhaustive, and there will probably be other discriminant experiments proposed.

(a) Microwave Limb-Brightening

Imagine that Venus is being observed from a flyby probe in the 1-cm wavelength region. Because of the close approach which the flyby makes to the planet, the disk can be resolved, and a scan can be made from the center of the disk to the limb. On the Ionospheric model, the ionosphere is becoming transparent around 1 cm, and a scan of the disk should reveal a pronounced limb-brightening. If the Ionospheric model is wrong, no such pronounced limb-brightening will be seen; indeed we might expect some limb-darkening.

(b) Microwave Emission Phase Effects

A critical test of the Aeolosphere model involves a search for strong phase effects at 3 cm and longer wavelengths. A flyby equipped with suitable microwave antennas can, in a short period of time, run through the entire 180° of phase angle. On the Aeolosphere model, there should be almost no variation of brightness temperature with phase, and the minimum brightness temperature should occur considerably after phase angle 180°. On both the Greenhouse and Ionospheric models, appreciable phase effects can be expected, with much more pronounced correlation between 180° phase angle and minimum brightness temperature.

(c) Active Radar Phase Effects

A direct test of the hypothesis that a hole exists in the night-time ionosphere of Venus can be performed by active radar carried by a flyby. The intensity of the returned signal should vary markedly with phase, dropping to zero in the illuminated hemisphere if the Ionospheric model is correct.

(d) Twilight Airglow

On the Ionospheric model there is a very high ion density in the daytime ionosphere. As twilight approaches, there should be a great flurry of recombinations of ions and electrons; the resulting recombination radiation should give a marked twilight airglow. The existence of such an airglow has not been demonstrated convincingly by earth-based experiments; but it could be checked with some precision by probe-borne ultraviolet spectrophotometry. However, the existence of a twilight airglow on Venus, while apparently a necessary condition for the Ionospheric model, is not by itself a demonstration that the Ionospheric model is true.

(e) Infrared Emission Windows

The Greenhouse model predicts a number of spectral regions—between 8 and 9 μ, and in the near infrared—where there is minimum attenuation by the Cytherean atmosphere. Therefore, especially where there are breaks in the clouds of Venus, enhanced emission should be observed at these window wavelengths. To gain the topographical resolution required to see breaks in the clouds, it is necessary to place an infrared spectrometer on a close flyby or orbiter.

(f) Polarimetric and Spectrometric Characterization of the Visible Cloud Layer

The Greenhouse and Aeolospheric models make very different predictions on the nature of the visible cloud layer: ice crystals on the one hand; and finely ground dust, possibly carbonates, on the other. Highly accurate polarimetry at several wavelengths, and spectroscopy in the near infrared should be able easily to distinguish between substances with such different indices of refraction and absorption coefficients.

8. Conclusions

Thus the distinct prospect exists of deciding among these diverse and mutually inconsistent models. In a way, it is gratifying to see that disagreement on the Cytherean surface conditions is not restricted by national boundaries. In the Soviet Union, Shklovsky, in *Izvestia,* has come out for the Greenhouse model; while Barabashov, in *Pravda,* has come out for moderate surface temperatures, which would put him in the Ionospheric model camp.

The differences among the three models are striking. The surface of

Venus on the Greenhouse model is hot as an oven, extremely dry, probably not very windy, and the sun can be seen dimly through a high cirrus overcast. On the Aeolosphere model, the surface is still as hot and as dry; but the winds are as intense as in the most severe terrestrial storms, and fairly large chunks of matter are being whipped about. Also, it is pitch dark; even in daytime the sun would not be visible. It is an incredibly dismal place. By contrast, if the Ionospheric model is true, the surface temperatures are probably below the boiling point of water; oceans and even life would then be possible.

Those planning entry and landing vehicles for Venus must be rather annoyed at the universal lack of agreement on the nature of the Cytherean physical environment. (I should probably be less provincial, and speak only of the planet-wide lack of agreement.) But it is a very exciting thought that the answers to our questions will soon be at hand.

There have been organisms on our planet for about four billion years. By a remarkable stroke of fortune, it is in the next few decades when we will first discover what is happening on the neighboring worlds. The probability of being alive at this particular time, taken on a random basis, is therefore about a millionth of a per cent. We are remarkably lucky to be living in this particular era.

NOTE ADDED IN PROOF: In the year which has elapsed between the presentation of this paper to the Symposium on Space Age Astronomy and its publication in the conference proceedings, our knowledge of the physical environment of Venus has advanced substantially. Very accurate measurements of the microwave emission from Venus have shown the spectrum to be very close to thermal at centimeter wavelengths, to show no significant day-to-day fluctuations, and to exhibit a marked phase effect [F. D. Drake, *Publ. Natl. Radio Astron. Obs.* **1**, 165 (1962)]. Drake considers these observations to eliminate the Aeolosphere and Ionospheric Models, and to leave only the Greenhouse Model with any plausibility.

A recent analysis of the 7820 Å CO_2 band on old Mt. Wilson spectra has revealed rotational temperatures and line contour pressures which vary together from plate to plate (H. Spinrad, *Publ. Astron. Soc. Pacific,* in press, 1962). The most reasonable interpretation of these data is that the Cytherean cloud cover varies from day to day. The surface pressures and temperatures on Venus will then be greater than the highest values obtained by Spinrad, 6 atm and 440°K. In fact three independent lines of evidence now suggest that the surface pressures on Venus are several tens of atmospheres, rather than the much lower values of previous models (C. Sagan, *Icarus,* in press, 1962). This same work indicates that one cloud level, at $T \simeq 234$°K is responsible for the bulk of the reflection and emission throughout the visible and infrared, and that the lapse rate in the dark hemisphere of Venus is subadiabatic. The direct evidence of high surface temperatures, and the indirect evidence of subadiabatic lapse rates, argue strongly against the Ionospheric and Aeolosphere Models, respectively.

It has recently been demonstrated that a fairly dense water droplet cloud layer with ice crystals above can adequately explain the microwave spectrum and the microwave phase effect (C. Sagan and L. Giver, 1962, to be published); but the quantity of water vapor required below the clouds is inconsistent with the very low water vapor mixing ratios indicated on those Mt. Wilson plates which see to the deepest levels beneath the Cytherean cloud deck (H. Spinrad, 1962, to be published). Spinrad's negative spectroscopic evidence is in contradiction to the infrared balloon spectroscopy of Strong which indicated the presence of water vapor, and to the infrared spectroscopy of Sinton which indicated that the cloud tops were composed of ice crystals. If the abundance of water vapor on Venus is very low, then another source of attenuation in the millimeter region must be found to explain the microwave spectrum, and another source of infrared opacity must be obtained if the Greenhouse Model is to be preserved. It now seems certain that not one of the three models discussed in the present paper is valid in its entirety; it will be interesting to see, from the vantage point of the next decades, how far from the truth we actually were in the murky days of 1961.

General References

The full report of the Planetary Atmospheres Study Panel has been published as

"The Atmospheres of Mars and Venus" (W. W. Kellogg and C. Sagan, eds.). Publication 944 of the Space Science Board, National Academy of Sciences, Washington, D. C., 1961.

The three models of the Cytherean environment discussed above are presented more fully in the following:

Greenhouse Model: Sagan, C., The radiation balance of Venus, Tech. Rept. 32-34, California Institute of Technology Jet Propulsion Laboratory, National Aeronautics and Space Administration (1960).

Aeolosphere Model: Öpik, E. J., The aeolosphere and atmosphere of Venus, *J. Geophys. Research* **66,** 2807 (1961).

Ionospheric Model: Jones, D. E., The microwave temperature of Venus, *Planetary and Space Sci.* **5,** 166 (1961).

Some other recent papers on these subjects include:

Kaplan, L. D., A new interpretation of the structure and CO_2 content of the Venus atmosphere, *Planetary and Space Sci.* **8,** 23 (1961).

Mintz, Y., Temperature and circulation of the Venus atmosphere, *Planetary and Space Sci.* **5,** 141 (1961).
Sagan, C., The planet Venus, *Science* **133,** 849 (1961).

Discussion

Dr. H. C. Urey: I greatly admire the review of the atmospheres of these planets as done by this *ad hoc* committee. They had asked me to join this group, but because of my work load I had to decline.

One of the curious things about Mars is the situation in regard to its equatorial bulge. The motion of the satellites indicates that if the planet has uniform composition, this bulge should be about 0.5%. On the other hand, direct observations by quite a number of very careful observers show that the bulge is about 1.2%. The difference amounts to a height in the equatorial region as compared with the polar region of about 24 km. This, if true, would indicate most remarkable conditions in the polar regions. An exceedingly thick atmosphere in the polar regions might be looked for.

The second thing that I would like to mention is what we may expect in the way of the development of this atmosphere. The presence of carbon dioxide indicates a very high state of oxidation. This state of oxidation does occur on a planet, probably as the result of the escape of hydrogen from compounds, due to radiation to which they are subjected. Generally, our terrestrial planets probably started out with reducing atmospheres, and the oxidation has proceeded by the escape of hydrogen. If we have an excess of water as compared with carbon on a planet, we get the situation on the earth: an excess amount of water and oxygen appears.

In the presence of plants, free oxygen occurs. On the other hand, if we should have an excess of carbon compounds as compared with water, we would expect an excess of carbon-hydrogen-nitrogen-oxygen compounds. These we might call organic, as we conventionally do, but they might have nothing whatever to do with living organisms. This situation might exist on Venus, and I do not know whether the ad hoc committee has considered this possibility. It was brought up some years ago by Professor Hoyle. In connection with this, if we look at Mars, we are a little surprised to see but a small amount of water in the atmosphere, and none on the surface. One would have thought that so small an amount of water would have disappeared by this time. It looks very much to me as though water is escaping from the interior of the planet, and hydrogen is going off into space at the present time. That is, we observe a steady-state situation, and not a microscopic fraction of solar history. Of course, I rather think we all hope that life exists on Mars. At least, I definitely hope so. It would be a most exciting thing to discover it, and I hope that treat is in store for us. But if this is the case, we must expect that there was liquid water on the planet at one time. Hence, oxygen must escape from the atmosphere of this planet. Now, since oxygen has a lower ionization potential than carbon dioxide or carbon monoxide, one would expect oxygen to escape from the planet as ions; for the effective atomic weight is lower for ions than neutral atoms. If oxygen and hydrogen both escape in this way, then there has been a way of removing water from the planet. This may have been much more effective in the past; hence, oceans may have escaped from this planet, and we may be seeing the end of a period of development of life. I mention this only to keep up your hopes that life still can be found on Mars in spite of its exceedingly arid condition. Living things have an enormous capacity to withstand adverse conditions, if sufficient time for evolution is allowed. And this might be true in the case of Mars.

PROFESSOR S. F. SINGER: I would like to comment very briefly on the question of the temperature of the surface of Venus inasmuch as several conflicting views have been set forth. The greatest argument against the Greenhouse theory is the large amount of water which has to be present; I believe 10 gm/cm was quoted. Now, it would seem that this is not borne out by the observations of Strong. His recent measurements at $1.1\,\mu$ support only on the order of 10^{-3} cm of H_2O above the cloud layer, and that cannot be condensed out, even if the lowest temperatures were assumed. Therefore, I think I should put forward the view that Professor Öpik maintains, that while his aeolosphere may be *ad hoc,* it is the only model which does not contradict any observational evidence.

I have another comment to make in connection with the question of the radiation belts of Mars; it has to do with what would be desirable features to observe. It appears to me that the most abundant constituent of any Martian exosphere may be CO^+, ionized carbon monoxide, and that therefore it would be extremely important and useful to look for the cometary bands of CO in any experiment that one undertakes in the vicinity of Mars. (See E. J. Öpik, The surface properties of Mars and Venus *in* "Progress in Astronautical Sciences," Vol. I. North Holland, Amsterdam, 1962.)

Another question that came up is the nature and origin of the Martian satellites, Phobos, and Deimos. Leaving aside the possibility that they are highly polished hollow spheres, the question really raises itself: Could they be spheres at all, natural spheres? I rather think that they are not spheres, but probably just pieces of rock, in which case they would have very irregular shapes. I think it would be important to plan an experiment which has a good enough resolution, that is, a resolution of a few kilometers, to determine whether the Martian satellites are, in fact, irregular bodies or whether they are spherical. There is a third possibility even, namely, that they might be an assembly of rubble, just weakly held together by their own gravitational field.

DR. C. SAGAN: Dr. Singer has said that the Aeolosphere model has the advantage of not postulating an amount of water vapor in the atmosphere of Venus which is inconsistent with the recent balloon observations of Strong. The observations of Strong give, though with very high probable error, an amount of water vapor of the order of 2×10^{-3} gm cm^{-2} above some level which must be in the vicinity of the visible *cloud* layer. The 10 gm cm^{-2} which arises in the Greenhouse model is the amount of water vapor above the *surface* of Venus. On the Greenhouse model the surface is some 36 km farther down. The amount of water above the clouds will, of course, be very much less than the amount of water vapor above the surface.

Indeed, if with a total water abundance of 10 gm cm^{-2}, a constant mixing ratio and an adiabatic lapse rate are both assumed, it is found that saturation and ice crystallization occur at a level corresponding to about 230°K. The amount of water vapor in equilibrium with ice at 230°K, in a convective atmosphere, is in good agreement with Strong's observations. There may be difficulties with the Greenhouse model, but this is not one of them.

Dr. Singer also claimed that the Aeolosphere model explains all the known facts about Venus. I would suggest that this is not correct. Both Sinton's evidence for an ice crystal cloud layer on Venus, and the evidence of Kuzmin, Salomonovich, and Lilley for brightness-temperature phase effects, are in contradiction with the Aelosphere model in its present form.

17.7 *Radiation Belts of Venus and of Mars (with Consideration of Sweeping Effect of Phobos)*

S. F. SINGER

UNIVERSITY OF MARYLAND, College Park, Maryland

A. Geomagnetically Trapped Radiation; Historical Introduction

The study of the motion of a charged particle in a magnetic dipole field was initiated by attempts to explain the polar aurora. More than 60 years ago in laboratory experiments Birkeland (*1*) investigated the behavior of a discharge in the vicinity of a terrella, a small magnetized sphere which simulated the earth. Inspired by these experiments, Poincaré analyzed the motion of a particle in the vicinity of a monopole and concluded that it would be reflected after it had approached to a minimum distance (*2*). A monopole, of course, is nowhere physically realized. Störmer (*3*), therefore, decided to study the motion of a charged particle in the vicinity of a magnetic dipole, since the earth's field may be approximated by a dipole. An examination of the equations of motion in a time-invariant magnetic field reveals at once one integral of the motion, namely the energy of the particle; hence the speed of the particle remains constant. In an axially symmetric field, such as the dipole field, another integral of the motion can be derived and is usually referred to as Störmer's integral. (Essentially, it refers to the z-component of angular momentum of the particle as given by a parameter γ.) A third integral of the motion can unfortunately not be found and therefore Störmer had to resort to numerical integrations to calculate particle trajectories. However, one general result can be stated as follows: a particle coming from infinity will either intersect the earth, or it will be deviated by the magnetic field and return to infinity. More particularly, there are "allowed" regions and "forbidden" regions around the earth which can be found by solving Störmer's integral using different values of γ. Störmer also showed that for γ less than -1 there is an allowed region within the normally forbidden region. But this inner allowed region is inaccessible to particles coming from infinity since they may not cross the forbidden region. While there is nothing in the equations of motion which would prevent particles from existing in this inaccessible region, Störmer, and others following him, assumed that the allowed inaccessible regions would be empty.

Particles in Trapped Orbits

Possibly the first suggestion that the inaccessible Störmer regions might be filled came from Alfvén in **1947** (*4*). It was generally believed at that time that the sun had a dipole field which acted on cosmic rays, and prevented low-energy cosmic rays from coming to the orbit of the earth, therefore causing a "knee" at the low end of the cosmic-ray energy spectrum. Rossi had pointed out that since the earth turns, one should observe as a necessary consequence a large diurnal variation of the low-energy cosmic rays (at high altitudes). In order to explain the experimental absence of this diurnal variation, Alfvén postulated that trapped orbits could exist in the sun's dipole field and that particles could be placed in these trapped orbits by being first scattered by the earth's magnetic field. He calculated roughly the equilibrium intensity and showed that the diurnal variation would indeed be very small. These ideas were developed with great precision by Wheeler and his students (*5*), and later by Treiman (*6*). While these workers did not apply the considerable simplification which comes from the use of adiabatic invariants, they developed the important concepts, such as injection rates, lifetime, etc. However, the idea of trapped particles in the solar dipole field was not taken up; further work suggested that this interplanetary field was not a dipole field and that, in any case, the motion of the conducting interplanetary gas would disturb the field considerably. Therefore, the assumption of the earth as the sole perturber of the field was perhaps not realistic.

For the case of the earth however, the dipole field proved to be a reasonably good approximation. Hence much laboratory work on the motion of charged particles in the field of a terrella was done following the pioneering efforts of Birkeland. Very precise work was carried out in Alfvén's Institute by Malmfors (*7*), by Brunberg and Dattner (*8*), and by Block (*9*), leading to model experiments on the trajectories of cosmic rays and on the origin of the aurora. Bennett (*10*), at the Naval Research Laboratory, carried out an especially elegant demonstration of the trajectories of electron streams in the vicinity of a terrella. Birkeland's earliest pictures and the Störmertron photographs of Bennett show very clearly the existence of particles which had been put into captive orbits around a dipole. No detailed analysis of this phenomenon was carried out; attention was concentrated mainly on the motion of particles in free orbits.

An important advance came from efforts to assess the contribution of cosmic-ray secondaries ("albedo") to rocket measurements of primary cosmic-ray flux. Using Störmer's integral, Treiman *(6)* showed that low-energy albedo particles would traverse the inner allowed region, crescent-shaped and characterized by large negative values of γ. Griem and Singer *(11)* investigated the effects of cosmic-ray albedo particles which were completely trapped in the earth's magnetic field, particularly near the equator. They showed that a particle would describe many loops in the low density atmosphere before being removed by collision loss, and calculated the contribution to the intensity as a function of particle energy and altitude *(12)*. No specific investigation on an injection mechanism was made at that time; the neutron albedo hypothesis was put forward only after the discovery of the radiation belt.

Ring Current

Störmer originally developed his theory of motion of particles in the geomagnetic field in order to account for the aurora. It turned out, however, that his results became useful mainly for the study of the trajectories of cosmic rays. Störmer himself pointed to a discrepancy between his results and observations of the aurora. The energy of particles causing the aurora can be roughly estimated from their range in the atmosphere; for particles of such low energy, the allowed points of incidence should be in the extreme proximity of the geomagnetic poles. The auroral zone, however, is some 20° from the magnetic pole. In order to circumvent this difficulty, Störmer made the *ad hoc* assumption that there existed around the earth a ring current of unspecified origin which deflected the auroral particles, which were supposed to be coming in from the sun, so as to cause them to hit in the auroral zone *(13)*. Much later, Chapman and Ferraro took up the idea of the ring current *(14)*, and postulated it as a means of explaining the *main phase* of magnetic storms: the large *decrease* in the magnetic field intensity (lasting 1 or 2 days) which generally follows the sudden commencement and initial phase increase of the magnetic field in a typical magnetic storm. In 1954 Alfvén *(15)* seriously criticized the particular ring current mechanism of Chapman and Ferraro and showed that it could not be stable. His discussion prompted Singer to look for another mechanism of producing a ring current, which was based on a hypothesis of particles trapped in the earth's magnetic field. Singer reasoned that even though a single particle could not be trapped (as shown by Störmer's theory), if a large number of particles were to arrive from the sun, their collective action could perturb the strict dipole field sufficiently to allow entry into the trapping region *(16)*. After the particle stream has passed the earth a certain number of particles may remain in this region.

Using a perturbation theory to describe the motion of the particles Singer showed that they would not immediately hit the earth but instead remain trapped for long periods of time. Their main motion would be a helical spiral about a line of force. As a result of the approximate constancy of the particle's magnetic moment, its pitch angle would increase as it moved along a line of force into a stronger magnetic field, up to a certain point where the pitch angle becomes 90°. There the particle is reflected, crosses the equator, and describes the same motion in the opposite hemisphere. In addition, the particle will also undergo a slow drift in azimuth about the dipole axis, protons toward the west and electrons toward the east. The drift produces a current, which Singer identified with the ring current required to account for the main phase of magnetic storms (*17*). He also pointed out that the trapped particles would be removed by interactions with the very tenuous atmosphere and by the scattering effects of magnetic field inhomogeneities.

It must be understood that the assumption of trapped solar particles was only a hypothesis designed to produce a ring current. Singer extended the discussion, however, and argued that a small number of these particles could be accelerated to auroral energies by the so-called Fermi acceleration mechanism, through collisions with magnetohydrodynamic waves (*18*). Chamberlain's observations (*19*), which suggest a power law energy spectrum of E^{-4} for auroral particles, can be accounted for most easily by this type of statistical acceleration mechanism. The waves are very likely connected with the micropulsations of the geomagnetic field which are often observed at sea level. In addition, Singer proposed that trapped particles traveling in bunches act as a source of extraterrestrial emissions in the very low frequency part of the spectrum (*20*). Earlier, Gallet had suggested fast solar particle streams as responsible for VLF emissions (*21*).

B. Direct Observations

An important advance came from the direct observations of auroral particles in rocket experiments conducted by Meredith *et al.* (*22*). While the radiation itself was identified as X-rays, it became fairly clear that these were produced by a particle flux of electrons. Subsequent experiments led to identification of the particles as electrons in the 10–100 kev range (*23*). Concurrently, theoretical work on the motion of such particles in the earth's field and their absorption in the auroral ionosphere led to the realization that they might be trapped (*17, 24*).

In order to check on the hypothesis of the existence of trapped particles specific experiments were suggested (*25*); one of these was to be carried out in the Far Side vehicle, a four-stage rocket launched from a high-altitude balloon designed to reach an altitude of 4000 miles. Unfortunately, the single successful flight in November 1957 did not carry the geiger counter intended for it, which would have detected the trapped radiation.

The discovery of geomagnetic trapped radiation was made by geiger counters in artificial satellites. Sputnik II (November 1957) showed a counting rate increase starting at 500 km; at 800 km, its maximum altitude, the rate was 50% above the ambient intensity (*26*). For Explorer I the maximum altitude was high enough to give an unmistakable increase in counting rate (by more than 100 times), which actually blocked the geiger counter. The correct interpretation of this radiation in terms of trapped particles was given by Van Allen in May 1958 (*27*). In his initial papers the trapped radiation was identified as of solar origin and held to be responsible for magnetic storms and aurorae (*28*). This view was also put forward by Dessler (*29*), who assumed local acceleration, and by Gold (*30*) who assumed that fast particles could be "conveyed" from the sun.

However, it seemed difficult to explain the existence of trapped solar radiation so very close to the earth near the equator (*31*). Hence Singer fell back on cosmic rays as a possible injection mechanism, and suggested fast cosmic-ray albedo neutrons as a likely source. He showed that this injection mechanism would give intensities which were in reasonable agreement with the observations, and he calculated the expected intensity-altitude distribution and also the energy spectrum of the trapped high energy *protons* which result from the decay of the high-energy neutrons (*32*). Kellogg investigated the possibility that decay *electrons* from thermal cosmic-ray albedo neutrons form a portion of the radiation belt (*33*). Independently, Vernov *et al.* suggested cosmic-ray neutrons as a source for the geomagnetically trapped radiation (*34*).

C. Existence and Cause of Two Belts

With the demonstration that cosmic-ray albedo neutrons could furnish a reasonable radiation belt, Singer (in November 1958) (*35, 36*) explicitly predicted the existence of two separate radiation belts, an inner belt (at 1 to 2 earth radii) of cosmic-ray origin and containing penetrating protons; and an outer one of solar origin containing only "soft" particles. Both the Pioneer III rocket and Lunik I observed two distinct belts with maxima at 1.5 and at about 3 to 4 earth radii, with a rather pronounced minimum in between (*37, 38*) (see Fig. 1).

The existence of a minimum ("slot") does not by itself indicate separate origins for the two belts. Dessler has made the important point

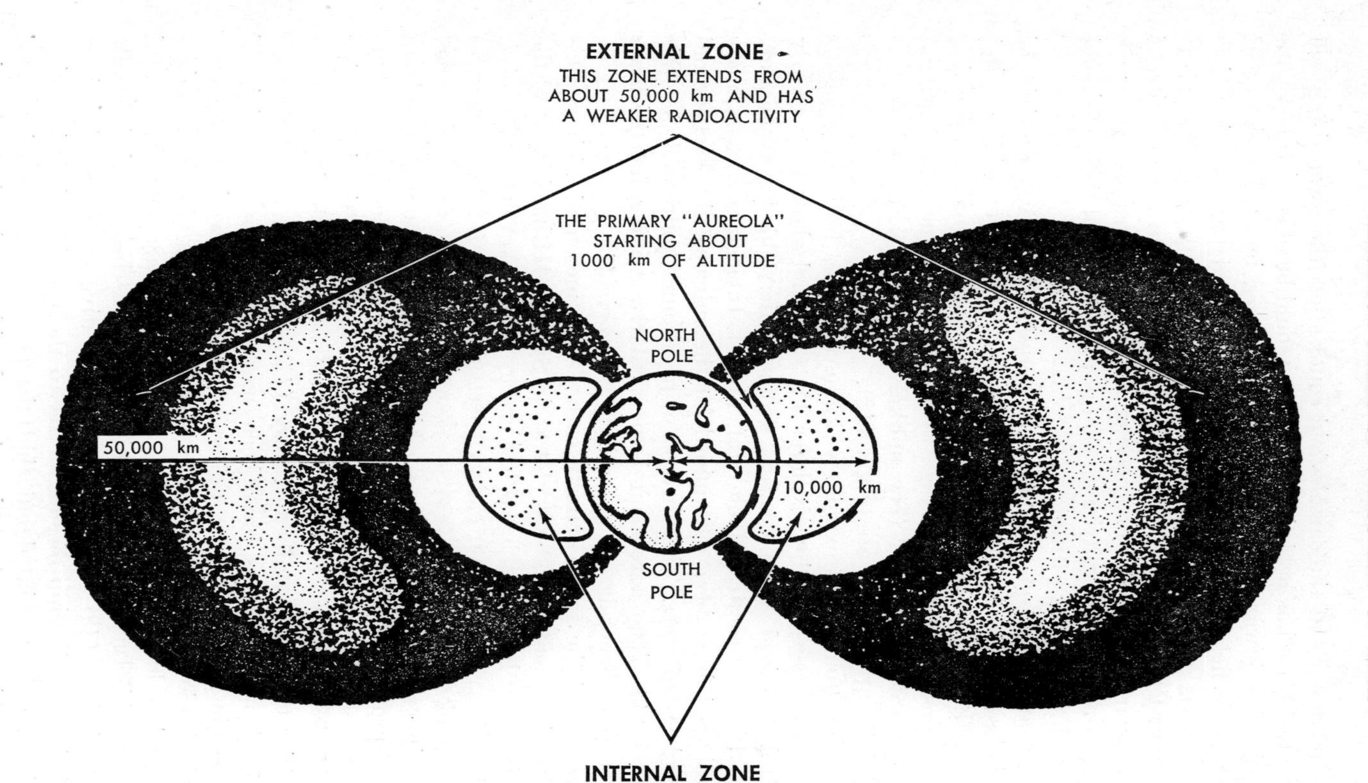

FIG. 1. Schematic diagram showing the inner (proton) and the outer (electron) belts around earth.

that large anomalies of the earth's field could affect the trapped particle intensity (*39*). Gold has held that both belts could be of solar origin with particles drifting inward, and with the slot caused by an instability of the geomagnetic field near a distance of 2 earth radii (*40*). On the other hand, Singer has proposed that the decrease in intensity of the inner belt beyond the first maximum may be due to a breakdown of the condition of adiabatic invariance in the magnetic moment of trapped particles; as a further consequence the maximum energy of the trapped protons should decrease with increasing altitude (*41*).

However, an important conclusion concerning the separate origin of the two belts was drawn by Christofilos from the observed fact that electrons, artificially injected by atomic bomb explosions, produced a shell whose position did not change with time. He argued that a radial drift of trapped particles is very unlikely and that therefore the two observed belts are of separate origin (*42*).

Intensity contours, approximately kidney-shaped, have been determined for the inner belt by Explorer IV (*28*) and show very clearly the control exercised by the actual geomagnetic field (approximately represented as an eccentric dipole) (cf. Fig. 2). Intensity contours, more crescent-shaped, have been determined for the outer belt by Pioneer and Lunik probes (*37, 38*). The theories can account quite well for this distribution (*43*). The agreement is particularly striking for the inner belt, where the theory is almost entirely *a priori* (*44*).

The nature of the trapped particles has been measured with various degrees of refinement. Krassovsky *et al.* in Sputnik III has identified the bulk of the outer belt particles as low energy (10–50 kev) electrons (*45*). Vernov *et al.* have given their energy spectra as E^{-5} to E^{-3} from measurements in Lunik I (*38*).

For the inner belt, the most detailed knowledge of the energy spectrum of trapped protons comes from the photographic emulsion measurements of Freden and White (*46*). If one takes account of the integrating feature of the emulsion, one finds good agreement with the spectrum predicted by the neutron albedo theory (*47*).

Two further suggestions have been made concerning the origin of the protons in the inner belt. Following the earlier work of Bennett, Harris *et al.* (*48*) have shown the existence of classes of Störmer orbits which spend a long time near the earth, and hence may be termed "quasi-trapped." Independently, similar work has been carried out by Gall and Lifshitz (*49*). However, no quantitative evaluation has been made of the contribution of such orbits to the radiation belt intensity. Alfvén has recently pointed out that the energy spectrum of trapped protons resembles a spectrum based on the idea of local acceleration

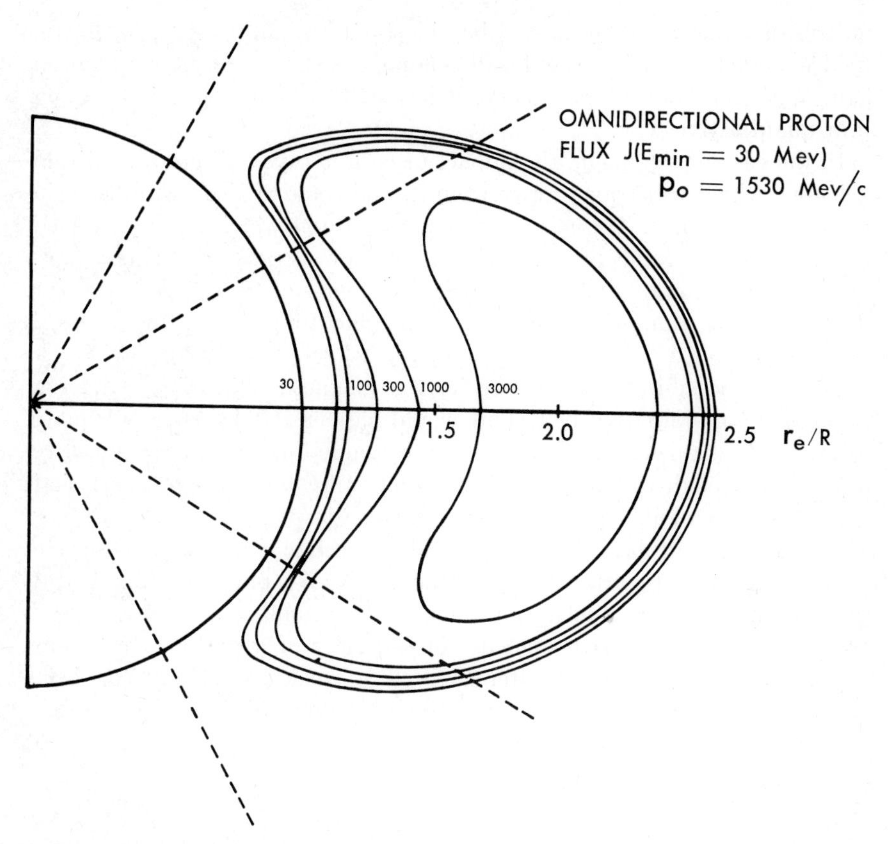

FIG. 2. Spatial distribution of proton flux around the earth (in particles/cm²/sec).

of these protons (*50*); again no complete quantitative assessment has been made of this theory.

Finally, the inner belt also contains a large flux of low-energy electrons (*33*). It is possible that they arise from the decay of thermal cosmic ray albedo neutrons but no quantitative assessment has as yet been made.

D. Radiation Belts of the Planets

If we adopt our point of view—namely, that the inner belt is caused by cosmic-ray neutron albedo, and the outer belt by injected solar corpuscular radiation—we can now make certain predictions about the radiation belts of other planets.

(1) The first statement which can be made is that a planet without a magnetic field cannot have belts of trapped radiation. It is generally believed that the moon has no appreciable magnetic field and, therefore, it should have no belt of trapped radiation. However, the matter is not

quite so simple. One also has to be able to state how strong a magnetic field a planet could have and still not possess an appreciable radiation belt. With the help of the theory, it is possible to answer this question in a quantitative way.

In the case of the moon, the impact of cosmic rays will produce albedo neutrons which will travel away from it, and some of them will decay in the moon's vicinity. The maximum energy proton which can be trapped in the vicinity of the moon is about 500 kev as given in Appendix I. Hence a detector having a total wall thickness of only 1 mg/cm^2 (or 0.0002 in.) of aluminum, would just be able to pick up this trapped radiation.

(2) It is possible for a body to have a magnetic field *without* having an appreciable radiation belt. This would happen if there is no adequate injection mechanism. Let us take as an example the planet Jupiter. If we assume (although this may be a somewhat unrealistic assumption) that practically all of its upper atmosphere consists of hydrogen, then very few neutrons will be created by incident cosmic rays, as opposed to the nitrogen-oxygen atmosphere of the earth. We must remember that nitrogen and oxygen nuclei contain an equal number of neutrons and protons, while a hydrogen nucleus consists only of a proton. Hence one would expect the planet Jupiter to have a weak inner radiation belt, but its outer radiation belt would also be quite weak since its distance from the sun is considerable.

E. Inner Belt of Mars and Venus

We now would like to apply some theoretical predictions to the planets Mars and Venus. These two planets are very similar to the earth in size and have, in general, conditions which are not too far different from those existing on the earth. If we make certain assumptions, we can then calculate something about the structure of the radiation belts of Mars and Venus.

(1) The magnetic dipole moment of the two planets is proportional to their volume. This is an arbitrary assumption, since the dipole moment depends on the nature of the *core* of the planet, and may therefore be more closely related to the past history of the planet, its internal heat sources, and possibly even its rate of rotation. Nevertheless, since the magnetic field of neither planet has been measured, we will proceed with the above assumption. Using the earth as a model, we therefore derive the magnetic moments shown in Table I.

(2) Next we can calculate the variation of the magnetic field intensity with altitude above the planet. This is shown in Table II. We now assume that the cosmic-ray intensity in the vicinity of Venus and Mars is similar

TABLE I[a]
(ASSUMED) MAGNETIC DIPOLE MOMENTS

	Earth	Mars	Venus
R (km)	6370	3400	6200
M (gauss-cm^3)	6.1×10^{25}	9.2×10^{24}	5.6×10^{25}

[a] If we assume that the planetary magnetic moment M is proportional to the volume $(4/3)\pi R^3$, then the sea level field at the equator, $B_e = M/R^3$, will be the same as for the earth, namely 0.3 gauss. Provided we measure distances r in terms of the planetary radius R, then for all planets $B = M/r^3$.

to that of the earth, i.e., that the cosmic-ray intensity does not vary appreciably throughout the inner solar system. We can then calculate

TABLE II
EQUATORIAL MAGNETIC FIELD (IN MILLIGAUSS) VS. DISTANCE

r(in planetary radii)	for Earth, Mars, and Venus
1	310
2	39
3	12
4	5
5	2.5

quite well the distribution of the inner radiation belt, using, however, the assumption that the exospheres of the two planets are similar to that of the earth. (Table III).

TABLE III[a]
INTENSITY OF PROTONS IN INNER BELT VS. ALTITUDE

r/R	1.0	1.1	1.2	1.4	1.6	1.8	2.0
Relative intensity	0	48	76.5	89.3	76	31	0

[a] From ref. (*41*).

F. The Structure of the Outer Belt of Mars and Venus

An approach to the study of the outer belt, presumably produced by solar corpuscular radiation, can be made by the following simple considerations. Assume that the solar corpuscular stream expands uniformly on its way from the sun to the earth. Then the particle density will be inversely proportional to the distance to the sun squared, provided the retardation is unimportant. In that case, the particle densities near Venus, Earth, and Mars will be given approximately in Table IV. Using the earth as a model, and noting that the outer belt has a maximum at 3 earth radii, we can derive the positions of the maxima for Venus and Mars by setting the kinetic energy density of the incoming beam equal to the magnetic field density in the exosphere of the planet. Using, therefore, the results of Table II, we derive the position of maxima of the outer belt given in Table IV. Assuming the particle density to be proportional to the magnetic field energy density, which varies approximately as $1/r^6$, we can sketch the probable distribution of particle intensity in the outer belt.

TABLE IV
POSITION OF MAXIMUM OF OUTER BELT

	Earth	Mars	Venus
Distance from sun (a.u.)	1.00	1.52	0.72
Relative density of solar stream	1.00	0.43	1.93
Maximum of outer belt (approx.) in terms of planetary radius	3.0	3.45	2.7

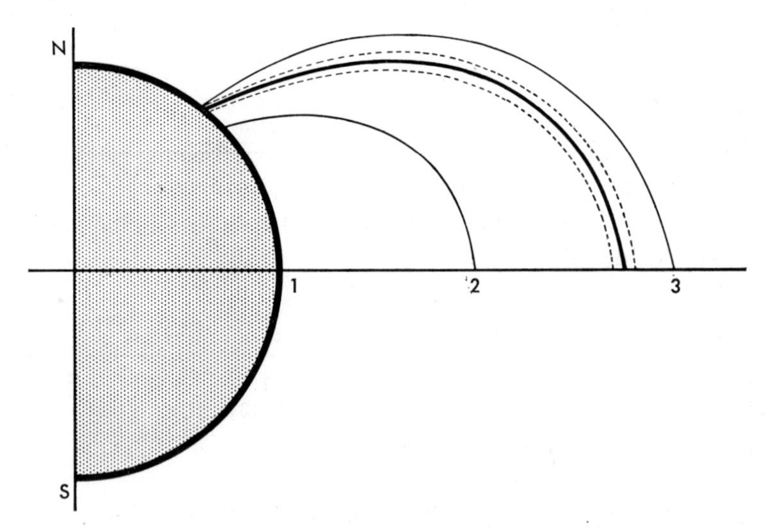

FIG. 3. Regions around Mars presumably swept by Phobos.

One interesting phenomenon occurs near Mars, which is not duplicated near the earth or Venus, and that is the sweeping effect (see Appendix II) produced by the Martian satellite Phobos. It has a diameter of the order of 16 km and moves at a distance of 9400 km from the center of Mars. Therefore, at the position of Phobos, the magnetic field will be 14.7 mgauss. For a 1-Mev electron, therefore, the radius of curvature will be 2.3 km. Hence, the channel swept clear by Phobos will have a radial dimension of approximately 20 km in the equatorial plane. We therefore expect to find a cleared region of the shape shown in Fig. 3. It is apparent, therefore, that Phobos represents an ideal observation base for the planet Mars. Not only is the radiation hazard much reduced in its vicinity, but also its low mass presents a small kinetic barrier for landing and takeoff.

G. Discussion of Results

One can now ask the question, what purpose is served by a calculation which is based on admittedly arbitrary assumptions? The best answer is that the radiation belts of Venus and Mars will undoubtedly be measured and the measured intensities will have to be interpreted. Using our present calculation (or one closely resembling it) we can then tell which of the assumptions need be modified.

It might be mentioned in conclusion that none of the planets are expected to have radiation belts intense enough to present any real health hazard. By far the greatest hazard to manned space flight still comes from cosmic radiation, in particular from the large cosmic-ray intensities which occasionally follow after a solar flare.

Appendix I

We can calculate the maximum energy of a particle which a magnetic field can trap from the critical Alfvén discriminant $x \equiv \rho[B/\text{grad } B]^{-1}$ [cf. ref. (*41*)]. Here ρ is the particle's radius of curvature in the field B, and is given by the expression ρ (in cm) = (momentum in ev)/$300B$. Empirically we found (*47*) that $x_{\text{critical}} = 0.06$. For a dipole field $B/\text{grad } B = r$, since $B = M/r^3$. Hence $\rho_{\text{crit}} = 0.06\, r$, and momentum (in ev) = $0.06 \times 300\, Br$. Near the moon's surface $r = 1.728 \times 10^8$ cm; we assume the maximum value of B which may have escaped detection to be 10^{-2} gauss. Hence the maximum momentum is 3×10^7 ev, and the maximum energy would be 30 Mev for trapped electrons and 500 kev for trapped protons.

Appendix II. The Sweeping Effect of Phobos on the Martian Radiation Belt

We have the following lengths:

$a = pc/eB$ radius of gyration of a trapped particle
$d =$ diameter of Phobos
$\Delta =$ distance of dipole from center of planet (dipole assumed to be in the plane of the Martian equator).

We calculate the probability of a trapped particle to hit Phobos (and be catastrophically absorbed).

General Discussion of Lifetime

Consider Phobos at distance R_p from the center of the dipole, oscillating about this mean position with a period of 7.7 hr and amplitude Δ; we may approximate this oscillation as

$$R = R_p + \Delta \sin \omega_p t. \tag{1}$$

Consider now a particle trapped at position r_e. It moves within a shell which intersects the (magnetic) equatorial plane in two circles of radius $r_e + a$ and $r_e - a$.

Special Cases

Case (1). $a < \Delta$; α very small: With small pitch angle α, the particle intersects the equatorial plane and spends very little time in its vicinity.

The problem can be viewed as follows: the area available to the particle in the equatorial plane is $4\pi r_e a$.

The area of Phobos $= A_p = \frac{1}{4}\pi d^2$; but the "effective" area is less, and proportional to the time interval which Phobos spends in the band $r_e - a$ to $r_e + a$.

$$A_{\mathrm{eff}} = \left(\frac{\pi}{4} d^2\right) \cdot \frac{1}{(\pi/2)} \left[\arcsin\left(\frac{r_e + a - R_p}{\Delta}\right) - \arcsin\left(\frac{r_e - a - R_p}{\Delta}\right)\right]. \tag{2}$$

For very small values of a the expression in square brackets becomes

$$\begin{aligned}\Delta\theta &= \frac{2a}{\Delta}\left[\cos\left(\arcsin \frac{r_e - R_p}{\Delta}\right)\right]^{-1} \\ &= \frac{2a}{\Delta}\left[1 - \left(\frac{r_e - R_p}{\Delta}\right)^2\right]^{-1/2}.\end{aligned} \tag{3}$$

The lifetime T of the particle is now given by the bounce time T_{NS} for a north-south oscillation along the line of force, multiplied by the probability of a strike,

$$T = T_{\mathrm{NS}} \,.\, 4\pi r_e a / A_{\mathrm{eff}} = T_{\mathrm{NS}}(8\pi r_e a/d^2)[\Delta\theta]^{-1}, \tag{4}$$

where $\Delta\theta$ may vary between zero and $\pi/2$, depending on the relation between Δ and a.

Case (2). $\Delta < a$. A minimum estimate of T can be given as follows: $\Delta\theta = \pi/2$.

$$\begin{aligned}T_{\mathrm{min}} &= T_{\mathrm{NS}} 16 r_e a/d^2 \\ &= k\beta^{-1} \times 16 r_e (mc/eB)\beta\gamma d^{-2} \\ &\simeq k 16 r_e (mc/eB) d^{-2},\end{aligned} \tag{5}$$

where k is approximately independent of β and equal to

$$k \sim [1.38 - 0.32(\sin^{1/2} \alpha_e + \sin \alpha_e)]2r_e/c$$
$$\sim 2r_e/c \sim 2 \times 9.4 \times 10^8/3 \times 10^{10} \sim 6 \times 10^{-2} \text{ sec.} \tag{6}$$

Since $\gamma \sim 1$ for all cases of importance, β cancels out and the lifetime is the same for particles of all energies. The profile of intensity in the equatorial plane will begin to decrease at a distance of $2a + \Delta$ from R_p.

Case (3). $\alpha \doteq 90°$. Here the particle remains in the equatorial plane and can, if $a < d$, be absorbed every time it circles Mars. However, the number of particles with $\alpha \doteq 90°$ is small and contributes little to the omnidirectional counting rate. Further, if the dipole is inclined, then Phobos will move above and below the equatorial (magnetic) plane.

It is clear that the lifetime cannot be too large since it ultimately must be set by the density of the Martian exosphere or by some other factor which limits the life of a particle. For purposes of discussion we will assume that it is the Martian exosphere which limits the lifetime, and that the density of the exosphere is of the order of 10^3 particles/cm^3 at the location of Phobos. The results are given in Table 1. Here $\bar{\rho}$ is

TABLE 1[a]

(DENSITY × LIFETIME) FOR PROTONS AND ELECTRONS

Proton Energy (Mev)	1.0	10	100
$\bar{\rho}T$ (cm^{-3} sec)	2×10^{10}	5×10^{11}	1.5×10^{13}
for a 300-kev electron $\bar{\rho}T \sim 4 \times 10^{11}$			

[a] A. M. Lenchek and S. F. Singer, *J. Geophys. Research* **67,** 1263 (1962).

the effective concentration (cm^{-3}) averaged over the spiral path of the particle.

We now distinguish the two cases of sweeping where (1) $a < d$ and (2) $a > d$, with $\Delta = 0$ in both.

(1) With $a < d$ the effective area of Phobos is $\sim 2\,ad$.

(2) With $a > d$ the effective area is simply $\pi/4\; d^2$. For reasonable values of the Martian field, case (2) is the more important.

The lifetime will be given by

$$T_{\text{NS}} \times (\text{probability of striking Phobos})$$
$$= T_{\text{NS}} 4\pi r_e a/A_{\text{eff}} = T_{\text{NS}} 16 r_e a/d^2.$$

An order of magnitude calculation gives for *protons:*

$$T_{\text{NS}} = \frac{10^4 \text{ km}}{\beta 10^{10} \text{ cm/sec}} = 10^{-1}\beta^{-1} \text{ sec.}$$

Therefore,

$$\begin{aligned}\text{Lifetime} &= 10^{-1}\beta^{-1} \times 16 \times 10^{9} \times (\tfrac{1}{300} \times 10^{9}\ \text{ev}\beta/B)/10^{12} \\ &= (5 \times 10^{3})/B\ \text{sec},\end{aligned}$$

independent of proton velocity. For fast electrons the lifetime is

$$\begin{aligned}&10^{-1} \times 16 \times 10^{9}(\tfrac{1}{300}\, 5 \times 10^{6}/B)/10^{12} \\ &= 30/B\ \text{sec}.\end{aligned}$$

Table 2 gives the lifetimes computed from these equations.

TABLE 2
RADIUS OF GYRATION AND LIFETIME AGAINST COLLISION WITH PHOBOS

	Magnetic field at Phobos (gauss)					
	$B = 10^{-1}$		$B = 10^{-2}$		$B = 10^{-3}$	
Nonrelat. protons	km	sec	km	sec	km	sec
$\beta = 0.1$; 5 Mev	31	5×10^{4}	310	5×10^{5}	3100	5×10^{6}
$\beta = 0.2$; 20 Mev	62	5×10^{4}	620	5×10^{5}	6200	5×10^{6}
$\beta = 0.43$; 100 Mev	140	5×10^{4}	1400	5×10^{5}	14000	5×10^{6}
~400 kev electron	2	300	20	3×10^{3}	200	3×10^{4}

We can now draw the following conclusions from our analysis and from Tables 1 and 2. In the region of Phobos, it sets the lifetime for high-energy particles, although for extremely low energy particles the atmospheric effects are sufficient to limit the lifetime eventually.

We can calculate quite easily the equilibrium intensity to be expected. From the *neutron albedo theory* we may compute an injection rate q_0 of the order of 10^{-14} per cm^3/sec which, when combined with the lifetime, gives the expression $n = q_0 T$ for the equilibrium concentration of trapped protons. For the remainder of the analysis we take the case where the radius of gyration is not too large, i.e., $d < a \ll R_p$.

It is to be noted that since the lifetime is energy independent over a wide range, the equilibrium concentration must exactly reflect the injection energy spectrum. However, the intensity which is *measured* does not, since the flux is concentration multiplied by a velocity. The flux to be expected is therefore given by the expression $J = nv$. Typical flux values are $\sim 1/\text{cm}^2$ sec.

It is therefore seen that the measured intensity can be used to *deduce the injection rate.*

Assuming the injection rate as taken above, we can now calculate also the equilibrium intensity at some distance from the orbit of Phobos, based on an assumed Martian exospheric density of 10^4 particles/cm^3. Here the absorption of particles is not catastrophic, and therefore the lifetime depends on energy in a manner which has already been discussed (see Table 1). The analysis now follows very closely our earlier one, and we arrive at the following results for the fluxes: Protons, $\sim 10^3$/cm^2 sec; and Electrons, $\sim 10^5$/cm^2 sec.

Comparing with the result in the vicinity of Phobos, we see that the density of the Martian exosphere can now be derived if we make the plausible assumption that the injection rate does not vary appreciably over a distance of a few tens of kilometers at 9400 km from the center of Mars.

In addition to the properties of the Martian exosphere and the injection rate, we can also derive d, *in principle,* if we perform measurements with different particles and different energy ranges, i.e., using different radii of gyration.

It is clear also that the injection rate at the different energies and for different particles can be used to derive the ultimate source of the trapped radiation in the vicinity of Mars, and can therefore shed a great deal of information on the source of trapped radiation for the terrestrial radiation belts.

Some Experimental Considerations

We estimate that the probe will traverse a distance corresponding to the diameter of Phobos in approximately 3 sec. An adequate time resolution would therefore be 0.3–0.5 sec. If a typical counting rate in the belt is 1000/sec for a small counter, then outside of Phobos each reading would include 300–500 counts, and the accuracy would be 5%. Within the Phobos band the counting rate might be only $\sim$1/sec.

We conclude that even a rough measurement of the electron and proton energy spectrum would be worthwhile and technically quite feasible. It would be necessary to read out data 2 to 3 times per second over an interval of perhaps 20 sec when the probe is in the vicinity of the orbit of Phobos.

References

1. K. Birkeland, See Fig. 161 in ref. (*3*), or Fig. 7 in ref. (*17*).
2. H. Poincaré, *Compt. rend. acad. sci. Paris* **123,** 530–533, 950 (1896) (see Störmer (*3*), p. 210).
3. For a summary of his work see, C. Störmer, "The Polar Aurora," pp. 209–334. Oxford Univ. Press, Oxford and New York, 1955.
4. H. Alfvén, Solar magnetic field and diurnal variation of cosmic radiation, *Phys. Rev.* **72,** 88 (1947).
5. E. O. Kane, T. J. B. Shanley, and J. A. Wheeler, Influence on the cosmic ray spectrum of five heavenly bodies, *Revs. Modern Phys.* **21,** 51–57 (1949).

6. S. B. Treiman, Cosmic radiation in the trapped orbits of a solar magnetic dipole field, *Phys. Rev.* **93,** 544–551 (1954).
7. K. G. Malmfors, Determination of orbits in the field of a magnetic dipole with application to the theory of the diurnal variation of cosmic radiation, *Ark. mat., astr. o. fysik* **32A,** No. 8 (1945).
8. E. A. Brunberg and A. Dattner, Experimental determination of electron orbits in the field of a magnetic dipole, *Tellus* **5,** 135 (1953).
9. L. Block, Model experiments on aurorae and magnetic storms, *Tellus* **7,** 65 (1955).
10. W. H. Bennett, Auroral and magnetic storm theory, *Astrophys. J.* **127,** 731–742 (1958).
11. H. Griem and S. F. Singer, Geomagnetic albedo at rocket altitudes at the equator, *Phys. Rev.* **99,** 608(A) (1955).
12. S. F. Singer, The primary cosmic radiation and its time variations, a chapter *in* "Progress in Elementary Particle and Cosmic Ray Physics," (J. G. Wilson and F. Wouthuysen, eds.), Vol. IX, pp. 203–335 (see p. 268 and Fig. 13). Interscience, New York, 1958.
13. C. Störmer, *Arch. sci. phys. et nat.* **32,** 33 (1911–12).
14. S. Chapman and V. C. A. Ferraro, A new theory of magnetic storms, *Terres. Mag. and Atmos. Elec.* **36,** 77, 171 (1931); **37,** 147 (1932); see also V. C. A. Ferraro, The origin of magnetic storms and aurorae, *Ann. geophys.* **11,** 284–304 (1955).
15. H. Alfvén, On the electric field theory of magnetic storms and aurorae, *Tellus* **7,** 50–64 (1955).
16. S. F. Singer, Trapped orbits in the earth's dipole field, *Bull. Am. Phys. Soc.* **1,** 229 (1956).
17. S. F. Singer, A new model of magnetic storms and aurorae, *Trans. Am. Geophys. Union* **38,** 175–190 (1957).
18. S. F. Singer, New acceleration mechanism for auroral particles, *Bull. Am. Phys. Soc.* **3,** 40 (1958).
19. J. W. Chamberlain, Theories of the aurora, *Advances in Geophys.* **4,** 109–215 (1958).
20. S. F. Singer, Geophysical effects of solar corpuscular radiation, *Ann. geophys.* **14,** 173–177 (1958).
21. R. M. Gallet, The very-low-frequency emissions generated in the earth's exosphere, *Proc. I.R.E.* **47,** 211–231 (1959).
22. L. H. Meredith, M. B. Gottlieb, and J. A. Van Allen, Direct detection of soft radiation above 50 kilometers in the auroral zone, *Phys. Rev.* **97,** 201–205 (1955).
23. L. H. Meredith, *Natl. Acad. Sci. IGY Rocket Rept. No.* **1,** 169 (July 30, 1958).
24. R. M. Rhodes, Masters Thesis, University of Maryland, 1955. Also published as Penetration of charged particles into auroral zones, Physics Section Rept. Zph-014, Convair, San Diego, California (April 1959).
25. S. F. Singer, Project Far Side, *Missiles and Rockets* **2,** 120–128 (Oct. 1958).
26. S. N. Vernov *et al.,* Artificial satellite measurements of cosmic radiation, *Doklady Akad. Nauk S.S.S.R.* **120,** 1231 (1958).
27. J. A. Van Allen, G. H. Ludwig, E. C. Ray, and C. E. McIlwain, Observation of high intensity radiation by satellites 1958 Alpha and Gamma, *Jet Propulsion* **28,** 588–542 (1958).
28. J. A. Van Allen, C. E. McIlwain, and G. H. Ludwig, Radiation observations with satellite 1958 Epsilon, *J. Geophys. Research* **64,** 271–286 (1958).

29. A. J. Dessler, Large-amplitude hydromagnetic waves above the ionosphere, *Phys. Rev. Letters* **1,** 68–69 (1958).
30. T. Gold, Origin of the radiation near the earth discovered by satellites, *Nature* **183,** 355 (1959).
31. S. F. Singer, Trapped albedo theory of the radiation belt, *Phys. Rev. Letters* **1,** 171–173 (1958).
32. S. F. Singer, Trapped albedo theory of the radiation belt, *Phys. Rev. Letters* **1,** 181–183 (1958).
33. P. J. Kellogg, Possible explanation of the radiation observed by Van Allen at high altitudes in satellites, *Nuovo cimento Suppl.* [10] **11,** 48–66 (1959).
34. S. N. Vernov *et al.,* Possible mechanism of production of "terrestrial corpuscular radiation" under the action of cosmic rays, *Soviet Phys. Doklady* **4,** 154–157 (1959).
35. S. F. Singer, Effects of environment on space vehicles, Chapter IV *in* "Symposium on Space-Physics and Medicine" (San Antonio, November 1958). Wiley, New York, 1959.
36. S. F. Singer, Artificial modification of the earth's radiation belt, *J. Astronaut. Sci.* **5,** 1–10 (1959) (Proc. 5th Ann. Meeting Am. Astronautical Soc., Washington, D. C., December 1958); also "Advances in Astronautical Science," Vol. IV, pp. 335–354. Plenum, New York, 1959.
37. J. A. Van Allen and L. A. Frank, Radiation around the earth to a radial distance of 107,400 kilometers, *Nature* **183,** 430–434 (1959).
38. S. N. Vernov *et al.,* The study of the terrestrial corpuscular radiation and cosmic rays during the flight of a cosmic rocket, *Doklady Akad. Nauk S.S.S.R.* **125,** 304–307 (1959).
39. A. J. Dessler, Effect of magnetic anomaly on particle radiation trapped in geomagnetic field, *J. Geophys. Research* **64,** 713–715 (1959).
40. T. Gold, Motions in the magnetosphere of the earth, *J. Geophys. Research* **64,** 1219–1224 (1959).
41. S. F. Singer, On the cause of the minimum in the earth's radiation belt, *Phys. Rev. Letters* **3,** 188 (1959).
42. N. C. Christofilos, The Argus experiment, *J. Geophys. Research* **64,** 869–875 (1959).
43. R. C. Wentworth, W. M. MacDonald, and S. F. Singer, Lifetimes of trapped radiation belt particles determined by Coulomb scattering, *Phys. Fluids* **2,** 499–509 (1959).
44. S. F. Singer, Latitude and altitude distribution of geomagnetically trapped protons, *Phys. Rev. Letters* **5,** 300 (1960).
45. V. I. Krassovsky *et al., Usp. fiz. Nauk* **64,** No. 3, 425 (1958). See also V. I. Krassovsky *et al.,* On fast corpuscles of the upper atmosphere, 10th Congr. Intern. Astron. Fed., London, 1959.
46. S. C. Freden and R. S. White, Protons in the earth's magnetic field, *Phys. Rev. Letters* **3,** 9 (1959).
47. A. M. Lenchek and S. F. Singer, Energy spectrum of geomagnetically trapped protons, *J. Geophys. Research* **67,** 1263 (1962).
48. I. Harris, R. Jastrow, and T. Kelsall, quoted in *Sci. American* **201,** 43 (Aug. 1959).
49. R. Gall and J. Lifshitz, Temporary capture of cosmic ray particles and their contribution to the high intensity belts, *Nuovo cimento* **12** (1960).
50. H. Alfvén, Momentum spectrum of the Van Allen radiation, *Phys. Rev. Letters* **3,** 459–460 (1959).

CHAPTER 18

Lunar Explorations

18.1 Exploration of the Moon in the U.S.S.R.

A. A. MIKHAILOV

PULKOVO OBSERVATORY, Leningrad, U.S.S.R

In the exploration of the moon two outstanding accomplishments have been achieved in the U.S.S.R. in recent years. First, the observation of an outburst of carbon-containing gas from the central peak of the crater Alphonsus by N. Kozyrev, and second, the photography of the reverse side of the moon by the third interplanetary rocket and the delineation of a map thereof.

On November 3, 1958 Kozyrev obtained several spectrograms of the crater Alphonsus with the 50-in. reflector of the Crimean Observatory, the slit being placed across the central peak (as shown in Fig. 1). On one spectrogram, exposed from 3^h0^m to 3^h30^m UT (Fig. 2), bright emission corresponding to the peak is clearly seen (Fig. 2). This emission ends abruptly at the wavelength 4740 Å and can be traced to about 4384 Å.

I shall not deal in detail with this observation as it was described by the author several times, for instance, in *Sky and Telescope*. Kozyrev himself was carried away by the success and luck of having witnessed such a rare phenomenon and was very enthusiastic about it. So, to make sure that the interpretation of the obtained spectrogram was strictly correct and above any suspicion of a possible partiality, I have asked a very able physicist of the staff of the Pulkovo observatory, Dr. Kalinyak, who at first was somewhat skeptical about the whole affair, to make an independent careful photometric study of Kozyrev's spectrogram.

It must be borne in mind that the emission in the spectrogram is superimposed over the usual solar spectrum as reflected by the moon's surface. This spectrum had to be subtracted photometrically in order to obtain the emission in pure form, which was a very tedious procedure. However, there remained another serious complication. The outflowing gas not only became fluorescent through excitation by the sun's radiation, but it also absorbed in the same wavelengths the light reflected by the moon's surface, so that the radiation registered in the spectrum was the balance

FIG. 1. Position of the spectrograph slit across Crater Alphonsus.

of these two opposite effects. Thus, according to the sum of these influences there could be either a bright emission or a dark absorption, or even no visible radiation at all. Dr. Kalinyak very accurately investigated this question theoretically and showed that the visible emission

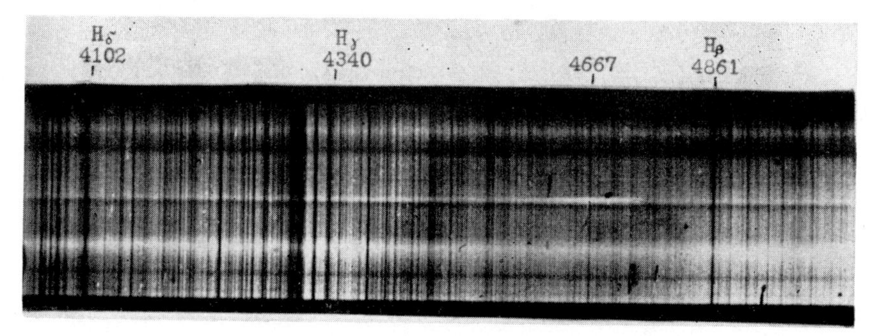

FIG. 2. Spectrum of Crater Alphonsus November 3, 1958, 3^h00^m to 3^h30^m. In the spectrum of the central peak can be seen an emission line 4737 Å of C_2 molecules.

down to a wavelength of 4720 Å was produced by a gas containing C_2 and showing most of the bands of the well-known Swan spectrum similar to the spectrum of cometary heads. The band at 5165 Å, due to transitions of the type (0-0), was absent; this was first thought to invalidate the identification with the Swan spectrum but later explained by the

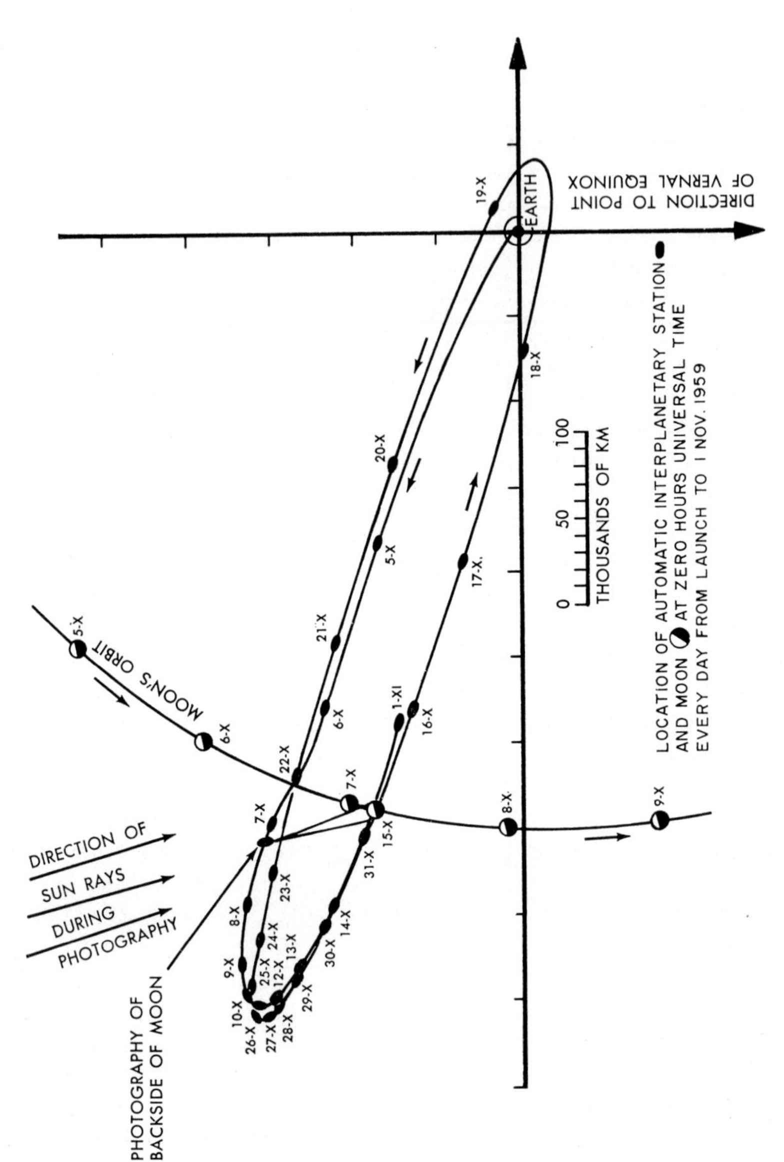

Fig. 3. Trajectory of vehicle carrying photographic equipment around moon.

interaction of emission and absorption, which canceled one another at this particular wavelength.

Thus the interpretation is that a volume of about one million cubic meters of gas (evaluated under normal conditions) escaped from a fissure in the central peak of Alphonsus and, rapidly expanding, formed a cloud 3–5 km in diameter which dissipated into the surrounding vacuum. This process lasted not longer than one hour, probably much less. Kozyrev is of the opinion that the observed phenomenon proves the volcanic origin of the crater Alphonsus and other similar formations on the moon.

The third interplanetary rocket launched on October 4, 1959 put into orbit an automatic station fitted with two cameras of 20 and 50 cm focal length. At 4^h UT on October 7th this station, when passing near the line joining the moon with the sun (ref. Fig. 3), and situated at about 117° selenographic longitude and +17° latitude, from a distance of 65,000 km took on a 35-mm standard-size film a number of photographs of the reverse side of the full moon (as seen from the station). These were developed, fixed, and dried in the station itself. A few days after, when the station was approaching the earth, the images from the negatives were transmitted by television, the signals being many million times weaker than in ordinary television. The pictures thus obtained showed much interference due to "noise" of different origin. A detailed study of nine transmitted negatives, overlapping as shown on Fig. 4, was made independently in Moscow at the Sternberg Astronomical Institute, at the Pulkovo observatory, and at the observatory of the University of Kharkov. Sample prints of four of these negatives are Figs. 5 and 6. The revealed features were divided into three groups according to the reliability of disclosure. The first group contains the 252 most reliable objects, among them about 100 on the visible marginal part of the moon, such as Mare Crisium, Marginis, etc. The second group consists of 190 less reliable features, and the third of 57 objects whose reality is least warranted. All these objects were entered into a catalogue with their selenographic coordinates and description. With the help of the Research Institute for Geodesy, Airsurvey and Cartography in Moscow, a map in an orthographic equatorial projection of the reverse side of the moon was drawn (Fig. 7). The results of this work were published by the Academy of Sciences of the U.S.S.R. The map shows that the reverse side of the moon contains very few maria (see Fig. 8)—only one small but very conspicuous sea being seen. A darkening near the SE border is possibly also an extended but less reliable mare. Thus the reverse side differs strikingly from the visible one. Curiously enough, this fact was anticipated by the German astronomer Julius Franz as stated in his booklet, "Der Mond," first published in 1906.

It seems that it is impossible to explain this difference by any influence of the earth. Three possible actions were thought of. First, only on the visible side of the moon solar eclipses can occur, when the earth's shadow falls on the moon. A total solar eclipse for a given point on the moon can have a duration up to about 1½ hours, during which time the surface temperature can drop more than 200°C—from over +100°C, to

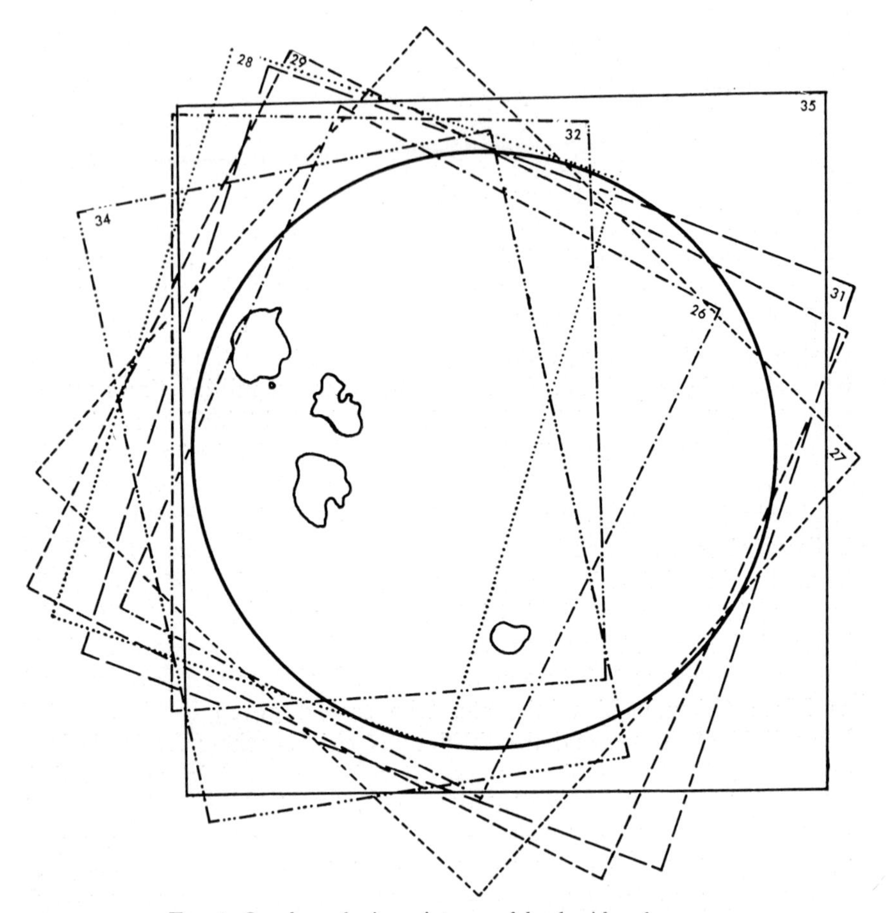

FIG. 4. Overlap of nine pictures of back side of moon.

which the moon's surface is heated at noon, to about —100°C in the earth's shadow. It was surmised that this sudden change could lead to a deterioration of the surface structure. However, we now know that the thermal conductivity of the upper layers on the moon is exceedingly low, so that an appreciable drop of temperature can penetrate only to a very small depth under the surface of the moon, probably only to a few

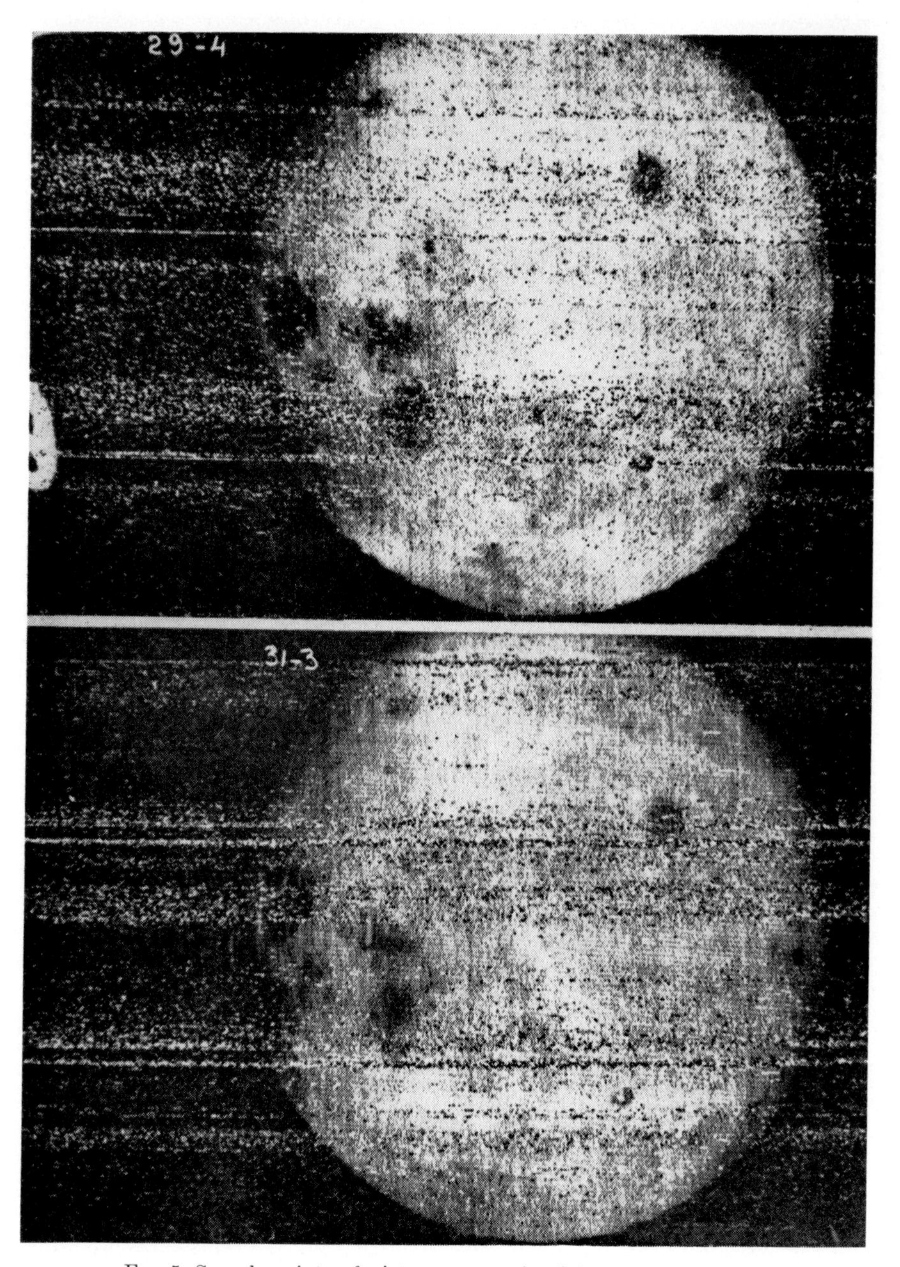

FIG. 5. Sample prints of pictures transmitted from lunar vehicle.

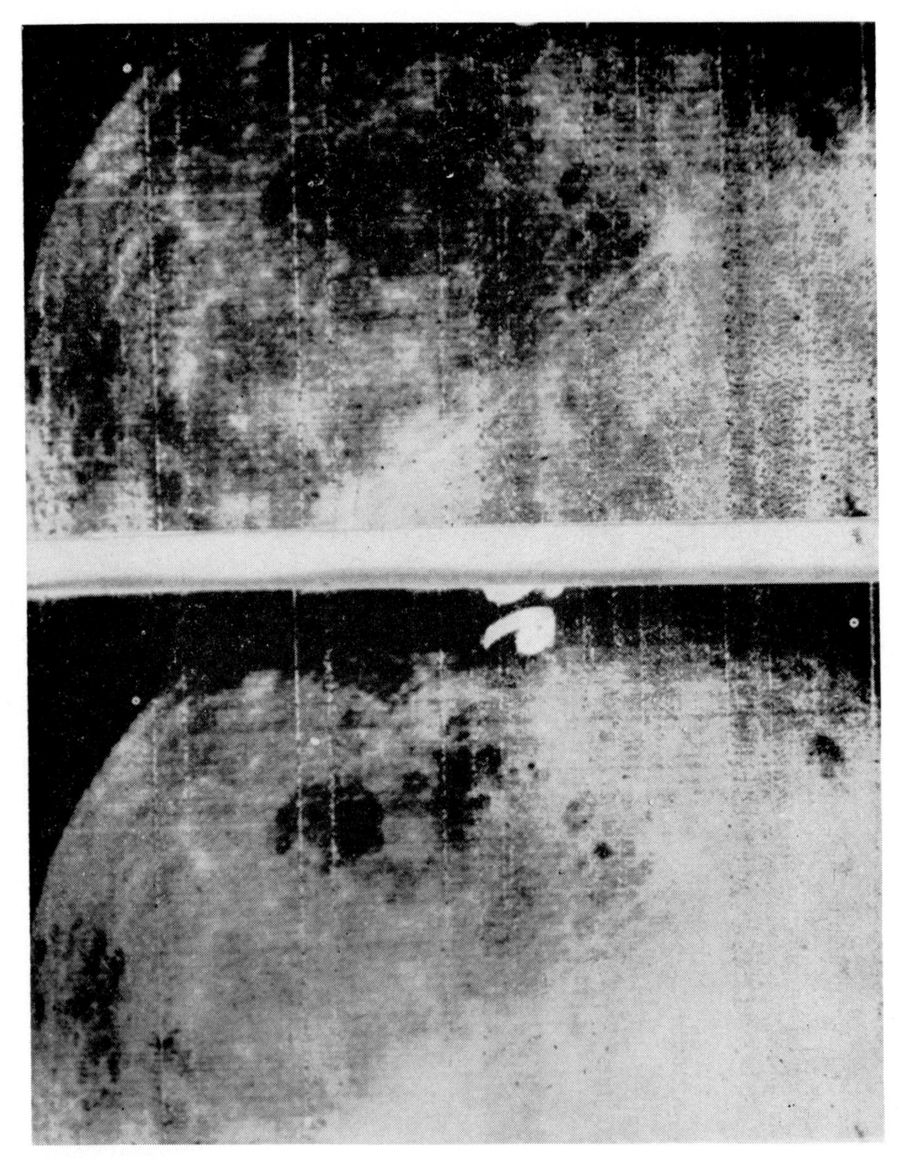

FIG. 6. Sample prints of pictures transmitted from lunar vehicle.

centimeters. Thus this cause cannot produce any such large change in the general features of the two hemispheres as revealed by our observations.

The second seemingly possible cause is the attraction of the earth as manifested by tidal forces. However, they act nearly symmetrically on

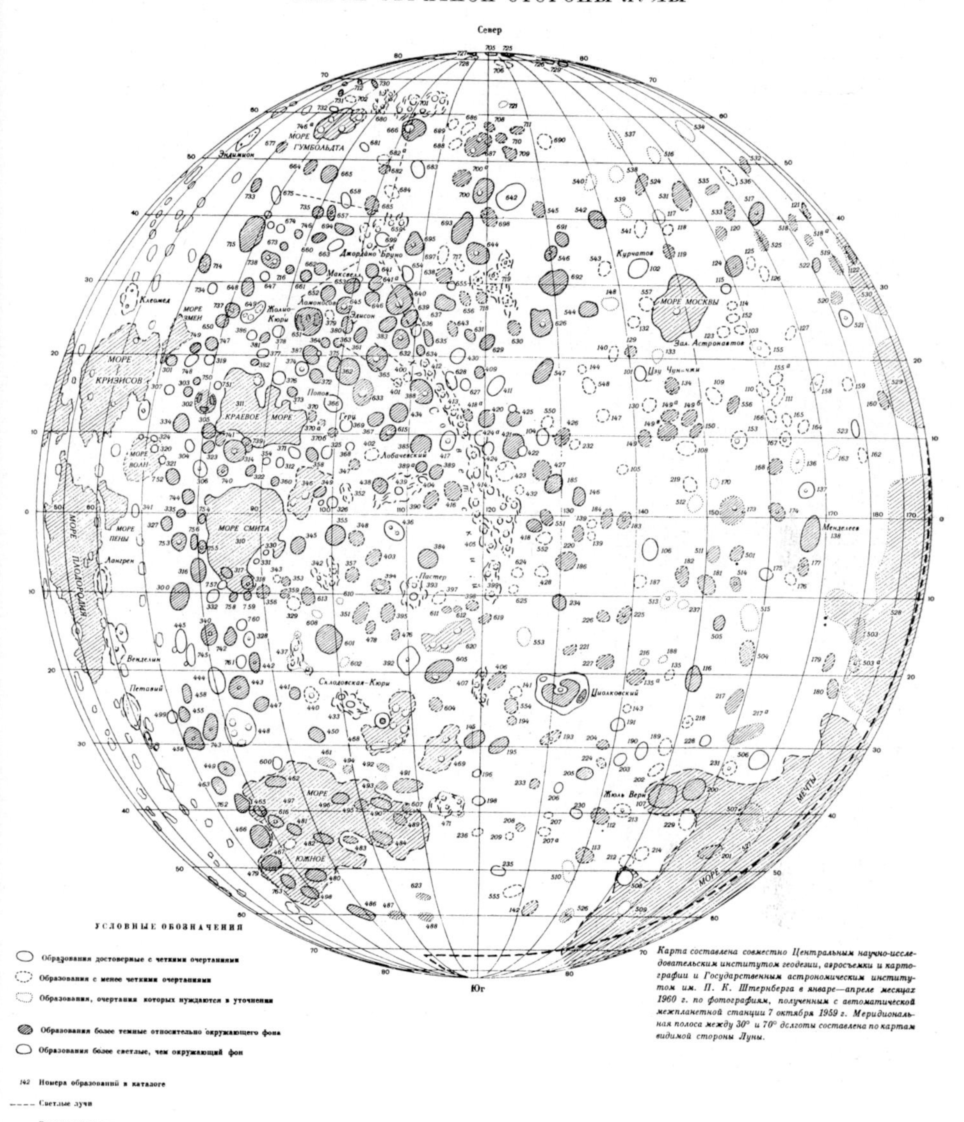

FIG. 7. Map of the reverse side of the moon from photographs taken by the automatic interplanetary station, October 7, 1959.

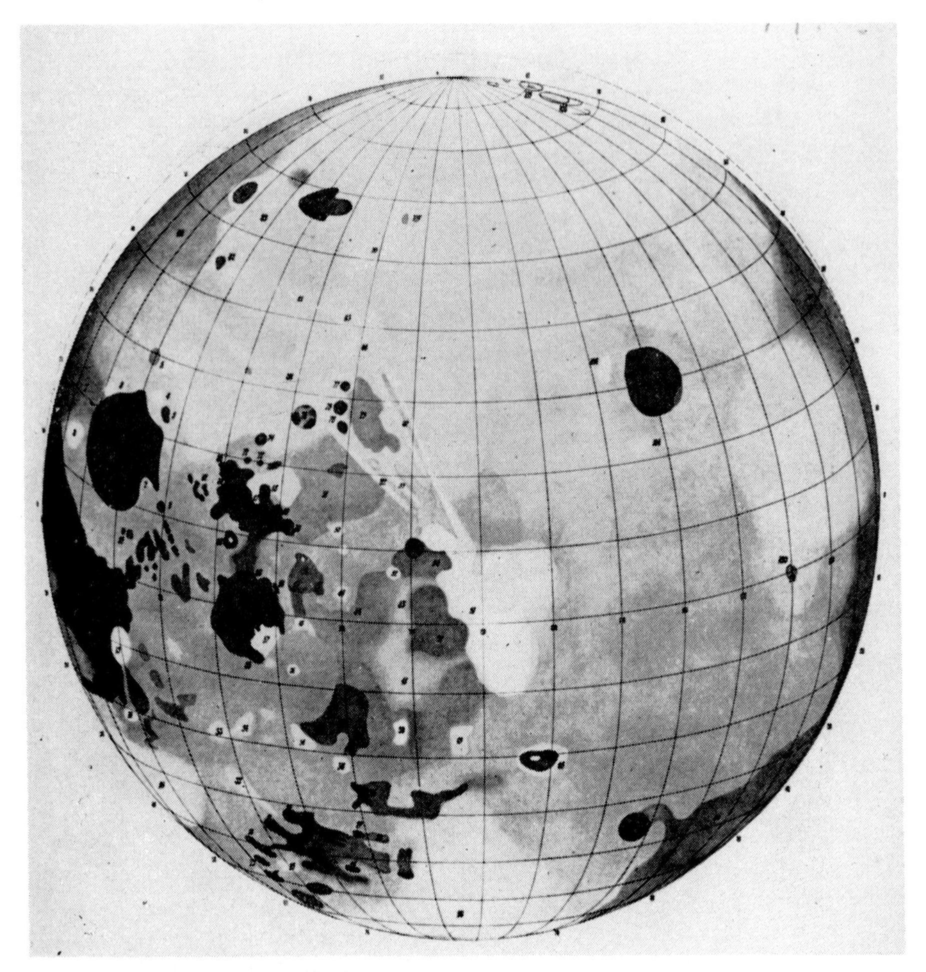

FIG. 8. Feature outlines on the reverse side of the moon. This composite drawing in external perspective projection as seen from the automatic interplanetary station was compiled from the original photographs at the Pulkovo observatory. On the left side are features visible from the Earth.

the two hemispheres, the tidal action on the reverse side being only by 0.5% weaker than on the front one. It is true, that if in the remote past the moon was much nearer to the earth than at present, this difference was larger. Still it is difficult to assign to this cause sufficient influence for producing the needed effect.

At last consideration was given to a shielding action of the earth on meteorites flying towards the moon. This action is very small, as the earth's disk seen from the moon covers only about 1/7000 of the whole celestial hemisphere on the moon. Besides there is another influence of opposite effect. Those meteorites which are not intercepted by the earth but fly near enough to its surface are attracted by the earth so that their paths are bent into the earth's "shadow." Those passing very near to the surface of the earth or having a small relative velocity are deflected so strongly as to leave the shadow much nearer than the moon. The paths of the more distant ones or of those with large velocities are bent insufficiently to hit the moon. Thus there are very restricted limits of distance and speed for meteorites to be deflected by the attraction of the earth just enough as to fall on the moon. Although an exact calculation is lacking, it is clear that we have to deal with two small and opposite effects, and therefore their combination must be still smaller.

Thus it seems that there is no external influence which could have produced the great difference in the extent of the maria on the two sides of the moon. Let us consider our earth, whose two hemispheres also differ in the distribution of land and sea, notwithstanding the quick axial rotation, which must have made all external influences of sufficient duration quite alike on the eastern and western hemispheres. It is probable, therefore, that the diversity of the two sides of the moon is the result of the action of internal forces which contributed to the formation of the surface of the moon.

There had been the difficulty of deciding at what time the photographs of the reverse side should be taken. At full moon the features are seen without any shadows and are therefore difficult to discern. On the other hand an oblique illumination, which brings out many more details, can show only a small part of the whole hemisphere of the moon. As part of the known side of the moon must also be presented on the photographs in order to provide a good connection and check, there would remain in this case only a small fraction of the reverse side. Taking into consideration these pro and contra, it was decided to include in the photos as much of the unknown side as possible, at the price of losing contrast of the features.

In the future, when the rapidly developing technique will allow us to see the moon's surface from a space-vehicle by television, there will be no restrictions of this kind, and the whole side of the moon which is not visible from the earth will be studied in conditions of different illumination with much greater precision and detail.

Discussion

Mr. A. H. Katz: Because they are unique, the photographs secured from the Soviets' Lunik III in 1959 are the best available photographs of the reverse side of our nonman-made satellite.

We performed two independent analyses of these photographs—analyzing them not for their contents, but with respect to the technical aspects of the photography itself (*1,2*).

In the process of this analysis, we found that there were several sets of "originals." In fact, no one has *the* originals which remained in the Lunik III capsule and suffered its fate. There were various derivatives, or generations, of the "best" series received by video in the Soviet Union from the Lunik III. Some sets of photos were degraded by the radio-photo process in transmission from the Soviet Union to New York, and some sets were further degraded by retransmission via wire-photo from New York to various points in the United States. We obtained several sets of "originals," including some very good photographs received directly from the Soviet Union without intermediate electronic processing.

There are at least two methods which permit one to estimate the quality of such photography. One method was used by my colleague M. Davies. He started with a "good" photograph of the visible half of the moon, a photograph produced by the Mount Wilson Observatory.

The reason that the description of that photograph—"good"—appears in quotation marks is that, based on my experience in aerial photography, I must confess that I have never seen a really good photograph of the moon, front or back. I have seen what are described as the "best" photographs of the front side of the moon, as well as the only and, therefore, "best" photographs of the back of the moon. The ground resolution—the detail visible on the surface—is still inadequate by several orders of magnitude by comparison with aerial photographs of the earth used for geologic interpretation.

In another paper Davies (*3*) describes and illustrates the degradation of a high-quality aerial photograph of Washington, D. C., to the level of a "good" photograph of the moon. When this is done, all detail disappears! Simply summarized, we need better photographs of the moon, front and back.

Davies started his analysis with the set of Soviet back-of-the-moon photographs available from wire-photo services. He then degraded the Mount Wilson photograph systematically and under control, so he could estimate the resolution of the degraded product. He thus constructed a visual go-no-go gage which enabled easy bracketing of the Soviet photos, and thus yielded an estimate of their quality.

Working completely independently of Davies, we estimated the quality by measuring the scanning lines, making small measurements of features, and so on.

We arrived at different but comparable results, the differences arising because Davies used a more degenerate set of "originals" than we did.

The quality estimates we made for the best of the Soviet moon photos were ground resolutions somewhat under 10 miles, for the photos secured from about 40,000 miles. I will not argue whether the resolution is 8 miles or 5 miles. The statement "under 10 miles" is good enough. Those of you who have anything to do with estimates of resolution know that this parameter lacks precision. By the time one adds up the exceptions and qualifications, side conditions, and caveats, "resolution" becomes a difficult parameter to use with meaning. We know how to order these numbers—that 10 miles is "better" than 20 miles, but we do not know how to interpret them precisely. These matters are discussed more fully in an earlier article (*4*).

This pair of numbers—10 miles at 40,000 miles—may be scaled to resolutions of the order of 150 to 200 ft from 150-mile satellite altitudes. The Tiros satellite performs an altogether different function than did the Soviet Lunik III. It covers a much greater angle of view, and from the same scaled altitude as in the example immediately above it would yield resolutions much inferior to Lunik III. The comparison is not meant to be invidious, and was made only because it is useful in thinking about the performance of Lunik III to refer to more familiar numbers and situations.

Let me return briefly to the matter of getting better photographs of the moon. About 15 years ago I was intrigued by a suggestion made by Dr. James G. Baker to the effect that it might be possible to sample the incoming wavefront, process the information, and compute and apply a correction in real time, thus greatly reducing atmospheric effects, and increasing resolution. Professor Kopal noted and discussed this idea in the introduction to his "Astronomical Optics." This is not the time nor am I the one to describe this class of ideas adequately.

The point is that when this kind of idea was originally suggested, 15 years ago, there was neither financial nor intellectual interest in such a project. The right climate was not present to entertain such a suggestion. I suggest that this is now a very good climate, intellectually and financially, to entertain suggestions like that. And I think we ought to thoroughly investigate the feasibility of improving the resolution of terrestrial instruments.

One of the reasons we ought to try getting better photographs from earth is to make it tough on space-borne instrumentation. Almost any experiment or data collection that we can do on earth is going to be less costly than the *same experiment* or the same data collection in space. Of course, there are experiments that can only be done in or from space, and such experiments are therefore not at all competitive with earth based experiments or data-collection systems.

Back again briefly to one of the points that we noted earlier. There are two ways of getting data back. In their Lunik III, the Soviets chose to construct a very beautiful system, which used film that was processed aboard the satellite. After chemical processing, the film was scanned by some sort of process analogous to wire-photo systems and the data were then transmitted to earth.

Of course, the pictures were rubbery and full of noise and all sorts of things that did not belong there. Despite all these defects, they were magnificent. In fact, so that my remarks are not misinterpreted now, I was and still am, much more impressed with *that* particular scientific experiment—putting this machine together, sending it around the moon, taking photographs, reading them out, and sending the photos back—than I am with the man in space work done so far. I think myself that Lunik III was a much more involved experiment than orbiting a man around the earth.

Nevertheless, we need still better pictures, and there are ways of getting them. The system in the Davies paper was based on a recoverable film system using a panoramic camera. The quality, in principle, can be quite high. We may suggest an interesting criterion: pictures should not be taken unless they are at least an order of magnitude better than what we can do from earth—except, of course, around the back of the moon where any pictures are better than those we take from earth.

The recovery of packages from distances corresponding to that of the moon has not yet been accomplished. Such systems will be available, and certainly they will be tried out before we are able to send a man round the moon and get him back. It might be interesting to speculate about combining video-playback with film recovery systems for insurance purposes. Although you would really like to get the film back, you are not sure you will, and while the machine is still out there you might be able to scan the film and transmit it via video. Then that is a safe and conservative thing to do, to make sure you obtain some results.

I noted earlier, and I will reiterate, that I am always amazed by the number of experiments that can be conjured up to substitute for old fashioned, high quality photography. Photography is such a basic exploration tool that it should be one of the first things attempted before planning any other experiments. Careful study of really high quality photographs of the moon would enable us, for example, to re-examine some of the poorer quality photographs and see what is really there, in terms of textures and tones that we cannot now interpret. This is a standard phenomenon in photo interpretation: once we have a high quality photograph and know what is really there, we are later able to identify and describe it even when limited to much poorer quality definition.

It strikes me that this role of photography in the space effort is not emphasized enough. Perhaps, as I indicated before, photography is so mundane and so well understood, and there are so many amateur photographers, that one would rather get on with all the other presumably more exciting and exotic experiments. I hold no brief for any one kind of experiment or data collection system. But I think photography needs a much stronger effort than it seems to be getting.

References

1. A. H. Katz, Analysis of Lunik III photographs, *Proc. Lunar and Planet. Exploration Colloq.* **2**(2), 27–44 (1960); The RAND Corporation, Paper P-2250 (March 17, 1960).
2. M. E. Davies, How good is the Lunik III moon photography?, The RAND Corporation Paper P-1892 (January 4, 1960); see also *ARS Journal* **30,** 28 (1960).
3. M. E. Davies, *in* Lunar exploration by photography from a space vehicle, "Proceedings of the Tenth International Astronomical Congress." Springer-Verlag, Vienna, 1960; see also The RAND Corporation Paper P-1671 (March 5, 1959).
4. A. H. Katz, Observation satellites, problems and prospects, *Astronautics,* April, June, July, August, September, October, 1960; The RAND Corporation, Paper P-1707 (May 29, 1959).

Dr. B. C. Murray: I would like to call attention to two aspects of the reconnaissance of the moon and of Mars that should be examined carefully with regard to a second-generation orbiting or fly-by vehicle. Firstly, it should be noted that recent work by Shorthill at Boeing Aircraft Company, which has been substantiated by Sinton at Lowell Observatory, has proven the existence of a considerable selenographic variation in the emitted infrared radiation from the moon. These variations in emission properties arise from corresponding variations in the thermal properties of the surface of the moon. Accordingly, high-resolution mapping of the moon in the long wavelength infrared can be expected to reveal variations in the surface properties in a manner analogous, for instance, to the way in which airborne magnetometer surveys on the earth reveal differences in the magnetic properties of the crust. Similar variations in infrared emission may well exist on the surface of Mars, arising from both temperature and emissivity variations on that surface. Again, high-resolution mapping from an orbiting or fly-by vehicle may provide otherwise unobtainable information regarding the surface properties of Mars.

A second application of long wavelength infrared observations may be emission spectroscopy of the same two bodies. The silicates, in particular, exhibit anomalous emissivity variations in this wavelength region, and it is possible that mineralogical information may be contained in fine structure superimposed on the thermal emission spectra of both the moon and of Mars.

It should be recognized, however, that both the photometric and spectroscopic significance of lunar and planetary infrared emission has yet to be investigated in detail from ground-based observation sites. The extra-terrestrial observations thus should await the full exploitation of this wavelength interval by ground-based instruments. Long wavelength infrared observations, therefore, should be considered for second-generation lunar and Martian probes, as well as for the later orbiting astronomical observatories.

Dr. H. Urey: I would like to ask Dr. Mikhailov whether he and Dr. Kozyrev and other scientists who have studied this subject in the Soviet Union believe that Kozyrev's observation of C_2 from the crater indicates volcanic action?

Professor A. A. Mikhailov: Well, the consensus is that there is volcanic action on the moon. But I think that is somewhat exaggerated. We could only say now that a gas escapes from a crevice, and that it was included in a hole, perhaps somewhere in the moon's crust under pressure, probably a cold gas. It escapes and evaporates into the vacuum very quickly. What is the origin of this gas? Whether it is produced in some cavities in the moon or in volcanic action, that is impossible to say.

Dr. H. Urey: Does Kozyrev still maintain that he saw evidence of C_3?

Professor A. A. Mikhailov: As far as I know, the last time he did not emphasize it.

Dr. H. Urey: May I ask another question of Professor Mikhailov in regard to the pictures of the back side of the moon? Do you not think that it may be that the distribution of maria on the two hemispheres is a matter of chance collisions of a relatively small number of objects?

Professor A. A. Mikhailov: I must confess that I am not a geologist. I never did occupy myself with the process by which the lunar surface was formed. But still I am of the opinion, although perhaps not on a sound basis, that the maria were caused not by meteorite impacts but by some volcanic or geologic processes in the moon itself.

Professor P. Swings: I understood from Dr. Mikhailov that he thought that the Swan bands were excited by shortwave radiation. Now the Swan system of C_2 from the electronic structure of the molecule will be excited only in the blue violet region, and that is the case for the comets. In the comets there is complete evidence that the excitation is by solar radiation ranging from 4300 to 5000 Å. I presume that in the case of the lunar molecules, the same should have taken place.

Dr. R. Boyd: I am accustomed to finding that any observation which we make in the United Kingdom has just been made either in the U.S.S.R. or in America, but in case this time that is not so, I would like to mention a figure for the albedo of the moon in the ultraviolet, which happened to come out of our recent ultraviolet scan of the southern sky. The band is rather wide. It peaks at about 1700 Å and stretches from 1600 to about 2300 Å. The albedo is about 3%. I would be interested to know whether this has already been measured and, if so, whether anyone else's figure is the same as ours.

Chairman Johnson noted that there was no contrary response from the audience.

18.2 *The Exploration of the Moon, the Planets, and Interplanetary Space**

A. R. HIBBS

JET PROPULSION LABORATORY, CALIFORNIA INSTITUTE OF TECHNOLOGY, Pasadena, California

I. Introduction

The National Aeronautics and Space Administration has undertaken a major exploratory program aimed to make direct measurements of the characteristics of the moon, the planets, and the space between them (*1*).

This program was initiated by the launching of the Pioneer series of space probes. Pioneer IV, launched in March of 1959, and Pioneer V, launched one year later, both escaped from the gravitational field of the earth. Pioneer IV telemetered information on cosmic-ray intensity to a range of about 400,000 miles. The radio signal from Pioneer V was detectable over a range of more than 20,000,000 miles, and good telemetry data were received from more than half of this distance, giving characteristics of charged-particle flux and magnetic-field direction and intensity in space well away from the vicinity of the earth.

The Ranger 1 and 2 spacecraft, scheduled for launching this year, will continue this interplanetary exploration program with a wide variety of sophisticated instrumentation. The engineering technique developed in these early Ranger flights will enable us to proceed with the spacecraft design for direct measurements of lunar and planetary characteristics by instruments to be flown close by and landed on the surfaces of these bodies.

The Jet Propulsion Laboratory of the California Institute of Technology has been assigned by NASA to carry out the Ranger, the Mariner, and the Surveyor projects, which will accomplish the first steps of this direct lunar and planetary exploration program. As a representative of that Laboratory, it is my purpose today to give you some information about the instrumentation which will be employed in this direct experimental investigation of the characteristics of the moon, the planets, and interplanetary space.

* This paper presents the results of one phase of research carried out at the Jet Propulsion Laboratory, California Institute of Technology, under Contract No. NASw-6, Sponsored by the National Aeronautics and Space Administration.

II. Rangers 1 and 2

Two vehicles, Rangers 1 and 2, will be launched in the last half of 1961 to begin the interplanetary exploration program. As can be seen in Fig. 1, each will be sent on a long elliptical trajectory, the apogee of which is approximately 10^6 km from earth. This means that they will

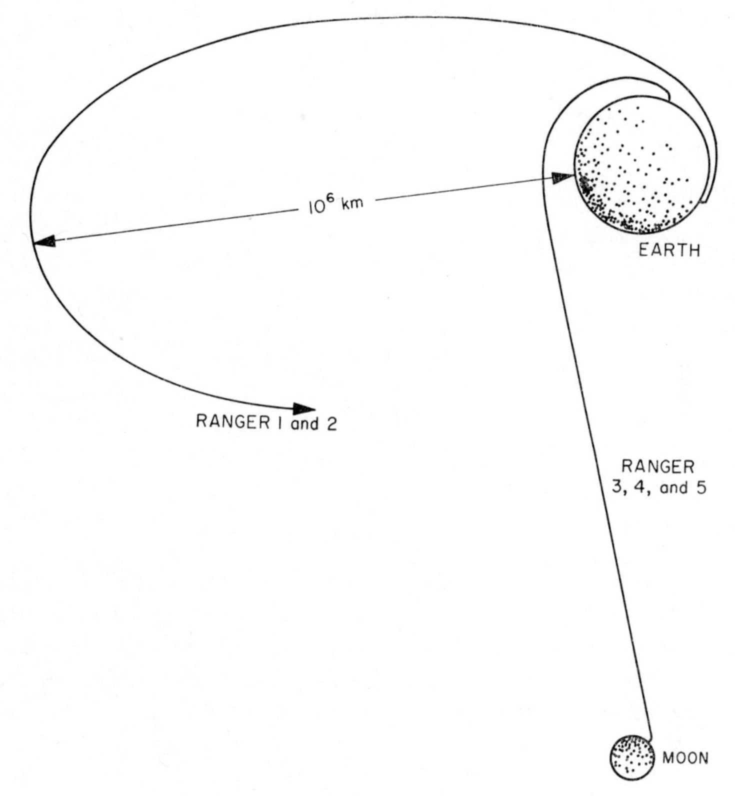

FIG. 1. Elliptical trajectory of the Ranger vehicles.

be launched with a speed only slightly less than escape speed. As a result, they will spend about 1 to 2 months measuring the characteristics of space at the order of several hundred thousand to a million kilometers from earth. Rangers 3, 4, and 5 will be sent on trajectories toward the moon and will carry with them a capsule containing a seismometer. This capsule will be detached from the main bus of the spacecraft, slowed by a retrorocket, and landed on the surface at a speed of a few hundred miles an hour.

Table I lists the scientific experiments which will be carried out by the first two Ranger spacecraft and the scientists assigned responsibility for them (*2*). Most of the experiments are directed toward the objectives of measuring interplanetary fields and charged particles. There are two exceptions to this category; namely, a measurement of the density of interplanetary dust, and an observation of the neutral hydrogen geocorona.

TABLE I

Scientific-Experiment Plan: Rangers 1 and 2

Experiment	Sponsoring agency and experimenter
Triple-coincidence telescopes	University of Chicago: C. Y. Fan, P. Meyer, and J. A. Simpson
Integrating ionization chamber	Caltech and JPL: H. V. Neher and H. R. Anderson
Medium-energy particle detectors	
(a) geiger tubes and CdS detectors	(a) State University of Iowa: J. A. Van Allen
(b) Au-Si detectors	(b) University of Chicago: C. Y. Fan, P. Meyer, and J. A. Simpson
Electrostatic analyzers	JPL: M. Neugebauer and C. W. Snyder
Magnetometer	NASA Goddard Space Flight Center: J. P. Heppner
Ly-α telescope	Naval Research Laboratory and JPL: T. A. Chubb and R. W. Kreplin
Cosmic-dust detectors	NASA Goddard Space Flight Center: W. M. Alexander

The charged-particle measurements will be carried out by instruments covering a range of energies. At the lowest energy range, there are electrostatic analyzers capable of examining the spectrum of protons from 0 to 5000 ev and the spectrum of electrons up to a few hundred electron volts. Medium-range particles will be detected by a group of counters relying both on the solid-state property of semiconductors and on traditional Geiger tubes. Ionization chambers, such as those flown on balloons in the earth's atmosphere, and triple-coincidence telescopes, such as those that were used on Pioneer V, will complete the charged-particle measurements by covering the highest energy range in the neighborhood of 10 to 100 Mev for protons.

Closely associated with the behavior of charged particles is, of course, the behavior of the interplanetary magnetic field. This will be measured with a rubidium vapor magnetometer which will detect the strength of the field by measuring the Larmor frequency separating the rubidium vapor lines, whose fine structure will be split by an amount proportional to the strength of the field.

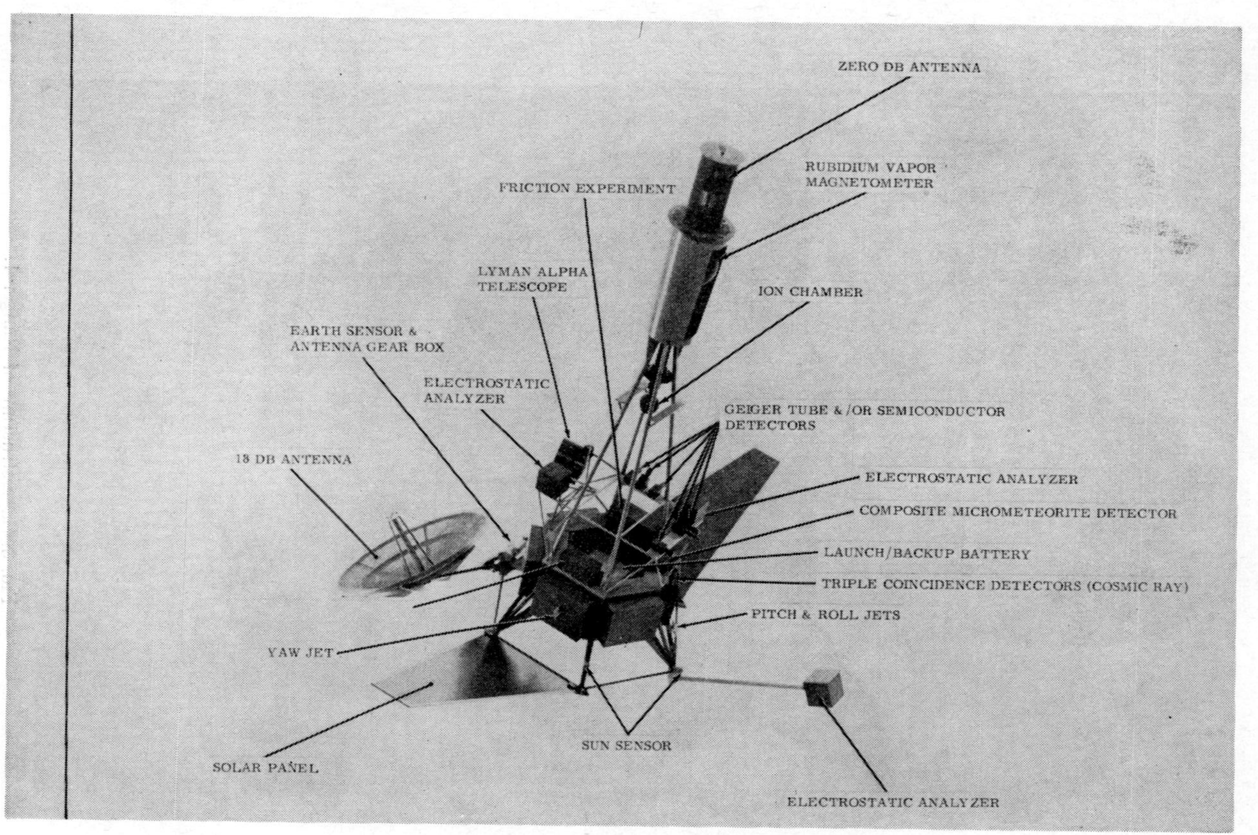

FIG. 2. Ranger A-1 and A-2 spacecraft.

FIG. 3. Superstructure of Ranger 1.

FIG. 4. Hexagonal base of Ranger 1.

The neutral hydrogen cloud around the earth will be observed by a scanning telescope that detects scattered radiation of the Ly-α frequency. As the spacecraft recedes from earth, this telescope will repeatedly scan the vicinity of the earth, including in its successive pictures a larger and larger field of view.

The micrometeorite detectors on the Ranger will give information on both the energy and momentum of the particles striking it.

Figure 2 shows the spacecraft for Rangers 1 and 2. The rubidium vapor magnetometer is located near the front end, where it is as far removed as possible from those parts of the spacecraft that may introduce a spurious magnetic field. The ionization chamber is below it, located in a position where it will be shielded as little as possible by the structure of the spacecraft. The six electrostatic analyzers are positioned in such a way that they can see freely along opposite directions of each of three coordinate axes.

The spacecraft itself is powered by solar panels that operate after the attitude-control system has successfully aimed the spacecraft directly at the sun. The attitude-control system will thereafter maintain this orientation throughout the lifetime of the experiment. The directional parabolic antenna will be aimed at earth with the same attitude-control system, by rolling the spacecraft around its longitudinal axis after the sun direction has been fixed. In this way, and by hinging the antenna out from the spacecraft to the appropriate angle, the antenna can be made to point at earth.

Figure 3 shows the superstructure of Ranger 1. The rubidium vapor magnetometer is inside the Fiberglas casing at the top of the structure; on a platform near the base, several of the charged-particle detectors can be seen in this figure.

Figure 4 shows the hexagonal base of the spacecraft. The six boxes positioned around this hexagonal base contain all the electronic parts required for the operation of the spacecraft and its scientific instruments.

III. Rangers 3, 4, and 5

The second group of Ranger spacecraft, 3, 4, and 5, is intended for lunar exploration. Table II lists the experiments selected for these flights. As the spacecraft approaches the moon, a succession of photographs will be taken by a vidicon camera, which is aimed toward the lunar surface (*3*). The vidicon tube will employ a 200-line scan, and the optics will be such as to take a picture measuring approximately 40 km on a side at the initiation of the picture-taking sequence, and decreasing steadily to 600 meters on a side for the last picture expected to be successfully recovered from the data.

The telescope optical system developed by Alan Dunk at JPL is basically a conventional Cassegrain-configuration astronomical telescope, as shown in Fig. 5, employing a primary concave parabolic mirror and a centrally located secondary convex hyperbolic mirror to reflect the lunar image back to the vidicon photoconductive image surface 0.5 in. in front of the primary mirror. An aperture of 7 in. and equivalent focal length of 40 in. is provided, yielding an equivalent light grasp of *f*/6.3. An initial optical resolving power of 5 sec of arc, or 40 optical line pairs/mm over the 1° telescope field of view, will be secured. This will, of course, be degraded by the vidicon scan to approximately 34 sec of arc or 6 optical line pairs/mm resolution.

TABLE II
SCIENTIFIC-EXPERIMENT PLAN: RANGERS 3, 4, AND 5

Experiments	Instruments and measurements	Cognizant agency and scientist
Capsule: seismology	Single axis seismometer	Caltech: F. Press Columbia U.: M. Ewing
Bus: photography of small lunar area	Vidicon television	JPL: E. F. Dobies
Gamma-ray spectroscopy	Gamma-ray spectrometer	U. of California: J. R. Arnold LASL: M. A. Van Dilla and E. C. Anderson JPL: A. Metzger

The significant deviations from usual astronomical telescope design consist of the use of fuzed quartz for the telescope mirrors, Invar for all temperature-sensitive metallic parts and, primarily, the use of an 8-in. diameter fuzed quartz tube as the basic rigid tubular structure separating the primary and secondary mirrors. These features have been emphasized in the design because of the large range of vehicle temperatures anticipated in the cislunar environment. Engineering models of the vidicon telescope employing this JPL design have successfully survived the simulated Atlas-Agena takeoff vibration tests without mechanical or optical deterioration.

A mechanical rotating sector shutter, operating on inertial principles with solenoid actuation, has been included in front of the vidicon face. This provides an exposure time of 20 msec on the photoconductor surface with a uniformly illuminated field. The shutter will prevent blurring of the image of the lunar surface due to motion of the spacecraft during the exposure time, and will also provide a closing of the optical system during the 13-sec scan and erase operation of the vidicon electronic system.

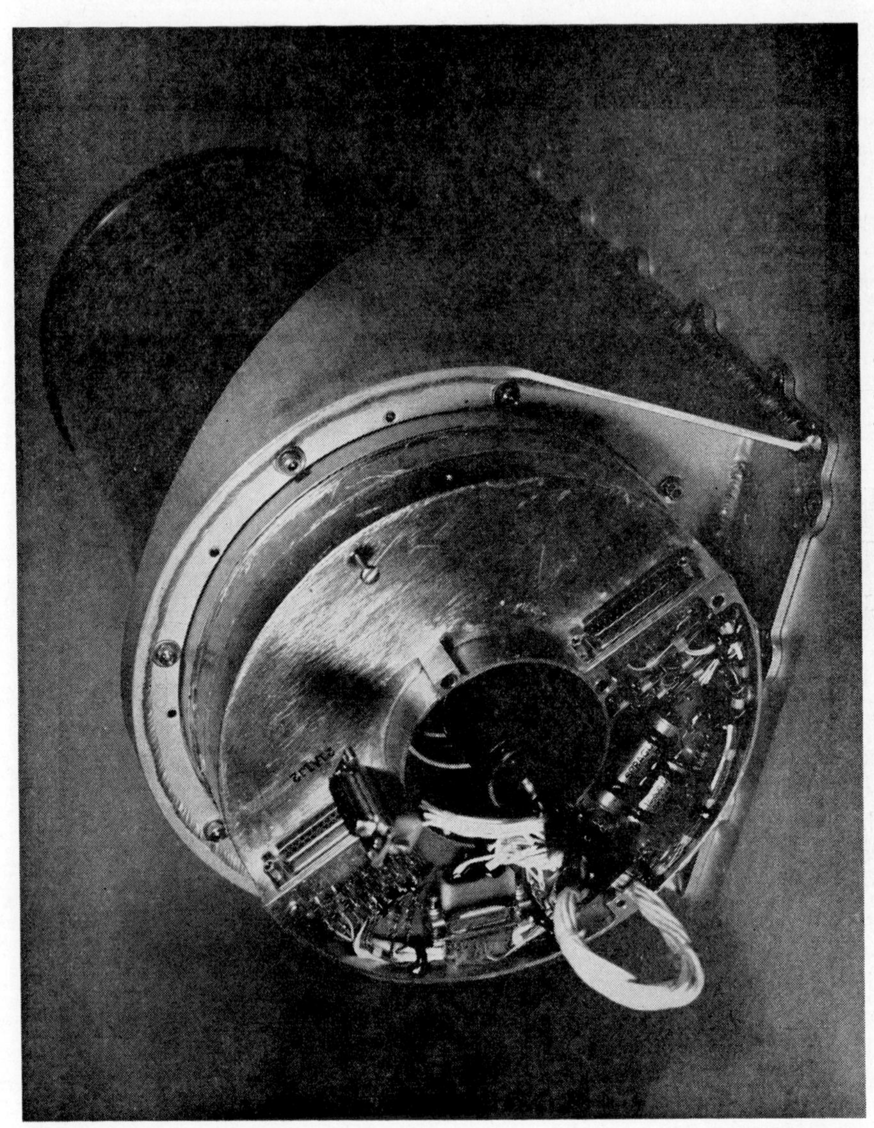

FIG. 5. Cassegrain-configuration astronomical telescope.

FIG. 6. Results of one of the numerous landing capsule impact tests.

The unit for holding the telescope optical elements and the vidicon tube and associated electronics within the telescope structure have been carefully designed to survive the shake, shock, and temperature environments anticipated. An auxiliary capping mechanism is provided to shield the telescope optics and the vidicon surface from the light of the sun during mid-course maneuvers, and to provide protection from micrometeorites and a proper temperature balance within the telescope in cislunar space. The telescope structure will be mounted to the spacecraft in such a way as to minimize misalignment of the longitudinal optical-mechanical axes during takeoff and under the temperature environment anticipated. While the vidicon is in operation, a gamma-ray spectrometer, positioned far from the spacecraft so as to avoid the effect of secondaries, will measure the ambient radioactivity in the region of the spectral line associated with the decay of potassium 40. This experiment has been so designed that, even if the moon is composed of material as low in natural radioactivity as the chondritic meteorites, the detector will observe the lunar potassium-40 line above the background expected from interplanetary and cosmic-ray sources.

Ranger 3, 4, and 5 spacecraft are similar in many ways to Rangers 1 and 2. However, the superstructure containing the scientific instruments has been replaced by a superstructure supporting an omnidirectional antenna and surrounding the lunar capsule together with its retromotor, which is being developed by Aeronutronic Corporation under subcontract to the Laboratory. This spacecraft is also powered by solar panels and communicates with earth by means of a directional parabolic antenna.

Approximately 30 km above the lunar surface, after the spacecraft has been properly positioned, the capsule, together with its retromotor, will be detached from the parent spacecraft. The capsule is spun to maintain its orientation. Thereafter, the retrorocket is ignited, which slows down the capsule to impact with a speed of about 30 meters/sec.

Variations in retromotor performance will, of course, result in a variation of landing speeds. The expected standard deviation of landing speeds is approximately 30 to 40 meters/sec. The landing capsule and all the instrumentation within it—that is, the seismometer, its amplifier, transmitter, and antenna, and power supply, righting mechanism, temperature-control device, zeroing motor, and automatic calibration device—have been designed to withstand several thousand G's of impact acceleration.

Figure 6 shows the results of one of the numerous tests that have been conducted to ensure that this design objective has been met. This is not a lunar crater but rather a terrestrial crater produced in blacktop by the impact of a seismometer dropped from a helicopter at 1000 ft.

The seismometer, lying on the ground beside the crater, operated properly after this drop test.

The seismometer carried in the capsule of Rangers 3, 4, and 5 is designed to operate for a period of 30 to 60 days. Even if no internal seismic activity occurs on the moon, it is likely that the impact of meteorites on the moon will create sufficient seismic disturbances to be detected by this device (*4*).

IV. Surveyor

The exploration of the lunar surface, begun with the series of Rangers 3, 4, and 5, will be continued with the Surveyor spacecraft. This spacecraft will be designed to land gently on the moon at a speed slower than the descent of a man in a parachute on earth, perform chemical analyses of lunar surface and subsurface, and relay back to earth television pictures of lunar features.

A full-scale mockup of the spacecraft, which stands 11 ft high, is shown in Fig. 7, which also carries identification of some of the instrumentation. The Surveyor will soft land 750 lb on the lunar surface. The landing will be accomplished by a solid-propellant retrorocket which will fire in a direction opposite to the flight of the spacecraft and slow it down to approximately 10 miles per hour. Of the 750 lb landed on the moon, more than 200 lb will be instruments.

The instrumentation will include several television cameras, a sensitive 3-axis seismometer to record moonquakes or meteoritic impacts, a sensitive magnetometer to measure the characteristics of the lunar magnetic field, a drill to penetrate the lunar surface, instruments to analyze the composition from the surface and from the drill hole, and instrumentation to measure radiation and the lunar atmosphere.

The drill will be extended from the Surveyor spacecraft and will be designed to penetrate at least 18 in. beneath the surface. As it drills, small fragments of the moon's surface and subsurface material will be brought into the spacecraft, where instrumentation will perform chemical analyses. One of the multiple television cameras will be used to monitor this operation.

The Hughes Aircraft Company in Culver City, California, is working under contract to the Jet Propulsion Laboratory to build the Surveyor spacecraft.

V. Mariner A

Direct exploration of planetary characteristics will begin with the Mariner-A spacecraft, shown in Fig. 8, designed for a close pass near the planet Venus. Scientific experiments have been selected for this

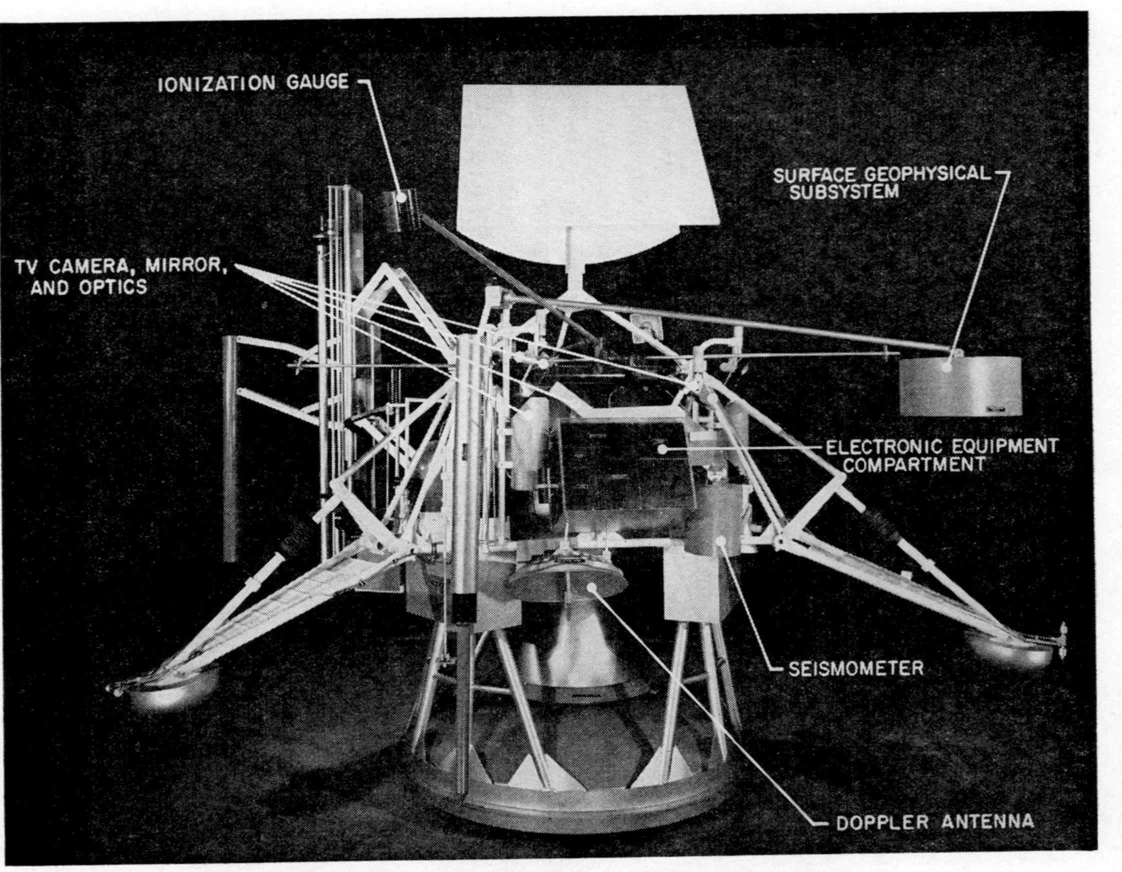

FIG. 7. Full scale model of Surveyor spacecraft.

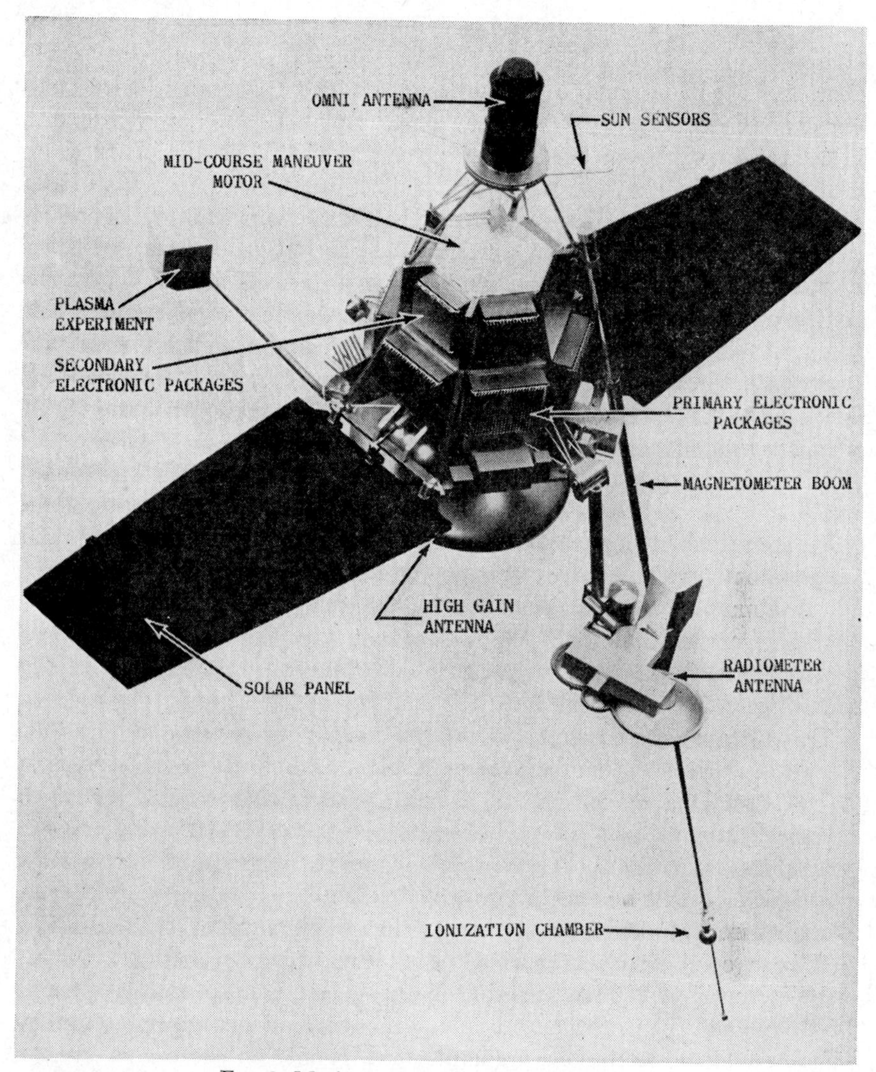

FIG. 8. Mariner A spacecraft configuration.

spacecraft, and the experimenters designated by NASA Headquarters.

The scientific instrumentation aboard Mariner A has four purposes: (1) the determination of the surface temperature and a rough temperature profile of the Cytherean atmosphere, (2) the identification of some of the constituents of the upper atmosphere, (3) the measurement of the planet's magnetic field and possible radiation belts, and (4) the exploration of the fields and particles of the interplanetary region between the earth and Venus.

The trajectory of Mariner A is a high-energy path in comparison to a Hohmann ellipse. The planes of the trajectory and of the planetary orbit near Venus will be inclined at perhaps 20°. The approach will be quite close, nominally about 27,000 km from the planet center, which results in a large curvature of the trajectory near Venus. Thus, the instruments on board Mariner A will see both the dark and lighted portions of the planet. The range in phase angle will be from about 145° on approach to 0° as the spacecraft swings around the planet.

At about 150,000 km, an infrared planet-seeker will locate Venus and center on it. At that time, the microwave radiometer experiment will begin. A short time later, the exact time being dependent upon the trajectory, the ultraviolet spectrophotometer will begin operation. Both spectrophotometer and radiometer are carried on an articulated head with an axis allowing scans along a line at an angle of 15° to the line through the cusps of Venus. The scans are to be step scans, thus allowing data to be taken from a comparatively localized area rather than integrated over large parts of the disk. A preprogramed command system controls the actual stepping, the program being designed to give the maximum geographical coverage possible at each point of the trajectory plus excursions off the planet to study the possible outer envelope of hydrogen (and conceivably other substances), and to calibrate the radiometer.

The ultraviolet spectroscopy experiment, under the direction of C. Barth of JPL, J. Chamberlain of Yerkes Observatory, Z. Sekera of UCLA, and D. Deirmendjian of The RAND Corporation, is intended to give measurements of the spectrum of the radiation coming from the Venus atmosphere on both the dark and sunlit sides. The radiation from the dark side will be due to emission by the gases in the upper atmosphere (aurora and airglow), whereas the radiation from the sunlit side will be a combination of such emission and scattered sunlight.

Below perhaps 2000 Å, emission features should be seen on either side of the planet. The off-planet scans will give data on the outer atmospheric envelope. At least semiquantitative results on the ozone, oxygen, hydrogen, and nitrogen of the upper atmosphere of Venus should result from this study. These additional data, plus those obtained by the radiometer and magnetometer also being carried, should help define the atmosphere of Venus.

The surface temperature of Venus and the temperature profile of its atmosphere are subjects of considerable speculation and debate. The temperature problems are inseparable from the unknowns in the atmospheric constituents, so that speculations on these subjects run parallel.

A set of microwave radiometers on board the Mariner spacecraft, designed under the direction of D. Jones of JPL, A. Lilley of Harvard, A. Barrett of the University of Michigan, and J. Copeland of the Army Ballistic Missile Agency, will attempt to measure the brightness temperature of the planet at four wavelengths. The location of the Cythereographical temperature sources will be found by scanning the disk with pencil beam antenna patterns. The sources in the ionized layers, if present, will be recorded by scanning across the limb.

The instrument will be pointed at the planet by an external pointing and scanning system. It will begin recording data on the primarily dark planet when it is within 150,000 km. The field of view of the instrument is 2°, which corresponds to a region 5800 km in diameter when the probe is 150,000 km from the planet.

The instrument system consists of four independent radiometers which utilize three parabolic antennas. The crystal audio radiometer is similar to a conventional Dicke type, and the crystal acts like a square-law device. The wavelengths of operation are 4, 8, 13.5, and 19 mm. The two longer wavelengths share a single parabolic antenna, whereas the shorter wavelengths utilize separate antennas. The weight of the entire unit is 20 lb, and the device requires a total of 10 watts of power.

The magnetometer experiment aboard Mariner A, under the direction of D. Jones of JPL, C. Sonett of NASA Headquarters, and L. Davis of the California Institute of Technology, has as its goals the measurement of the interplanetary field in the region between the orbits of the earth and Venus as well as the Cytherean magnetic field itself. Complete vector measurements will be made, the direction and magnitude of the field being of great importance in both regions of interest.

The magnetometer instrument is a three-component fluxgate type which will have a maximum value of zero offset of $0.5\,\gamma$ and will be capable of resolving fields to within $0.25\,\gamma$ on the most sensitive scale. It will have a dynamic range of from essentially 0.5 to $\pm 3000\,\gamma$, which is covered in three ranges. The basic magnetometer will measure fields with periods down to a fraction of a second, although data sampling will increase this to several seconds.

In addition to obtaining information regarding dc and slowly varying interplanetary and planetary magnetic fields, the Mariner magnetometer will obtain information regarding the magnetic fluctuations in the region from 1 to 30 cps in three bands. This will be obtained by opening up the bandpass and tapping a signal out prior to synchronous detection. Variations in amplitude of these frequency components will be measured to within $1.5\,\gamma$ and peak amplitudes up to $150\,\gamma$ can be measured. This part of the magnetometer instrument is primarily for a survey type experiment as frequency components in this realm may not be measurable by any previous instrument system, although some indication may be obtained from RA-1 and -2.

The Mariner A spacecraft also contains a variety of detectors to measure the flux, energy spectrum, and anisotropy of charged particles which will be encountered during the flight from earth to Venus.

A planetary flyby toward Mars is being planned. This spacecraft is tentatively identified as the Mariner B (*5*), and its basic purpose is to study the planet Mars from a close hyperbolic orbit about the planet and to study the physics of the interplanetary medium during the flight of earth to Mars.

The exploration of the moon and planets, carried out with the spacecraft and instrumentation which has briefly been described in this report, represents a combination of the techniques of astronomy and geology. In fact, as the program progresses, geological investigations, including geophysical and geochemical measurements, will gradually dominate the mission objectives. This tendency is indicated by the increasing number of scientists with a geological background who are now entering the lunar and planetary exploration program.

It is very important, therefore, that a spirit of close cooperation be established and maintained between these two disciplines—astronomy and geology. Not only is it necessary that the geologists discover what has already been learned about the moon and planets by astronomers who have for so long been the almost exclusive investigators of these bodies, but it is also necessary that the experiments carried on rocket-launched spacecraft be those which actually require a spacecraft to make their measurements. We are all keenly aware of the fact that many observations of the moon and planets can be done from the surface of the earth or from balloons in the high atmosphere with expenditures of time and money far below that required for rocket-borne investigations. It is primarily the astronomers who are aware of the possibilities and limitations of these more traditional techniques.

However, one problem now becomes apparent. For the past many decades, the main stream of astronomy has turned toward the stars and away from the planets. Thus, there are few professional astronomers today whose acquaintance with planetary astronomy is any greater than that of the geologist. Thus, although the techniques and instrumentation for astronomical observations of the moon and planets are available at many places around the world, trained astronomers, capable of making efficient use of these instruments, interested in planetary research and experienced in the field of planetary astronomy, are few and far between.

It appears, therefore, that astronomers today have some very real possibilities to pursue in the field of space-age astronomy. Within the last few days there have been many discussions from astronomers about experiments which can be carried out on rockets. We do not want to discourage these suggestions. Some of them are useful or interesting. But at the same time the astronomers have not discharged their responsibilities in space age astronomy by suggesting experiments for the engineers to fly 20 years from now. There is also a responsibility of suggesting what they, the astronomers, can do right now here on the ground or from balloons. Certainly, we at the Jet Propulsion Laboratory, assigned the responsibility for building spacecraft to make direct exploration of the moon and planets, would be most interested to learn about lunar and planetary astronomical research projects which might be carried out from the ground or from balloon-borne instruments, and we would like even more to know the people who are interested in carrying out such projects themselves.

References

1. A. R. Hibbs, The national program for lunar and planetary exploration, *J. Geophys. Research* **66,** 2003–2012 (1961).
2. Scientific experiments for Ranger 1 and 2, Tech. Rept. No. 32-55, California Institute of Technology, Jet Propulsion Laboratory, Pasadena (January 3, 1961).
3. Space programs summary no. 37-9, Volume 1, Period March 1, 1961 to May 1, 1961, Jet Propulsion Laboratory, California Institute of Technology, Pasadena (June 1, 1961).
4. F. Press, P. Buwalda, and M. Neugebauer, A lunar seismic experiment, *J. Geophys. Research* **65,** 3097–3105 (1960).
5. W. W. Kellogg and C. Sagan, eds., Proceedings of the *Ad Hoc* Panel on Planetary Atmospheres, Space Science Board, Natl. Acad. Sci. (to be published).

CHAPTER 19

Engineering Problems to be Solved for Implementation of Above Tasks

19.1 Problems of Cost and Complexity

RONALD SMELT

LOCKHEED MISSILES AND SPACE COMPANY, DIVISION OF LOCKHEED AIRCRAFT CORPORATION, Sunnyvale, California

The papers at this symposium, and indeed the recent writings of many astronomers and astrophysicists, contain a large number of proposals for the application of space vehicle technology to astronomical investigation. Some of these are quite straightforward, and we have already made a start on them with our present space vehicles and instruments. Others are further in the future, usually because they require the solution of some specific problem; examples are the problems of extremely precise stabilization of an orbiting observatory and of adequate communications over interplanetary distances. Instead of singling out one or two of these specific subjects for detailed examination, we shall concentrate upon two more general problems which extend throughout space vehicle technology at the present time.

It is evident that many of the experimental needs, particularly of the astrophysicists, can be satisfied with relatively simple instruments—counters, magnetometers, spectrometers—weighing only a few pounds or even ounces. These are, of course, the instruments which have already permitted satellites and space probes to make definite contributions to astronomy; we can expect developments here to be in the direction of improved instruments of wider range. The real requirement for experiments of this type is an increase in the variety of orbits and trajectories, in the number of flights, and in the ease with which the experimenter can utilize space vehicles. The author has no hesitation in presenting these as engineering problems, since there is an underlying requirement for an order-of-magnitude reduction in the cost of launching small space vehicles. Dr. Hyatt in this symposium quoted the cost of the cheapest NASA vehicle, the Scout, as $1,000,000 per shot, or about $6000 per pound of useful payload. According to the popular press, this is about the same as the cost per pound of building the first prototype of a new automobile model; the figure drops to about $1.00 per pound in full production of the same model. We have a major engineering problem, in both building and launching space vehicles, to move from the experimental prototype to the production version of the space taxicab.

If we carry the automobile analogy a little further, the space omnibus is cheaper transportation than the space taxicab. Dr. Hyatt's figure of $6000 per pound of Scout payload compares with about $1000 per pound on Agena or Centaur (quoting Dr. Garber's figures from Chapter 14.1); and there is another decrease of at least one order of magnitude in the cost per lb of the very large payloads which can be carried by nuclear rockets (see Hunter and Merrilees, Chapter 14.3). Considerable economy is therefore effected by pooling many experiments on a common space vehicle, provided that all can use the same trajectory and there is no mutual interference. Fortunately, the National Aeronautics and Space Administration in the United States has been willing to shoulder this coordination problem in projects such as the Orbiting Geophysical Observatory and the Ranger moon vehicles.

The second engineering problem which we shall discuss relates to the more complex space experiments which have been put forward during the symposium. Having put into space the final detecting equipment of the astronomical observatory, it is natural next to want to add the telescope itself; its stabilizing equipment; its accurate thermal control; command from the ground; programming and analysis devices; and finally the astronomer himself, first young and then somewhat more mature. As a further step, we then take the manned station with its equipment to the moon and the planets. The significant point here is that there is no theoretical limit to the possibilities which present themselves in this manner by straightforward extension of our present technology. In practice, however, there are real limitations, and it is important that we appreciate them fully. One is the element of cost, already discussed; the other is the steadily increasing complexity of the equipment to be put into space, and its relation to lifetime.

It is not easy to define complexity numerically; but fortunately, since we are dealing with order-of-magnitude effects, we can be very crude. The electronic engineers have been concerned over this problem for some years, and have introduced a unit of complexity, an "active element group," which is typically one stage of an amplifier with its associated transistors, capacitors, and resistors. Using statistics from experience on commercial equipment, airborne radio and control devices, and large-scale computers, rough relations have been developed between complexity and lifetime, i.e., mean time to failure of the equipment. Figure 1 shows the best of these curves—from computers in which particular attention has been given to long-life requirements, from undersea cable equipment, etc. In applying them to space we tacitly assume that the special environmental problems associated with operation in high vacuum and in radiation fields can be solved; there is a very large amount of development effort currently being applied to such problems.

A typical simple stabilization system for a satellite, with its power

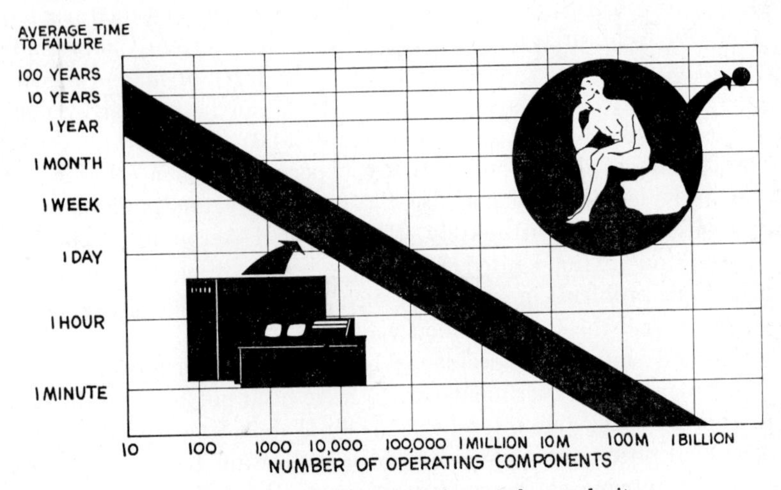

Fig. 1. Relation between lifetime and complexity.

supplies and monitoring telemetering equipment, will represent a complexity of several hundreds of active element groups. A programmer or analyzer can be even more complex. In fact, it is easy, within a payload of 5000 lb, to achieve a complexity measured in tens of thousands, and a corresponding probable failure time of only a few days, even if we utilize best current practice. With forthcoming developments in microminiaturization of electronic equipment we can expect to change this by one or two orders of magnitude. This does not imply that large satellites will then be useless; on the contrary, they offer opportunities for the introduction of redundancy into the equipment, thus alleviating the problem.

Another solution to the problem is indicated by the point on the upper right-hand side of Fig. 1, representing rough estimates of the complexity and lifetime of a human being. He is evidently much more reliable than the equipment which he produces. We have an obvious engineering problem, throughout our space equipments, to incorporate the same features of multiple redundancy, and the same self-healing techniques which man uses to achieve his extraordinary reliability. Since it is not likely that these developments in improved reliability will be accomplished within the very near future, there appear to be two rules which should be applied to all space vehicle payloads of the present era. Firstly, the equipment should be kept as simple as possible, avoiding long chains of components which must function successfully in series to attain the desired experimental result. Secondly, if the objectives of the experiment necessitate complexity above an acceptable level defined as in Fig. 1, it appears desirable to take along a man as operator and repairman. Since Fig. 1 is admittedly crude, there is a secondary engineering problem in obtaining much more definite relations between lifetime and complexity, for the equipments and environments of space vehicles.

19.2 Problems of Surface Exploration of the Moon and the Planets

ROBERT K. RONEY
HUGHES AIRCRAFT COMPANY, Culver City, California

As we have heard from the various speakers of this symposium, use of spacecraft for astronomical observations may be either by distant observation from low altitude earth satellites, or by direct exploration where the spacecraft is taken to the immediate vicinity of an astronomical body. Within the latter category, observations may be made either by a fly-by or probing experiment, by going into a low altitude orbit around the object body, or finally, by entering the atmosphere or landing directly on its surface. It is this final class of experiments, chiefly, which we shall comment upon from the point of view of the engineering problems. It is quite well understood that we are limited in the astronomical use of spacecraft for lunar and planetary exploration by the weight considerations, or the ability to carry sufficient instruments, and this is doubly important for a craft which must carry equipment to provide for landing. But this is simply a matter of booster size.

However, contrary to popular opinion, we are not particularly limited with respect to guidance accuracy for probing the planets or striking the moon. Guidance techniques of today clearly allow sufficient accuracy for encounter with the closer planets, and for landing on the moon to within a few miles, i.e., within of a few resolution elements as seen from the earth. When greater accuracy is required, or the ability to rendezvous in closer proximity to a specified point, we will require further refinement, using terminal reference. Thus, what we may consider practical in the early future is an uncontrolled, or random, penetration of the atmosphere of the nearer planets, and touchdown on the lunar surface to within a specified circle of a few miles, on the eastern (leading) face of the moon. With the use of suitable beacons, it will become practical to make multiple landings within a much closer radius of one another. But to land within a matter of hundreds of yards of a preselected lunar feature will require substantial development in terminal reference techniques.

Thus, not transit guidance, but controlled descent and landing is the critical consideration. *This* problem is clearly understood; it is soluble within certain limitations. Landing on the surface involves two entirely different operations depending upon whether there is an atmosphere, as on the planets, or not, as on the moon. Most practical entry and landing techniques in the atmosphere of a planet are closely related to the similar process of re-entry to the earth's atmosphere. Of the planets, Mars, Earth, and Venus, the most difficult problems in design of a satisfactory entry vehicle are probably offered by Venus. The parabolic velocity is comparable to that of earth. Although the structure and composition of the atmosphere are not definitely known, the surface density may be an order of magnitude higher than that of earth, and the surface temperature is possibly as high as 300°C, CO_2 appears to be a major constituent. While these conditions are speculative, and possibly far from what would actually be encountered, they are believed to be the severest conditions that could be encountered by an entry vehicle. A preliminary design study of a vehicle under these assumptions has shown that it can probably survive the entry into the atmosphere of Venus until the planetary surface is reached, for entry angles from 10° to 90°.

However, landing in the vacuum on the surface of the moon presents an entirely different set of requirements. In the first place, we are relieved of the problem of aerodynamic heating due to an atmosphere, but by the same token, we cannot use atmospheric drag for reduction of our velocity. About two-thirds of the weight of the spacecraft arriving at the moon must be expended in rocket fuel to slow it down for landing. In addition, a means is required for the sensing of velocity relative to the surface of the moon and for control of the rocket impulse vector in response to the sensing. Probably the most important engineering requirement for lunar landing is the development of adequately throttlable vernier rockets. The use of radar doppler measurements for terminal velocity sensing is straightforward and practical, but some aspects remain speculative; further measurements are needed to assure touchdown of unlimited softness. For example, since for any particular landing we must have adequate reflectivity at the specific spot of the landing, we are dependent on the surface reflectivity in detail; but our knowledge today is limited to the average reflectivity of large areas, as measured from the earth. Furthermore, we depend on the operation of the radar in close proximity to the plume of a rocket operating in a vacuum. While we believe that this constitutes no substantial hazard for moderate landing velocity, we do not today have certain knowledge of the velocity noise which will result. Finally, the exact nature of the surface of the moon is of course uncertain. It is not easy to engineer a touchdown system which is optimum, or even adequate, for alighting on any surface from smooth granite to randomly piled boulders or to deep, loose dust. Aside from the mechanical difficulties associated with the touchdown itself if the surface should be dust, there is the problem of terminal sensing and general disturbance arising out of the action of the jet. We may therefore be required, for certain purposes, to drop from some specified height without rocket support. Many of these difficulties will be largely overcome if use is made of a beacon previously placed at the landing site.

The gathering of scientific information, or the conduct of experiments on the surface of the moon, presents perhaps the most challenging problems of all. Some of these are associated with the gathering, grinding, and otherwise preparing lunar material for scientific analysis; and with the recording of the gathered information and its communication to earth. In the first place, the equipment must operate in an extreme environment of near perfect vacuum, with temperatures changing in some places sharply between daylight and night-time operations from about 130°C to —150°C. During the 14 dark days of frigidity, the apparatus must operate without benefit of solar power. Indeed, power provisioning, environmental control, and plain reliability probably are the keys to long duration observations on the surface of the moon. As far as we now know, the most severe environmental hazard is simply the temperature, since relatively little time is spent in the Van Allen belt. Suitable nuclear power sources will be of immense value to lunar spacecraft for both power and thermal control.

The collected data may be communicated to earth either by radio transmission or by the actual physical return of sample material or records. Of these, radio transmission is clearly more straightforward, but there are serious technical limits to the information that can be returned. If we visualize, for example, the collection of photographic information over one hemisphere of view to a resolution of 0.1 milliradian, the transmission at 300,000 bits per second would take approximately one hour without redundancy. With the sensitive receivers available at the Deep Space Instrumentation Facility, the spacecraft power and antenna requirements for this operation are reasonable for lunar distances today. A similar transmission from Venus, a hundred times farther at its closest, would require 10,000 hr for the same amount of data using the same radio equipment. It is clear that much more elaborate spacecraft equipment or data retrieval systems will be required for future missions, if we are not to be satisfied with very limited information transmission.

19.3 Propulsion Developments

D. W. HEGE

ROCKETDYNE, A DIVISION OF NORTH AMERICAN AVIATION, INC., Canoga Park, California

There are several types of propulsion systems that can be applied for space exploration, as indicated by Fig. 1. These propulsion system types vary from vehicles using all solid propellant systems, through vehicles using combinations of solid propellant and liquid propellant systems, to all liquid propellant systems, combination liquid and nuclear systems, and all nuclear systems. For missions with a high amplification factor (gross wt/payload) and a low required velocity increment, an all solid propellant propulsion system will suffice. As the velocity increment grows larger for more ambitious missions, such as a lunar orbit and return, or lunar landing and return, it will be necessary to use a multistage all liquid propulsion system. In liquid propellant systems, the upper stages will undoubtedly carry liquid oxygen and liquid hydrogen for this is one of the most efficient liquid propellant combinations known today. For still more ambitious missions, such as a near-planet landing and return or even a lunar landing and return, a combination of a liquid propellant booster with nuclear propulsion upper stages, or all nuclear propulsion systems, will be required to maintain a maximum payload and a minimum gross weight (comparatively low amplification factor).

The primary characteristics of these propulsion systems may be stated in terms of specific impulse and of engine thrust per pound of engine weight. The measure of efficiency common in rocket propulsion technology is specific impulse. This is defined as the number of pounds of thrust generated per pound of propellant consumed. The various types of propulsion systems fall into the performance ranges shown in Fig. 2. In terms of efficiency as indicated by specific impulse, the electrical system is the highest, with the nuclear and chemical following in that order. However, the engine thrust per pound of engine weight must also be considered, along with the efficiency of the propulsion system, when determining the type of propulsion system for a specific application. As shown in Fig. 1, chemical systems and nuclear systems will be used for booster and upper-stage applications. This is because of the high efficiencies of these systems, and because the engine thrust per pound of

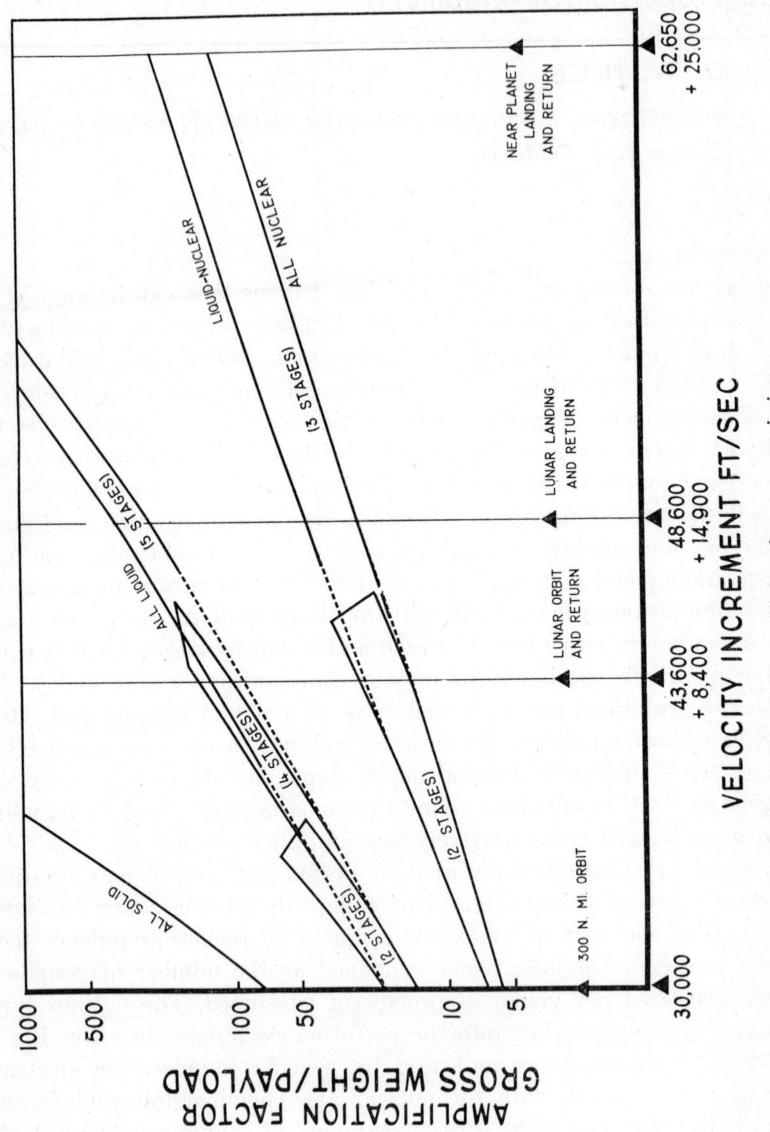

FIG. 1. Gross weights for space missions.

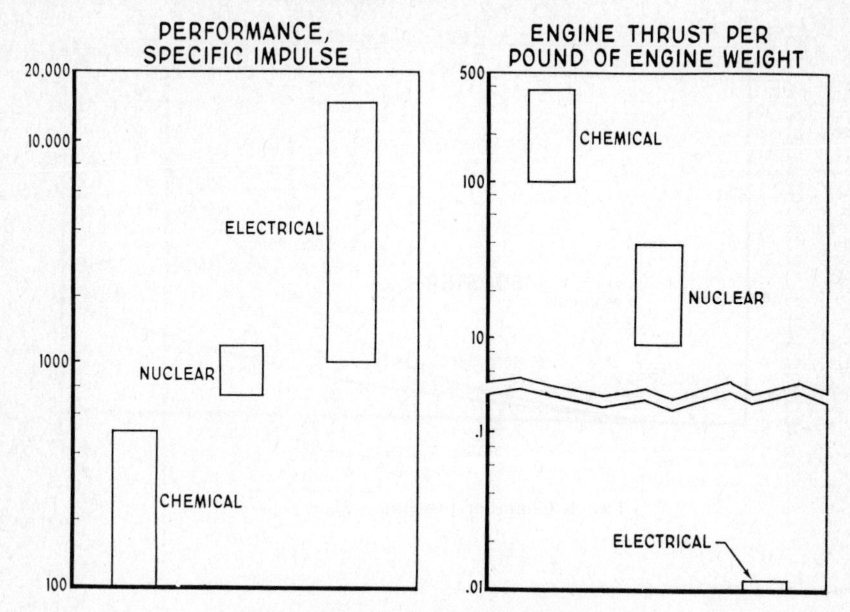

FIG. 2. Primary engine characteristics.

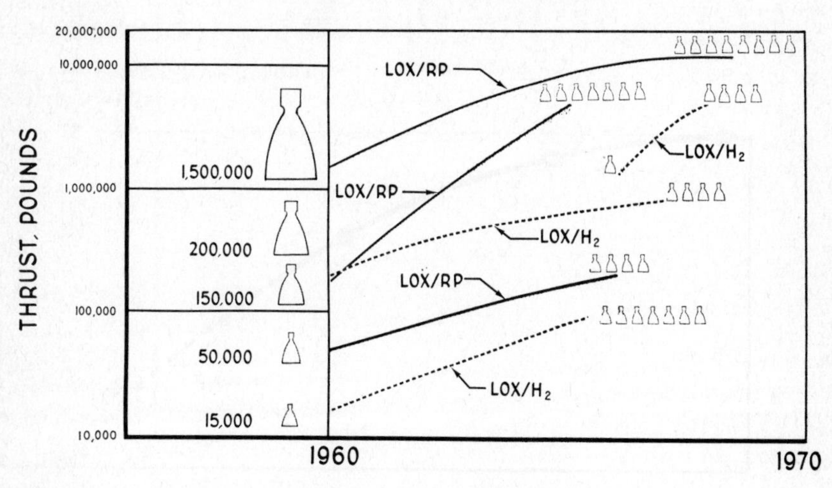

FIG. 3. Propulsion thrust trend.

engine weight yields an acceptable amplification factor. Electrical propulsion systems, although having high efficiencies in terms of specific impulse, have very low engine thrust per pound of engine weight, due to the heavy weight of the electrical generating equipment. However, this type of propulsion system will be required to sustain, maneuver, and

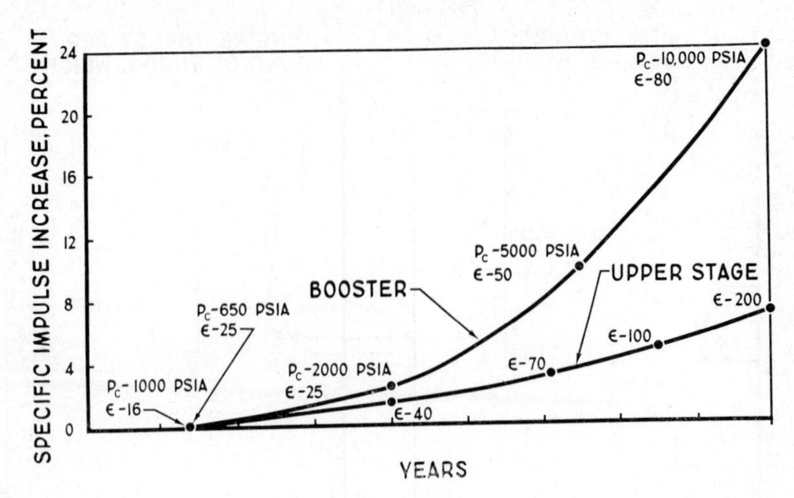

FIG. 4. Chamber pressure and area ratio.

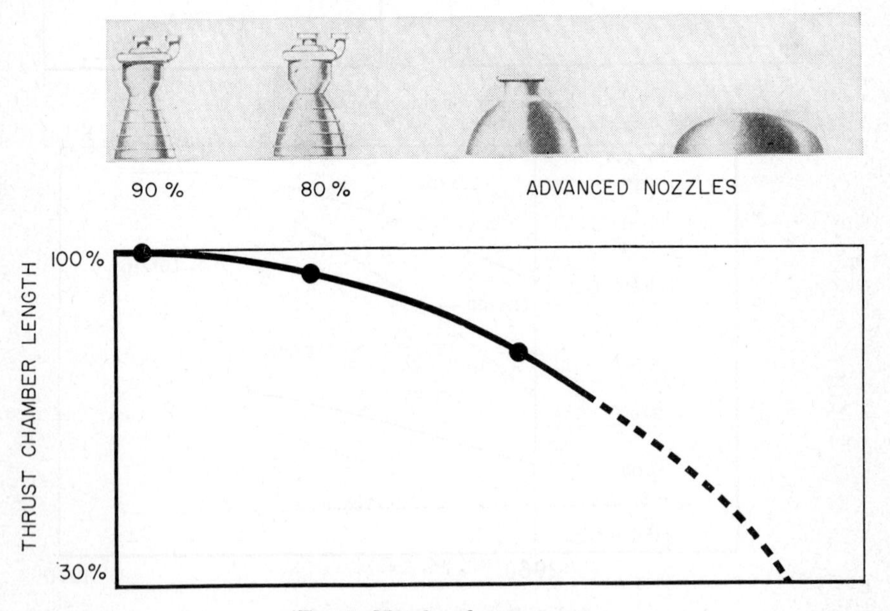

FIG. 5. Nozzle advancements.

control the attitude of space vehicles, and possibly even to provide thrust for orbit-to-orbit transfer to the farther planets.

Since the first rocket propulsion system was built, there has always been a desire for higher thrust and more efficient propulsion systems. Rocket propellant systems have now been designed and built in thrust ranges up to 1,500,000 lb (Fig. 3). The higher thrust has been achieved

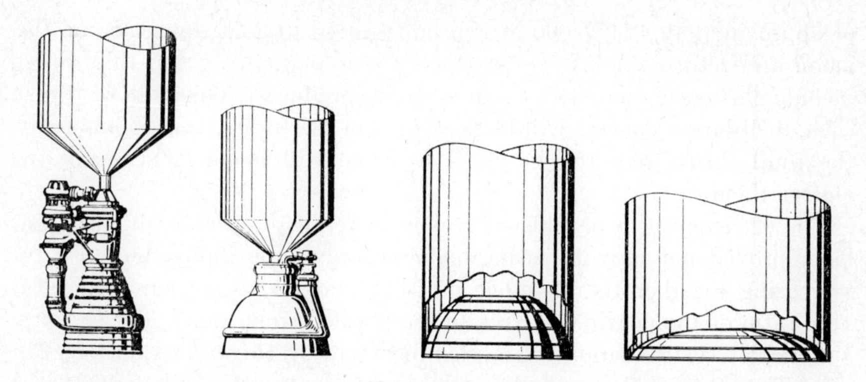

FIG. 6. Engine packaging. Advantages: compact; lightweight; elimination of concentrated thrust loads; short high-pressure ducting; reduced missile lengths; reduced bending moment.

by clustering rocket propulsion systems. For example, the 188,000-lb-thrust H-1 engine is now being clustered in the Saturn vehicle to produce approximately 1,500,000 lb of thrust. To obtain more efficient systems, higher energy propellants have been used. The higher energy propulsion

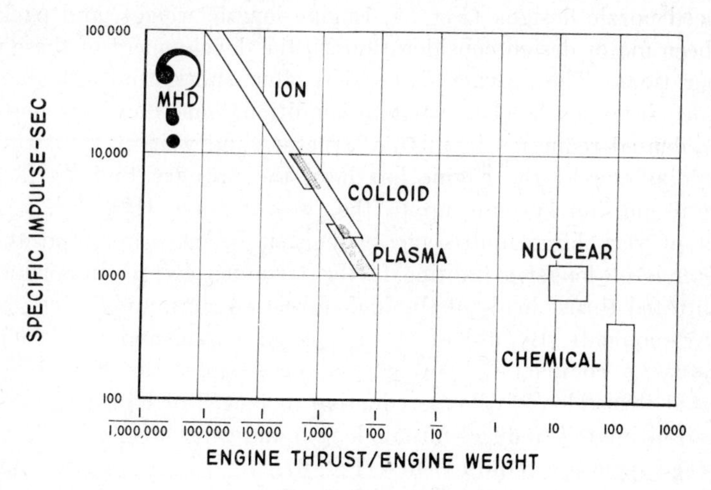

FIG. 7. Propulsion areas.

systems will also be clustered, to give a combination of a higher thrust and more efficient vehicles. For example, two propulsion systems of 15,000 lb of thrust each, utilizing liquid oxygen/hydrogen, are being clustered today for use in the Centaur vehicle. The J-2 engine, with a thrust rating of 200,000 lb using liquid oxygen/hydrogen, will be clustered in upper-stage systems for the Saturn vehicle. A booster thrust of approximately 12,000,000 lb will be required to land three men on the moon and return them to the earth. Present plans to obtain this thrust include clustering eight F-1 engines, which produce 1,500,000 lb of thrust each. Still larger engines will be necessary in the future, and undoubtedly the total thrust required in years to come will make it necessary to cluster them.

The efficiency of a propulsion system in terms of specific impulse may be improved not only by using higher energy propellants, but also by increasing together the chamber pressure and the expansion area ratio (the ratio of the nozzle exit area to the nozzle throat area). The German V-2 rocket system employed a chamber pressure of approximately 220 psia. The state of the art today has allowed us to raise this to 1000 psia and above. As we increase the chamber pressure and the expansion area ratio for a booster propulsion system, it will be possible to augment the specific impulse as shown in Fig. 4. Upper-stage systems will be affected primarily by changes in the expansion area ratio, allowing a more nearly optimal system to be designed for any specific mission.

Thrust chamber nozzle development has proceeded from the early conical type of the V-2 engine to the currently used bell and into advanced nozzle designs (Fig. 5). Engine length, weight, and packaging have been major design considerations in the development of these nozzle configurations. The advanced nozzles offer substantially higher performance from sea level to vacuum conditions, and they also permit an unprecedented reduction in missile structure and weight.

The diameter of the engine has been the primary limiting factor in rocket propulsion systems up to the present time. However, with the advent of very large multistage systems, it becomes apparent that the diameter is no longer a limiting factor. Of much greater importance are concentrated thrust loads of the high-thrust engines, missile lengths, and bending moments. By use of the advanced nozzle and new packaging techniques, a compact light-weight system results; this eliminates concentrated thrust loads, allows reduction in length of high-pressure ducting, and ultimately reduces missile length and gross weight by decreasing interstage structure requirements (Fig. 6).

In looking at all of the propulsion systems that will be applied for space exploration in the years to come, we find that there will be places for chemical, nuclear, plasma, colloid, ion, and possibly magnetohydrodynamic devices (Fig. 7). The chemical and nuclear systems will be used for booster and upper-stage propulsion systems, whereas the electrical systems will be reserved primarily for orbit-correction devices and long-duration low-thrust devices for long-range cruising vehicles.

19.4 Space Electronics

S. STERNBERG

RCA, Princeton, New Jersey

This discussion of Space Electronics will dwell specifically on three very practical phases: communications, electronic image-sensing, and production of electrical power on board spacecraft.

Communications

At this symposium, we have heard some advocates of putting man in space in order to increase the reliability of our instrumentation. However, there is another viewpoint worthy of consideration: that is, providing a space communications capability that will take the man "out of space," and put him back on the telephone. The communications equipment that we are putting into space now is quite reliable. It can, of course, still stand some improvement.

The frequency allocations that may be considered suitable for space use range from 1 to 16 kMc. Nature has limited the low end by cosmic noise, and the high end by atmospheric-absorption noise. By next year, the requirement for high-frequency generation at high power will be met (based on present progress) by a device called the Traveling Wave Tube, or TWT. The TWT, at present, can operate within the band from 2 to 12 kMc, generating power outputs of the order of 2 to 35 watts. However, the future of this major element of space communication (that is, high-frequency generation) is in the more reliable solid-state devices. The big advantage of solid-state devices lies not in amplification, but in frequency multiplication. One new device, the Varactor, is a PN junction which operates as a nonlinear reactor. It has low internal power dissipation and is an excellent frequency multiplier in the range of interest. At the moment, we can generate approximately one watt of RF output at 2 kMc. It seems quite reasonable to assume that, in the not too distant future, 10 watts will be reached at frequencies between 1 and 10 kMc.

Along with the development of high-frequency-generation circuitry, emphasis is being placed on antennas of large aperture, and also on efficient, reliable attitude stabilization systems.

Image Sensing

The present factors of greatest interest in image sensing are sensitivity, resolution, and the storage of image data. Also of importance is the compression of bandwidth, to conserve power.

Present imaging tubes range in sensitivity from a low value of about 10^{-3} ft-candle-sec to a high value typified by the Intensifier Image Orthicon, which in a $\frac{1}{30}$ sec exposure can detect a 100 television-line display with illumination of the photocathode at 2×10^{-9} ft-candles.

Good spacecraft stabilization permits a longer look at pictorial data, which can be used to give an improved signal-to-noise ratio for the transmitted data, as well as better resolution at these sensitivities.

Marked improvement in sensitivity is not likely to come in the immediate future. This must await the development, or discovery, of new materials with much higher quantum efficiencies than those we know at present.

Commercial image-sensing tubes used in television applications give a resolution of about 700 lines per frame. For special applications, tubes can be produced with a capability of 5000 lines per frame. It now appears that, in the near future, electronic imaging capabilities will be as good as that available by silver halide photography. A few of the interesting things in space, which we will be concerned with for possible imaging in the near future, might be mentioned here. One is the zodiacal light seen at night (which has an estimated brightness lying between 2×10^{-4} and 2×10^{-5} candles/sq ft). This will require a space-qualified Image Orthicon. Another is the surface of Mars. Pictures taken from a space-stabilized spinning spacecraft require a high-sensitivity sensor exposed for only about 15 μsec to prevent smearing of the picture. Mapping of the moon is a task that has been discussed before in the symposium and is already under way. Finally, balloon-borne telescopes, or stratoscopes, are observing ninth-magnitude stars in a one-degree field. System interface problems concerned with image sensing are stabilization, which has been mentioned, and thermal control.

Dielectric storage of imaged information seems, at the moment, to be the most favorable. With such techniques, a high-resolution picture that is imaged in 1 msec can be read off (and transmitted) during several minutes, allowing a very favorable bandwidth compression. In the future, we look for read-off times of several hours.

Spacecraft Electrical Power

All of the subsystems and devices just discussed require electrical power for their operation. At this time, the energy source we draw on is the sun. To convert this solar energy to electricity, we are limited to conversion devices that will work in space. I would like to mention three of them. The conversion device being used in the first-generation satellites, the solar cell, converts photons directly to electrical power. Next, we must consider the thermocouple and the thermionic converter—both of which are heat engines, and convert heat to electrical energy. Solar cells, although by far the simplest device for conversion, are limited in power output for reasonable amounts of surface area—not more than a few kilowatts of power are readily obtainable. When tens of kilowatts are needed, then we must look to the heat-engine system.

The thermocouple works at a much lower temperature than the thermionic converter. This is an advantage if the sun is the sole source of heat, since the aiming or stabilization accuracy of the collector does not have to be as good as for the high-temperature device. On the other hand, the low-temperature radiator requires large radiation surfaces. The thermionic converter, which operates at a "cold" temperature of 875°K, requires a much smaller radiation surface.

As to the system interfaces for the power supply, the structure will be determined by the kind of power supplies chosen, the thermal characteristics of the satellite or space probe, and again, stabilization.

19.5 *Guidance and Navigation Problem Areas for Interplanetary Missions*

B. P. BLASINGAME

A. C. SPARK PLUG DIVISION, GENERAL MOTORS CORPORATION, Milwaukee, Wisconsin

Certainly the problems associated with stabilization, navigation, guidance and control for space travel are diverse—almost as numerous as are the types of space missions that have been proposed. In terms of scientific usefulness in the near future, the space missions which deserve the most attention are probably Mars or Venus shots requiring close passage to the target planet followed by safe recovery on the earth.

For missions of this type, the general consensus is that for successful mission accomplishment, midcourse (and terminal) guidance is a system requirement. The two factors which make midcourse guidance necessary are imperfect boost guidance and imperfect knowledge of the astronomical constants.

For example, for Venus close-approach shots, the error coefficients, which are dependent on launch time and trajectory, are typically 1 to 10 thousand N. mi miss distance/fps error in boost burnout velocity, and 1 to 10 thousand N. mi/minute of arc error in burnout velocity direction. The error coefficients for the return to earth are larger by at least an order of magnitude (i.e. 10 to 100 thousand N. mi/fps error in boost burnout velocity). (Magness *et al.*, 1959 and Mickelwait *et al.*, 1959) Considering these error coefficients in the light of the state-of-the-art or near-future expectations in boost guidance accuracy, the need for midcourse guidance is apparent.

Even with perfect boost guidance, uncertainties in the astronomical constants can lead to sizeable errors without midcourse guidance. For example, the lack of knowledge of the precise value of the astronomical unit causes an uncertainty in the distance of closest approach to the target planet on the order of 600 N. mi for Mars, and 200 N. mi for Venus. In addition, effects such as solar radiation pressure over the prolonged flight time may cause comparable errors.

When considering all factors such as equipment weight, required power, and the great transmission distances involved, we are led to conclude that midcourse guidance and control will be obtained, in all probability, by completely self-contained means. Even for systems in which the guidance is commanded from earth-bound tracking and transmitting stations, there must be a vehicle-borne means of determining vehicle attitude so that thrust applications can be made in the correct direction. This implies heavy reliance on optical systems for sighting on planets and/or stars to provide orientation and/or position information from which guidance maneuvers can be determined. Besides the optical devices, inertial instruments will be required for short term attitude reference and control and for monitoring corrective velocity application. And indeed, a study of all literature on presently proposed space systems reveals that without exception, these systems consist of one or more optical devices, inertial instruments of one form or another, and a central computer.

In most instances, a highly specialized digital computer occupies a central position in the over-all system mechanization. It is intimately connected to all sensing and control equipment, and it serves to control and sequence all the necessary measurements and vehicle maneuvers.

Most presently proposed systems, utilizing combinations of optical and inertial instruments properly sequenced by a digital computer, appear to be entirely adequate in terms of accuracy. As an example, the space probe described by Trageser (1960) was designed to pass within 4700 miles of Mars and return to earth for safe recovery, after a total trip time of over three years; it has the following accuracy characteristics:

At closest approach distance to Mars:

~200-mi miss in intended arrival distance;
~125-fps velocity error in intended 11,400-fps arrival velocity;
~0.8-hr arrival time error for 2.4-year trip to Mars

At earth return:

~80-mi error in impact point;
~10-min error in arrival time.

Several midcourse guidance corrections based on navigational position fixes obtained with the aid of optically measured angles are necessary to realize these accuracies. No use is made of external information sources such as radio tracking and command. The assumptions used in arriving at these results are:

1. there is a 0.1% booster guidance error;
2. there is a 10 sec error in optical angle measurements;

3. time can be measured to an accuracy of 1 part in 10^5; and
4. velocity corrections can be applied with an error of 1%.

These assumed values are certainly within the limits of present-day capabilities. Theoretically, then, the guidance and navigation problems for interplanetary missions lie not in the requirement for high accuracy, but in certain other related areas.

Rather than cataloging the various technical problems that come to mind—most of which are created by the space environment—we will discuss only the foremost and most difficult requirement that must be met. This is the assurance of reliability.

The magnitude of the reliability problem becomes apparent when it is realized that an interplanetary mission to Venus or Mars may take several years. To achieve a 99% probability of mission success—a figure which is perhaps a minimum allowable if the mission is to be manned—the equipment mean-time-to-failure must be on the order of half a century.

In the case of unmanned probes, where human life is not a factor, a degraded probability of mission success might be tolerated. However, even if we were to accept only a 50% probability of mission success, a mean-time-to-failure of the order of 5 years would be required. This lifetime is still beyond present engineering standards.

The equipment longevity problem is not one for which a solution is readily available. The magnitude of the task puts burdens on both the equipment designer and the engineers and scientists responsible for the integration of all the equipment into a workable space vehicle. In effect, while the instrument designer is striving to extend the working lifetime of the equipment, the guidance and navigation engineer, with the aid of scientists in other fields, must find ways to ease the load of the equipment designer in achieving reliability. Several ways in which this might be accomplished are by (1) designing the system to lower the guidance-equipment accuracy requirements, (2) designing the system to simplify the guidance and navigation concept, and (3) by designing for variable probability of success as a function of number and type of failures.

Relaxed accuracy requirements: One of the main incentives for highly accurate navigation fixes and guidance correction determination and execution is fuel economy. Unfortunately, the limitations on the amount of energy available for orbit corrections requires that these corrections be made infrequently and precisely. That is to say, there is a tradeoff between available energy and guidance accuracy. As the number of allowable corrections is increased by use of higher energy chemical propellants or continuous-thrust ion engines, the less accurate need be the overall guidance system, since the effects of past errors can be compensated for by later corrections.

Although this decreased accuracy requirement in no way increases the lifetime of certain elements of the guidance system (e.g., the photosensors of the optical devices), it may allow the utilization of coarser but more rugged servo control loops, gyros, and accelerometers.

Simplified guidance concept: Many of the proposed guidance schemes for interplanetary travel require the near-simultaneous measurement of angles between several pairs of celestial bodies for position determination and subsequent computation of guidance corrections. Since in many of these proposals only two "telescopes" are provided in the vehicle, a typical procedure is as follows:

1. The telescopes are first positioned by some search and acquisition scheme in order that the angle between, say, two stars can be measured.
2. The vehicle and/or the telescope(s) are reoriented so that the angle between a star and sun is measured.
3. The vehicle and/or the telescope(s) are again slewed to allow sighting between a planet and the sun or a star.
4. This procedure is continued until a sufficient number of angles are measured.

It is apparent that this scheme puts heavy demands not only on the vehicle attitude control system and on the telescope pointing servos, but also on the proper sequencing of operations for each position fix. If the guidance system can be simplified to the point where only the one angle between the same two celestial bodies need be measured repeatedly, the equipment demands and subsequent wear and tear can be reduced considerably.

Variable probability of success: The devising of guidance schemes in which the failure of certain subsystems or modes does not jeopardize the entire mission, but rather leads only to a lowered probability of success, can help to lessen the reliability problem. This stratagem can be most effectively employed in the logical organization of the digital computer.

In digital computer programming it is generally assumed that all failures or malfunctions are equally significant, and that these failures should be prevented from occurring. If any one element (and, in some cases, its redundant replacement) fails, the entire computer was supposed to become inoperable. However, by utilizing special logical design techniques and by providing special programs, it is possible to ensure that the computer, at a certain level of component failure, only degrades in performance rather than becomes completely inoperable. That is, the computations might be less accurate or take longer, or some less important computations may be omitted; but the essential answers will still be obtained.

In conclusion, it is believed that the reliability problem is the greatest obstacle confronting us at the present time. It is not immediately clear how satisfactory reliability and equipment lifetime are to be achieved. The attainment of these goals will require the concerted effort of engineers in all fields.

References

Magness, T. A., McGuire, J. B., and Smith, O. K. (1959), Accuracy requirements for interplanetary ballistic trajectories, "Proceedings of the IXth International Astronautical Congress, Amsterdam 1958," Vol. I, pp. 286–306. Springer-Verlag, Wien.

Mickelwait, A. B., Tompkins, E. H., and Park, R. A. (1959), Three dimensional interplanetary trajectories, *IRE Trans. on Military Electronics,* **MIL-3,** 149–159.

Trageser, M. B. (1960), A recoverable interplanetary space probe, *ARS Journal* **30,** 32–35, 116–120.

19.6 Survival

E. B. KONECCI*

DOUGLAS AIRCRAFT COMPANY, INC., Santa Monica, California

The exploration of space is a human challenge. It will require the application of man's knowledge collected through 3000 years of civilization, that is, use of the hoarded thoughts winnowed and sifted through millions of minds living and dead to guide us on our way in the design and fabrication of the space vehicles and equipment needed to explore the Universe. This year, 1961, is an historic one which will be marked as the one in which the first man went into space and returned safely. It is therefore no longer a problem of will or should man go into space, but rather, how long can he *survive* in space. Survival alone is not sufficient. We must not lose the dignity of man by the imposition of needless restrictions and stresses on him. We have it within our present engineering technology to provide man with an adequate environment so that he may perform either as a pilot, an observer, or a passenger in a space vehicle.

Safety is, and must always be, a cardinal element in civilian aviation. Similarly, in astronautics the ultimate success of manned space flight exploration and extensive transportation, will depend on the overall reliability of the space vehicle system, especially the design adequacy of the life support system. The average life span today is remarkably close to the biblical three-score and ten years. As far as the dangers to his body are concerned man has begun to conquer his environment on earth. The improvement in life expectancy of a new-born baby represents man's conquest of the infectious diseases, his control of bacteria, but more than anything else, it is the decrease in infant mortality. By or shortly after the year 2000, with our present rapid rate of progress in the field of antibiotics, with the hope of conquering degenerative diseases like arteriosclerosis and with the conquest of cancer, future generations may look forward to a life expectancy of over 100 years.

What man does not understand he mistrusts. In the last several years we have heard of space flight as involving the penetration into a hostile environment. As information becomes available about the space environment, the scientific and engineering community have been able to offset

* Present address: NASA, Washington, D. C.

this so-called hostile environment and perform useful experiments in space. Table I outlines some of the areas of concern in a closed ecological system. As an example, we know very little about the effects of prolonged weightlessness. The radiation environment will have to be more adequately determined. The effects of combined psychophysiological stresses

TABLE I

SOME FACTORS IN A CLOSED ECOLOGICAL SYSTEM

		Temperature	
		Pressure	
		Humidity	
	Physical →	Radiation	
		Gravity	
		(acceleration)	
		Dust	
		Air ionization	
		Organisms	
		bacteria, spores, viruses, etc.	
	Biological →	Metabolism	
		Algal system	
Environment →		Atmosphere	→ Man
		Water	
		Food	
	Chemical →	Drugs	
		Odors	
		Toxicity	
		Fuels	
		Fire	
		Missions	
		Logistics	
		Cabin space	
	Situational →	Tasks	
		physical	
		mental	
		Emergencies	

offer a large area of fruitful research. The need for an adequate and reliable life support system is evident; however, research that has been conducted and work that is planned should establish the proper life science requirements.

Comments that man will not be able to survive in space because of the many multiple risks involved are no longer justified. Certainly we cannot eliminate all of the risks. How safe are we on earth? Last year the highway death rate in U.S.A. was one fatal accident for each 45,000,000 miles of travel; we lost 25,000 U.S.A. citizens. In aircraft accidents, 326 people died, while only 32 deaths resulted from train accidents. The U.S.A. aircraft rate was one fatal accident for each 99,000,000 passenger miles and only one fatality for each 663,000,000 passenger miles on trains.

Although the U.S.S.R. and the U.S.A. have been fortunate to begin the manned space flight era without a fatality, we must expect some tragedy as the manned space operations are expanded. By 1980, with nuclear space transportation systems scheduled flights to the moon, Venus, and Mars should become commonplace. By that time the reliability of these space transports should be very high, and our knowledge of the space environment should be substantial, so that safe round trips between the planets will become the rule rather than the exception. Increased propulsion capability will significantly reduce flight times to the near planets and make all year around transportation possible. Even so, there may also be room for longer flight time "tourist" flights. Although their cost might be less, the increased exposure time to the space environment (e.g., meteoroids, ionizing radiation) would increase the possible risks.

Since space exploration is a human challenge, we believe that some of the astronomers in this room might be willing to personally go into space or land on the moon in order to do their cosmic observations without the annoyances and disturbances of the blanket of atmosphere which covers the earth. Willing, that is, if they could be assured with some reasonable degree of safety that they would be able to survive the journey and return safely to earth. We sincerely believe that this possibility does exist and that it is definitely within our present engineering capability to provide an adequate life support system for such astronomical ventures. Life support systems can be designed and developed to provide not only test pilot astronauts but scientists and eventually civilian passengers with an adequate environment for travel in space. We can presently foresee physical and chemical systems for the control of the atmosphere, giving an adequate amount of oxygen, absorbing the carbon dioxide, and providing a regulated temperature and humidity within the space cabin. The recycling of waste water is certainly feasible and has been performed successfully in the laboratories. Although there has been much discussion of algae systems for the control of the atmosphere, as well as providing food for the astronauts, there does not seem to be a requirement for such a system nor the necessity for imposing an all algae diet on the astronauts as far as vehicular systems are concerned. As the field of astronautics progresses, so will our propulsion capability, and with increases in velocity capability the travel times between the earth, the moon, Mars, and Venus will be significantly decreased to where it will not be necessary to remain in the vehicle for more than a few months. Biological systems such as algae may be a requirement on permanent lunar and planetary bases, and for such long duration uses may be competitive with the physical and chemical means (such as molecular sieves, KO_2) of providing life support. However, even in the case of a planetary base, it is doubtful that space travelers would want to endure a monotonous algae diet just for the sake of maintaining a near closed ecological system. Nuclear rocket propulsion will significantly reduce the cost per pound of payload delivered to the lunar or planetary bases. This is significant, since we presently pay premium prices in the world market for desired commodities.

We are confident one of the future Astronomical Congresses will be held on the moon.

Discussion

Vice Chairman Puckett: One of the most interesting questions that has come up here is one on which we have heard two sides: the matter of the man in the spacecraft. The real engineering question is whether his inclusion in the proper manner will, in fact, turn out to be necessary as an engineering device from the standpoint of reliability or even permitting completion of missions or whether, on the other hand, he will turn out to be a complicating and undesirable burden which we take along strictly because the propensities of the human race are to do things like this.

Dr. R. Smelt: I do not think you can escape the limits given by the thick line on my chart. The complexity and lifetime which we will demand from our space equipment in the near future will lie well above this line, and we therefore cannot omit man until we can guarantee corresponding improvements in our equipment. We are a long way from this at the present, although we are trying hard.

Perhaps by adopting the same processes as the human adopts in his thinking and his control habits by building into our equipment multiple redundancy, self-healing and similar advances in computer technology which we talk about but have not yet achieved, then we could achieve sufficient reliability to omit the man. It may sound as though in this process we will be building a robot. It might be simpler just to use a man, who is produced by unskilled labor, as X-15 test pilot Scott Crossfield remarked several years ago.

Mr. S. Sternberg: I am not quite so pessimistic, perhaps, about the capability of some of our equipment. I also believe that putting a man in a spaceship requires additional equipment, which in itself could be very unreliable. For this reason I do not believe you are really going to gain very drastically in reliability by putting a man in a spaceship. The comparison to the number of neurons in a man's brain, made by Dr. Smelt, is all right if you keep the man for the purpose of thinking rather than doing. His capability in deductive logic is tremendous compared to anything we can do mechanically. However, operationally he is not necessarily much better than what we can achieve with a good control system.

Dr. R. K. Roney: It seems to me that discussion of whether or not we need a man in a spacecraft is perhaps a bit beside the point. Man in space is actually also an objective in the game of astronautics. Without intending to be irreverent in this assembly at all, I am conscious of the fact that the money that these programs cost are paid by the public, and they just naturally have more interest in putting a man in space than in making astronomical observations there. It is one of the facts of life. Perhaps putting the man there has more bearing on the demand for reliability than it has on yielding reliability.

DR. R. SMELT: There is an exception which should be made to Dr. Roney's comment, viz., that larger payloads, although less expensive in dollars per pound, will be less reliable. In operations like the Ranger experiment, which Dr. Hibbs described, we put in a lot of little experiments side by side; and we can be sure, on straight probability arguments, that some of these are going to fail. However, they are not in a serial arrangement such that the failure of any one of them would ruin the experiment for the rest. The reliability and lifetime problems occur when we attempt experiments that require many things to operate in series. I must emphasize strongly the difference between this arrangement and the parallel experiments that are planned in projects like the Ranger.

DR. B. P. BLASINGAME: I want to straddle the fence on the question of man's place in space exploration. To me, a voyage to the moon for which the time of flight is measured in days, not years, is one in which it is practical for a man to participate; his inclusion will improve the probability of success of the mission. The man can do some things that are very difficult to do with machines, and he can do them better. For example, a man using an optical device like a sextant can measure the angle between two celestial objects, or the angle subtended by the moon even though there will be a great difference in brightness of its sides. From a series of such measurements, position in space can be determined accurately by an automatic computer, or approximately by a nomograph. Locating the chosen stars or accommodating a large difference in brightness is done easily by a man, but only with difficulty and complexity by machine. Further, the man may be more accurate than the machine in this situation. On a trip to the moon where it is practical to carry a man, his presence can contribute to the success of the mission. On the other hand, on an interplanetary trip, where the time of the journey may be measured in years, it is far less practical to include the man. Whenever the time of flight is a significant fraction of man's normal life span or his mean-time-between-illnesses, then it would seem that we should try to use machines rather than men.

DR. E. B. KONECCI: I would like to comment that it really depends on what your objective is. I do not think anybody really wants to put a man in a system where a man does not belong. However, we are going to get into space whether some like it or not. This has been a dream from prehistoric times; man wants to go. There are astronomers here, who privately or openly have stated the desire to go to the moon to be able to make some observations without the hindrance of the earth's atmosphere. This, then, becomes an objective. If it is an objective, then these people will want to go as passengers. They will not particularly care to control the vehicle.

In jet transport safety meetings not more than five or six years ago, we were not even sure that passengers could board a jet aircraft without having to take a full medical physical examination. We were worried about the possibility of a passenger having a heart attack in case of cabin decompression. But this was taken care of by imposing definite requirements on the designer. To my knowledge, we have not had one explosive decompression in commercial jets since the 1954 Comet accidents.

So, basically, if we are going to transport people around in space, we must protect them. We can certainly do this from an engineering standpoint. In certain experiments we do not want a man. Take, for example, many of the atomic experiments. We do not want a man inside of a reactor; we instrument it. The same thing applies to space. It is not a question of man or machine, but of the best effective combination of the two to do the task at hand.

New Horizons for Astronomy

JOHN P. HAGEN

DIRECTOR, OFFICE FOR THE UNITED NATIONS CONFERENCE NATIONAL AERONAUTICS AND SPACE ADMINISTRATION

Mr. Chairman, it is a pleasure to speak to this group of astronomers, space engineers, and scientists who are searching for the best means of expanding the horizons of astronomy, on the one hand, and of enriching the program of space exploration, on the other. The National Aeronautics and Space Administration welcomes this activity and awaits with interest the outcome of your deliberations.

When I accepted your invitation to come here, I was not, of course, aware of the plans of our Soviet counterparts to put a man into space around the earth and keep him there for one full day. We commend this achievement and recognize it as a natural development of their earlier success in propelling a man once around the earth and a forward step in their program for space exploration. It is important to determine that a man can withstand the stress of long journeys in space. We hope for reports of the results of this experiment which may point to the use of man for scientific observations for long periods outside the atmosphere of the earth.

We should anticipate that, as time goes on, multimanned vehicles will be put in orbit around the earth and then, when radiation and re-entry problems have been brought into focus, man will travel toward the moon, circumnavigate it, and return to earth. Much of the success of the manned exploration of space depends on the scientific information gathered by the many satellites and space probes which have been launched as the forerunner of man. This all points up the need to accelerate and intensify the exchange of scientific experience.

It is now more than ten years ago that the first ultraviolet spectrograph was flown into space on the nose of a probing rocket by Tousey and his co-workers. The rewards were immediate and rich; we soon saw the spectrum unfold as the rocket rose above the earth's absorbing atmosphere. Later spectrographs of higher resolution were flown to photograph the Lyman alpha line and from its profile to determine the temperature of its place of origin in the chromosphere and, as an interesting by-product, to also observe absorption by hydrogen clouds near the earth. Meanwhile, Friedman and his group using ionization chambers had observed X-ray radiation from the sun and during an eclipse had demonstrated that the principal source of X-ray radiation was associated with active regions in the sun's atmosphere. This work was culminated by a remarkable X-ray photograph of the disk of the sun taken with a pinhole camera clearly identifying the hot X-ray regions with known active regions.

These are but two of the earlier demonstrations of the value to astronomy and astrophysics of the new opportunity to perform observations beyond the atmosphere of the earth. The richness of the rewards that have come to astronomy may stand as a symbol of the hopes we have that all science may benefit as our ability to place complex payloads into space advances.

These more complex payloads will provide powerful telescopes fitted out with ultraviolet and infrared spectroscopes making available for study those stars whose spectra extend beyond the wavelength limits of the optical window in our atmosphere. Observation from well-stabilized telescopes beyond our turbulent atmosphere will, as already demonstrated by Schwarzschild, make high resolution photography of the surface of the sun, planets, and other objects in space possible in a way never available to us here on our earthly mountain tops.

The rewards from extending conventional observations are but one aspect of this new opportunity. Another aspect is the ability to make observations of a totally new kind. A good example of this is the work in gamma-ray astronomy now being carried out in the satellite Explorer XI. The results from this experiment are still incomplete and have not yet been announced. The purpose of the experiment is to detect gamma rays from cosmic sources. One source of gamma radiation is the annihilation of matter as high energy cosmic rays collide with material in space. One intriguing possibility is that gamma-ray telescopes will map out for us the distant regions in space where cosmic rays abound, permitting us to chart this distribution as radio astronomers have charted the distribution of un-ionized hydrogen in our own galaxy. The sources of cosmic rays may outline the boundaries of the universe as the radio radiation from neutral hydrogen has helped to outline the structure of our galaxy.

The President of the United States in his recent message has stated a goal toward which we will work: to land a man on the moon and provide for his safe return. This is an exciting prospect, and astronomy more than any other science may be revolutionized as man conquers the limitations of space and learns to live and operate outside the protective but selectively opaque atmosphere of the earth. No longer will the astronomer be limited to those experiments which can be performed by automatically and remotely controlled apparatus; then he will be able to survey and assess the universe as seen in the full electromagnetic spectrum, the moon and the planets as seen close to. As a scientist he may direct his efforts and observations most effectively to probe more deeply into those areas promising an expansion of our knowledge and to report these new findings to the scientific community. Machines have already played and will continue to play a role in space science and exploration; great advances are being made in automatic computing machines; however, we will surely have the capability of placing man as an observer in space long before the art of automatic computation has reached the point where machines to replace man will have the required flexibility and range of discrimination to observe complex patterns and to make perceptive decisions based on the observations.

In the course of the attainment of the goal of placing an observer on the moon and safely returning him to earth, we must necessarily improve our knowledge and our techniques in many diverse fields of science and technology. If history repeats itself, the research and development efforts expended here will advance other fields of science in ways one cannot now predict. The concentration of effort on the goal of man in space does not detract from the effort expended on other developing fields of scientific and technical effort. That this is so may be seen by noting that, as our expenditure on space research and development has increased, so, too, has there been an increase in our expenditure for astronomy, geophysics, oceanography, and high energy physics.

It is heartening to see this great increase in scientific activity in constructive directions. We have for too long now been impressed with the ability of science to increase our power of destruction. The world is ready and waiting for science to be allowed to apply its talents and direct its efforts toward this expansion of the knowledge and understanding of our universe. It will stimulate the intellect of man to know that he may give free rein to his thoughts and that what he achieves will be of permanent value in the advance of our civilization, in our continual struggle to understand the forces of nature and to bend them to the betterment of man.

The exploration of the moon and the planets and the increase in scope of astrophysical observations are perhaps the ultimate present objectives of the space programs. There are, however, other benefits to man that will come along the way. Two examples of these are in the fields of communications and meteorology. Pilot experiments have already demonstrated the feasibility of communicating over long distances using broad-band microwave beams reflected off great satellites, or using satellites equipped with receivers, memory devices, and transmitters to receive microwave beams and retransmit them from the satellite's great height long distances around the curved earth. Early experiments have also successfully televised large areas of the earth's surface, revealing the structure of the assemblages of clouds defining the weather systems. This first historic opportunity to see in perspective the structure of a massive weather system and its development in time has excited meteorologists about the future capability of satellites as a tool in weather research and forecasting.

There will be other like benefits of space research uncovered. Again, the benefits accrue in the first instance to one nation, but in the long run to the people of all nations. Cooperation between nations in the early development and use of these beneficial activities in space is highly to be desired. Cooperation on this scale is only achieved when all parties feel assured that the contributions of each matches his capabilities, that the results of the effort can be freely exchanged among all, and that all will share in the benefits.

The achievements of the past and the promise of the future make it clear that this is a field not for one nation alone, nor for a select group of nations, but it is a field in which international cooperation in its broadest sense must be exercised. The machinery for getting into space is complex and expensive. The development of large-thrust, multistage space rockets and the facilities for launching them has been accomplished by only two nations, and will remain for a long time beyond the reach of some nations whose scientists have a rich background, unquestioned ability, and a great desire to perform original experiments in space. The ability to perform experiments beyond the earth's absorbing atmosphere will be recognized as one of the historic great breakthroughs of science. To carry on the work of science with this new tool, and not make the tool available to the foremost scientific talent of the world, would be morally wrong in that it would impede scientists in their continuing catholic effort of extending the frontiers of man's knowledge.

To this end, NASA has already initiated programs wherein scientists of other nations will participate with us in space research. An example of this is the "top side sounder," an ionospheric research program in which the satellite-borne experiment, and the satellite itself, are being prepared in Canada, the launching vehicle in the United States, and the observational program will be participated in by many nations. There is also in being a program wherein a complex of satellite experiments is being prepared in England. The experiments being prepared will measure cosmic rays, ion mass spectra, electron densities and temperatures, and solar radiation. The above experiments will be flown from Wallops Island early next year in American Scout rockets. This is a small beginning, but as it is successfully completed, even more complex payloads may be considered. Not only in satellites, but in sounding rockets, tracking, and ground-based experimental work, our joint work with other nations is increasing.

The real drain on the national resources and, more importantly, the actual technological capability of any one nation, limits severely its ability to carry out complex space programs. This situation becomes more critical when other complex scientific needs of a state must be met from the same pool of human and economic resources. In other technological fields, such as the peaceful uses of atomic energy, international programs of cooperation have proved of great benefit to many countries throughout the world. We, who are concerned with the administration of space projects, might look at this experience to see how adaptable it might be to cooperative space efforts.

As we look far into the future and see man sending his emissaries on missions taking months and years to perform, exploring the moon and visiting the planets, it is difficult now to see how this could be done by or for one nation alone; how or why it should be done by nations in competition; but only that it should be done by all men for the benefit of all mankind.

The drain on the scientific and technical resources of the world will be great, as will the drain on the financial resources. The drain will not compare with that found in war; and being for a constructive purpose, it will represent a forward social movement when man has learned to turn his new technology toward his improvement, not his destruction, and when he has learned to increase his consumption of goods and services through the expansion of his frontiers.

With this impending scientific breakthrough into space within our grasp, we must overcome the barriers preventing us from its accomplishment. Keeping in mind the incentives involved in such an exploitation, we would encourage open and periodic discussion of the scientific progress achieved by our respective countries. Although some national security requirements are recognized, there is the need for a closer exchange of experiences which would further progress in peaceful space exploration. The lack of full discussion has led to a diminution of knowledge from our scientific efforts. With full and open discussion, mankind as a whole would learn more of the atmosphere surrounding the earth and what it may expect as man reaches out to the moon and the planets.

We here should feel proud of the fact that international cooperation in science and in the exploration of outer space can greatly increase mutual understanding among nations and promote the cause of peace. Those of us who are astronomers have a rich background of fruitful international cooperation. As we join together in the exploration of space beyond the earth, the new perspective gained will strengthen the knowledge that we as human beings will make the great strides forward and our differences here on earth will become more petty. No more appropriate mutual step to facilitate international scientific cooperation could be taken than to review, exchange, and assess experiences jointly with respect to outer space activities conducted to date. That such an international conference be held under the auspices of the United Nations was proposed by the Soviet Union and endorsed by the United States as a valuable meeting ground for scientists actively engaged in outer space activities and others actively interested in the results of these activities. An international conference would be in keeping with the emphasis placed by the Ad Hoc Committee of the United Nations on the desirability of openness in the conduct of space activities.

Negotiations to arrange for a conference under the U. N. Resolution have been in progress for some time and it is to be hoped that this spur to international cooperation in the penetration of the new frontier of space can be arranged.

Every nation on this earth, no matter how advanced scientifically, can benefit in some way in this space age through cooperation with other nations. Whether it is a direct exchange of information on some perplexing scientific problem, or assisting each other in tracking spacecraft, man's knowledge will be more complete and his life richer through such collaboration. The first space voyagers leaving this earth could confirm just how small the planet earth really is as a part of the universe. We need not wait until that time, however, to be confronted with the necessity of acting as members of the same planet, capable of discussing openly problems of a mutual nature. As scientists, let us, therefore, strive to dissipate and eventually destroy the barriers to a free exchange of scientific experience and let us increase international cooperation, so that we may further the cause of science and derive from it its enriched benefits.

Subject Index

U

V

W

X